Chemical Analysis

CHEMICAL ANALYSIS

AN ADVANCED TEXT AND REFERENCE

Herbert A. Laitinen

PROFESSOR OF ANALYTICAL CHEMISTRY
UNIVERSITY OF ILLINOIS

McGRAW-HILL BOOK COMPANY

New York   Toronto   London

1960

545
2146

CHEMICAL ANALYSIS

Not the fact avails, but the use you make of it.
RALPH WALDO EMERSON

Preface

This book is intended primarily to serve as a textbook at the advanced undergraduate and beginning graduate level for courses stressing the fundamental principles of analytical chemistry. In addition, it is hoped that it will serve as a reference work and guide to the literature for instructors in quantitative analysis and for practicing analytical chemists.

Although centered around the "classical" or "wet chemical" methods, the treatment includes background material for those instrumental methods which involve prior chemical operations or separations.

My aim has been to cover the principles in a rigorous fashion, striving for clarity of expression rather than beauty of style. To keep the length of this work within the bounds of a single volume, it has been necessary to avoid all detailed descriptions of analytical procedures and to describe only the features that contribute to an understanding of basic principles. Most of the chapters could have been written more easily at twice their length; I can only hope that clarity has not been sacrificed too often in my zeal for brevity.

The material has been collected from a wide variety of sources, which are documented in detail in the text. In addition to the standard reference books and specialized monographs, an important source of material has been the research literature. No attempt has been made to survey exhaustively the literature of any topic. The references have been chosen to represent (a) important historical references that serve to mark the pioneers in each field and to give a temporal perspective to the development of analytical chemistry as a science, (b) readily accessible review papers that can serve as sources of literature references and for supplementary reading, (c) research monographs and textbooks, to serve the same purpose as review papers, and (d) selected research papers, chosen to describe theoretical advances and experimental verification of theoretical principles.

Firmly believing in the value of numerical problems in gaining a working knowledge of theory, I have included many example problems throughout the text. The student is strongly urged to work through these examples in detail and to work the problems at the ends of the chapters. I have tried to make these problems represent real situations as nearly as possible.

I wish to express my appreciation to colleagues and graduate students, past and present, who have encouraged me through stimulating discussions to undertake the writing of this book. Special thanks are due to those who have examined and critically reviewed the manuscript, or portions of it: Professor Donald D. DeFord, Northwestern University; Professor David N. Hume, Massachusetts Institute of Technology; Professor I. M. Kolthoff, University of Minnesota; and Professor Ward B. Schaap, Indiana University. A number of graduate students also have read portions of the manuscript and have made valuable suggestions. To Mrs. Robert F. Scarr, who finished typing the final manuscript, and to Mr. Robert F. Scarr, who helped with its proofreading, I extend my thanks. The help of Mr. M. S. Chao with the reading of galley proofs and in checking references is gratefully acknowledged.

I am especially grateful to my wife, Marjorie Gorans Laitinen, for her constant encouragement throughout the years. By typing much of the first draft of the manuscript, she played an important role in its preparation and did much to relieve the tedium and solitude that are inevitable components of scholarship.

Herbert A. Laitinen

Contents

1. Introduction

With the spectacular advances in instrumentation and automation of analytical operations that have taken place in the last generation, a question may well be raised about whether it is necessary to study in detail the basic principles of some of our oldest classical methods of gravimetry and titrimetry. To put this question into its proper perspective, it should first be realized that instrumentation and automation are often introduced rather late in an analytical scheme. Preliminary operations may have included such steps as sampling, dissolution, treatment with prior oxidant or reductant, removal of excess reagent, adjustment of pH, addition of complex formation reagents, precipitation or extraction of interfering materials, concentration of the desired component, etc. The instrumental aspects of many analytical schemes are concerned only with the final measurement step, which has been preceded by a number of necessary chemical operations. Indeed, the instrumental observation may be merely a substitute for an indicator in the classical scheme.

The classical methods will long continue to be important for several reasons. In the first place, they are inherently simple. For an occasional determination or standardization, the use of a visual indicator titration or gravimetric determination involves no prior calibration, no investment in expensive equipment, and no high degree of specialized knowledge or training. Secondly, the classical methods are accurate. Many of the instrumental methods are designed for speed or sensitivity rather than for accuracy, and depend upon the classical methods for calibration. Thirdly, it is often possible to gain valuable information by a simple additional step of weighing or titration. For example, if it is necessary for silica to be removed by volatilization with hydrofluoric acid, its quantitative determination is only a matter of ignition and weighing.

Much of the theory of quantitative analysis is concerned with the causes of nonquantitativeness, which may arise either from unfavorable

1

equilibria, from undesirable side reactions, or from catalyzed or induced reactions. In gravimetric analysis through precipitation of a sparingly soluble salt, we are concerned with loss of precipitate through solubility or peptization, with coprecipitation and postprecipitation of foreign materials, with incompleteness of loss of moisture during ignition, with decomposition or oxidation during ignition, and with hygroscopic behavior during weighing. In acid-base titrations, we are concerned with a lack of coincidence of indicator response with the equivalence point due to unfavorable equilibrium conditions. In redox titrations, we may also be concerned with unfavorable equilibrium situations, but more often the lack of exact stoichiometry must be traced to slow reactions, side reactions, and totally unexpected occurrences like induced reactions.

Equilibrium calculations primarily are involved in ion-combination reactions (acid-base, precipitation, complex formation), which are usually rapid. In recent years significant progress has been made in acid-base titrations, taking advantage of nonaqueous solvents to gain advantageous equilibrium situations. Although much of the work has been highly empirical in nature, several important theoretical and experimental studies have yielded insight into the equilibria involved, at least in the simpler solvent systems. The principal complication is that in many problems several simultaneous equilibria must be considered. It is our objective to simplify the mathematical operations by suitable approximations, without loss of rigor. Frequently the greatest uncertainty in equilibrium calculations is imposed not so much by the necessity to approximate as by the existence of equilibria which may be unsuspected or for which quantitative equilibrium-constant data are not available. Many of these calculations are based on the use of concentrations rather than activities. This procedure is often justified on the very practical ground that the value of the equilibrium constant was in fact obtained by determining equilibrium concentrations at finite ionic strengths and that no extrapolated value at zero ionic strength is available. Often the true thermodynamic value based on activities may be less useful than the practical value determined under conditions comparable to those in which it is used. Similarly, the thermodynamically significant standard electrode potential may be of less immediate value than the formal potential measured under the actual conditions of use.

Kinetic considerations are of primary importance in several aspects of quantitative analysis. Among the nonequilibrium situations commonly encountered are (1) formation and aging of precipitates, (2) irreversible electrode behavior, and (3) slow oxidation-reduction reactions. It is often of tremendous value to our understanding of nonquantitative behavior to examine the mechanism of a kinetic process, for an unstable intermediate substance may take part in reactions that the reactants and

products do not undergo.   Through insight into the intermediate steps
we may gain knowledge about the mechanism of catalysis, side reactions,
or induced reactions that disturb the stoichiometry of the main reaction.

As by-products of the study of reaction rates and mechanisms, new
types of analytical methods have emerged.   For example, the rate of a
catalyzed homogeneous reaction is often proportional to the concentration
of catalyst and can, therefore, serve as the basis of a quantitative method
for determining the catalyst.   Again, if two constituents of a sample
undergo parallel reactions by identical mechanisms but at different rates,
the determination of the over-all rate is useful in determining the concentrations of the two constituents.

Considerable recent progress has been made in the field of analytical
separations.   The process of precipitation from homogeneous solution has
greatly improved many of the time-honored precipitation separations.
Extraction separations have benefited from systematic studies of the
equilibria involved in the formation of metal chelates and their extraction
from aqueous solutions.   Electrodeposition separations have been greatly
improved by the use of controlled-potential electrolysis techniques.   In
addition, some separations that only a relatively short time ago would
have been considered impossibly difficult for quantitative purposes have
been rendered practicable by techniques involving a multiplication of
many stages of phase-distribution equilibria.   An outstanding example
is the use of ion-exchange resins for the quantitative separation of rare
earth ions, which previously had required many thousands of separate
recrystallizations in some cases.   Another example is gas chromatography, which has seen truly spectacular development in recent years.
By multiplication of gas-liquid partition equilibria to occur in many
stages, even supposedly pure distillation fractions have been resolved into
several separate components.   Once a separation has been effected, the
quantitative determination by physical means is quite straightforward.

The topic of sampling has long been neglected in analytical chemistry
courses.   Although everyone recognizes that an analysis can be no better
than the sample upon which it was performed, the fundamental principles
are too elusive for rigorous discussion in a first course.   By its very
nature, the sampling operation involves statistical concepts.   For this
reason this topic is reserved for the very end of the book even though it
might appear logical to discuss it first, as the first "unit operation" of
quantitative analysis.

The field of statistics has made important contributions to the less
exact sciences for a long time, but the analytical chemist has been slow
to recognize its important contributions to several phases of his field.
Even today, many practicing analysts and analytical research chemists
do not go beyond calculating the standard deviation of a set of supposedly

identical determinations.   Many seem to have an erroneous notion that
enormous bodies of data are required to use more advanced statistical
methods.   A point that often seems to be overlooked is that a relatively
small number of systematically planned observations may yield much
more information than a larger number of repeated identical observations.
Another concept that may be intuitively difficult to accept is that it is
not the most efficient mode of experimentation to vary each variable
separately and systematically in turn, while holding all the other variables
constant.   A statistical experimental design, properly planned, can lead
to more efficient evaluation of the effects of individual variables, and
in addition it can give information about the interaction of more than
one variable.

In summary, it is the thesis of this book that the field commonly called
"wet analysis" or classical analytical chemistry is still alive with challeng-
ing unsolved problems of a fundamental nature.   By searching for the
answers to these problems, the analytical chemist can make important
contributions not only to the fields of chemical and instrumental analysis
but to the larger subject of chemistry as a whole.

2. Equilibrium and Activity

Many of the practical calculations of the analytical chemist involve reactions carried out at appreciable ionic concentrations; yet the equilibrium constants that are of most fundamental value are the thermodynamic values obtained by extrapolation to zero ionic strength. It is our purpose here to estimate the magnitudes of the errors made by neglecting ionic strength effects and to consider the extent to which it is possible to avoid these errors by suitable corrections.

2-1. The Condition of Equilibrium

A chemical reaction is at equilibrium when the sum of the chemical potentials of the reactants is equal to that of the products. Thus for the reaction

$$m\mathrm{M} + n\mathrm{N} \rightleftharpoons p\mathrm{P} + r\mathrm{R} \tag{2-1}$$

the condition of equilibrium is

$$m\mu_\mathrm{M} + n\mu_\mathrm{N} = p\mu_\mathrm{P} + r\mu_\mathrm{R} \tag{2-2}$$

where μ is the chemical potential. At constant temperature and pressure, the chemical potential is the partial molal free energy, and Eq. (2-2) is equivalent to saying that, at constant temperature and pressure, the free energy change of a reaction is zero at equilibrium.

G. N. Lewis[1] defined the chemical activity a by the equation

$$\mu_i = k_i + RT \ln a_i \tag{2-3}$$

where a_i = chemical activity of species i

R = gas constant

T = absolute temperature

k_i = value of μ_i at $a_i = 1$ and depends on the concentration scale in which a_i is expressed as well as on the temperature and pressure

[1] Lewis, G. N., *Proc. Natl. Acad. Sci. U.S.*, **37**, 45 (1901); **43**, 259 (1907).

Substituting Eq. (2-3) into (2-2), we have

$$\frac{mk_M + nk_N - pk_P - rk_R}{RT} = \ln \frac{a_P^p a_R^r}{a_M^m a_N^n} = \ln \mathbf{K}_{eq} \tag{2-4}$$

and the equilibrium constant

$$\mathbf{K}_{eq} = \frac{a_P^p a_R^r}{a_M^m a_N^n} \tag{2-5}$$

is a function of temperature and pressure.

2-2. The Standard State

According to Eq. (2-3), the change in chemical potential $\Delta\mathbf{\mu}_i$ or free energy ΔF accompanying the transfer of a mole of substance i from a state of activity a_1 to activity a_2 is

$$\Delta F = \Delta\mathbf{\mu}_i = RT \ln \frac{a_2}{a_1} \tag{2-6}$$

The free energy change is determined by the *ratio* of activities. Consequently, we may adopt some *arbitrary* standard state of a substance and assign to it a unit activity at any given temperature and pressure. The value of k_i will depend on the standard state chosen; therefore, the value of the equilibrium constant will depend on the choice of standard states. It is important, therefore, that for each substance in a particular reaction a consistent standard state be chosen.

Pure liquids at the specified temperature and pressure are taken to be in their standard states, that is, to have unit activity. Pure solids in their *most stable crystalline state* are assigned unit activity. Ideal gases are considered at unit activity at unit partial pressure (1 atm). We shall not consider the behavior of nonideal gases.

For solutions, either of two conventions is useful. (1) Each component may be defined as having an activity given by

$$a_i = N_i\gamma_i \tag{2-7}$$

where N_i is the mole fraction and γ_i is the activity coefficient. Obviously, Eq. (2-7) constitutes a definition of γ_i; and, since $a_i = 1$ when $N_i = 1$ (pure substance), $\gamma_i = 1$ for a pure substance. Also, if the activity is equal to the mole fraction (Raoult's law), $\gamma_i = 1$, and the solution is ideal. This convention is most frequently used for mixtures of two or more liquids, for solid solutions, and for situations in which it is convenient to compare the activity in a mixture with that of a pure substance. Thus, for example, the activity of water in a sodium chloride solution may be compared with that of pure water.

The other convention for solutions is to define an activity coefficient by an equation of the type

$$a_i = C_i f_i \qquad (2\text{-}8)$$

where the concentration C_i may be expressed either in moles per liter of solution (molarity) or in moles per kilogram of solvent (molality). In dilute aqueous solutions, the molarity and molality are very nearly equal, but the molarity varies slightly with temperature. Analytical chemists usually find it convenient to express concentration in molarity rather than in molality. To emphasize this distinction, square brackets will be used here to indicate molarity, and f will be used to denote the activity coefficient, rather than γ, which is frequently used by physical chemists who employ molality as a concentration unit.

The term *formal* is used by some authorities to express concentrations based on *formula weights*. Either *weight formal* (formula weights per kilogram of solvent) or *volume formal* (formula weights per liter of solution) units of concentration may be used. The advantage is that there is involved no implication about the actual species present in solution. For example, 8 vF HCl contains 8 formula weights of hydrogen chloride per liter, whatever species may actually be present. We shall, however, use the symbol C to represent *analytical concentration* when we need to distinguish between the moles of solute added per liter and the *equilibrium concentration*, which is represented by the square brackets.

It is experimentally true, as well as theoretically predicted, that the activity coefficient f_i approaches unity as the concentration approaches zero.

In this convention, the standard state is defined by the molar concentration which, multiplied by the activity coefficient at the concentration in question, gives a product of unity. Clearly, there is no simple relationship between this standard state and the pure state of the same substance. For example, 1.5 M sodium chloride solution, in which the activity coefficient of sodium chloride is 0.66, has about unit activity.[1] When an expression for an equilibrium constant is used, such a dual convention need not cause confusion, provided that the same standard state is used that had been used in evaluating the equilibrium constant.

2-3. Debye-Hückel Theory

In 1923, Debye and Hückel[2] made a very important contribution to our knowledge of the theory of solutions by deriving a theoretical expression for the activity coefficients of individual ions and the mean activity coefficients of strong electrolytes.

The derivation is based upon the application of two laws to describe

[1] Harned, H. S., and Nims, L. F., *J. Am. Chem. Soc.*, **54**, 423 (1932).
[2] Debye, P., and Hückel, E., *Physik. Z.*, **24**, 185 (1923).

the interaction among the ions of an electrolyte. These are Coulomb's law (the inverse-square law of attraction for particles of unlike charge and of repulsion for particles of like charge) and the Boltzmann distribution law, which describes the tendency for thermal agitation to counteract the effects of electrical attraction and repulsion. In the simplest form of the Debye-Hückel derivation, the ions are assumed to be point charges and their finite sizes are neglected. We shall first examine the consequences of the simplest treatment (the Debye-Hückel limiting law, or DHLL) and then consider the more exact treatments, which take ion size and ion hydration into consideration.

According to the Boltzmann distribution law,

$$C_i = C_i^\circ \exp\left(\frac{-Z_i\epsilon\psi}{kT}\right) \tag{2-9}$$

where ψ = electrical potential of a point in solution with respect to an electrically neutral point (ψ is positive around a cation and negative around an anion)

$Z_i\epsilon\psi$ = electrical potential energy of ith ion (of charge $Z_i\epsilon$) with respect to a neutral point

C_i° = concentration of ith ion at an electrically neutral point

C_i = concentration of ion at potential ψ

k = Boltzmann constant

T = absolute temperature (kT is a measure of thermal energy)

According to the Boltzmann expression, the concentration of like-charged ions (Z_i and ψ both positive or both negative) is diminished in the vicinity of a particular ion, whereas unlike-charged ions are concentrated to form an *ion atmosphere*. The total charge in the ion atmosphere surrounding a particular ion is equal to the charge of the central ion, because the solution as a whole is electrically neutral.

The distribution of charge around an ion falls off exponentially with distance, and depends upon the temperature, because at higher temperatures thermal agitation tends to counteract the electrical attraction of unlike ions [Eq. (2-9)].

In the simplest derivation, in which the ions are assumed to be point charges, the activity coefficient f_i of an ion of charge $Z_i\epsilon$ in a solvent of dielectric constant D is given by the equation

$$\ln f_i = -\frac{Z_i^2\epsilon^2\kappa}{2DkT} \tag{2-10}$$

The quantity κ, which is proportional to the square root of the concentration of any particular electrolyte, may be interpreted as the reciprocal of the radius of the ionic atmosphere. In other words, the charge in the ionic atmosphere may be regarded as being uniformly distributed over the surface of a sphere of radius $1/\kappa$.

The relationship between κ and concentration is given by

$$\kappa = \sqrt{\frac{8\pi\epsilon^2 N}{1,000DkT}}\ \sqrt{\mu} = 0.33 \times 10^8\ \sqrt{\mu} \qquad \text{for water at } 25°C \quad (2\text{-}11)$$

where $N =$ Avogadro's number and $\mu =$ ionic strength,[1] given by

$$\mu = \tfrac{1}{2}\Sigma C_i Z_i^2 \qquad (2\text{-}12)$$

For any given electrolyte, the ionic strength is proportional to the concentration. Thus, for molarity C of the following electrolytes, we have

$$
\begin{array}{llll}
A^+B^- & \mu = 1/2(C_A Z_A^2 + C_B Z_B^2) & = 1/2(C_A + C_B) = C \\
A^{++}B_2^- & C_A = C \quad C_B = 2C & \mu = 1/2(4C + 2C) = 3C \\
A^{++}B^= & C_A = C_B = C & \mu = 1/2(4C + 4C) = 4C \\
A^{3+}B_3^- & C_A = C \quad C_B = 3C & \mu = 1/2(9C + 3C) = 6C \\
A_p^{m+}B_q^{n-} & C_A = pC \quad C_B = qC & \mu = C(pm^2 + qn^2)/2
\end{array}
$$

The radius $1/\kappa$ of the ionic atmosphere depends upon the charge type of the electrolyte as well as on the concentration, as shown by Table 2-1.

TABLE 2-1. RADIUS OF IONIC ATMOSPHERE $1/\kappa$, CM, CALCULATED FOR AQUEOUS SOLUTIONS AT 25°C FOR ELECTROLYTES A_pB_q OF ION CHARGE Z_A AND Z_B

C, moles liter^{-1}	$Z_A = Z_B = 1$	$Z_A = 2$ or 1 $Z_B = 1$ or 2	$Z_A = 2$ $Z_B = 2$	$Z_A = 3$ or 1 $Z_B = 1$ or 3
10^{-1}	9.5×10^{-8}	5.5×10^{-8}	4.8×10^{-8}	3.9×10^{-8}
10^{-3}	9.5×10^{-7}	5.5×10^{-7}	4.8×10^{-7}	3.9×10^{-7}
10^{-5}	9.5×10^{-6}	5.5×10^{-6}	4.8×10^{-6}	3.9×10^{-6}

It is apparent from Eqs. (2-10) and (2-11) that, for the case of ions of point charge, the Debye-Hückel limiting law (DHLL) takes the form

$$-\log f_i = A Z_i^2\ \sqrt{\mu} \qquad (2\text{-}13)$$

where the constant A is proportional to the $-\tfrac{3}{2}$ power of both the dielectric constant of the solvent and the absolute temperature, and contains the conversion factor to convert natural to Briggsian logarithms. For water at 25°C, A is very nearly equal to 0.5 and we may write

$$-\log f_i = 0.5 Z_i^2\ \sqrt{\mu} \qquad (2\text{-}14)$$

[1] The symbol μ is frequently used in thermodynamics both for chemical potential and for ionic strength. Since we will have little occasion to refer to the chemical potential, it should cause no confusion to use the boldface $\mathbf{\mu}$ for chemical potential and the ordinary μ for ionic strength.

For an ionic electrolyte A_mB_n the *mean activity coefficient* $f_\pm$ is defined by the equation

$$(m + n) \log f_\pm = m \log f_A + n \log f_B \qquad (2\text{-}15)$$

By combining Eqs. (2-14) and (2-15) it can readily be shown that the DHLL can be written

$$- \log f_\pm = 0.5 \sqrt{\mu} \, \frac{mZ_A^2 + nZ_B^2}{m + n} = 0.5 Z_A Z_B \sqrt{\mu} \qquad (2\text{-}16)$$

in which Z_A and Z_B are taken without regard to sign.

It is interesting to observe that G. N. Lewis[1] had introduced the concept of ionic strength before the derivation of the Debye-Hückel equation and had shown that, in very dilute solutions, the logarithm of the activity coefficient of a strong electrolyte is in general a linear function of the square root of the ionic strength. It is a triumph of the Debye-Hückel theory that not only is the linear dependence predicted without any *ad hoc* assumptions but even the slope of the curve is quantitatively predicted. Thus the ionic strength, which had been introduced as an empirical quantity, was given a sound theoretical interpretation.

Example 2-1. Use the DHLL to calculate the activity coefficients of each of the ions and the mean activity coefficient of the salt in a 10^{-4} M solution of potassium sulfate.

Answer. The ionic strength is $3C = 3 \times 10^{-4}$, and $- \log f_{K^+} = 0.5(3 \times 10^{-4})^{1/2}$, or $f_{K^+} = 0.980$. Similarly, $- \log f_{SO_4^-} = 0.5 \times 2^2 \times (3 \times 10^{-4})^{1/2}$, or $f_{SO_4^-} = 0.922$; and $- \log f_\pm = 0.5 \times 2 \times (3 \times 10^{-4})^{1/2}$, or $f_\pm = 0.961$.

According to the DHLL, the activity coefficient of a given ion is determined by its charge and the *total* ionic strength of the solution, not primarily by its own concentration.

For example, in a saturated solution of silver chloride in 0.01 M potassium chloride, the concentration of silver chloride is only about 10^{-8} M and makes no appreciable contribution to the total ionic strength. Nevertheless, the activity coefficient of the silver ion is equal to that of potassium or chloride ions ($= 0.89$, from the DHLL).

The Debye-Hückel limiting law does not take into account the finite sizes of ions. Obviously, if the radii of all (hydrated) ions are equal to a, the nearest approach of their centers is $2a$, and, in calculating the distribution of ions in the ion atmosphere, it is not correct to consider any approach closer than $2a$. The DHLL, therefore, tends to overcorrect for the effects of interionic attraction and repulsion. However, it is useful as an approximation at low ionic strengths.

In their original paper Debye and Hückel took into account the finite sizes of ions and introduced a parameter a, described as "the mean distance of approach of the ions, positive or negative." They derived the

[1] Lewis, G. N., and Randall, M., *J. Am. Chem. Soc.*, **43**, 1141 (1921).

equation

$$- \log f_i = \frac{A Z_i^2 \sqrt{\mu}}{1 + \kappa a}$$

which, in view of (2-11), becomes

$$- \log f_i = \frac{A Z_i^2 \sqrt{\mu}}{1 + 0.33 \times 10^8 a \sqrt{\mu}} \qquad \text{for water at 25°C} \qquad (2\text{-}17)$$

For many ions the ion size parameter a is of the order of 3×10^{-8} cm, or 3Å (angstroms), and

$$- \log f_i = \frac{A Z_i^2 \sqrt{\mu}}{1 + \sqrt{\mu}} \qquad (2\text{-}18)$$

For an electrolyte $A_p B_q$ the mean activity coefficient is given by

$$- \log f_{\pm} = \frac{A Z_A Z_B \sqrt{\mu}}{1 + 0.33 \times 10^8 a \sqrt{\mu}} \cong \frac{A Z_A Z_B \sqrt{\mu}}{1 + \sqrt{\mu}} \qquad (2\text{-}19)$$

We shall refer[1] to Eq. (2-18) or (2-19) as the extended Debye-Hückel equation, or EDHE; this pair of equations will give results appreciably different from the DHLL when $\mu > 0.01$ (that is, $\sqrt{\mu} > 0.1$, appreciable compared with unity). For comparison, some ionic activity coefficients calculated from Eqs. (2-14) and (2-18) are listed in Table 2-2.

TABLE 2-2. CALCULATED ACTIVITY COEFFICIENTS OF IONS

f_{ion} Ion charge	From DHLL, for $\mu =$				From EDHE, for $\mu =$			
	0.005	0.01	0.05	0.1	0.005	0.01	0.05	0.1
1	0.92	0.89	0.78	0.70	0.93	0.90	0.81	0.76
2	0.73	0.63	0.36	0.23	0.74	0.65	0.43	0.33
3	0.48	0.36	0.10	0.039	0.50	0.39	0.15	0.083
4	0.28	0.17	0.017	0.003	0.30	0.18	0.035	0.013

Unfortunately, it is not possible to check the calculated values of f_i by direct experiment, because in principle all experimental methods yield the mean activity coefficient $f_{\pm}$ rather than the individual ionic values.[2] By use of the definition given in Eq. (2-15), the experimentally determined value $f_{\pm}$ can be apportioned to give f_A and f_B. This procedure is theoretically justified only at high dilution, where the DHLL is valid by virtue of the fact that the limiting slope of $\log f_{\pm}$ plotted against $\sqrt{\mu}$ is found experimentally to be $0.5 Z_A Z_B$, as required by Eq. (2-16). At higher

[1] Guggenheim, E. A., and Schindler, T. D., *J. Phys. Chem.*, **38**, 533 (1934).
[2] Lewis and Randall, *op. cit.*

values of μ, where the ion size parameter a must be introduced, the latter must be regarded as a "mean distance of closest approach" for the electrolyte.

Kielland[1] assigned to *each* ion an empirical value of a parameter a and used Eq. (2-17) to calculate its activity coefficient. A selection of

TABLE 2-3. INDIVIDUAL ION ACTIVITY COEFFICIENTS

Ion	Ion size parameter a, Å ($= 10^{-8}$ cm)	Ionic strength			
		0.005	0.01	0.05	0.1
H^+	9	0.933	0.914	0.86	0.83
$(C_3H_7)_4N^+$	8	0.931	0.912	0.85	0.82
$(C_3H_7)_3NH^+$, $\{OC_6H_2(NO_2)_3\}^-$	7	0.930	0.909	0.845	0.81
Li^+, $C_6H_5COO^-$, $(C_2H_5)_4N^+$	6	0.929	0.907	0.835	0.80
$CHCl_2COO^-$, $(C_2H_5)_3NH^+$	5	0.928	0.904	0.83	0.79
Na^+, IO_3^-, HSO_3^-, $(CH_3)_3NH^+$, $C_2H_5NH_3^+$	4	0.927	0.901	0.815	0.77
K^+, Cl^-, Br^-, I^-, CN^-, NO_2^-, NO_3^-	3	0.925	0.899	0.805	0.755
Rb^+, Cs^+, NH_4^+, Tl^+, Ag^+	2.5	0.924	0.898	0.80	0.75
Mg^{++}, Be^{++}	8	0.755	0.69	0.52	0.45
Congo red anion$^-$	7	0.755	0.685	0.50	0.425
Ca^{++}, Cu^{++}, Zn^{++}, Mn^{++}, Ni^{++}, Co^{++}, $C_6H_4(COO)_2^-$	6	0.749	0.675	0.485	0.405
Sr^{++}, Ba^{++}, Cd^{++}, $H_2C(COO)_2^-$	5	0.744	0.67	0.465	0.38
Hg_2^{++}, SO_4^-, CrO_4^-	4	0.740	0.660	0.445	0.355
Al^{3+}, Fe^{3+}, Cr^{3+}, La^{3+}	9	0.54	0.445	0.245	0.18
$\{Co(en)_3\}^{3+}$	6	0.52	0.415	0.195	0.13
Citrate^{3-}	5	0.51	0.405	0.18	0.115
PO_4^{3-}, $Fe(CN)_6^{3-}$, $\{Co(NH_3)_6\}^{3+}$	4	0.505	0.395	0.16	0.095
Th^{4+}, Zr^{4+}, Ce^{4+}	11	0.35	0.255	0.10	0.065
$Fe(CN)_6^{4-}$	5	0.31	0.20	0.048	0.021

[From Kielland, J., *J. Am. Chem. Soc.*, **59**, 1675 (1937).]

Kielland's values is listed in Table 2-3. As a justification of Kielland's procedure can be offered the fact that the values of $f_\pm$ calculated for various electrolytes from the individual ionic values are in satisfactory agreement with the experimental values up to an ionic strength of about 0.1. For mixtures of electrolytes such as are commonly encountered in analytical chemistry, the justification is less straightforward, and the approximation is less exact.[2]

[1] Kielland, J., *J. Am. Chem. Soc.*, **59**, 1675 (1937).

[2] Harned, H. S., and Owen, B. B., "The Physical Chemistry of Electrolytic Solu-, tions," 3d ed., chap. 14, Reinhold Publishing Corporation, New York, 1958.

Nevertheless, the values in Table 2-3 can serve as a useful approximation even in mixed electrolytes up to a *total* ionic strength of about 0.1.

From the Debye-Hückel theory, we can deduce the following guiding principles, which are of practical value to the analytical chemist and which are valid at moderate ionic strengths.

1. In a given solution, neutral molecules may be regarded as ideal in behavior. Ions of ± 1 charge as a group are less ideal; ions of ± 2 charge are still less ideal, etc. In each group, the activity coefficient increases with increasing hydrated-ion radius.

2. In a given solution, ions of a given charge have approximately the same activity coefficients regardless of their individual concentrations.

3. In solvents of low dielectric constant, the deviation from ideality is greater than in solutions of high dielectric constant [A in Eq. (2-13) is larger], and departure from the DHLL occurs at lower ionic strengths. However, if ion association is very pronounced (cf. glacial acetic acid as a solvent, Chap. 4) the ionic strength is so low that activity coefficients may actually be nearer unity than they are in a solvent of high dielectric constant.

2-4. Activity Coefficients of Nonelectrolytes

According to the Debye-Hückel theory, molecular solutes would behave ideally and exhibit activity coefficients of unity at all ionic strengths. Experimentally, it is true that the deviations of activity coefficients from unity are much smaller for molecular solutes than for ionic solutes. Qualitatively, however, it is clear that, if addition of electrolyte has a "salting-out effect," the activity coefficient must increase with increasing ionic strength. Suppose that S_w, the solubility of a nonelectrolyte in water is greater than S_s, its solubility in a salt solution. Both saturated solutions can exist in equilibrium with the pure solid; hence the activities of the nonelectrolyte are equal in the two solutions. Thus $a_w = f_w S_w = a_s = f_s S_s$, leading to $f_s > f_w$.

An electrostatic theory of activity coefficients of nonelectrolytes was derived by Debye and McAulay,[1] who arrived at an equation of the form

$$\log f_0 = k\mu \qquad (2\text{-}20)$$

indicating that the logarithm of the activity coefficient should be proportional to the ionic strength. The proportionality constant k is positive if the solute has a lower dielectric constant than the solvent, as would usually be the case for aqueous solutions. Although Debye and McAulay expressed k as a function of the ionic radii, the relationship has not been found to hold experimentally, and k must be regarded as an empirical constant. As a first approximation, an equation of the form (2-20) is

[1] Debye, P., and McAulay, J., *Physik. Z.*, **26**, 22 (1925).

valid for many solutes up to an ionic strength of the order of unity.[1] The quantity k, called the *salting coefficient*, depends upon the natures of the solute and the electrolyte, and usually has values of the order of 0.01 to 0.10. In a few instances negative values, indicating a "salting in" effect, are noted.

From the practical viewpoint we may conclude that molecular solutes have activity coefficients very near to unity up to an ionic strength of 0.1 and that the deviations are only moderate even at ionic strengths of the order of unity.

2-5. Activity Coefficients at High Ionic Strengths

For solutions of *single electrolytes* of the 1:1 or 1:2 charge types, several theoretical approaches have proved to be useful in interpreting the variation of the *mean* activity coefficient up to relatively high concentrations. Without considering the details, it is of interest to compare some of the methods that have been used to attack this problem.

A purely mathematical refinement of the Debye-Hückel theory was made for electrolytes of symmetrical charge type by Gronwall, La Mer, and Sandved,[2] who used several terms of a power-series expansion of the Boltzmann distribution expression instead of taking only the first-order term as had been done in the original theory. The same approach was extended to electrolytes of unsymmetrical charge type by La Mer, Gronwall, and Greiff.[3] The resulting equations are too complicated to describe in detail. For our purpose it suffices to mention that, although the extended equations lead to a more precise representation of activity coefficient data in the intermediate ionic-strength range, they fail at high ionic strengths. It is clear that the failure is not due to mathematical limitations but rather to fundamental assumptions in the theory.

In an early modification due to Hückel,[4] a term similar in form to Eq. (2-20) was added to Eq. (2-19), yielding

$$\log f_{\pm} = \frac{-AZ_A Z_B \sqrt{\mu}}{1 + \kappa a} + BC \qquad (2\text{-}21)$$

The term BC was included to correct for the change in dielectric constant of the solvent upon addition of electrolyte. Harned and Owen[5] state: "Although there is no doubt that the dielectric constant is altered by addition of ions, it is also certain that this effect is not the only important factor in concentrated solutions. Therefore, this equation must be

[1] Harned and Owen, *op. cit.*, p. 531 *et seq.*

[2] Gronwall, T. H., La Mer, V. K., and Sandved, K., *Physik. Z.*, **29**, 358 (1928).

[3] La Mer, V. K., Gronwall, T. H., and Greiff, L. J., *J. Phys. Chem.* **35**, 2245 (1931).

[4] Hückel, *Physik. Z.* **26**, 93 (1925).

[5] Harned and Owen, *op. cit.*, p. 508.

regarded as mainly empirical." Equations of the form of Eq. (2-21) have been used extensively in the representation of activity coefficient data.[1] Such equations, containing two empirical constants, are satisfactory for 1:1 electrolytes up to an ionic strength of the order of unity. Equations containing second- or higher-order terms of concentration and containing three or more empirical constants have been used, but such equations lack a theoretical foundation and are to be regarded solely as empirical representations of experimental data.

Stokes and Robinson[2] achieved remarkable success with a one-parameter equation, the single parameter being a hydration number. For a salt of the type AB or AB_2 they wrote the equation

$$\log \gamma_{\pm} = \frac{-0.50 Z_A Z_B \sqrt{\mu}}{1 + 0.33 \times 10^8 a \sqrt{\mu}} - \frac{n}{\nu} \log a_w - \log \{1 - 0.018(n - \nu)m\}$$

$$(2\text{-}22)$$

where $\gamma_{\pm}$ = mean activity coefficient, molality scale

μ = ionic strength, in volume units

n = number of water molecules bound by one "molecule" of solute

ν = number of ions per "molecule" of solute

a_w = activity of water

m = molality

The first term on the right-hand side is recognized as the Debye-Hückel term, which is always negative in sign. The second term, or "solvent term," corrects for the decreased activity of water in the salt solution and is always positive in sign because a_w is always less than unity. The third term, or "scale term," takes into account the hydration of the ions, with the consequent binding of n water molecules with ν ions to remove them from acting as solvent molecules. Depending upon whether $n > \nu$, $n = \nu$, or $n < \nu$, the scale term is positive, zero, or negative. Thus, a highly hydrated solute will tend to have an abnormally high activity coefficient, which can even exceed unity at sufficiently high concentrations.

Equation (2-22) as it stands has two arbitrary constants a and n. In principle, however, the ion size parameter a should be related to the hydration parameter n. Stokes and Robinson suggested that the ion size parameter could be estimated from the crystallographic radii of the unhydrated ions and the hydration number n, if it is assumed that the water of hydration is associated largely with the cations of the salt. If a semiempirical relationship between a and n is introduced into Eq. (2-22), the hydration number n becomes the only parameter, which is

[1] Robinson, R. A., and Harned, H. S., *Chem. Revs.*, **28**, 420 (1941).

[2] Stokes, R. H., and Robinson, R. A., *J. Am. Chem. Soc.*, **70**, 1870 (1948).

then found by trial and error. It is noteworthy that the hydration number is regarded as being independent of the salt concentration.

The remarkably good agreement between experiment and the fitted one-parameter equation up to an ionic strength of the order of 4 is evident from Figs. 2-1 and 2-2. In general, the equation breaks down

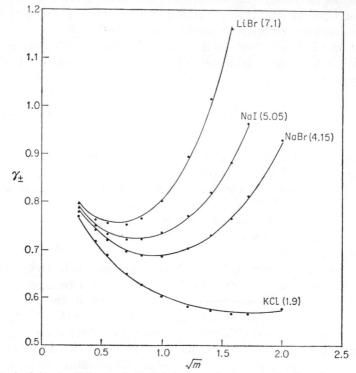

FIG. 2-1. Activity coefficients of alkali halides. Parameter n is given in parentheses. [*With permission from Stokes, R. H., and Robinson, R. A., J. Am. Chem. Soc.,* **70**, 1870 (1948).]

when the product nm, or hydration number times molality, exceeds 10 or 15. Considering the fact that just 55.5 moles of water are available for m moles of salt, it is reasonable to expect that n would begin to decrease with concentration when neighboring ions begin to compete for the available water. The hydration numbers, which are shown in parentheses near each curve, are reasonable in magnitude and show the expected trends with the nature of the cation. However, they should not be taken too literally. For instance, Glueckauf,[1] using a statistical theory, derived an equation quite as effective as Eq. (2-22) in expressing activity coefficients but containing hydration numbers about one-half as large as

[1] Glueckauf, E., *Trans. Faraday Soc.,* **51**, 1235 (1955).

those of Stokes and Robinson. Miller,[1] using a free volume theory, obtains hydration numbers roughly twice as large as those of Stokes and Robinson. Diamond[2] has discussed the significance of the hydration number parameter and has pointed out the necessity of considering other types of ion-water, ion-ion, and water-water interactions. This discus-

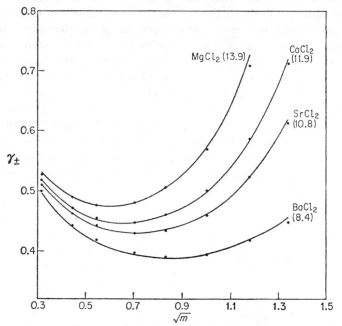

FIG. 2-2. Activity coefficients of alkaline earth halides. Parameter n is given in parentheses. [*With permission from Stokes, R. H., and Robinson, R. A., J. Am. Chem. Soc.*, **70**, 1870 (1948).]

sion is for the most part beyond the scope of the present treatment. However, ion association has long been recognized as a complicating factor.

Ion association was first considered in detail by Bjerrum,[3] and later by Fuoss and Kraus.[4] The formation of ion pairs and higher ion clusters becomes increasingly important as the charges of the ions increase and the dielectric constant of the medium decreases. For particularly large ions, such as the complex ions of heavy metals, the forces of interionic attraction are only moderately large, and even electrolytes of higher

[1] Miller, D. G., *Phys. Chem.*, **60**, 1296 (1956).

[2] Diamond, R. M., *J. Am. Chem. Soc.*, **80**, 4808 (1958).

[3] Bjerrum, N., *Kgl. Danske Vidensk. Selskab*, **7**, no. 9 (1926).

[4] Fuoss, R. M., and Kraus, C. A., *J. Am. Chem. Soc.*, **55**, 1019, 2387 (1933); **57**, 1 (1935); Fuoss, *ibid.*, **56**, 1027 (1934).

charge types can be handled.[1,2] Alkaline earth halides act as strong electrolytes,[3] but alkali metal sulfates and alkaline earth nitrates show some evidence of association,[4] as do the sulfates of divalent metals.[5]

2-6. Activity Coefficients in Mixed Electrolytes

A problem frequently encountered by the analytical chemist is that of maintaining as nearly as possible a constant ionic environment while varying the concentration of one component of an electrolyte mixture. For example, in evaluating the successive formation constants of halide complexes of a metal ion, it is necessary to vary the halide ion concentration over wide limits. The practice generally adopted is to use an electrolyte such as sodium perchlorate, which is believed not to form competing complexes, and to compensate for the increased concentration of, say, sodium chloride, by a corresponding decrease in sodium perchlorate concentration. In this manner, a constant ionic strength is maintained at a high level, say 1 or 2 M. There arises some question of the validity of the assumption that ionic activity coefficients are maintained at a constant level in this procedure.

By measurement of solubilities of sparingly soluble electrolytes or by appropriate cell emf measurements, the *mean* activity coefficient of one electrolyte can be determined as a function of composition in solutions of mixed electrolytes. From the discussion given by Harned and Owen,[6] one can draw the conclusion that, for mixed electrolytes of the 1:1 charge type, the mean activity coefficient of one component, say, AgCl, is accurately determined by the total ionic strength as expected from the Debye-Hückel theory, at least up to ionic strengths of the order of 0.1. For mixtures of unlike charge types, for example, 1:1 and 2:1, the situation is far less satisfactory. For example, in studies of the solubilities of 2:1-charge-type cobalt ammines, the best value of the ion size parameter a for the cobalt salt depended on the specific nature of the cosolute in an unpredictable way.[7] In general, the difficulties are much more pronounced the higher the charge type of the electrolyte.[8]

One may conclude that the procedure of maintaining a constant ionic strength by electrolyte substitution should be practiced only with

[1] Brønsted, J. N., and La Mer, V. K., *J. Am. Chem. Soc.*, **46**, 555 (1924).

[2] Brubaker, C. H., Jr., *J. Am. Chem. Soc.*, **78**, 5762 (1956).

[3] Harned, H. S., and Mason, C. M., *J. Am. Chem. Soc.*, **54**, 1439 (1932).

[4] Righellato, E. C., and Davies, C. W., *Trans. Faraday Soc.*, **26**, 592 (1930).

[5] Davies, *J. Chem. Soc.*, **140**, 2093 (1938).

[6] Harned and Owen, *op. cit.*

[7] Partington, J. R., and Stonehill, H. J., *Phil. Mag.*, [7], **22**, 857 (1936).

[8] For a discussion of activity coefficients in mixtures of HCl with $BaCl_2$, $SrCl_2$, $AlCl_3$, and $CeCl_3$, see Argersinger, W. J., Jr., and Mohilner, D. M., *J. Phys. Chem.*, **61**, 99 (1957).

electrolytes of the same charge type and that the most satisfactory results are to be expected when both electrolytes are of the $1:1$ charge type, as in the $NaCl-NaClO_4$ example cited above. Even here, the procedure is subject to criticism because of the varying charge types of the successive chloride complexes. Thus, the formation constants evaluated in this way cannot be expected to be valid even in solutions alike in ionic strength but widely different in composition. Nor is it valid, as has sometimes been suggested, to evaluate equilibrium constants only at ionic strengths of $1\ M$ and $2\ M$, extrapolating the values thus obtained to zero ionic strength.

2-7. Salt Effects on Equilibrium Constants

The equilibrium constant expression Eq. (2-5), written in terms of activities of the reactants, shows no salt effect. However, in practice, an equilibrium constant is usually determined experimentally in terms of concentrations, and we write

$$K = \frac{[P]^p[R]^r}{[M]^m[N]^n} \tag{2-23}$$

and, substituting concentrations times activity coefficients in (2-5),

$$\mathbf{K} = \frac{[P]^p[R]^r}{[M]^m[N]^n}\frac{f_P^p f_R^r}{f_M^m f_N^n} = K\frac{f_P^p f_R^r}{f_M^m f_N^n} \tag{2-24}$$

We shall distinguish between the boldface $\mathbf{K}$ written in terms of activities (sometimes called the thermodynamic equilibrium constant) and K written in terms of concentrations. The particular case of activity product $\mathbf{K}_{ap}$ and the solubility product K_{sp} are distinguished also by the subscripts. Since the f's in the equation approach unity at infinite dilution, it is usual practice to extrapolate the experimental values of K at various ionic strengths to obtain $\mathbf{K}$, which is the limiting value at infinite dilution.

An estimate of the magnitude of the salt effect can be obtained from the Debye-Hückel theory. Defining

$$p\mathbf{K} = -\log \mathbf{K} \tag{2-25}$$

and
$$pK = -\log K \tag{2-26}$$

we may rewrite Eq. (2-24)

$$pK = p\mathbf{K} + p \log f_P + r \log f_R - m \log f_M - n \log f_N \tag{2-27}$$

and the values of the activity coefficients can be estimated from the DHLL or EDHE. A few examples will serve to illustrate the method.

Example 2-2. Estimate the effect of ionic strength on the solubility product of $BaSO_4$. The solubility equilibrium

$$BaSO_4 \rightleftharpoons Ba^{++} + SO_4^{-}$$

is represented by the activity product $\mathbf{K}_{ap}$, which is independent of ionic strength:

$$\mathbf{K}_{ap} = a_{Ba^{++}} a_{SO_4^{--}} = [Ba^{++}][SO_4^=] f_{Ba^{++}} f_{SO_4}$$
$$= K_{sp} f_{Ba^{++}} f_{SO_4^-}$$

Defining $\mathbf{pK}_{ap} = -\log \mathbf{K}_{ap}$
and $\mathbf{pK}_{sp} = -\log K_{sp}$
we have $\mathbf{pK}_{sp} = \mathbf{pK}_{ap} + \log f_{Ba^{++}} + \log f_{SO_4^-}$
From the DHLL,

$$\log f_{Ba^{++}} = \log f_{SO_4^-} = -0.5 \times 4 \sqrt{\mu}$$
and $$\mathbf{pK}_{sp} = \mathbf{pK}_{ap} - 4 \sqrt{\mu}$$
Or, from the EDHE,

$$\mathbf{pK}_{sp} = \mathbf{pK}_{ap} - \frac{4 \sqrt{\mu}}{1 + \sqrt{\mu}}$$

Example 2-3. Estimate the effect of ionic strength on the two successive ionization constants of a dibasic acid composed of neutral molecules H_2A. For the first ionization

$$H_2A \rightleftharpoons H^+ + HA^-$$
$$\mathbf{K}_1 = \frac{a_{H^+} a_{HA^-}}{a_{H_2A}} = K_1 \frac{f_{H^+} f_{HA^-}}{f_{H_2A}}$$
$$\mathbf{pK}_1 = \mathbf{pK}_1 + \log f_{H^+} + \log f_{HA^-} - \log f_{H_2A}$$

From the DHLL,

$$\log f_{H^+} = \log f_{HA^-} = -0.5 \sqrt{\mu}$$
$$\log f_{H_2A} = 0$$
and $$\mathbf{pK}_1 = \mathbf{pK}_1 - \sqrt{\mu}$$
Or, from the EDHE,

$$\mathbf{pK}_1 = \mathbf{pK}_1 - \frac{\sqrt{\mu}}{1 + \sqrt{\mu}}$$

For the second ionization

$$HA^- \rightleftharpoons H^+ + A^=$$
$$\mathbf{pK}_2 = \mathbf{pK}_2 + \log f_{H^+} + \log f_{A^-} - \log f_{HA^-}$$
From the DHLL,

$$\mathbf{pK}_2 = \mathbf{pK}_2 - 2 \sqrt{\mu}$$
or, from the EDHE,

$$\mathbf{pK}_2 = \mathbf{pK}_2 - \frac{2 \sqrt{\mu}}{1 + \sqrt{\mu}}$$

Example 2-4. The solubility of barium iodate is 22 mg per 100-ml solution. Calculate the solubility in (a) 0.03 M KIO_3, (b) 0.01 M $MgCl_2$.

The molar solubility is $\dfrac{22 \times 10^{-3}}{Ba(IO_3)_2} \times 10 = 4.5 \times 10^{-4} M$.

$$K_{sp} = [Ba^{++}][IO_3^-]^2 = (4.5 \times 10^{-4})(9.0 \times 10^{-4})^2 = 3.65 \times 10^{-10}$$
$$\mu = 3 \times 4.5 \times 10^{-4} = 1.35 \times 10^{-3}$$

From the DHLL, $f_{Ba^{++}} = 0.845$, $f_{IO_3^-} = 0.958$.

$$\mathbf{K}_{ap} = K_{sp} f_{Ba^{++}} f_{IO_3^-}^2 = 2.83 \times 10^{-10}$$

In 0.03 M KIO_3

$$\mu = 0.03 + 3S$$

where S = solubility.   Neglecting S and calculating from the DHLL,

$$f_{Ba^{++}} = 0.451$$
$$f_{IO_3^-} = 0.819$$

$$K_{sp} = \frac{K_{ap}}{f_{Ba^{++}}f_{IO_3^-}^2} = 9.36 \times 10^{-10}$$

$$S = [Ba^{++}] = \frac{K_{sp}}{[IO_3^-]^2} = 1.04 \times 10^{-6}\ M$$

In 0.01 M MgCl$_2$

$$\mu = 0.03 + 3 \times 5 \times 10^{-4} = 0.0315$$

From the DHLL,

$$f_{Ba^{++}} = 0.442$$
$$f_{IO_3^-} = 0.815$$
$$K_{sp} = 9.64 \times 10^{-10}$$
$$S = [Ba^{++}] = x$$
$$[IO_3^-] = 2x$$
$$4x^3 = K_{sp} = 9.64 \times 10^{-10}$$
$$x = 6.2 \times 10^{-4}\ M$$

PROBLEMS

2-1. The solubility of AgCl in water is $1.278 \times 10^{-5}\ M$.   Using the DHLL, calculate the following: (a) the activity product; (b) the solubility in 0.01 M KNO$_3$; (c) the solubility in 0.01 M K$_2$SO$_4$.   *Ans.* (a) 1.620×10^{-10}; (b) 1.43×10^{-5}; (c) 1.55×10^{-5}.

2-2. The solubility product of CaSO$_4$ at 10°C is 6.4×10^{-5}.   (a) Using the DHLL and EDHE, estimate the activity product.   (b) Using the EDHE, calculate the solubility in 0.01 M MgCl$_2$ and in 0.01 M MgSO$_4$.   *Ans.* (a) 1.2×10^{-5}, 1.58×10^{-5}. (b) In MgCl$_2$, $\mu = 0.07$, $S = 1.07 \times 10^{-2}$; in MgSO$_4$, $\mu = 0.065$, $S = 6.2 \times 10^{-3}$.

2-3. Using the data given in Table 2-3, estimate the activity product of mercurous sulfate at an ionic strength of 0.1.   The solubility is 60 mg per 100 ml.   *Ans.* 1.8×10^{-7}.

2-4. Using the EDHE, write expressions for the equilibrium constants of the following reactions as a function of the ionic strength: (a) Ca$_3$(PO$_4$)$_2$(solid) $\rightleftharpoons$ 3Ca^{++} + 2PO$_4^{3-}$; (b) HPO$_4^=$ $\rightleftharpoons$ H$^+$ + PO$_4^{3-}$; (c) Fe(C$_2$O$_4$)$_3^{3-}$ $\rightleftharpoons$ Fe(C$_2$O$_4$)$_2^-$ + C$_2$O$_4^=$; (d) I$_3^-$ + 2S$_2$O$_3^=$ $\rightleftharpoons$ 3I$^-$ + S$_4$O$_6^=$.   *Ans.* $pK = pK - \{\sqrt{\mu}/(1 + \sqrt{\mu})\}y$, where $y = $ (a) 15; (b) 3; (c) -2; (d) -1.

2-5. Using the DHLL, derive an expression for the solubility product of a precipitate A$_m$B$_n$, composed of ions of charge $+Z_A$ and $-Z_B$ units, as a function of ionic strength. *Ans.* $pK_{sp} = pK_{ap} - 0.5(mZ_A^2 + nZ_B^2)\sqrt{\mu}$.

2-6. Show that, for a salt A$_m$B$_n$, the quantity $(mZ_A^2 + nZ_B^2)/(m + n)$ appearing in Eq. (2-16) is equal in absolute magnitude to $Z_A Z_B$.   *Hint:* Using the electroneutrality condition $mZ_A = nZ_B$, express the numerator and denominator to contain the factor $(Z_A + Z_B)$, which can be canceled.

3. Acid-Base Equilibria in Water

The Brønsted-Lowry concept of acids and bases, which will be discussed in more detail in Chap. 4 in connection with nonaqueous solvents, is also useful in discussing aqueous solutions. If all types of proton donors are regarded as acids, it is unnecessary to distinguish between the ionization of acetic acid and the hydrolysis of ammonium ion. Likewise, the behavior of acetate ion as a base ("hydrolysis") is identical in principle with the behavior of ammonia as a base ("ionization"). It is possible, therefore, to simplify considerably the quantitative treatment of acid-base equilibria by eliminating the unnecessary concept of hydrolysis. On occasion we shall find it useful to compare our equations with those derived from the classical viewpoint, mainly to emphasize the advantages of the more modern concept.

3-1. Equilibrium in Pure Water

The autoionization of water can be represented by

$$2H_2O \rightleftharpoons H_3O^+ + OH^- \tag{3-1}$$

or conventionally by

$$H_2O \rightleftharpoons H^+ + OH^- \tag{3-2}$$

if it is understood that the symbol H^+ represents the *hydrated proton*.

The equilibrium constant of (3-2) is generally written as the ion activity product of water

$$\mathbf{K}_w = a_{H^+}a_{OH^-} \tag{3-3}$$

since the activity of pure water is unity by convention.

The equilibrium constant of Eq. (3-1) in terms of activities is

$$\mathbf{K}_i = \frac{a_{H_3O^+}a_{OH^-}}{a^2_{H_2O}} \tag{3-4}$$

22

where K_i is the ionization constant of water, equal to the ion activity product only in pure water.

In an aqueous solution the activity of water is less than that of pure water, a convenient measure being the (partial) vapor pressure p of water in equilibrium with the solution.

Thus

$$a_{H_2O} = \frac{(p_{H_2O})_{soln}}{(p_{H_2O})_{pure}} \qquad (3\text{-}5)$$

However, for all practical purposes, in dilute aqueous solutions the activity of water may be regarded as unity, because, even in 1 M solutions of electrolytes, the vapor pressure is diminished by only 2 to 4 per cent.[1]

3-2. Definition of the pH Scale

The negative logarithm of hydrogen ion *concentration* was originally defined by Sørensen[2] as the pH. For the sake of clarity, this quantity is now often written pcH.

Actually Sørensen did not measure hydrogen ion concentrations, but something more nearly related to activities. He measured the emf of galvanic cells such as

$$H_2, Pt \mid buffer\ X \left| \begin{matrix} KCl \\ salt\ bridge \end{matrix} \right| 0.1\ N\ calomel\ electrode \qquad (3\text{-}6)$$

and attempted to eliminate the liquid junction potentials by an extrapolation procedure due to Bjerrum.[3] At the time of Sørensen's original work, electromotive force measurements were interpreted in terms of the classical theories of Arrhenius and Nernst. Thus, if two such cells were measured with different solutions X_1 and X_2, the difference in cell emf was interpreted as measuring the ratio of hydrogen ion concentrations in the solutions, according to the equation

$$E_1 - E_2 = \frac{RT}{F} \ln \frac{[H^+]_2}{[H^+]_1} \qquad (3\text{-}7)$$

Now, to establish a pH scale, it was necessary to use as a standard a solution of known hydrogen ion concentration, for which Sørensen took a dilute hydrochloric acid solution. He considered that the concentration of hydrogen ion in such a solution was given by αC, where C is the concentration of hydrochloric acid and where α is a "degree of dissociation"

[1] Harned, H. S., and Owen, B. B., "The Physical Chemistry of Electrolytic Solutions," 3d ed., Reinhold Publishing Corporation, New York, 1958.

[2] Sørensen, S. P. L., *Biochem. Z.*, **21**, 131, 201 (1909).

[3] Bjerrum, N., *Z. physik. Chem. Leipzig*, **53**, 428 (1905).

determined from conductance measurements. We now realize that there are several theoretical objections to this procedure: (1) There is evidence that the extrapolation procedure does not actually reduce the liquid junction potential of cell (3-6) to zero; (2) the modern form of Eq. (3-7) is written in terms of activities rather than concentrations; and (3) the concentration of hydrogen ion in dilute hydrochloric acid is C rather than αC.

The Sørensen pH unit, which is often designated by psH, is not, therefore, related directly either to the concentration or to the activity of hydrogen ion. However, it happens to resemble very closely the modern "operational" pH scales, as will be seen below. Clark[1] has given a value of 0.3376 volt for the standard potential of cell (3-6) at 25°C, corresponding to psH = 0. An operational definition of psH is, therefore,

$$\text{psH} = \frac{E - 0.3376}{0.05916} \qquad \text{at 25°C} \qquad (3\text{-}8)$$

Extensive compilations of the psH values of buffer solutions are available.[1,2]

When the concept of thermodynamic activity became established, Sørensen and Linderstrøm-Lang[3] defined the term paH as the negative logarithm of hydrogen ion activity. Thus

$$\text{paH} = -\log a_{H^+} = -\log [H^+]f_{H^+} \qquad (3\text{-}9)$$

Unfortunately, since individual ion activity coefficients cannot be evaluated without extrathermodynamic assumptions, the paH of this definition cannot be rigorously related to experimental quantities. If we consider cell (3-6), the cell emf is given by

$$E = E^0 - \frac{2.303RT}{F} \log (a_{H^+})_1(a_{Cl^-})_2 + E_j \qquad (3\text{-}10)$$

where $(a_{H^+})_1$ = activity of hydrogen ion in buffer X
$\quad(a_{Cl^-})_2$ = activity of chloride ion in 0.1 N potassium chloride
$\quad E_j$ = algebraic sum of the two liquid junction potentials
$\quad E^0$ = cell emf of a hypothetical cell in which $(a_{H^+})_1$ and $(a_{Cl^-})_2$ are unity and the liquid junction potential E_j is zero

From (3-9) and (3-10),

$$\text{paH} = \frac{(E - E^0 - E_j)}{0.05916} + \log a_{Cl^-} \qquad \text{at 25°C} \qquad (3\text{-}11)$$

[1] Clark, W. M., "The Determination of Hydrogen Ions," 3d ed., The Williams & Wilkins Company, Baltimore, 1928.

[2] Britton, H. T. S., "Hydrogen Ions," 4th ed., vol. 1, D. Van Nostrand Company, Inc., Princeton, N.J., 1956.

[3] Sørensen, S. P. L., and Linderstrøm-Lang, K., *Compt. rend. trav. lab. Carlsberg*, **15**, no. 6 (1924).

But, since neither E_j nor a_{Cl^-} can be determined rigorously, the best that can be done is to assume that E_j remains constant between measurements and to lump it together with the other constant quantities of Eq. (3-11) to obtain

$$paH = \frac{E - const}{0.05916} \quad at\ 25°C \tag{3-12}$$

which has exactly the same form as Eq. (3-8) for the psH value. The best value of the constant is about 0.3356 volt;[1] so

$$paH = \frac{E - 0.3356}{0.05916} = psH + 0.04 \tag{3-13}$$

Several attempts have been made to define pH scales that are not subject to the theoretical limitations of psH or paH and yet are capable of experimental measurement. These various scales are discussed in detail by Bates,[2] Gold,[3] and Feldman.[4] Suffice it to say that the "thermodynamic scales" that have precise theoretical meaning are not practical scales in the sense that they fit established or convenient measurement procedures.

From the viewpoint of the analytical chemist, a practical scale of acidity should permit the interpretation of the most important experimental measurements, namely, those with the glass electrode and saturated calomel electrode, represented by the cell

Glass electrode | buffer X | saturated calomel electrode   (3-14)

This cell closely resembles the original Sørensen cell, with a glass electrode substituted for the hydrogen electrode. Inasmuch as a glass electrode is subject to an unpredictable *asymmetry potential*,[5] in practice, a pH measurement is always made by substituting a standard buffer for the unknown buffer X and then comparing the pH of the unknown with the pH of the standard, pH_s, according to the equation

$$pH = pH_s + \frac{(E - E_s)F}{2.303RT} \tag{3-15}$$

Similar calibrations can also be performed conveniently when any pH electrode, such as the hydrogen electrode or quinhydrone electrode, is substituted for the glass electrode in cell (3-14).

Equation (3-15) is the basis of the present practical definition of pH

[1] Bates, R. G., "Electrometric pH Determinations," John Wiley & Sons, Inc., New York, 1954.
[2] *Ibid.*
[3] Gold, V., "pH Measurements," Methuen & Co., Ltd., London, 1956.
[4] Feldman, I., *Anal. Chem.* **28**, 1859 (1956).
[5] Dole, M., "The Glass Electrode," John Wiley & Sons, Inc., New York, 1941.

endorsed by the National Bureau of Standards[1] and other standardizing groups in this country and abroad. The value of pH_s is determined once and for all by making careful measurements of cells such as

$$H_2, Pt \mid solution \ S, AgCl \mid Ag$$

without liquid junction, making reasonable assumptions about activity coefficients in such a way as to make pH_s represent as nearly as possible $- \log a_{H^+} = - \log [H^+] f_\pm$, where $f_\pm$ is the mean activity coefficient of a typical univalent electrolyte in the standard buffer.

Evidently, a pH scale could be defined in terms of a single standard buffer. However, every practical pH reading involves a liquid junction potential, and the difference in liquid junction potential between the readings of cell (3-14) for the unknown and the standard is tacitly involved in Eq. (3-15). The liquid junction potential is sensibly constant for all solutions of intermediate pH values, say, pH 3 to 11, but beyond these limits it varies appreciably because of the appreciable concentrations of ions of unusually high mobility, H^+ or OH^-. This would not affect the definition of pH by Eq. (3-15), but the value of pH would deviate appreciably from the known "best" values of $- \log a_{H^+}$ for solutions of high acidity and alkalinity. For this reason, the National Bureau of Standards has adopted a series of standard values of pH_s. For an experimental determination, it is recommended that the pH standard chosen be that nearest to the unknown. By using two standard buffers, preferably one on each side of the unknown, the response of the pH indicator electrode can be checked, and results of comparatively great reliability can be attained.

At each temperature, a different set of pH_s values must be adopted; in effect there is a different pH scale for each temperature. Selected values of pH_s for several standards are shown for purposes of illustration in Table 3-1. Various other reference solutions are described by Bates.[2]

With regard to the significance of pH values, it may be concluded that, at best, pH may be regarded as an estimate of $- \log a_{H^+}$, but how good an estimate it is depends upon how accurately the liquid junction potential remains constant for the measurement of standard and unknown. Bates[3] suggests that the measured pH of dilute solutions (less than 0.1 M) having pH values between 2 and 12 may be considered to conform to the equation

$$pH = - \log [H^+] f_\pm \pm 0.02 \tag{3-16}$$

[1] NBS Letter Circular LC993, National Bureau of Standards, Washington, D.C., 1950; ASTM Method E 70-52T, American Society for Testing Materials, Philadelphia, 1952.

[2] Bates, *op. cit.*

[3] *Ibid.*, p. 90.

where $f_{\pm}$ is the mean activity coefficient of a typical uniunivalent electrolyte in the solution. For most applications, the pH value may be regarded as a practical measure of acidity, and no attempt need be made to interpret it in terms of single-ion activity.

TABLE 3-1. pH$_s$ VALUES OF NBS STANDARDS

Temp., °C	0.05 M K tetroxalate	KH tartrate (sat'd at 25°C)	0.05 M KH phthalate	0.025 M KH$_2$PO$_4$ 0.025 M Na$_2$HPO$_4$	0.01 M borax
0	1.67	–	4.01	6.98	9.46
15	1.67	–	4.00	6.90	9.27
25	1.68	3.56	4.01	6.86	9.18
30	1.69	3.55	4.01	6.85	9.14
40	1.70	3.54	4.03	6.84	9.07
60	1.73	3.57	4.10	6.84	8.96

[Selected values reprinted with permission from Bates, R. G., "Electrometric pH Determinations," p. 74, John Wiley & Sons, Inc., New York, 1954.]

In many calculations, the hydrogen ion concentration is more accessible than the activity. For example, the electroneutrality condition is written in terms of concentrations rather than activities. Also, from stoichiometric considerations, the concentrations of solution components are often directly available. Therefore, the hydrogen ion concentration is readily calculated from equilibrium constants written in terms of concentration. If a comparison with measured pH values is necessary, an estimation of the hydrogen ion activity coefficient can be made by application of the Debye-Hückel theory.

3-3. Equilibria in a Single Acid-Base System and Water[1]

If a Brønsted acid A or its conjugate base B (cf. page 57) or both are added to water, we have to consider the equilibria

$$A + H_2O \rightleftharpoons H_3O^+ + B \qquad (3\text{-}17)$$

or, conventionally,

$$A \rightleftharpoons H^+ + B \qquad (3\text{-}18)$$

and

$$H_2O \rightleftharpoons H^+ + OH^- \qquad (3\text{-}19)$$

If C_A and C_B are the analytical concentrations of A and B, and [A] and [B] are the equilibrium concentrations, we have the relations

$$[A] = C_A - ([H^+] - [OH^-]) \qquad (3\text{-}20)$$
$$[B] = C_B + ([H^+] - [OH^-]) \qquad (3\text{-}21)$$

which are apparent if we consider the fact that the analytical concentra-

[1] Charlot, G., *Anal. Chim. Acta*, **1**, 59 (1947); DeFord, D. D., *J. Chem. Ed.*, **27**, 554 (1950).

tion of A is diminished by the amount of hydrogen ion produced in reaction (3-18), which in turn is the total hydrogen ion concentration minus the hydroxyl ion concentration.

The equilibrium constant K_{eq} of reaction (3-18) in terms of concentration is

$$K_{eq} = \frac{[\text{H}^+][\text{B}]}{[\text{A}]} = K_a \qquad (3-22)$$

where K_a is by definition the acid dissociation constant, or ionization constant of the acid A.

Solving for hydrogen ion concentration,

$$[\text{H}^+] = K_a \frac{[\text{A}]}{[\text{B}]} = K_a \frac{C_\text{A} - [\text{H}^+] + [\text{OH}^-]}{C_\text{B} + [\text{H}^+] - [\text{OH}^-]} \qquad (3-23)$$

Equation (3-23) is used conveniently for calculating hydrogen ion concentration in various situations that involve a single acid-base system as well as water. To illustrate, we shall consider several examples.

Solution of Strong Acid. A strong acid, by definition, is one for which Eq. (3-17) is complete to the right, so that [A] is zero. From (3-20),

$$[\text{H}^+] = C_\text{A} + [\text{OH}^-] \qquad (3-24)$$

The total concentration of hydrogen ion is that from the strong acid plus that from the water (equal to [OH⁻]). Unless the solution is very dilute ($C_\text{A} < 10^{-6}\ M$) the second term may be neglected.

Consider, for example, $C_\text{A} = 10^{-6}$. As a first approximation,

$$[\text{H}^+] = 10^{-6}$$

and, therefore, $[\text{OH}^-] = 10^{-14}/10^{-6} = 10^{-8}$; this represents only a 1 per cent correction on the first approximation.

Solution of Strong Base. A strong base, by definition, is one for which [B], the equilibrium concentration of base other than hydroxyl ion, is zero. Thus, from (3-21),

$$[\text{OH}^-] = C_\text{B} + [\text{H}^+] \qquad (3-25)$$

an expression analogous to (3-24).

Solution of Weak Acid. If A but not B is added to water, $C_\text{B} = 0$, and, since hydrogen ions are added, $[\text{H}^+] \gg [\text{OH}^-]$; so Eq. (3-23) becomes

$$[\text{H}^+] = K_a \frac{C_\text{A} - [\text{H}^+]}{[\text{H}^+]} \qquad (3-26)$$

which can be written

$$[\text{H}^+] = \sqrt{K_a(C_\text{A} - [\text{H}^+])} \qquad (3-27)$$

and, as a first approximation, if the degree of dissociation is small

$([H^+] \ll C_A)$,

$$[H^+] \cong \sqrt{K_a C_A} \tag{3-28}$$

Example 3-1. Calculate the hydrogen ion concentration of a 10^{-3} N solution of acid HA, of ionization constant $K_a = 10^{-7}$.

Answer. From (3-28),

$$[H^+] \cong \sqrt{10^{-7} \times 10^{-3}} = 10^{-5}$$

Since $[H^+]$ is only 0.01 C_A [see (3-27)], the approximation is valid.

Example 3-2. Calculate the hydrogen ion concentration of 10^{-3} N solution of acid HA, of ionization constant $K_a = 10^{-5}$.

Answer. From (3-28),

$$[H^+]' = \sqrt{10^{-5} \times 10^{-3}} = 10^{-4}$$

From (3-27), $\qquad [H^+]'' = \sqrt{10^{-5}(10^{-3} - 10^{-4})} = 9.5 \times 10^{-5}$

(Note that successive approximations are indicated by primes.)

$$[H^+]''' = \sqrt{10^{-5}(10^{-3} - 9.5 \times 10^{-5})} = 9.5 \times 10^{-5}$$

Therefore, the second approximation was close enough.

Example 3-3. Calculate the hydrogen ion concentration of 10^{-3} N solution of acid HA, of ionization constant $K_a = 10^{-3}$.

Answer. From (3-28), $[H^+]' = \sqrt{10^{-3} \times 10^{-3}} = 10^{-3}$.

From (3-27), no answer is possible, using $[H^+]'$ as a first approximation.

From (3-26), $[H^+]^2 + K_a[H^+] - K_a C_A = 0$.

From quadratic solution, $[H^+] = 6.2 \times 10^{-4}$.

Note that nothing has been said about the charge of acid A, which can be a neutral molecule HA or a cation BH^+ such as the ammonium ion. The acid cannot, however, be an anion HA^-, because in general such an anion is also a weak base and so *two* acid-base systems in addition to water are involved. The classical expression for the hydrolysis of the cation of a weak base

$$BH^+ + H_2O \rightleftharpoons BOH + H^+$$

is an example of Eq. (3-18), and the same equilibrium expression is valid, using the ionization constant of the cation acid BH^+, which is K_w/K_b, the classical "hydrolysis constant."

Example 3-4. Calculate the hydrogen ion concentration of a 0.01 M solution of ammonium chloride, $K_b = 2 \times 10^{-5}$.

$$[H^+] \cong \sqrt{(K_w/K_b)C_A} = \sqrt{(10^{-14}/2 \times 10^{-5}) \times 0.01} = 2.2 \times 10^{-6}$$

Solution of Weak Base. If B but not A is added to water, $C_A = 0$, and, with hydrogen ions removed, $[H^+] \ll [OH^-]$. Equation (3-23) becomes

$$[H^+] = K_a \frac{[OH^-]}{C_B - [OH^-]} = \frac{K_w}{[OH^-]} \tag{3-29}$$

Solving for $[OH^-]$, we have

$$[OH^-] = \sqrt{(K_w/K_a)(C_B - [OH^-])} \tag{3-30}$$

Approximately, if $[OH^-] \ll C_B$,

$$[OH^-] \cong \sqrt{(K_w/K_a)C_B} \qquad (3\text{-}31)$$

Comparing (3-30) or (3-31) with the classical expressions, K_w/K_a is the hydrolysis constant K_h if B is the anion of a weak acid undergoing the reaction

$$A^- + H_2O \rightleftharpoons HA + OH^- \qquad (3\text{-}32)$$

For the classical molecular weak base, such as NH_3, the equilibrium expression

$$NH_3 + H_2O \rightleftharpoons NH_4^+ + OH^- \qquad (3\text{-}33)$$

leads to equations identical with (3-30) or (3-31) with K_w/K_a replaced by K_b, the classical ionization constant of a weak base.

Example 3-5. Calculate the pH of 0.05 M sodium acetate if $K_a = 2 \times 10^{-5}$.
Answer. From (3-31),

$$[OH^-] = \sqrt{(10^{-14}/2 \times 10^{-5}) \times 0.05} = 5.0 \times 10^{-6}$$
$$pOH = 6 - \log 5 = 5.30$$
$$pH = 14 - 5.30 = 8.70$$

Compare with (3-30) to verify approximation.

Example 3-6. Calculate the hydroxyl ion concentration of 10^{-3} M pyridine, $K_b = 10^{-9}$.
Answer. From (3-31),

$$[OH^-] \cong \sqrt{10^{-9} \times 10^{-3}} = 10^{-6}$$

Compare with (3-30) to verify approximation.

Solution of Weak Acid and Its Conjugate Base.   If both A and B are added to water, hydrogen ions may be either added or removed.   Therefore, we have either one of two situations, depending upon whether the solution becomes acidic or alkaline.

For an acidic solution, $[H^+] \gg [OH^-]$, and Eq. (3-23) becomes

$$[H^+] = K_a \frac{C_A - [H^+]}{C_B + [H^+]} \qquad (3\text{-}34)$$

which often can be replaced by the approximate expression

$$[H^+] \cong K_a \frac{C_A}{C_B} \qquad (3\text{-}35)$$

if C_A and C_B are both much greater than $[H^+]$.   Equation (3-35) is sometimes known as the *Henderson equation*.[1]

For an alkaline solution, $[H^+] \ll [OH^-]$, and Eq. (3-23) becomes

$$[H^+] = K_a \frac{C_A + [OH^-]}{C_B - [OH^-]} \qquad (3\text{-}36)$$

[1] Henderson, L. J., *J. Am. Chem. Soc.*, **30**, 954 (1908).

which again reduces to (3-35) if C_A and C_B are both much greater than [OH⁻].

Example 3-7. Calculate the hydrogen ion concentration of a solution containing 0.10 M HA, and 0.002 M A⁻ if $K_a = 10^{-5}$.

Answer. From (3-35),

$$[H^+]' = 10^{-5}\frac{0.10}{0.002} = 5 \times 10^{-4}$$

From (3-34),

$$[H^+]'' = 10^{-5}\frac{0.10}{0.0025} = 4.0 \times 10^{-4}$$

$$[H^+]''' = 10^{-5}\frac{0.10}{0.0024} = 4.2 \times 10^{-4}$$

Example 3-8. Calculate the hydrogen ion concentration of a solution containing 0.001 M HA and 0.1 M A⁻ if $K_a = 10^{-8}$.

Answer. From (3-35),

$$[H^+]' = 10^{-8}\frac{0.001}{0.1} = 10^{-10} \qquad [OH^-]' \cong 10^{-4}$$

From (3-36), $\qquad [H^+]'' = 10^{-8}\frac{0.0011}{0.1} = 1.1 \times 10^{-10}$

3-4. Equilibria in Multiple Acid-Base Systems

When more than one conjugate acid-base pair is in equilibrium with water and its ions, the exact mathematical relationships become extremely complex, especially if a single equation is to represent all possible initial conditions.[1,2] The derivation of such equations has the advantage of pointing out clearly the nature of approximations made in practical applications. In many cases, however, an enormous simplification can be achieved at the outset by using crude calculations to estimate the concentrations of the major species concerned. In most practical cases, a simple equation gives a result as precise as is justified by the reliability of the equilibrium constants that are available. If the concentration levels or equilibrium constants are so abnormal that the simple equations are not valid, the exact equations of Ricci[2] can be used.

Solution of Polybasic Acid. It will be shown that a solution containing only a polybasic acid H_nA and water can almost always be treated by considering only the first step of ionization.

To illustrate, if the dibasic acid H_2A is added to water, we have the equilibria

$$H_2A \rightleftharpoons H^+ + HA^- \qquad K_1 = \frac{[H^+][HA^-]}{[H_2A]} \tag{3-37}$$

$$HA^- \rightleftharpoons H^+ + A^= \qquad K_2 = \frac{[H^+][A^=]}{[HA^-]} \tag{3-38}$$

[1] DeFord, *Anal. Chim. Acta*, **5**, 345, 352 (1951).

[2] Ricci, J. E., "Hydrogen Ion Concentration," Princeton University Press, Princeton, N.J., 1952.

which, together with the stoichiometric equation

$$C_A = [H_2A] + [HA^-] + [A^=] \qquad (3\text{-}39)$$

and the electroneutrality condition

$$[H^+] = [HA^-] + 2[A^=] \qquad (3\text{-}40)$$

give four equations in four unknowns.

The rigorous solution of the equations could be awkward; fortunately it can be avoided by simple approximations.

As a first approximation, ignore the second ionization step. Thus

$$[H^+]' \cong [HA^-]' \qquad (3\text{-}41)$$

and, from (3-27),

$$[H^+]' = \sqrt{K_1(C_A - [H^+]')} \qquad (3\text{-}42)$$

as for a monobasic acid. To check the validity of the approximation, consider (3-38) and (3-41); whence

$$[A^=]' \cong K_2 \qquad (3\text{-}43)$$

which states that the divalent anion concentration is given approximately by the second ionization constant, *independent of the acid concentration.*

If necessary, second and further approximations may be made by combining (3-40) with (3-41) to give

$$[H^+]'' = [HA^-]' + [A^=]' \qquad (3\text{-}44)$$
$$[HA^-]'' = [HA^-]' - [A^=]' \qquad (3\text{-}45)$$

From the new values of $[H^+]''$ and $[HA^-]''$, a better value of $[A^=]$, namely, $[A^=]''$, is calculated, which can be used in place of $[A^=]'$ in (3-44) and (3-45).   However, these further steps are hardly ever necessary, as will be shown by examples of calculations.

Example 3-9. Calculate the hydrogen ion concentration of a 10^{-2} M solution of acid H_2A, of ionization constants $K_1 = 10^{-6}$, $K_2 = 10^{-7}$.
   Answer. From (3-42),
$$[H^+]' = [HA^-]' = 10^{-4}$$
From (3-43), $[A^=]' = 10^{-7}$

Therefore, the second ionization is negligible, and the approximation is valid.
   Example 3-10. Calculate the hydrogen ion concentration of a 10^{-3} M solution of acid H_2A, of ionization constants $K_1 = 10^{-3}$, $K_2 = 10^{-4}$.
   Answer. From (3-42) by quadratic solution,

$$[H^+]' = [HA^-]' = 6.2 \times 10^{-4}$$
From (3-43), $[A^=]' = 10^{-4}$
From (3-44), $[H^+]'' = (6.2 + 1.0)10^{-4} = 7.2 \times 10^{-4}$
From (3-45), $[HA^-]'' = (6.2 - 1.0)10^{-4} = 5.2 \times 10^{-4}$

From (3-38), $[A^=]'' = \dfrac{5.2}{7.2} 10^{-4} = 7.2 \times 10^{-5}$

From (3-44), $[H^+]''' = (6.2 + 0.7)10^{-4} = 6.9 \times 10^{-4}$

From (3-45), $[HA^-]''' = (6.2 - 0.7)10^{-4} = 5.5 \times 10^{-4}$

It will be observed that, even in this extreme case, a very dilute solution of an acid of two closely adjoining ionization steps, the second approximation is essentially correct. In almost all practical cases, the first approximation is sufficient.

Solution of Ampholyte. In this section, the equilibria involved in a solution of the monohydrogen salt HA^- of a dibasic acid H_2A will be considered. In general, the equations will be independent of the charge type of the acid; therefore, they will be valid also for solutions of a salt BH^+A^-, where BH^+ is the cation acid of a weak base B, as well as for intermediate states of neutralization of polybasic acids (H_2A^-, $HA^=$, etc.).

If HA^- is added to water, it can act as an acid or as a base, and the water is subject to autoionization:

$$HA^- \rightleftharpoons A^= + H^+ \qquad K_2 = \frac{[H^+][A^=]}{[HA^-]} \qquad (3\text{-}46)$$

$$HA^- + H^+ \rightleftharpoons H_2A \qquad \frac{1}{K_1} = \frac{[H_2A]}{[HA^-][H^+]} \qquad (3\text{-}47)$$

$$H_2O \rightleftharpoons H^+ + OH^- \qquad K_w = [H^+][OH^-] \qquad (3\text{-}48)$$

From stoichiometric considerations, the concentration of hydrogen ion is that present from (3-46) plus that from (3-48) minus that from (3-47), or

$$[H^+] = [A^=] + [OH^-] - [H_2A] \qquad (3\text{-}49)$$

Or, making use of the equilibrium constants,

$$[H^+] = K_2 \frac{[HA^-]}{[H^+]} + \frac{K_w}{[H^+]} - \frac{[H^+][HA^-]}{K_1} \qquad (3\text{-}50)^*$$

Clearing fractions and rearranging,

$$[H^+]^2(K_1 + [HA^-]) = K_1 K_2 [HA^-] + K_1 K_w$$

or $$[H^+] = \sqrt{\frac{K_1(K_2[HA^-] + K_w)}{K_1 + [HA^-]}} \qquad (3\text{-}51)$$

Equation (3-51) may usually be simplified by appropriate approximations. If C is the analytical concentration of salt, $[HA^-] \cong C$.

In the numerator of (3-51), K_w is often negligible in comparison with K_2C; then

$$[H^+] \cong \sqrt{K_1 K_2 C/(K_1 + C)} \qquad (3\text{-}52)$$

* Equation (3-50) can equally well be derived by considering the OH^- produced and consumed, rather than the H^+.

Now, if C is large compared with K_1, Eq. (3-52) becomes

$$[H^+] \cong \sqrt{K_1 K_2} \qquad (3\text{-}53)$$

so the hydrogen ion concentration to a first approximation is independent of salt concentration.   If $K_1 K_2 > K_w$, the solution is acidic; if $K_1 K_2 < K_w$, it is alkaline.   Apparently the approximation in going from (3-51) to (3-52) is valid in particular if the solution is acidic, for then K_2 cannot be comparable to K_w.

Now, if the solution is alkaline, and Eq. (3-51) is rearranged to give

$$[H^+]^2 = \frac{K_1 K_2 C}{K_1 + C} + \frac{K_1 K_w}{K_1 + C} \qquad (3\text{-}54)$$

at reasonable values of C, K_1 can be neglected in comparison with C, and

$$[H^+] \cong \sqrt{K_1 K_2 + K_1 K_w / C} \qquad (3\text{-}55)$$

which once more reduces to (3-53) if $K_1 K_w / C$ is negligible compared with $K_1 K_2$, as it will be for the usual values of C (K_1/C small) unless K_2 is smaller than K_w.   Thus the limiting forms of (3-52) and (3-55) are both (3-53), but the effects of concentration in the two cases are somewhat different.

Example 3-11.   Calculate the hydrogen concentration of 0.01 M NaHS, taking $K_1 = 10^{-7}$, $K_2 = 10^{-15}$.

Answer.   Since $K_1 K_2 < K_w$, the solution is alkaline.   Because of the small value of K_2, Eq. (3-55) must be used, giving $[H^+] \cong \sqrt{K_1 K_w / C} \cong 3 \times 10^{-9}$.   Note that the approximation (3-53) would give $[H^+] \cong 10^{-11}$.

According to Eq. (3-53), $\sqrt{K_1 K_2}$ is an approximate expression for the hydrogen ion concentration at the first end point of the titration of a dibasic weak acid.   It can also be used in a more general way to describe the successive intermediate end points of the titration curve of a polybasic acid, i.e.,

$$[H^+] \cong \sqrt{K_2 K_3} \qquad \text{or} \qquad [H^+] \cong \sqrt{K_3 K_4}$$

provided that the concentration is not too low and that the other ionization constants are sufficiently different from the two in question for their effects to be ignored.

Equation (3-51) and its simplifications can also be used to describe the hydrogen ion concentration of a solution of the salt of a weak acid and a weak base.   According to the Brønsted concept, a solution of the salt BH^+A^- may be regarded as the half-neutralized solution of an equimolar mixture of the acids HA and BH^+.   In order for the salt BH^+A^- to form, HA must be a stronger acid than BH^+.   Thus the ionization constants K_1 and K_2 may be replaced by the constants K_a and K_w/K_b, where K_b is the classical dissociation constant of the base B.   Thus Eq. (3-51) becomes

$$[H^+] = \sqrt{\frac{K_w K_a (C + K_b)}{K_b (C + K_a)}} \tag{3-56}$$

which is valid if $K_a K_b \gg K_w$.* If the concentration C is large compared with K_a and K_b, Eq. (3-56) reduces to

$$[H^+] = \sqrt{K_w K_a / K_b} \tag{3-57}$$

which is analogous to Eq. (3-53).

Solution of Multivalent Anions. In the Brønsted sense, a multivalent anion A^{n-} is a multiacidic base, which can add protons stepwise. If the protons originate from water, we commonly speak of "hydrolysis," which can be described by the classical hydrolysis constants. Consider, for example, the two stages of hydrolysis of the ion $A^=$:

$$A^= + H_2O \rightleftharpoons HA^- + OH^- \qquad K_{h_1} = \frac{K_w}{K_2} \tag{3-58}$$

$$HA^- + H_2O \rightleftharpoons H_2A + OH^- \qquad K_{h_2} = \frac{K_w}{K_1} \tag{3-59}$$

where K_{h_1} and K_{h_2} might equally well be called the base dissociation constants of $A^=$ and HA^-.

Equations (3-58) and (3-59) bear a relation to each other similar to that between Eqs. (3-37) and (3-38) for the successive ionization steps of multibasic acids. Therefore, in general, the *second and higher stages of hydrolysis may be ignored* except in situations involving extreme dilution and close proximity of the constants K_1 and K_2.

The simple equations (3-30) or (3-31) may, therefore, be used in almost all practical situations involving titration end points. However, in calculating the solubilities of sparingly soluble salts of polybasic weak acids, the concentration of anion may be so low that successive hydrolysis steps must be considered (cf. Sec. 6-3).

3-5. Calculation of Concentrations of Species Present at a Given pH

In many situations it is necessary to be able to calculate the concentrations of the constituents of a solution at a given pH value. Such calculations are involved in finding the relative concentrations of the two forms of an acid-base indicator at a given pH value, in calculating the ionic strength of a buffer, or in calculating the concentration of complexing agents in buffers where the actual complexing species is not the major component of the solution.

We will consider first a single acid-base system, as in the equation

$$A \rightleftharpoons B + H^+ \qquad K_a = \frac{[B][H^+]}{[A]} \tag{3-60}$$

* Ricci, *op. cit.*, p. 125.

Let α_A and α_B be the fractions of the total concentration $[A] + [B]$ in the forms A and B, respectively. Clearly, since $[A] = [B][H^+]/K_a$,

$$\alpha_A = \frac{[A]}{[A] + [B]} = \frac{[H^+]}{[H^+] + K_a} \quad \text{and} \quad \alpha_B = \frac{K_a}{[H^+] + K_a} \quad (3\text{-}61)$$

Consider next a dibasic acid system, H_2A and its ions, and let us calculate the fractions α_0, α_1, and α_2 in the forms H_2A, HA^-, and $A^=$, respectively. The total concentration is

$$C_A = [H_2A] + [HA^-] + [A^=] \quad (3\text{-}62)$$

which, by substitution from (3-37) and (3-38), can be written in terms of $[H_2A]$ as follows:

$$C_A = [H_2A] + \frac{K_1[H_2A]}{[H^+]} + \frac{K_1K_2[H_2A]}{[H^+]^2} \quad (3\text{-}63)$$

so,

$$\alpha_0 = \frac{[H_2A]}{C_A} = \frac{[H^+]^2}{[H^+]^2 + K_1[H^+] + K_1K_2} \quad (3\text{-}64a)$$

similarly,

$$\alpha_1 = \frac{[HA^-]}{C_A} = \frac{K_1[H^+]}{[H^+]^2 + K_1[H^+] + K_1K_2} \quad (3\text{-}64b)$$

and

$$\alpha_2 = \frac{[A^=]}{C_A} = \frac{K_1K_2}{[H^+]^2 + K_1[H^+] + K_1K_2} \quad (3\text{-}64c)$$

The same type of treatment for the general case of a polybasic acid gives a similar result, in which the denominator is a polynomial

$$[H^+]^n + K_1[H^+]^{n-1} + K_1K_2[H^+]^{n-2} + \cdots + K_1K_2 \cdots K_n \quad (3\text{-}65)$$

containing $n + 1$ terms, and in which the fractions $\alpha_0, \alpha_1, \ldots, \alpha_n$ are obtained by taking each of the $n + 1$ terms in turn as the numerator of the fraction, as follows:

$$\alpha_0 = \frac{[H^+]^n}{[H^+]^n + K_1[H^+]^{n-1} + K_1K_2[H^+]^{n-2} + \cdots + K_1K_2 \cdots K_n} \quad (3\text{-}66a)$$

$$\alpha_1 = \frac{K_1[H^+]^{n-1}}{[H^+]^n + K_1[H^+]^{n-1} + K_1K_2[H^+]^{n-2} + \cdots + K_1K_2 \cdots K_n} \quad (3\text{-}66b)$$

$$\alpha_2 = \frac{K_1K_2[H^+]^{n-2}}{[H^+]^n + K_1[H^+]^{n-1} + K_1K_2[H^+]^{n-2} + \cdots + K_1K_2 \cdots K_n} \quad (3\text{-}66c)$$

$$\cdot \quad \cdot \quad \cdot \quad \cdot \quad \cdot \quad \cdot \quad \cdot \quad \cdot \quad \cdot \quad \cdot \quad \cdot \quad \cdot \quad \cdot \quad \cdot$$

$$\alpha_n = \frac{K_1K_2 \cdots K_n}{[H^+]^n + K_1[H^+]^{n-1} + K_1K_2[H^+]^{n-2} + \cdots + K_1K_2 \cdots K_n} \quad (3\text{-}66d)$$

Example 3-12. Calculate the concentration of HPO_4^- in a 0.1 M phosphate buffer of pH = 7, given $pK_1 = 2.16$, $pK_2 = 7.13$, $pK_3 = 12.30$.

Answer. At pH = 7, the denominator is given by

$$10^{-21} + 10^{-16.16} + 10^{-16.29} + 10^{-21.59} = 10^{-15.92}$$

and

$$\alpha_2 = \frac{10^{-16.29}}{10^{-15.92}} = 10^{-0.37} = 0.426$$

The concentration of HPO_4^- is equal to $0.426 \times 0.10 = 0.0426\ M$.

3.6. Buffer Capacity

The *buffer capacity* of a solution is its tendency to resist changes in pH upon the addition of acid or base.   Quantitatively, it is convenient to define[1] the buffer capacity as the number of moles of strong base that, added to a liter of solution, will cause a unit increase of pH.   Since buffer capacity π in general varies with composition (and, therefore, with pH), it is best defined in differential terms; that is,

$$\pi = \frac{db}{d\mathrm{pH}} = -\frac{da}{d\mathrm{pH}} \qquad (3\text{-}67)$$

where $-da$ and db represent, respectively, the number of moles of strong acid or strong base required to bring about a pH change of dpH.

The buffer capacity at any point of a titration is inversely proportional to the slope of the titration curve at that point.   If a titration curve of an acid is plotted in terms of the fraction X of the stoichiometric quantity of base added against pH, then the slope of the titration curve is given by $d\mathrm{pH}/dX$.   But, since $db = C_A\,dX$, where C_A is the analytical concentration of acid at the beginning of the titration corrected for dilution at the point X of the titration curve, we have

$$\pi = \frac{C_A\,dX}{d\mathrm{pH}} \qquad (3\text{-}68)$$

Various authors have derived equations for the slopes of titration curves and for buffer capacities during the entire course of the titration.[2-4] We shall consider in detail only the most important type of buffer solution composed of a weak acid or base and its conjugate, in which the hydrogen ion concentration is given accurately enough for the present purpose by the approximation $[H^+] = K_a C_A / C_B$.   Taking $pcH = -\log [H^+]$ as an approximation to pH,

$$\pi = \frac{db}{d\mathrm{pH}} = -2.3\,\frac{db}{d\ln[H^+]} = -2.3[H^+]\frac{db}{d[H^+]} \qquad (3\text{-}69)$$

[1] Van Slyke, D. D., *J. Biol. Chem.*, **52**, 525 (1922).

[2] Kilpi, S., *Z. physik. Chem. Leipzig*, **A173**, 223, 427 (1935).

[3] Grunwald, E., *J. Am. Chem. Soc.*, **73**, 4934 (1951).

[4] Ricci, *op. cit.*

Considering that the total buffer concentration $C = C_A + C_B$ = constant, we have $dC_B = -dC_A$. Thus the addition of db moles of strong base per liter causes an increase dC_B in the analytical concentration of B and an equal decrease in the analytical concentration of A.

From the expression for $[H^+]$,

$$\frac{d[H^+]}{db} = \frac{d[H^+]}{dC_B} = -K_a \frac{C_A + C_B}{C_B^2} \tag{3-70}$$

and, from Eq. (3-69),

$$\pi = 2.3 \frac{C_A C_B}{C_A + C_B} = 2.3 \frac{C_A C_B}{C} \tag{3-71}$$

To determine the condition of maximum buffer capacity, the derivative $d\pi/dC_B$ is set equal to zero, which is true for $C_A = C_B = C/2$. In other words, for a given total concentration of buffer components, the buffer capacity is at a maximum for equal concentrations of the two components. For a given ratio C_A/C_B, the buffer capacity is proportional to the total concentration C. It is important to realize that, when strong acid or base is added to a buffer solution, the concentrations C_A and C_B of both components are changed. Therefore it is not sufficient to have a high concentration of acid A to buffer against the effect of addition of strong base, or vice versa. This is clearly evident from Eq. (3-71), which contains the product of the two concentrations.

Sometimes a solution of an acid salt is used as a "buffer," for example, in using potassium biphthalate as a pH standard for the calibration of a pH meter. Such a solution has the advantage of showing only small changes in pH with changes of concentration [Eqs. (3-52), (3-55)]. However, since the composition corresponds to the first end point of the titration of a dibasic weak acid, the buffer capacity is actually at a minimum, and it is of interest to evaluate it quantitatively. Ricci[1] has derived an equation for the buffer capacity of an acid salt of concentration C,

$$\pi \cong 2.3 \times 2C \frac{\sqrt{K_2/K_1}}{1 + 2\sqrt{K_2/K_1}} \tag{3-72}$$

For the analytically important case where $K_2 \ll K_1$, this reduces to

$$\pi \cong 2.3 \times 2C \sqrt{K_2/K_1} \tag{3-73}$$

which shows that the buffer capacity is proportional to the salt concentration and becomes smaller as the ratio of K_2 to K_1 decreases.

Example 3-13. Calculate the buffer capacity of the phosphate buffer described in Example 3-12.

Answer. We calculate $[H_2PO_4^-] = 0.10 \times 10^{-16.16}/10^{-15.92} = 0.0575$, and, from Eq. (3-71), $\pi = 2.3 \times 0.0575 \times 0.0426/0.1 = 0.056$ mole liter^{-1}.

[1] Ricci, *op. cit.*, p. 249.

Example 3-14. Calculate the buffer capacity of 0.05 M potassium biphthalate, given that $K_1 = 1.3 \times 10^{-3}$ and that $K_2 = 3.9 \times 10^{-6}$.

Answer. From Eq. (3-73), $\pi = 2.3 \times 2 \times 0.05 \sqrt{3.9 \times 10^{-6}/1.3 \times 10^{-3}} = 0.0126$ mole liter^{-1}, as compared with the more exact value 0.0114 mole liter^{-1} calculated from Eq. (3-72).

3-7. Titration Curves

From the viewpoint of analytical applications, the titration curves of greatest importance are those involving a *strong* acid or base as the titrant,

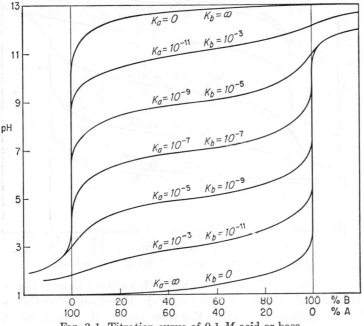

FIG. 3-1. Titration curve of 0.1 M acid or base.

because the sharpest possible end points are thus obtained. According to the Brønsted concept, the titration of monobasic weak acids and of weak bases can be described by the same curves, as illustrated by the family of curves shown in Fig. 3-1, calculated for 0.1 N acid or base, neglecting dilution. Since all the necessary equations have already been presented, the details of the calculations will be omitted here. However, an important practical consideration is that the sharpness of the end point varies with the concentration and the strength of the acid or base being titrated. This is illustrated by the family of curves in Fig. 3-2, calculated for 0.001 N acids or bases.

According to the calculations of Roller,[1] an inflection point occurs at all concentrations for "symmetrical" acid-base titrations, such as titra-

[1] Roller, P. S., *J. Am. Chem. Soc.*, **50**, 1 (1928); **54**, 3485 (1932); **57**, 98 (1935).

tion of a strong acid with a strong base or vice versa, or the titration of all but the last hydrogen of a polybasic weak acid. Moreover, the inflection point in such a titration coincides theoretically with the equivalence point. On the other hand, for an "unsymmetrical" titration, such as

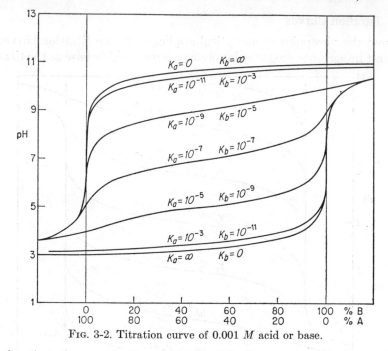

FIG. 3-2. Titration curve of 0.001 M acid or base.

the titration of a monobasic weak acid with a strong base or the last step of the titration of a polybasic weak acid, the inflection point theoretically precedes the equivalence point. For very weak acids at extreme dilution, no inflection at all appears, unless the quantity CK_a is greater than $27K_w$. The theoretical percentage errors of other values of CK_a are given in Table 3-2. The theoretical error is negligible for CK_a greater than 10^{-10} and is, therefore, of concern only over a relatively small range of values of CK_a.

TABLE 3-2. THEORETICAL TITRATION ERROR OF WEAK ACIDS

CK_a	Per cent error (relative)
10^{-8}	-0.0003
10^{-10}	-0.03
10^{-11}	-0.3
10^{-12}	-3.0

[From Roller, P. S., *J. Am. Chem. Soc.*, **50**, 1 (1928).]

A titration curve of a dibasic acid is essentially a composite of the titration curves of an equimolar mixture of two weak acids with dissociation constants K_1 and K_2. In the two buffer regions, where the simple Henderson equation applies, the shape is readily calculated from Eq. (3-35) if $K_1 \gg K_2$. The hydrogen ion concentration at the first end point is approximately given by $\sqrt{K_1 K_2}$, and at the second end point it is very nearly the same as that for the titration of a monobasic weak acid with $K_a = K_2$.

If K_1 is not very large compared with K_2, the above approximations are no longer valid, but, as will be seen below, the precision of the intermediate end point is so low under these conditions that it is no longer of analytical value. From a theoretical viewpoint, however, it is of interest that, if a dibasic acid has two ionization processes that are equivalent and independent, the limiting value of K_1/K_2 is 4. This relationship, which appears to have been first pointed out by Adams,[1] is evident from the following simple consideration.

Suppose that a dibasic acid HAH has two independent ionization processes with equilibrium constants K_1' and K_1'', yielding the anions HA$^-$ and AH$^-$, respectively. These in turn ionize, with equilibrium constants K_2' and K_2'', to yield the same anion A$^=$. Clearly, $K_1' K_2' = K_1'' K_2''$. Now, the ordinarily defined K_1 and K_2 are written in terms of the total concentration [HA$^-$] + [AH$^-$]. It follows that $K_1 = K_1' + K_1''$ and that $K_2 = K_2' K_2''/(K_2' + K_2'')$. Now, if $K_1' = K_1'' = K$, then $K_2' = K_2'' = K$; so $K_1 = 2K$ and $K_2 = K/2$ and $K_1 = 4K_2$.

The titration curve of such an acid can be shown[2] to be identical in every respect with the titration curve of a monobasic acid of one-half its molecular weight and with dissociation constant $K_1/2$.

If the ratio K_1/K_2 exceeds 16, an inflection point appears[3] at the first equivalence point. The titration curve, however, is too shallow for quantitative analytical use, unless K_1/K_2 exceeds 10^3 or 10^4.

3-8. Relative Precision of Acid–Base Titrations

In deciding whether it is feasible to determine an end point we shall follow Benedetti-Pichler,[4] who defined the "relative precision" of an end point as a measure of the steepness of the titration curve in the immediate vicinity of the end point. The *relative precision* is the fraction of the stoichiometric quantity of reagent required to traverse the region represented by a ± 0.1 pH unit on either side of the end point.

[1] Adams, E. Q., *J. Am. Chem. Soc.*, **38**, 1503 (1916). Cf. Bjerrum, N., *Z. physik. Chem. Leipzig*, **106**, 219 (1923); Greenspan, J., *Chem. Revs.*, **12**, 339 (1933).

[2] Ricci, *op. cit.*, p. 95.

[3] Ricci, *op. cit.*, p. 25.

[4] Benedetti-Pichler, A. A., "Essentials of Quantitative Analysis," The Ronald Press Company, New York, 1956.

The change of ± 0.1 pH unit represents about the limit of visual observation of indicator color change using a color comparison method. A relative precision of 10^{-3} indicates an expected end-point sensitivity of the order of 1 part per thousand.

Since both the relative precision and the buffer capacity are inversely related to the slope of the titration curve at the end point, the two quantities are closely related. Taking the titration curve to be approximately linear in the region of the end point, we have for $\Delta pH = 0.2$ unit, in view of Eq. (3-68):

$$\text{rp} = \left(\frac{dX}{dpH}\right)_{x=1} \Delta pH = 0.2 \frac{\pi_{\text{equiv}}}{C} \qquad (3\text{-}74)$$

where π_{equiv} is the buffer capacity at the equivalence point, $X = 1$, and C is the end-point concentration.

We now wish to apply Eq. (3-74) to several cases of practical interest. **Strong Acid–Strong Base Titration.** Taking

$$[H^+] = (1 - X)C + \frac{K_w}{[H^+]}$$

in the region immediately before the end point, we calculate X corresponding to 0.1 pH unit before the end point by setting down the condition $- \log [H^+] = - \log \sqrt{K_w} - 0.1$, or $[H^+] = 1.26 \sqrt{K_w}$. The corresponding value of $1 - X$ is given by $1 - X = \sqrt{K_w}/C(1.26 - 1/1.26)$, or $1 - X \cong 0.5 \sqrt{K_w}/C$. Invoking the condition of symmetry about the equivalence point, we estimate $\text{rp} \cong \sqrt{K_w}/C$.

An alternative approach is to use the value of π_{equiv} given by Ricci,[1] that is, $2.3 \times 2 \sqrt{K_w}$, which gives, by Eq. (3-74),

$$\text{rp} = 2.3 \times 2 \times 0.2 \frac{\sqrt{K_w}}{C} \cong \frac{\sqrt{K_w}}{C}$$

Example 3-15. Estimate the relative precision of the titration of $10^{-4} M$ HCl. *Answer.* Neglecting dilution, $\text{rp} = \sqrt{10^{-14}}/10^{-4} = 10^{-3}$, or 1 part per thousand.

Weak Acid–Strong Base Titration. Taking

$$[H^+] = \frac{K_a(C_A + [OH^-])}{C_B - [OH^-]}$$

and setting $C_A = (1 - X)C$, $C_B = C$, we calculate for

$$[OH^-] = \frac{1}{1.26} \sqrt{\frac{K_w C}{K_a}}$$

---

[1] Ricci, *op. cit.*, p. 138.

the corresponding value $1 - X \cong 0.5 \sqrt{K_w/K_aC}$, from which

$$rp \cong \sqrt{\frac{K_w}{K_aC}}$$

Alternatively, the value $\pi_{\text{equiv}} \cong 2.3 \times 2 \sqrt{K_wC/K_a}{}^*$ substituted into Eq. (3-74) gives $rp \cong 2.3 \times 2 \times 0.2 \sqrt{K_w/K_aC} \cong \sqrt{K_w/K_aC}$.

Example 3-16. Estimate the relative precision of the titration of 10^{-3} M acetic acid.

Answer. Neglecting dilution, $rp = \sqrt{10^{-14}/1.8 \times 10^{-5} \times 10^{-3}} = 0.00075$, or 0.75 parts per thousand.

Intermediate End Points of Polybasic Acid Titration. From Eqs. (3-73) and (3-74), the relative precision is estimated to be

$$rp \cong 2.3 \times 2 \times 0.2 \sqrt{K_2/K_1} \cong \sqrt{K_2/K_1}$$

for the first end point of a dibasic acid titration.

Qualitatively, it is clear that the relative precision should be independent of concentration for reasonably high values of the concentration and relatively large K_2/K_1, because the hydrogen ion concentration is, to a first approximation, independent of initial acid concentration in both buffer regions and also in the vicinity of the first end point.

Example 3-17. Estimate the relative precision of the intermediate end point of the titration of sodium carbonate with a strong acid.

Answer: $rp \cong \sqrt{K_2/K_1} = \sqrt{4.5 \times 10^{-11}/3.5 \times 10^{-7}} = 0.011$

For polybasic acids, the relative precision for the second intermediate end point is similarly estimated by $\sqrt{K_3/K_2}$, etc. The final end point is handled the same way as that of a monobasic weak acid.

3-9. Effect of Temperature on Acid-Base Equilibria

The temperature coefficient of an acid dissociation constant is determined by the enthalpy change of the dissociation reaction, as is evident from the thermodynamic relationship

$$-2.303 \frac{d\mathbf{pK}}{dT} = \frac{d \ln \mathbf{K}}{dT} = \frac{\Delta H°}{RT^2} \tag{3-75}$$

The standard enthalpy change $\Delta H°$ varies with temperature according to

$$\frac{d \Delta H°}{dT} = \Delta C_p \tag{3-76}$$

where ΔC_p is the difference in molal heat capacities of the products and

---

* Ricci, *op. cit.*, p. 161.

reactants. According to Pitzer[1] and Everett and Wynne-Jones,[2] ΔC_p is independent of temperature for many acid dissociation reactions, so it is possible to write

$$\Delta H° = \Delta H_0° + \Delta C_p T \qquad (3\text{-}77)$$

where $\Delta H_0°$ is a hypothetical standard enthalpy change[3] at absolute zero. $\Delta H_0°$ should be regarded as an extrapolated limiting value that has no physical reality, because ΔC_p does not remain constant down to absolute zero. For many acids, $\Delta H_0°$ is a positive quantity and ΔC_p is negative, so that, at some temperature T_m, calculated from $T_m = -\Delta H_0°/\Delta C_p$, $\Delta H°$ is zero. At this temperature $d \ln \mathbf{K}/dT$ is zero, and the ionization constant passes through a maximum (Fig. 3-3). Qualitatively, the maximum

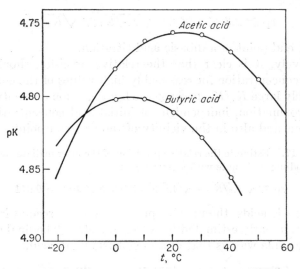

FIG. 3-3. Variation of ionization constant with temperature. [*With permission from Everett, D. H., and Wynne-Jones, W. F. K., Trans. Faraday Soc.,* **35,** 1380 (1939).]

ionization constant occurs when the tendency toward increased proton transfer with rising temperature has been just counterbalanced by the decreasing tendency toward charge separation. The latter effect is explained in part by the decreasing dielectric constant (electrostatic effect) and in part by the decreasing orientation of solvent molecules around the solute ions, with a resultant decrease in heat capacity. For cation acids, there is no net separation of charged species, with the result that the ionization constant increases regularly with rising temperature.

[1] Pitzer, K. S., *J. Am. Chem. Soc.,* **59,** 2365 (1937).
[2] Everett, D. H., and Wynne-Jones, W. F. K., *Trans. Faraday Soc.,* **35,** 1380 (1939).
[3] Or free energy change, since $\Delta F° = \Delta H°$ at $T = 0$.

The quantitative behavior may be expressed as follows.

Since $\qquad\qquad \Delta F^\circ = -RT \ln \mathbf{K} = \Delta H^\circ - T \Delta S^\circ$ $\qquad\qquad$ (3-78)

and $\qquad\qquad \Delta S^\circ = \Delta S_0^\circ + \Delta C_p \ln T$ $\qquad\qquad$ (3-79)

where ΔS° = standard entropy change at temperature T
$\qquad \Delta S_0^\circ$ = intercept of Eq. (3-79); ΔS° corresponding to $\ln T = 0$
$\qquad \Delta F^\circ$ = standard free energy change
from Eqs. (3-77) and (3-79) it follows that

$$-RT \ln \mathbf{K} = \Delta H_0^\circ - T(\Delta S^\circ - \Delta C_p) \qquad (3\text{-}80a)$$

and $\qquad\qquad \ln K = \dfrac{-\Delta H_0^\circ}{RT} + \dfrac{\Delta C_p}{R} \ln T + \dfrac{\Delta S_0^\circ - \Delta C_p}{R} \qquad (3\text{-}80b)$

Equation (3-80) has been shown to be valid for a large number of acids by Everett and Wynne-Jones,[1] who used it to evaluate the various thermodynamic constants. A selection of their values is given in Table 3-3.

TABLE 3-3. THERMODYNAMIC FUNCTIONS FOR ACID DISSOCIATION REACTIONS

Acid	$\dfrac{\Delta H_0^\circ}{2.303R}$	$\Delta C_p,$ cal deg^{-1}	$\Delta F_{298.1}^\circ,$ cal	$\Delta H_{298.1}^\circ,$ cal	$\Delta S_{298.1}^\circ,$ cal deg^{-1}	$T_m,$ °K
Water	6,274.0	−51.0	19,122	13,490	−18.9	564.0
Formic	2,684.1	−41.4	5,114	−40	17.3	297.0
Acetic	2,358.9	−36.6	6,483	−100	−22.1	295.3
Butyric	2,098.0	−34.6	6,570	−700	−24.4	278.0
Benzoic	2,362.6	−36.2	5,682	40	−18.9	300.0
Salicylic	3,327.8	−47.7	4,055	1,000	−10.2	320.0
Glycine:						
1st step	2,455.0	−33.8	3,304	1,100	−7.3	333.0
2d step	4,175.0	−28.5	13,328	10,600	−9.2	671.0
Phosphoric:						
1st step	2,691.8	−47.4	2,895	−1,790	−15.7	260.3
2d step	3,236.4	−47.0	9,823	820	−30.2	315.6
Ammonium ion	2,706.0	0.0	12,562	12,400	−0.54	–
Methyl-ammonium ion	2,374.0	+7.5	14,484	13,092	−4.7	–
Anilinium ion	1,553.0	0.0	6,265	7,105	2.8	–

[By permission from Everett, D. H., and Wynne-Jones, W. F. K., *Trans. Faraday Soc.*, **35**, 1380 (1939).]

It is noteworthy that, for various uncharged acids, the quantity ΔC_p has a relatively large and constant negative value, of the order of -40 cal

[1] Everett and Wynne-Jones, *op. cit.*

deg^{-1}. Evidently this regularity is associated with the formation of a hydrogen ion and an anion the nature of which exerts only a minor effect. The temperature T_m of maximum ionization constant falls below 25°C for acids showing negative $\Delta H_{298.1}$ values. For water, T_m is so high that a regular increase in ionization constant is observed. The entropy changes $\Delta S°$ also have large negative values, primarily because of the pronounced orientation of solvent molecules in the immediate vicinity of the ions.

Baughan[1] has considered the temperature dependence of ionization constants in relation to changes of dielectric constant. He found that the simple electrostatic model developed by Gurney,[2] which takes into consideration the electrical work of separation of charges in a medium of dielectric constant D, properly accounts for the temperature effects for uncharged or anionic acids. For cationic species forming dipolar ions (amino acids) the simple electrostatic model is no longer adequate.

For certain cationic acids, e.g., anilinium or ammonium ions, the temperature dependence is adequately expressed[3] by

$$\log \mathbf{K} = A - \frac{B}{T}$$

which corresponds to Eq. (3-80) with $\Delta C_p = 0$. For methyl anilinium ion (Table 3-3), ΔC_p is a small positive quantity. In either case, there is no maximum in the curve of $\log \mathbf{K}$ against temperature. Corresponding to the large positive ΔH values, a regular increase in ionization constant with increasing temperature is observed. The entropy change is smaller than for uncharged or anionic acids, because of the relatively small net change in orientation of solvent molecules.

It is interesting to contrast this viewpoint with the classical description of the temperature effect.[4] For the "salt of a weak base" the hydrogen ion concentration is given by

$$[H^+] = \sqrt{(K_w/K_b)C_s}$$

where K_b (like K_a) is insensitive to temperature but K_w increases rapidly with temperature. It is, of course, more straightforward to consider the proton transfer from BH^+ to water in a single step.

3-10. Acid-Base Indicators

According to the classical theory of acid-base indicators due originally to Wilhelm Ostwald, it is convenient to distinguish between *indicator acids* and *indicator bases*, depending upon whether the molecular form of

[1] Baughan, E. C., *J. Chem. Phys.*, **7**, 951 (1939).
[2] Gurney, R. W., *J. Chem. Phys.*, **6**, 499 (1938).
[3] Baughan, *op. cit.*
[4] Schoorl, N., *Chem. Weekblad*, **3**, 719, 771, 807 (1903).

the indicator is an acid or a base.[1] The Brønsted concept of acids and bases, however, makes it unnecessary to make this distinction. Instead, emphasis is placed upon the charge types of the acid and alkaline forms of the indicator, which are important in relation to salt and solvent effects and the effect of temperature.

It is beyond the scope of this book to discuss the large number of acid-base indicators that are available. Instead, a selection (Table 3-4) of three common types of commonly used indicators (phthaleins, sulfonephthaleins, and azo compounds) covering a wide pH range, will be considered.

TABLE 3-4. TRANSITION INTERVALS OF COMMON ACID-BASE INDICATORS

Trade name	Chemical name	Acid color	Base color	pH transition interval
Thymol blue	Thymolsulfonephthalein	Red	Yellow	1.2– 2.8
Tropaeolin OO	Diphenylaminoazo-p-benzenesulfonic acid	Red	Yellow	1.3– 3.0
Methyl yellow	p-Dimethylaminoazobenzene	Red	Yellow	2.9– 4.0
Methyl orange	p-Dimethylaminazobenzenesulfonic acid	Red	Orange-yellow	3.1– 4.4
Bromcresol green	Tetrabromo-m-cresolsulfonephthalein	Yellow	Blue	3.8– 5.4
Methyl red	Dimethylaminoazobenzene-o-carboxylic acid	Red	Yellow	4.2– 6.3
Bromthymol blue	Dibromothymolsulfonephthalein	Yellow	Blue	6.0– 7.6
Phenol red	Phenolsulfonephthalein	Yellow	Red	6.4– 8.0
Cresol red	o-Cresolsulfonephthalein	Yellow	Red	7.0 8.8
Thymol blue	Thymolsulfonephthalein	Yellow	Blue	8.0– 9.6
Phenolphthalein	Phenolphthalein	Colorless	Red-violet	8.0– 9.8
Thymolphthalein	Thymolphthalein	Colorless	Blue	9.3–10.5

[Abstracted with permission from Kolthoff, I. M., and Laitinen, H. A., "pH and Electro Titrations," p. 29, John Wiley & Sons, Inc., New York, 1941.]

The analytically important color-change reactions of the three types of indicators are represented by the following classical structure changes. For further details and for discussion of the mechanism on the basis of resonance, the reader is referred to the monographs of Kolthoff and Rosenblum[2] and Tomiček[3] and to the papers of Schwarzenbach et al.[4]

[1] Kolthoff, I. M., and Rosenblum, C., "Acid-Base Indicators," chap. 7, The Macmillan Company, New York, 1937.

[2] Ibid.

[3] Tomiček, O., "Chemical Indicators," translated by A. R. Weir, Butterworth & Co. (Publishers), Ltd., London, 1951.

[4] Schwarzenbach, G., et al., Helv. Chim. Acta, 20, 490, 498, 627, 654 (1937).

Phthaleins (example, phenolphthalein):

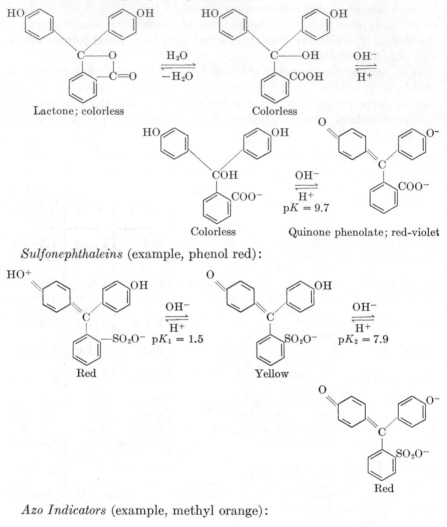

Lactone; colorless   Colorless

Colorless   Quinone phenolate; red-violet

Sulfonephthaleins (example, phenol red):

Red   Yellow

Red

Azo Indicators (example, methyl orange):

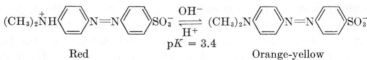

Red   Orange-yellow

The "zwitterion," or dipolar ion form, behaves like a cationic acid (if the influence of the relatively distant negative charge can be ignored). On the other hand, from the viewpoint of salt effects, it can approach the behavior either of a neutral molecule or of two univalent ions, depending upon the ionic strength, as will be seen on page 51.

Color-change Equilibrium. The equilibrium between the acid form In_A of an indicator In and the alkaline form In_B may be written

$$In_A \rightleftharpoons H^+ + In_B \tag{3-81}$$

and the corresponding equilibrium constant is

$$K_{In} = \frac{a_{H^+} a_{In_B}}{a_{In_A}} \tag{3-82}$$

The color of an indicator, as perceived by the eye, is determined primarily by the ratio of concentrations $[In_A]/[In_B]$, which is given by

$$\frac{[In_A]}{[In_B]} = \frac{a_{H^+}}{K_{In}} \frac{f_{In_B}}{f_{In_A}} \tag{3-83}$$

where f_{In_A} and f_{In_B} are the activity coefficients of the acid and alkaline forms of the indicator. Writing Eq. (3-83) in logarithmic form and rearranging,

$$- \log a_{H^+} = pH = pK_{In} + \log \frac{[In_B]}{[In_A]} + \log \frac{f_{In_B}}{f_{In_A}} \tag{3-84}$$

The *apparent indicator constant* pK'_{In} is defined by the equation[1]

$$pK'_{In} = pK_{In} + \log \frac{f_{In_B}}{f_{In_A}} \tag{3-85}$$

The color-change equilibrium at any particular ionic strength (constant-activity-coefficient term) can be described by the equation

$$pH = pK'_{In} + \log \frac{[In_B]}{[In_A]} \tag{3-86}$$

By a color comparison or spectrophotometric method, the ratio $[In_B]/[In_A]$ is determined experimentally. If the eye is able to perceive a color change in the interval $0.1 < [In_B]/[In_A] < 10$, the corresponding pH interval according to Eq. (3-86) is $pH = pK'_{In} \pm 1$. A wider pH interval can be covered spectrophotometrically. Of course, if the color intensity of either form is much greater than that of the other form, the transition interval is unsymmetrical with respect to pK'_{In}. For most indicators, the transition interval judged visually is less than two units, showing that more than 10 per cent must be present in a given form to show a perceptible color. For a one-color indicator, the transition interval is indeterminate unless the total concentration of indicator is defined.

[1] It will be noted that pK'_{In} and pK_a are defined in different ways. Here the activity coefficient of hydrogen ion is omitted in order to express Eq. (3-86) as nearly as possible in terms of the pH measured by the modern operational pH scale.

Mixed Indicators. For certain titrations, particularly in titrating to a definite end-point pH value, it is desirable to sharpen the color change of an indicator. This can be done by adding a substance that exhibits the color complementary to that of one of the forms of the indicator, so that a gray color exists over a relatively narrow pH range.

Two general methods are used. In the first, a pH-insensitive dye is added to produce the complement of one of the indicator colors. A common example is the addition of xylene cyanol to methyl orange.[1] At a pH of 3.8, the blue color of xylene cyanol complements the orange-yellow color of methyl orange to produce a neutral gray shade. Another example is the addition of methyl green, which complements the red-violet alkaline color of phenolphthalein. At a pH of 8.4 to 8.8, a transformation of gray to pale blue is observed.[2]

The other method is to use two indicators of closely adjoining pK'_{In} values, such that the overlapping colors are complementary at an intermediate pH value. Examples are bromcresol green and methyl red, showing a transition color at pH 5.1; bromcresol green and chlorphenol red at pH 6.1; neutral red and bromthymol blue at pH 7.2; cresol red and thymol blue at pH 8.3, and thymol blue and phenolphthalein at pH 9.0. In order to achieve a satisfactory color balance it is necessary to adjust the relative amounts of the two indicators. These and other mixed indicators are described by Kolthoff and Rosenblum[3] and by Kolthoff and Stenger.[4]

Salt Effects. The effect of neutral electrolytes on the color of acid-base indicators is of two types: (1) change in the color intensity (absorbancy) of one or both forms, and (2) effects of the electrolytes on the indicator equilibrium. Of these effects, the first is more apt to be serious at relatively high ionic strengths and is difficult to consider in a general way because the effects are markedly different for various indicators and salts. Thus von Halban and Kortüm[5] noted large increases in the absorbancy of dinitrophenolate ions in the presence of divalent and trivalent cations, but decreases in absorbancy in the presence of univalent cations. Anion effects were also observed, and even nonelectrolytes like urea had an influence. There seems to be no relationship between the magnitude of the effects and the ionic activity coefficient, but rather an interaction between the added solute and the solvent molecules surrounding the indicator ion. Sidgwick, Worboys, and Woodward[6] found that

[1] Hickman, K. C. D., and Linstead, R. P., *J. Chem. Soc. London*, **121**, 2502 (1922).

[2] Kolthoff and Rosenblum, *op. cit.*, p. 172.

[3] *Ibid.*

[4] Kolthoff, I. M., and Stenger, V. A., "Volumetric Analysis," 2d ed., vol. 2, p. 58, Interscience Publishers, Inc., New York, 1947.

[5] Von Halban, H., and Kortüm, G., *Z. physik. Chem. (Leipzig)*, **A170**, 351 (1934); Kortüm, G., *ibid.*, **B30**, 317 (1935).

[6] Sidgwick, N. V., Worboys, W. J., and Woodward, L. A., *Proc. Roy. Soc. London*, **A129**, 537 (1930).

uniunivalent salts increased the absorbancy of both forms of methyl orange with increasing salt concentration in a linear way, so that the color ratio remained essentially constant. Specific anion effects were not observed.

In contrast to the specific salt effects of this type, the general effects of electrolytes on the indicator equilibrium can be interpreted reasonably well on the basis of the Debye-Hückel theory. As a first approximation, at low ionic strengths, indicators of various charge types can be regarded as ionic electrolytes.

Returning to the definition of the apparent indicator constant pK'_{In} [Eq. (3-85)], we see that the salt error is reflected in the variation of pK'_{In} due to the variation of the ratio f_{InB}/f_{InA}.

From the Debye-Hückel limiting law, we have, approximately, for the three charge types of indicators:

$$HIn^+ \rightleftharpoons H^+ + In \qquad pK'_{In} = pK_{In} + 0.5 \sqrt{\mu} \qquad (3\text{-}87)$$

$$HIn \rightleftharpoons H^+ + In^- \qquad pK'_{In} = pK_{In} - 0.5 \sqrt{\mu} \qquad (3\text{-}88)$$

$$HIn^- \rightleftharpoons H^+ + In^= \qquad pK'_{In} = pK_{In} - 1.5 \sqrt{\mu} \qquad (3\text{-}89)$$

There is, however, an important complication that must be taken into account, particularly at higher ionic strengths. Bjerrum[1] pointed out long ago that indicators that exist as "zwitterions," or dipolar ions, should be regarded as existing as two separate univalent ions rather than as neutral molecules. Bjerrum postulated a relationship

$$\log {}_+f_- = 2 \log f_- \qquad (3\text{-}90)$$

between the activity coefficient ${}_+f_-$ of a dipolar ion and f_- of the monovalent anion. In terms of the more modern Debye-Hückel concept, this relationship holds because the electrical work involved in charging two separate ions is twice that for charging a single ion.[2] This is true only if the separation of charges is great enough so that the ionic atmospheres of the two ends of the dipolar ion do not overlap. From Table 2-1 we see that the quantity $1/\kappa$, which is a measure of the radius of the ionic atmosphere, is 9.5 Å$(= 10^{-8}$ cm) at an ionic strength of 0.1 for a 1:1 electrolyte and varies inversely with the square root of the ionic strength. Since this distance is comparable to the distance of separation of the charges in a dipolar indicator ion, the Bjerrum relationship would be expected to hold only at relatively high ionic strengths. According to the results of Güntelberg and Schiödt,[3] the ratio f_{InB}/f_{InA} [Eq. (3-85)] for methyl orange is less than 1 for low ionic strengths ($\mu < 0.1$), but increases with ionic strength until it becomes substantially greater than 1 at high ionic strengths. This behavior is qualitatively reasonable, because the

[1] Bjerrum, Z. physik. Chem. Leipzig, **104**, 147 (1923).

[2] Kolthoff, I. M., and Guss, L. S., J. Am. Chem. Soc., **60**, 2516 (1938).

[3] Güntelberg, E., and Schiödt, E., Z. physik. Chem. Leipzig, **135**, 393 (1928).

dipolar ion behaves like a neutral molecule at very low ionic strengths but like two separate charges at high ionic strengths. Therefore the salt error is negligible in the intermediate interval of ionic strengths.

On the other hand, the sulfonephthaleins show a relatively large salt effect. According to Schwarzenbach,[1] the charge separations may be represented by

$$C_6H_4(SO_3^-)C^+(C_6H_4OH)_2 \rightleftharpoons C_6H_4(SO_3^-)C^+ \begin{matrix} C_6H_4OH \\ \diagup \\ \diagdown \\ C_6H_4O^- \end{matrix}$$

Acid form   Yellow form

$$\rightleftharpoons C_6H_4(SO_3^-)C^+ \begin{matrix} C_6H_4O^- \\ \diagup \\ \diagdown \\ C_6H_4O^- \end{matrix}$$

Alkaline form

If we ignore the dipolar ion character for purposes of first approximation, the principal color-change reaction may be represented by

$$H_{In}^- \rightleftharpoons In^= + H^+$$

which, according to Eq. (3-89), shows a large salt effect.

Actually, however, the quantitative relationships are complicated by the dipolar ion character and by the relatively large separation of charges. Particularly at high ionic strength and in solvents of relatively low dielectric constant, each species is best regarded as consisting of n univalent ions, where n is the total charge including the dipolar charges.[2]

Kolthoff[3] has listed salt corrections for various indicators, taking as a reference a buffer solution of ionic strength 0.1. A selection of values is given in Table 3-5. It is striking that the indicators that exhibit dipolar ion structure (methyl orange, methyl red, thymol blue in its acid range) show very small salt errors. The sulfonephthaleins (bromcresol green, thymol blue, chlorphenol red) and phenolphthalein show relatively large salt effects.

Temperature Effects. From the general consideration of the effect of temperature on acid dissociation constants, (Sec. 3-9) we may expect that the various indicators could profitably be classified by charge type in considering their sensitivity to temperature changes. Indicators that are molecular or anionic acids would be expected to show relatively small changes of K_{In} with temperature. Indeed, the sulfonephthaleins and phthaleins do show a negligible temperature effect.

[1] Schwarzenbach, et al., Helv. Chim. Acta., 20, 490 (1937).

[2] Guss and Kolthoff, J. Am. Chem. Soc., 62, 249 (1940).

[3] Kolthoff, J. Phys. Chem., 32, 1820 (1928).

TABLE 3-5. SALT CORRECTIONS FOR INDICATORS*

Indicator	Ionic strength				
	0.01	0.02	0.05	0.01	0.5 (KCl)
Methyl orange	−0.02	0.00	0.00	0.00	0.00
Methyl red	0.00	0.00	0.00	0.00	0.00
Bromcresol green	0.16	0.14	0.05	0.00	−0.12
Thymol blue:					
Acid range	0.00	0.00	0.00	0.00	0.00
Alk. range	0.12	0.09	0.05	0.00	−0.12
Chlorphenol red	0.13	0.12	0.05	0.00	−0.16
Phenolphthalein	0.12	0.10	0.05	0.00	−0.16

[Reprinted with permission from Kolthoff, I. M., *J. Phys. Chem.*, **32**, 1820 (1928).]
* Correction in pH units to be added to measured value.

Cationic indicator acids might be expected to show relatively large temperature effects. However, such indicators normally exhibit dipolar ion structure (e.g., methyl orange) which makes them behave somewhat like molecular acids. The temperature effects, although larger than those of the phthaleins or sulfonephthaleins, are not so large as might be expected from typical cationic acids.

Another consideration is that the ionization constant of water is especially sensitive to temperature ($pK_w = 14.2$ at 18°C and 12.2 at 100°C).[1] Therefore, indicators that show an invariant pH transition interval (same pK_{In}) at various temperatures are subject to large changes of pOH transition interval, and vice versa.

The effect of temperature on several indicators is shown in Table 3-6. Nitramine (picrylmethylnitramine) is interesting in that it shows a constant pOH interval at 18 and at 100°C.

The effect of temperature on the color of an indicator in a given solution is of course determined (1) by the effect of temperature on the pH of the solution and (2) by its effect on the response of the indicator. Thus the pH of dilute hydrochloric acid is insensitive to heating, whereas the pOH decreases markedly. Thymol blue in its acid range, if adjusted to its transition color with hydrochloric acid, does not change color upon heating. On the other hand, the pOH of dilute sodium hydroxide is insensitive to heating, whereas the pH decreases markedly. Therefore, phenolphthalein adjusted to its transition color with sodium hydroxide shifts to its acid (colorless) form upon heating.

A buffer of acetic acid and sodium acetate changes pH very little upon heating, whereas a buffer of pyridinium ion and pyridine shows a decrease

[1] Kohlrausch, F., and Heydweiller, A., *Ann. Physik.* [4], **28**, 512 (1909).

TABLE 3-6. EFFECT OF TEMPERATURE ON INDICATOR TRANSITION INTERVALS

Indicator	18°C		100°C	
	pH	pOH	pH	pOH
Thymol blue 1	1.2– 2.8	13.0–11.4	1.2– 2.6	11.0– 9.6
Tropaeolin OO	1.3– 3.3	12.9–10.9	0.8– 2.2	11.2–10.0
Methyl orange	3.1– 4.4	11.1– 9.8	2.5– 3.7	9.7– 8.5
Methyl red	4.2– 6.3	10.0– 7.9	4.0– 6.0	8.2– 6.2
Phenolphthalein	8.3–10.0	5.9– 4.2	8.1– 9.0	4.1– 3.2
Thymol blue 2	8.0– 9.6	6.2– 4.6	8.2– 9.2	4.0– 3.0
Nitramine	11.0–12.5	3.2– 1.7	9.0–10.5	3.2– 1.7

[Reprinted with permission from Kolthoff, I. M., and Rosenblum, C., "Acid-Base Indicators," p. 196, The Macmillan Company, New York, 1937.]

of pH (increase of K_a) upon heating. Consequently, methyl red, which is insensitive to temperature in its pH transition interval, shows little change of color upon heating in an acetate buffer, but shifts toward its acid form when heated in a pyridine–pyridinium ion buffer.

Solvent Effects. The effect of addition of alcohol to various indicators has been determined by Kolthoff. A few selected values of the corrections are given in Table 3-7, mainly to illustrate the magnitudes of the

TABLE 3-7. CORRECTIONS FOR ALCOHOL ERRORS*

Indicator	Per cent alcohol by volume:				
	10	20	30	50	70
Tropaeolin OO	−0.06	−0.23	−0.6	−1.4	−1.9
Methyl orange	−0.10	−0.20	−0.47	−1.2	−1.8
Thymol blue:					
Acid range	0.00	0.02	0.07	0.21	0.30
Alk. range	0.15	0.3	0.5	0.8	1.0
Phenolphthalein	0.06	0.10	0.15	1.0	2.2
Thymolphthalein	0.1	0.3	0.6	1.3	1.9

[Reprinted with permission from Kolthoff, I. M., and Rosenblum, C., "Acid-Base Indicators," p. 357, The Macmillan Company, New York, 1937.]
* Corrections to be added to measured pH values.

effects. In pure ethanol and methanol (page 71) the various indicators behave in a regular fashion, depending upon the charge type of the indicator. Molecular and anionic acids show pK increase of the order of 5 units in going from water to ethanol or methanol, whereas cationic acids show only a very small change. The data in Table 3-7 show much less regularity. It appears possible that the effects of alcohol on the actual pH values of the buffers were not adequately taken into account. A reinvestigation using the more recent data on acid dissociation constants in mixed solvents would seem desirable.

Colloid Effects. One of the important limitations on the use of indicators for colorimetric pH determinations is that colloids may cause relatively large errors. Klotz[1] has classified protein effects into four types, which will be mentioned in turn.

1. *Micelle equilibria.* Proteins have been shown[2] to disturb monomer-polymer equilibria of dyes, even in media where both the dye and the protein have similar electrical charges. Such effects are of relatively little analytical significance because the important indicators exist as individual ions or molecules rather than as polymers or micelles.

2. *Adsorption of indicator on protein of opposite charge.* Thiel and Schulz[3] found that the color of methyl orange was strongly shifted toward the alkaline form by proteins such as egg albumin. The positively charged protein forms a complex with the anionic indicator, thus decreasing the concentration of the acid form of the indicator in solution. With bromcresol green, which is anionic in both forms, Danielli[4] found a protein error only in solutions of pH below the isoelectric point of the protein, where the protein is positively charged.

3. *Formation of protein complex with dye ions of the same charge.* The anion of methyl orange has been shown to interact with serum albumin even at pH values above the isoelectric point of the protein.[5]

4. *Alteration of absorption spectrum.* The complex formed between a protein and indicator may have a substantially different absorption spectrum than the free indicator.[6]

Other types of colloidal systems can cause profound changes in the colors of indicators. Inorganic precipitates, e.g., silver halides, preferentially adsorb indicator ions of opposite charges, although adsorption of neutral molecules and of like-charged ions may also occur. Adsorbed hydroxyl ions on the surface of colloidal hydrous oxides may cause an adsorbed indicator to exhibit its alkaline color on the surface. Soaps exert an effect of "solubilization" of indicator molecules in the colloidal soap micelles, thus altering the indicator equilibrium in the aqueous phase.[7]

[1] Klotz, I. M., *Chem. Revs.*, **41**, 373 (1947).
[2] Michaelis, L., and Granick, S., *J. Am. Chem. Soc.*, **67**, 1212 (1945).
[3] Thiel, A., and Schulz, G., *Z. anorg. u. allgem. Chem.*, **220**, 225 (1934).
[4] Danielli, J. F., *Biochem. J.*, **35**, 470 (1941).
[5] Klotz, *J. Am. Chem. Soc.*, **68**, 2299 (1946).
[6] *Ibid.*
[7] Corrin, M. L., Klevens, H. B., and Harkins, W. D., *J. Chem. Phys.*, **14**, 480 (1946).

PROBLEMS

3-1. Cell (3-14) is used to follow the kinetics of the reaction $PtCl_4^- + H_2O \rightarrow PtCl_3(OH)^{-2} + H^+ + Cl^-$ starting with a solution of K_2PtCl_4 of initial concentration $0.010\ M$ in pure water. Assuming that the pH meter reading corresponds to $-\log a_{H^+}$, use the EDHE to calculate the concentration of $PtCl_4^-$ corresponding to a pH meter reading of 3.00. *Ans.* $\mu = 0.031$; $C = 8.8 \times 10^{-3}\ M$.

3-2. A 50-ml aliquot of $0.100\ M\ H_2A$ is titrated with $0.100\ M$ NaOH. The thermodynamic constants K_1 and K_2 are 1.00×10^{-4} and 1.00×10^{-6}, respectively. For each of the titration points listed below, calculate the pH (a) neglecting activity coefficients completely, and (b) using the EDHE to estimate activity coefficients. Volume NaOH added = 0, 10, 50, 75, 100 ml. *Ans.* (a) 2.51, 3.41, 5.00, 6.00, 9.26; (b) 2.51, 3.45, 4.82, 5.67, 9.02.

3-3. Neglecting activity coefficient corrections, calculate the pH of each of the following solutions: (a) Water in equilibrium with CO_2 of the air. $C_{H_2A} = 1.3 \times 10^{-5}$; $K_1 = 3 \times 10^{-7}$, $K_2 = 6 \times 10^{-11}$. (b) Water in part (a) which has been brought to pH = 7.00 with NaOH, and allowed to reach equilibrium again with CO_2. (c) Standard $0.100\ N$ hydrochloric acid, in equilibrium with CO_2 of the air, treated with an equal volume of NaOH, of total alkalinity $0.100\ N$, but contaminated with carbonate to the extent of 2 per cent (relative). *Ans.* (a) 5.74; (b) 6.40; (c) 4.92.

3-4. The titration in Prob. 3-3c is continued (a) to pH 7.0, and (b) to pH 9.0. Estimate the titration errors, in relative percentages. *Ans.* (a) 0.75 per cent; (b) 1.05 per cent.

3-5. Calculate (a) the concentrations of the various forms of orthophosphate in a buffer of total phosphate concentration equal to 0.200 and of pH 8.00; $pK_1 = 2.16$, $pK_2 = 7.13$, $pK_3 = 12.30$. Calculate (b) the ionic strength of the buffer. *Ans.* (a) $[H_3PO_4] = 3.5 \times 10^{-8}$, $[H_2PO_4^-] = 0.024$, $[HPO_4^-] = 0.176$, $[PO_4^{-3}] = 9 \times 10^{-6}$; (b) $\mu = 0.552$.

3-6. Derive the expressions given in Sec. 3-8 for the relative precisions of a strong acid–strong base and a weak acid–strong base titration, and also for the first end point of the titration curve of a dibasic weak acid.

3-7. Derive an expression for the relative precision of the titration of the salt of a weak acid (or a weak base) with a strong acid. *Ans.* $\sqrt{K_a/C} \equiv \sqrt{K_w/K_bC}$.

3-8. Calculate the relative precision values for the following titrations which involve a strong base as the reagent, neglecting dilution: (a) strong acid, $C_A = 10^{-3}$; (b) weak acid, $K_a = 10^{-5}$, $C_A = 10^{-1}$; (c) $K_a = 10^{-5}$, $C_A = 10^{-3}$; (d) 0.1 M phthalic acid, $K_1 = 1.3 \times 10^{-3}$, $K_2 = 3.9 \times 10^{-6}$. *Ans.* (a) 10^{-4}; (b) 10^{-4}; (c) 10^{-3}; (d) first end point 0.055, second end point 1.6×10^{-4}.

3-9. Calculate the relative precision values for the titration of $0.05\ M\ Na_2CO_3$ with $0.1\ M$ HCl, assuming no loss of CO_2. $K_1 = 4 \times 10^{-7}$, $K_2 = 4 \times 10^{-11}$. *Ans.* First end point, 10^{-2}; second end point, $\sqrt{K_1/C} = 10^{-4}$.

3-10. Derive Eqs. (3-72) and (3-73) for the buffer capacity of an ampholyte. From Eq. (3-24) write an expression for the buffer capacity of a solution of a strong acid.

3-11. Compute the buffer capacities of (a) an equimolar acetic acid–sodium acetate buffer of total concentration 0.1 M; (b) same as (a) except for a mole ratio $C_A/C_B = 0.1$; (c) a 0.1 M potassium biphthalate solution; (d) 0.1 M hydrochloric acid. *Ans.* (a) 0.057; (b) 0.019; (c) 0.025; (d) 0.23 mole liter^{-1}.

4. Acid-Base Equilibria in Nonaqueous Solvents

Of the various acid-base concepts, that of Brønsted and Lowry is the most useful to analytical chemists, because it allows a quantitative description of acid-base equilibria in all solvents that can donate or accept protons. It was proposed independently in 1923 by Brønsted[1] in Denmark and Lowry[2] in England. According to this concept, an *acid* is any species (molecule or ion) that acts as a proton donor. In losing a proton, an acid is transformed into its *conjugate base*. If we designate a proton by the symbol[3] p^+, a conjugate acid-base pair is represented by

$$A \rightleftharpoons B + p^+ \qquad (4\text{-}1)$$

A base, in general, is a species that acts as a proton acceptor, thereby forming its conjugate acid.

Equation (4-1) can be said to represent an *acid-base half-reaction*, analogous to an oxidation-reduction half-reaction, which involves electrons rather than the protons involved here. Protons, like electrons, do not exist to any appreciable extent in a free state. Therefore an acid will dissociate to yield protons only if a base is available to accept the protons. Several conjugate acid-base pairs, arranged in order of decreasing acidity of A and, therefore, of increasing basicity of B, are listed in Table 4-1. Clearly, the Brønsted-Lowry definition of acids and bases is more general than the classical Arrhenius definition, for it includes cations, anions, and neutral molecules as acids and bases. Morton[4] has compared

[1] Brønsted, J. N., *Rec. trav. chim.*, **42**, 718 (1923).
[2] Lowry, T. M., *J. Soc. Chem. Ind. London*, **42**, 43 (1923).
[3] The symbol p^+, commonly used in nuclear chemistry to indicate the proton, is used here rather than H^+, which is often used to represent a solvated (especially hydrated) proton.
[4] Morton, A., *Chem. Revs.*, **35**, 1 (1944).

the proton-donor properties of a number of organic compounds, including alcohols, hydrocarbons, and amines.

TABLE 4-1. SOME CONJUGATE ACID-BASE PAIRS

Acid	Base
$HClO_4$	$\rightleftharpoons ClO_4^- + p^+$
H_2OAc^+	$\rightleftharpoons HOAc + p^+$
H_3O^+	$\rightleftharpoons H_2O + p^+$
$HOAc$	$\rightleftharpoons OAc^- + p^+$
NH_4^+	$\rightleftharpoons NH_3 + p^+$
H_2O	$\rightleftharpoons OH^- + p^+$
$EtOH$	$\rightleftharpoons OEt^- + p^+$
NH_3	$\rightleftharpoons NH_2^- + p^+$
OH^-	$\rightleftharpoons O^= + p^+$

The equilibrium constant of the acid-base half-reaction (4-1) could be taken as a measure of the intrinsic acidity of A and its reciprocal as a measure of the intrinsic basicity of B. Thus[1]

$$\mathbf{K}_{acidity} = \frac{a_B a_{p^+}}{a_A} = \frac{1}{\mathbf{K}_{basicity}} \tag{4-2}$$

For a complete acid-base reaction

$$A_1 + B_2 \rightleftharpoons A_2 + B_1$$

the equilibrium constant then is

$$\mathbf{K}_{eq} = \frac{a_{A_2} a_{B_1}}{a_{A_1} a_{B_2}} = (\mathbf{K}_{acidity})_1 (\mathbf{K}_{basicity})_2 \tag{4-3}$$

As an example, consider an acid-base system A,B in a solvent S,

$$A + S \rightleftharpoons B + SH^+ \tag{4-4}$$

The equilibrium constant of Eq. (4-4) is the ionization constant of the acid A in the solvent S, which could formally be considered to be

$$\mathbf{K}_i = \frac{a_B a_{SH^+}}{a_A a_S} = (\mathbf{K}_{acidity})_A (\mathbf{K}_{basicity})_S \tag{4-5}$$

Equation (4-5) illustrates the role of solvent basicity in determining the strength of a solute acid.

Equation (4-5) is of little direct use because there are no methods of evaluating the constants $\mathbf{K}_{acidity}$ and $\mathbf{K}_{basicity}$. Suppose, however, that we wish to compare the ionization constants of two acids A_1 and A_2 in a

[1] Brønsted, *Z. physik. chem. Leipzig*, **A169**, 52 (1934).

given solvent S. From (4-5),

$$\frac{(K_i)_1}{(K_i)_2} = \frac{(K_{acidity})_{A_1}}{(K_{acidity})_{A_2}} \tag{4-6}$$

and the basicity of the solvent drops out. Now, according to this picture, to compare two solvents S_1 and S_2, the ratio $(K_i)_1/(K_i)_2$ for a pair of acids should be independent of the nature of S_1 and S_2.

Actually, Eq. (4-5) does not describe completely the acid-base reaction (4-4) as we usually determine it experimentally. Reaction (4-4) describes only the *proton transfer*, or "ionization," but experimentally we are usually interested in the concentrations or activities of the separate species B and SH⁺. This can be expressed formally:

$$A + S \xrightleftharpoons{\hspace{1cm}} BSH^+ \xrightleftharpoons{\hspace{1cm}} B + SH^+ \tag{4-7}$$

Ionization   Dissociation

In solvents of high dielectric constant the dissociation step may be essentially complete, but in low-dielectric-constant solvents the distinction is important.[1] The equilibrium constants for the two steps are the ionization constant K_i and the dissociation constant K_d. The over-all dissociation constant K_a is usually determined experimentally. The quantitative relationships will be discussed below.

Returning now to the problem of comparing intrinsic acidity constants of the half-reactions listed in Table 4-1, there is another problem, namely, that of standard state. Usually, in any solvent, we take the solvent, by convention, to be in its standard state, and we set its activity equal to unity. Now consider the equilibrium

$$NH_3 + H_2O \rightleftharpoons NH_4^+ + OH^-$$

which has equilibrium constants

$$K_{H_2O} = \frac{a_{NH_4^+} a_{OH^-}}{a_{NH_3}} \quad \text{or} \quad K_{NH_3} = \frac{a_{NH_4^+} a_{OH^-}}{a_{H_2O}} \tag{4-8}$$

depending upon whether water or ammonia is the solvent. Both constants are much smaller than unity; therefore, we can conclude qualitatively that ammonium ion is a stronger acid than water (or, what amounts to the same thing, that ammonia is a weaker base than hydroxyl ion). However, a direct quantitative comparison is not possible, for, even if we introduce the molalities of water and ammonia into Eqs. (4-8), the two expressions do not become identical. If a reference solvent were chosen, so that both ammonia and water could be compared in dilute solution, the strengths of ammonia and hydroxyl ion as bases could be measured quantitatively. However, as will be seen below, the relative

[1] Kolthoff, I. M., and Bruckenstein, S., *J. Am. Chem. Soc.*, **78**, 1 (1956).

strength would actually depend to some extent upon the reference solvent chosen.

In general, the following properties of a solvent are important in determining the acid-base behavior of solutes: (1) the proton donor and acceptor properties, i.e., the acidic and basic properties of the solvent; (2) the autoprotolysis constant; and (3) the dielectric constant. These properties will be discussed in turn.

4-1. Acidic and Basic Properties of Solvents

Solvents may be classified into several types on the basis of their proton donor-acceptor properties; a solvent may be (1) *amphiprotic*, that is, both acidic and basic; (2) *aprotic*, that is, neither acidic nor basic; (3) basic but not acidic; or (4) acidic but not basic. No solvents of the last class are known. Most of the analytically important solvents are amphiprotic in character and, therefore, undergo *autoprotolysis* or self-ionization, as illustrated by the following reactions:

$$2H_2O \rightleftharpoons H_3O^+ + OH^- \tag{4-9}$$
$$2EtOH \rightleftharpoons EtOH_2^+ + OEt^- \tag{4-10}$$
$$2HOAc \rightleftharpoons H_2OAc^+ + OAc^- \tag{4-11}$$
$$2NH_3 \rightleftharpoons NH_4^+ + NH_2^- \tag{4-12}$$

or, in general,

$$2S \rightleftharpoons SH^+ + S^- \tag{4-13}$$

where SH^+ is the solvated proton, or *lyonium ion*, and S^- is the *lyate ion*.[1]

Aprotic solvents, having neither acidic nor basic properties, do not act as ionizing solvents for Brønsted acids or bases. Examples are benzene and carbon tetrachloride.

Certain solvents, such as ether, have weakly basic properties but no appreciable acidic properties. No autoprotolysis equilibrium can be written for such solvents.

Amphiprotic solvents may be dominantly acidic or basic in their properties. Thus we may regard glacial acetic acid as a very acidic solvent, liquid ammonia as a very basic solvent, and ethanol as neither strongly acidic nor basic. Depending upon its acidic and basic properties, a solvent may exert a *leveling effect* (a term originally due to Hantsch[2]) upon solute acids and bases.

Thus, if a solute acid is a much stronger proton donor than the solvated proton in a given solvent, the reaction

$$HA + S \rightleftharpoons SH^+ + A^- \tag{4-14}$$

goes to completion as far as can be determined experimentally, and the

[1] Bjerrum, N., *Chem. Revs.*, **16**, 287 (1935).
[2] Hantsch, A., *Z. Elektrochem.*, **29**, 221 (1923).

acid HA may be said to be *leveled* to the strength of the solvated proton. In water, acids such as $HClO_4$, HCl, and HNO_3 are stronger proton donors than H_3O^+; therefore, all are leveled to the same strength, i.e., that of the hydronium ion. In a less basic solvent, e.g., glacial acetic acid, perchloric acid is a much stronger acid than hydrochloric acid. Glacial acetic acid acts as a *differentiating solvent* because it levels acids at a higher ultimate strength, namely, that of H_2OAc^+. The picture is actually more complicated, as will be seen below, because acetic acid is a solvent of low dielectric constant; therefore, the solvated protons H_2OAc^+ are present largely as ion pairs or higher aggregates. In a solvent more basic than water, e.g., liquid ammonia, solute acids are leveled to the strength of ammonium ion, which is inherently weaker than hydronium ion. Therefore, acetic acid, which is weak in water, is strong in liquid ammonia.

Analogous leveling effects exist for solute bases. In water, any base stronger than hydroxyl ion will be leveled to the strength of the hydroxyl ion. Thus oxide ions or amide ions cannot exist in measurable concentrations because of the quantitative reactions:

$$O^= + H_2O \rightarrow 2OH^- \qquad\qquad (4\text{-}15)$$
$$NH_2^- + H_2O \rightarrow NH_3 + OH^- \qquad\qquad (4\text{-}16)$$

Liquid ammonia acts as a differentiating solvent for much stronger bases than water does. On the other hand, in glacial acetic acid, bases stronger than acetate ion will be leveled to its strength. However, the degree of dissociation is not necessarily the same for all acetates, and so different acetates are not equally basic.

In two solvents S_1 and S_2, both of which have moderately high dielectric constants, a particular acid HA will have dissociation constants that are determined primarily by the basic properties of the solvent. That is, if we write the equilibria:

$$HA + S_1 \rightleftharpoons S_1H^+ + A^- \qquad K_1 \qquad\qquad (4\text{-}17)$$
$$HA + S_2 \rightleftharpoons S_2H^+ + A^- \qquad K_2 \qquad\qquad (4\text{-}18)$$

the ratio K_1/K_2 will be determined by the relative tendencies for S_1 and S_2 to act as bases. Since this is true for all acids of the same charge type, it follows that *the relative strengths of any two acids of the same charge type are approximately the same in all solvents of similar dielectric constants.* This is illustrated by the data of Wooten and Hammett[1] for a number of uncharged acids in *n*-butyl alcohol $(D = 17.4)$ and in water (Fig. 4-1). In spite of the relatively large difference between the dielectric constants of the solvents, the relative strengths of the acids are essentially independent of the nature of the acid. Therefore, the effect must be determined largely by the relative basicities of the two solvents.

[1] Wooten, L. A., and Hammett, L. P., *J. Am. Chem. Soc.*, **57**, 2289 (1935).

As will be seen below, the dielectric constant of the solvent and the charge type of the acid exert important influences; caution must, therefore, be exercised, and indiscriminate comparisons of this sort must be avoided, particularly with solvents of dielectric constant below about 20.

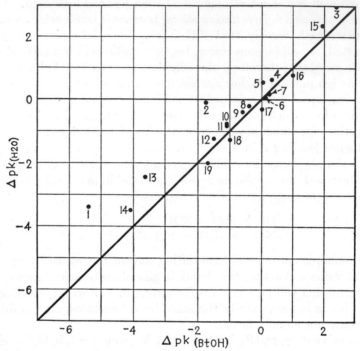

FIG. 4-1. Strengths of acids in water and *n*-butyl alcohol relative to benzoic acid in each solvent. (*With permission from Hammett, L. P., "Physical Organic Chemistry," Fig. IX-1, p. 259, McGraw-Hill Book Company, Inc., New York, 1940.*)

4-2. The Autoprotolysis Constant

In general, the extent of ionization of a pure amphiprotic solvent is measured by the autoprotolysis constant K_s, defined by

$$2S \rightleftharpoons SH^+ + S^- \qquad K_s = a_{SH^+}a_{S^-} \tag{4-19}$$

Since the autoprotolysis reaction results in the formation of both solvent cations and anions, the autoprotolysis constant is a measure of the differentiating ability of a solvent. If a solvent has a relatively large K_s, its leveling influence prohibits the existence in it of a wide range of acid strengths or basic strengths.

Since autoprotolysis is an acid-base reaction in which one molecule of solvent acts as an acid and another as a base, the extent of autoprotolysis is determined (1) by the acid strength, (2) by the basic strength, and (3) by the dielectric constant of the solvent.   The acid strength and basic strength are not reciprocally related, because, for each autoprotolysis reaction, we are concerned with *two* acid-base conjugate pairs.   Thus, to compare the acidities of two solvents S_1 and S_2, it is necessary to determine the equilibrium constant of the reaction

$$S_1 + S_2^- \rightleftharpoons S_1^- + S_2 \tag{4-20}$$

whereas, to compare basicities, one determines the equilibrium constant of the reaction

$$S_1H^+ + S_2 \rightleftharpoons S_1 + S_2H^+ \tag{4-21}$$

For example, comparing ethanol and water as acids in isopropanol solution, Hine and Hine[1] found ethanol to be 0.95 as acidic as water, but Kolthoff[2] found ethanol to be 0.0025 as basic as water.   Similarly, Goldschmidt and Dahll[3] found methanol to be about 0.01 as basic as water, but Hine and Hine found methanol to be 3.3 times as acidic as water.   Thus, on the basis of acid and basic properties alone, we might expect the autoprotolysis constants of ethanol and methanol to be 2.4×10^{-17} and 3.3×10^{-16}, respectively.   The actual values are smaller: 3×10^{-20} for ethanol[4] and 2×10^{-17} for methanol.[5]   Evidently the low dielectric constants (25 and 32, respectively) cause the degree of dissociation to be smaller than would be expected on the basis of acid-base properties alone.   The associated structure of water and alcohols in the liquid state causes complications in any estimate of this type, because the relative acidities and basicities are measured in another solvent where association is minimized.

The very low autoprotolysis constant of liquid ammonia (10^{-33} at $-50°C$)[6] suggests that the strongly basic properties of ammonia in comparison with water are more than counterbalanced by the very weak acidic properties.   Once more, the relatively low dielectric constant (22) contributes to a minor extent.

Glacial acetic acid represents the other extreme from ammonia, that of a solvent strongly acidic but very weakly basic compared with water.   These two factors by themselves would cause glacial acetic acid to have a relatively high autoprotolysis constant.   However, owing to the low

[1] Hine, J., and Hine, M., *J. Am. Chem. Soc.*, **74**, 5266 (1952).

[2] Kolthoff, *J. Phys. Chem.*, **35**, 2732 (1931).

[3] Goldschmidt, H., and Dahll, P., *Z. phys. Chem. Leipzig*, **108**, 121 (1924); cf. Goldschmidt, *ibid.*, **60**, 728 (1907); **81**, 30 (1912); **89**, 129 (1914).

[4] Kilpi, S., and Warsila, H., *Z. physik. Chem. Leipzig*, **A177**, 427 (1936).

[5] Bjerrum, N., Unmack, A., and Zechmeister, L., *Kgl. Danske Videnskab Selskab, Mat. fys. Medd.*, **5**, no. 11 (1925).

[6] Pleskov, V. A., and Monosson, A. M., *Acta Physicochim. U.R.S.S.*, **1**, 713 (1935).

dielectric constant (6.13), the autoprotolysis constant turns out to be about the same as that of water[1] (pK_s = 14.45).

Formic acid is more acidic than acetic acid, but has a high dielectric constant (62). The autoprotolysis constant is so large (pK_s = 6.2)[2] that formic acid is relatively useless as a titration medium. Mixtures of formic acid with low-dielectric-constant solvents could be of interest, however. Sulfuric acid likewise has a high autoprotolysis constant (pK_s = 3.85) and a high dielectric constant. Although of little importance as a titration medium, sulfuric acid may be of considerable interest for spectrophotometric work.

4-3. Effect of Dielectric Constant

Qualitatively, the effect of the dielectric constant of a solvent is evident if we consider the equilibrium

$$A + S \rightleftharpoons B + SH^+ \qquad (4\text{-}22)$$

The acid A and its conjugate base B differ by a proton and, therefore, by 1 unit of charge. If A is a neutral molecule and B is a monovalent anion, reaction (4-22) involves not only a proton transfer but a separation of charges. The reaction will be favored by a high-dielectric-constant solvent in which the work of charge separation is minimal. On the other hand, if A is a cation and B is a neutral molecule, reaction (4-22) involves no charge separation, and the equilibrium constant should be independent of dielectric constant (although, of course, dependent on the basicity of the solvent).

Quantitatively, the effect of solvent may be considered by writing reaction (4-22) for solvents S_1 and S_2 for the same acid-base system A,B. The activities of the various species are written $(a_A)_1$, $(a_A)_2$, etc., in the two solvents, using the usual convention for standard state, namely, that each activity approaches the concentration as the concentration approaches zero and that the activity of each solvent is taken as unity. The equilibrium constants in the two solvents are

$$K_1 = \frac{(a_B)_1 (a_{S_1H^+})_1}{(a_A)_1} \quad \text{and} \quad K_2 = \frac{(a_B)_2 (a_{S_2H^+})_2}{(a_A)_2} \qquad (4\text{-}23)$$

Several authors have written the relationships between K_1 and K_2 in terms of partition coefficients of the species A, B, and H^+ between the two solvents. We define

$$P_2^1 X = \frac{(a_X)_1}{(a_X)_2} = \frac{(f_X)_1 [X]_1}{(f_X)_2 [X]_2}$$

---

[1] Bruckenstein and Kolthoff, *J. Am. Chem. Soc.*, **78**, 2974 (1956).

[2] Hammett, L. P., and Deyrup, A. J., *J. Am. Chem. Soc.*, **54**, 4239 (1932).

where f represents the usual activity coefficient in the particular solvent. The same type of definition was used by Bjerrum and Larsson,[1] who spoke of "partition coefficients P"; by Brønsted,[2] who used the symbol f for "activity coefficients referred to water," and by Grunwald,[3] who used f for "degenerate activity coefficients." We shall follow Bjerrum and Larsson's notation, to avoid confusion with the ordinary activity coefficient f.

The partition coefficient for uncharged species is identical with the usual distribution coefficient for uncharged substances, but applied to miscible solvents. If the solute undergoes no dimerization and if its saturated solutions in both solvents may be regarded as ideal, the partition coefficient is simply the ratio of solubilities in the two solvents, or

$$P_2^1 X = \frac{[X]_{1,sat}}{[X]_{2,sat}} \tag{4-24}$$

Introducing the partition coefficients into Eq. (4-23), we have

$$K_1 = K_2 \frac{P_2^1 H^+ \cdot P_2^1 B}{P_2^1 A} \tag{4-25}$$

Equation (4-25) could be used to relate acid-base equilibrium constants in different solvents if the partition coefficients could be evaluated. Unfortunately, it is not possible to determine directly the partition coefficient of a charged species.[4] The condition of equilibrium is that the free energy change be zero; for a charged species X in equilibrium in two phases, this implies

$$(\mu_X)_1 - (\mu_X)_2 - Z_X \epsilon (\psi_2 - \psi_1) = 0 \tag{4-26}$$

where $(\mu_X)_1$, $(\mu_X)_2$ = chemical potentials of species X in phases 1 and 2, respectively

Z_X = charge of species X

ϵ = charge of the electron

$\psi_2 - \psi_1$ = difference in electrical potential of the two phases at equilibrium

Thus $Z_X \epsilon (\psi_2 - \psi_1)$ is the electrical work per mole done in transferring X from phase 1 to phase 2. If $Z_X = 0$, Eq. (4-26) reduces to the usual condition that $(\mu_X)_1 = (\mu_X)_2$ at equilibrium and, therefore, that $(a_X)_1 / (a_X)_2$ be a constant, equal to $P_2^1 X$. Another way of writing (4-26) is

$$(\mu_X)_1 + Z_X \epsilon \psi_1 = (\mu_X)_2 + Z_X \epsilon \psi_2 \tag{4-27}$$

[1] Bjerrum, N., and Larsson, E., Z. phys. Chem. Leipzig, **127**, 358 (1927).

[2] Brønsted, Chem. Revs., **5**, 231 (1928).

[3] Grunwald, E., J. Am. Chem. Soc., **73**, 4939 (1951).

[4] Guggenheim, E. A., J. Phys. Chem., **33**, 842 (1929); cf. also Bjerrum, Acta Chem. Scand., **12**, 945 (1958).

which states that the *electrochemical potential*[1] $\mu + Ze\psi$ is the same in the two phases at equilibrium. Since there is no method available for evaluating a single phase-boundary potential difference $\psi_2 - \psi_1$, it follows that there is no way to evaluate the partition coefficient of a charged species.

Now, in every acid-base equilibrium we are necessarily dealing with at least two charged species: the proton and either A or B or both. Therefore, there is no direct way of evaluating the relationship between K_1 and K_2 in Eq. (4-25). There are, however, two different approaches that have been taken in attempts to make use of Eq. (4-25).

The first approach is to estimate on theoretical grounds the magnitudes of the partition coefficients of ionic species. Brønsted[2] took water and methanol as solvents and estimated on purely electrostatic grounds the electrical work per mole involved in transferring solutes from one of these solvents to the other. Qualitatively, work must be done to transfer a charged species from water to methanol, for the solvent of higher dielectric constant is more polar than the other and interacts more strongly with positive or negative ions. As a quantitative estimate of the work of transference from solvent 1 to solvent 2, Brønsted wrote

$$kT \ln P_2^1 = \frac{Z^2\epsilon^2}{2r}\left(\frac{1}{D_2} - \frac{1}{D_1}\right) \tag{4-28}$$

where D_1, D_2 = dielectric constants of solvents 1 and 2, respectively
$\quad\quad r$ = ion radius
$\quad\quad k$ = Boltzmann constant
$\quad\quad T$ = absolute temperature

According to this equation, neutral molecules ($Z = 0$) would have partition coefficients of the order of unity. Taking $D_1 = 81$ for water and $D_2 = 31$ for methanol, Brønsted estimated that, for univalent ions, the partition coefficient P could be expected to lie in the range 100 to 500 and that, for divalent ions, P would be expected to be of the order of 10^4 to 10^5.

From Eqs. (4-25) and (4-28), taking all ionic radii to be equal to r,

$$\Delta pK = pK_2 - pK_1 = \log\frac{K_1}{K_2} = \frac{\epsilon^2}{2.3 \times 2kTr}\left(\frac{1}{D_2} - \frac{1}{D_1}\right)(Z_{H^+}^2 + Z_B^2 - Z_A^2)$$

But $\quad\quad\quad\quad\quad Z_{H^+}^2 = 1 \quad\quad$ and $\quad\quad Z_A = Z_B + 1$

so $\quad\quad\quad\quad\quad\quad Z_{H^+}^2 + Z_B^2 - Z_A^2 = -2Z_B$

and $\quad\quad\quad\quad\quad \Delta pK = \frac{Z_B\epsilon^2}{2.3kTr}\left(\frac{1}{D_1} - \frac{1}{D_2}\right) \tag{4-29}$

[1] Guggenheim, *op. cit.*
[2] Brønsted, *loc. cit.*

From (4-29), it follows that $\Delta pK = 0$ for a cation acid ($Z_B = 0$) but that $\Delta pK = pK_2 - pK_1$ should be a positive quantity for a molecular acid ($Z_B = -1$), given two solvents such that $D_2 < D_1$. Taking solvent 2 to be methanol and solvent 1 to be water, Brønsted estimated on the basis of Eq. (4-29) that molecular acids should be 2.48 pK units weaker in methanol than in water.

The low basicity of methanol compared with water causes ΔpK to be actually larger than the value calculated from Eq. (4-29), which takes into consideration only the electrostatic effect. Thus, acetic acid is actually 4.89 pK units weaker in methanol than in water. Likewise, ammonium ion is 1.70 pK units weaker, whereas, from Eq. (4-29), ΔpK should be zero.

Wynne-Jones[1] showed that, by measuring ratios of acid dissociation constants, that is, by choosing a reference acid, the basicity of the solvent could be eliminated. If acid A_0 is chosen as a reference acid against which the strength of A is to be measured, $K_r = K_A/K_{A_0}$. The relative dissociation constant K_r is actually the equilibrium constant of the reaction

$$A + B_0 \rightleftharpoons B + A_0$$

which is to be compared in two solvents S_1 and S_2. By an approach identical with Brønsted's, Wynne-Jones wrote the following expressions, taking $r_A = r_B = r$, $r_{A_0} = r_{B_0} = r_0$, and the charges of the bases B and B_0 equal to $Z\epsilon$ and $Z_0\epsilon$, respectively:

$$\Delta \ln K_r = \ln \frac{(K_r)_1}{(K_r)_2} = \frac{\epsilon^2}{2kT}\left(\frac{2Z+1}{r} - \frac{2Z_0+1}{r_0}\right)\left(\frac{1}{D_1} - \frac{1}{D_2}\right) \quad (4\text{-}30)$$

If both acids are uncharged, $Z = Z_0 = -1$, and

$$\Delta \ln K_r = \frac{\epsilon^2}{2kT}\left(\frac{1}{r_0} - \frac{1}{r}\right)\left(\frac{1}{D_1} - \frac{1}{D_2}\right) \quad (4\text{-}31)$$

If both acids are univalent cations, $Z = Z_0 = 0$, and

$$\Delta \ln K_r = \frac{\epsilon^2}{2kT}\left(\frac{1}{r} - \frac{1}{r_0}\right)\left(\frac{1}{D_1} - \frac{1}{D_2}\right) \quad (4\text{-}32)$$

Wynne-Jones showed that plots of $\Delta pK_r (= -0.434 \ln K_r)$ were linear functions of $1/D$ for a large number of acids in water, ethanol, and methanol. A similar functional relationship with the reciprocal of the dielectric constant has been given by Hammett[2] and confirmed for various solvents of dielectric constant down to about 25.* However, the

---

[1] Wynne-Jones, W. F. K., *Proc. Roy. Soc. London*, **A140**, 440 (1933).

[2] Hammett, *J. Chem. Phys.*, **4**, 613 (1936); *J. Am. Chem. Soc.*, **59**, 96 (1937).

* Minnick, L. J., and Kilpatrick, M., *J. Phys. Chem.*, **43**, 259 (1939); Wooten, L. A., and Hammett, L. P., *J. Am. Chem. Soc.*, **57**, 2289 (1935); Kilpatrick, M., and Mears, W. H., *J. Am. Chem. Soc.*, **62**, 3047, 3051 (1940).

linear relationship breaks down for low-dielectric-constant solvents such as dioxane-water mixtures.[1,2] Elliott and Kilpatrick[3] attributed the failure to preferential orientation of dioxane molecules around the solute, causing an abnormally low dielectric constant in the vicinity of the water molecules. Brande and Stern,[4] however, felt that the proton affinity of water molecules in dioxane-water mixtures is actually higher than in pure water because of the disruption of the hydrogen-bonded structure of water.

4-4. Acid-Base Equilibria in Alcohol-Water Mixtures

The other approach to relating acid-dissociation constants in different solvents is the empirical approach, developed, for example, by Grunwald et al.[5,6] for ethanol-water mixtures. These workers measured the dissociation constants of acids of the general type RZH reacting with a solvent S,

$$RZH + S \rightleftharpoons RZ + SH^+ \tag{4-33}$$

where R is the organic radical and Z is the functional group. Two different charge types (HA and BH$^+$) of acids will be considered. Purely empirically, it was found that the ΔpK values for a given acid in two solvents S_1 and S_2 could be expressed by the equations

$$\Delta pK_{HA} = pK_2 - pK_1 = A + m_- Y_- \tag{4-34}$$
$$\Delta pK_{BH^+} = pK_2 - pK_1 = A + m_0 Y_0 \tag{4-35}$$

where A is a constant, later to be identified as $\log P_2^1 H^+$, where $P_2^1 H^+$ is the partition coefficient of hydrogen ion, dependent only upon the nature of solvents 1 and 2, independent of R or Z.

Y_- and Y_0 are *activity functions* of the solvent; they depend only on the nature of the solvent. Y_- and Y_0 were arbitrarily assigned the values of zero in water and 1.000 and -1.000, respectively, in anhydrous ethanol. Experimental values were determined for mixtures of water and ethanol, as shown in Table 4-2.

The quantities m_- and m_0 are empirical constants characteristic of the acid and independent of the solvent. Primarily, m_- and m_0 depend on the charge type and, to a lesser extent, on the nature of the particular acid, as can be seen from the values in Table 4-3.

[1] James, J. C., and Knox, J. G., *Trans. Faraday Soc.*, **46**, 254 (1950).
[2] Elliott, J. H., and Kilpatrick, M., *J. Phys. Chem.*, **45**, 485 (1941).
[3] *Ibid.*
[4] Brande, E. A., and Stern, E. S., *J. Chem. Soc.*, **1948**, 1976.
[5] Grunwald, E., and Berkowitz, B. J., *J. Am. Chem. Soc.*, **73**, 4939 (1951).
[6] Gutbezahl, B., and Grunwald, E., *J. Am. Chem. Soc.*, **75**, 559, 565 (1953).

TABLE 4-2. VALUES OF Y_-, Y_0, AND LOG $P_2^1H^+$ FOR ETHANOL-WATER

Wt % ethanol	Y_-	Y_0	log $P_2^1H^+$
0.0	0.000	0.000	0.000
20.0	0.349	−0.057	0.008
35.0	0.596	−0.136	0.042
50.0	0.816	−0.266	0.251
65.0	0.924	−0.379	0.542
80.0	0.964	−0.570	1.152
100.0	1.000	−1.000	4.707

[With permission, from Gutbezahl, B., and Grunwald, E., *J. Am. Chem. Soc.*, **75**, 565 (1953).]

TABLE 4-3. VALUES OF m_0 AND m_-

Acid	m_-	Acid	m_0
Formic	0.765	Ammonium ion	3.480
Acetic	1.035	Anilinium ion	3.614
Propionic	1.255	o-Toluidinium ion	3.823
Butyric	1.352	m-Toluidinium ion	3.803
Chloracetic	1.059	p-Toluidinium ion	3.505
Lactic	0.860	N-Methylanilinium ion	4.639
Succinic	1.019	Monomethylammonium ion	4.311
Benzoic	1.571	Dimethylammonium ion	4.556
Salicylic	0.934	Trimethylammonium ion	5.121

[With permission from Grunwald, E., and Berkowitz, B. J., *J. Am. Chem. Soc.*, **73**, 4939 (1951); Gutbezahl, B., and Grunwald, E., *ibid.*, **75**, 559 (1953).]

If Eq. (4-25) is written in logarithmic form, we have

$$\Delta pK = pK_2 - pK_1 = \log P_2^1H^+ + \log \frac{P_2^1B}{P_2^1A} \qquad (4-36)$$

Comparing (4-34) and (4-35) with (4-36), the term A can be empirically identified as log $P_2^1H^+$, and the terms m_-Y_- and m_0Y_0 both as log (P_2^1B/P_2^1A). Thus, empirical justification is given for the usefulness of the concept of individual ion-partition coefficients. Moreover, if either A or B is a neutral molecule, its partition coefficient can be determined by experiment, and the partition coefficient of the other can then be calculated from Eq. (4-36).

Gutbezahl and Grunwald[1] have used the concept of individual ion-partition coefficients to estimate liquid junction potentials between aqueous potassium chloride solution and solutions of acids in ethanol-

[1] *Ibid.*

water mixtures.　Such liquid junctions are involved in pH meter readings using an aqueous calomel reference electrode.　Gutbezahl and Grunwald reached the interesting conclusion that, up to 35 per cent ethanol, the liquid junction potential should be 6 mv or less.　For solvents containing higher percentages of alcohol, the liquid junction potential increases rapidly (25 mv for 50 per cent, 44 mv for 65 per cent, and 75 mv for 80 per cent ethanol).　A word of caution should be interjected against interpreting the numerical values too literally, particularly as the composition approaches ethanol.　An "electrically neutral" phase in each solvent corresponds to equal numbers of positive and negative ionic charges, but the "absolute" electrostatic potentials of such electrically neutral phases are not necessarily equal.[1]　The calculated liquid junction potential, therefore, contains an indeterminate term.

As implied by Eqs. (4-34) and (4-35), acids of a given charge type should have similar values of ΔpK_a for any two alcohol-water mixtures taken as solvents.　Taking pure water and pure ethanol, the comparisons in Table 4-4 show this relationship in a striking fashion.　A large number

TABLE 4-4. COMPARISON OF pK_a VALUES IN WATER AND ANHYDROUS ETHANOL AT 25°C

Acid	pK_a in ethanol	pK_a in water	ΔpK_a
Formic	9.15	3.75	5.40
Acetic	10.32	4.76	5.56
Cyanoacetic	7.49	2.47	5.02
Benzoic	10.25	4.20	6.05
Salicylic	8.68	3.00	5.68
Anilinium ion	5.70	4.63	1.07
o-Toluidinium ion	5.55	4.46	1.09
m-Toluidinium ion	5.78	4.77	1.01
p-Toluidinium ion	6.24	5.10	1.14
N-Methylanilinium ion	4.86	4.84	0.02

[With permission from Gutbezahl, B., and Grunwald, E., *J. Am. Chem. Soc.*, **75**, 563 (1953); Grunwald, E., and Berkowitz, B. J., *ibid.*, **73**, 4939 (1951).]

of acid dissociation constants in alcohol-water mixtures are listed by Michaelis and Mizutani.[2]　Oiwa[3] has made a detailed study of the thermodynamic properties of hydrochloric acid in mixtures of water with various organic solvents, especially the lower alcohols.

[1] Guggenheim, *op. cit.*

[2] Michaelis, L., and Mizutani, M., *Z. physik. Chem. Leipzig*, **116**, 135 (1925); Mizutani, *ibid.*, p. 350.

[3] Oiwa, I. T., *Sci. Repts. Tôhoku Univ., First Ser.*, **41**, nos. 2 and 3 (1957).

Acid-base indicators show similar behavior, as shown by the data of Table 4-5. The various indicators can be characterized according to the charges present on the acid and alkaline forms of the indicator.

TABLE 4-5. INDICATOR CONSTANTS IN ETHANOL AND METHANOL

Indicator	pK_{In,H_2O}	$pK_{In,EtOH}$	$pK_{In,MeOH}$
Tropaeolin OO	2.0	2.3	2.2
Methyl yellow	3.25	3.55	3.4
Methyl orange	3.45	3.4	3.8
Methyl red 1	2.3	3.55	4.1
Thymol blue 1	1.65	5.35	4.7
Neutral red	7.4	8.2	8.2
Bromphenol blue	4.1	8.9	9.5
Methyl red 2	5.0	10.45	9.2
Bromcresol green	4.9	10.65	9.8
Bromcresol purple	6.4	12.05	11.3
Bromthymol blue	7.3	13.2	12.4
Phenol red	8.0	13.55	12.8
Thymol blue 2	9.2	15.2	14.0

[With permission from Guss, L. S., and Kolthoff, I. M., *J. Am. Chem. Soc.*, **62,** 249 (1940).]

1. The sulfonephthaleins (bromphenol blue, bromcresol green, bromcresol purple, phenol red, and thymol blue 2), which are transformed from singly charged negative ions to doubly charged negative ions, undergo a relatively large change in pK_{In} in going from water to ethanol. Even though both forms possess dipolar ion character, it is predominantly the change in charge separation accompanying the color-change reaction $HIn^- \rightleftharpoons In^= + H^+$ that determines the large change in pK_{In}.

2. The cation acid indicators (methyl yellow and neutral red) undergo a small change in pK_{In}, because of the small change in charge separation in the reaction $InH^+ \rightleftharpoons In + H^+$. The low-pH color-change reaction of thymol blue is characteristic of the ionization of a cationic acid, which forms a dipolar ion rather than a neutral molecule, $HIn^+ \rightleftharpoons {}^+In^- + H^+$, with a consequent large separation of charges and large change in pK_{In}.

3. Indicators that exist as dipolar ions in the acid form and as singly charged anions in the alkaline form (methyl orange) undergo a small change in pK_{In}. Here the color-change reaction may be represented by ${}^+HIn^- \rightarrow In^- + H^+$, which indicates once more only a small change in charge separation.

Methyl red represents a special case in which the intermediate form (red 2) acts as a neutral molecule rather than as a dipolar ion. Consequently, its first transition (at low pH) is characteristic of a cationic acid, whereas its second transition is characteristic of a molecular acid. The salt effects of methyl red in ethanol and methanol also point to a neutral molecular species as the intermediate form.[1] It should be borne in mind that the *degree* of dipole ion character would be expected to diminish with decreasing dielectric constant of the solvent.

Titration curves and indicator equilibria in ethanol-water mixtures can be calculated as in water. Values of K_s, the autoprotolysis constant, are close to K_w for mixtures containing only a moderate amount of ethanol. On the other hand, even a trace of water in ethanol causes a large increase in K_s. According to Gutbezahl and Grunwald,[2] pK_s is 14.33, 14.57, 14.88, 15.29, 15.91, and 19.5 for 20, 35, 50, 65, 80, and 100 wt per cent of ethanol, respectively.

With solvents of dielectric constant lower than about 25, the acid-base and indicator equilibria are more complicated. For this reason, we shall discuss separately the use of glacial acetic acid, which is a solvent of low dielectric constant.

4-5. Acid-Base Equilibria in Glacial Acetic Acid

Glacial acetic acid is strongly acidic and very weakly basic compared with water. In addition, its dielectric constant is only 6.13; so there is a strong tendency toward incomplete dissociation of ion aggregates. It is important to distinguish between ionization and dissociation,[3] described by the following reactions for an acid HA and a base B:

$$HA + HOAc \underset{\text{Ionization}}{\rightleftharpoons} H_2OAc^+A^- \underset{\text{Dissociation}}{\rightleftharpoons} H_2OAc^+ + A^- \quad (4\text{-}37)$$

$$B + HOAc \rightleftharpoons BH^+OAc^- \rightleftharpoons BH^+ + OAc^- \quad (4\text{-}38)$$

As in any other solvent, the corresponding equilibrium constants can be written in terms of activities or approximately in terms of concentrations. However, owing to the low dielectric constant of glacial acetic acid, even "strong" electrolytes have dissociation constants only of the order of 10^{-5}, so that high ionic strengths are never encountered. Therefore, it is a good approximation to write concentrations rather than activities of all species.[4]

The ionization constant of an acid HA is written

$$K_i^{HA} = \frac{[H_2OAc^+A^-]}{[HA]} \quad (4\text{-}39)$$

[1] Guss, L. S., and Kolthoff, I. M., *J. Am. Chem. Soc.*, **62**, 249 (1940).
[2] Gutbezahl and Grunwald, *J. Am. Chem. Soc.*, **75**, 565 (1953).
[3] Kolthoff and Bruckenstein, *J. Am. Chem. Soc.*, **78**, 1 (1956).
[4] *Ibid.*

The dissociation constant is

$$K_d^{HA} = \frac{[H_2OAc^+][A^-]}{[H_2OAc^+A^-]} \tag{4-40}$$

and the over-all dissociation constant is

$$K_{HA} = \frac{[H_2OAc^+][A^-]}{[HA] + [H_2OAc^+A^-]} = \frac{[H_2OAc^+][A^-]}{C_{HA}} = \frac{K_i^{HA}K_d^{HA}}{1 + K_i^{HA}} \tag{4-41}$$

where C_{HA} is the total concentration of undissociated acid, that is, $[HA] + [H_2OAc^+A^-]$.

Corresponding expressions for bases are:

$$K_i^B = \frac{[BH^+OAc^-]}{[B]} \tag{4-42}$$

$$K_d^B = \frac{[BH^+][OAc^-]}{[BH^+OAc^-]} \tag{4-43}$$

$$K_B = \frac{[BH^+][OAc^-]}{[B] + [BH^+OAc^-]} = \frac{[BH^+][OAc^-]}{C_B} = \frac{K_i^B K_d^B}{1 + K_i^B} \tag{4-44}$$

where C_B is the total concentration of undissociated base, that is, $[B] + [BH^+OAc^-]$.

An acid may, rather arbitrarily, be called a strong acid in glacial acetic acid if $K_i^{HA} \geq 1$. Thus perchloric acid is a strong acid; yet its over-all dissociation constant is only $10^{-4.87}$ because it exists largely as ion pairs.[1]

Bruckenstein and Kolthoff[1] used spectrophotometric and potentiometric measurements to establish an acidity scale and to determine dissociation constants of a number of acids and bases (Table 4-6). The autoprotolysis of acetic acid was found to be described by the equilibrium

$$2HOAc \rightleftharpoons H_2OAc^+ + OAc^- \qquad pK_s = 14.45 \tag{4-45}$$

Compared with their counterparts in water solution, acid-base titrations in glacial acetic acid are subject to several peculiar effects.[2] We shall consider here the several equilibria involved in the titration of weak base B with perchloric acid, assuming first that the change in acidity is indicated by the change in potential of an electrode, and then that an indicator is used.

Solution of a Base B. If the total undissociated base concentration is given by $C_B = [B] + [BH^+OAc^-]$ and if the analytical concentration of base is designated $(C_B)_t$, then

$$(C_B)_t = C_B + [BH^+] = C_B + [OAc^-] \tag{4-46}$$

[1] Bruckenstein and Kolthoff, *J. Am. Chem. Soc.*, **78**, 10, 2974 (1956).
[2] Kolthoff and Bruckenstein, *J. Am. Chem. Soc.*, **79**, 1 (1957).

TABLE 4-6. OVER-ALL DISSOCIATION CONSTANTS OF ACIDS, BASES, AND
SALTS IN GLACIAL ACETIC ACID

	Compound	pK
Acids	Perchloric acid	4.87
	Sulfuric acid	7.24
	p-Toluene sulfonic acid	8.46
	Hydrochloric acid	8.55
Bases	Tribenzylamine	5.36
	N,N-Diethylaniline	5.78
	Pyridine	6.10
	Potassium acetate	6.10
	p,p'-N,N'-dimethylaminazobenzene	6.32
	Sodium acetate	6.58
	Lithium acetate	6.79
	2,5-Dichloroaniline	9.48
	Urea	10.24
Salts	Sodium perchlorate	5.48
	Diethylaniline perchlorate	5.78
	Tribenzylamine hydrochloride	6.71
	Diethylaniline hydrochloride	6.84
	Potassium chloride	6.88
	Urea hydrochloride	6.96
	Lithium chloride	7.08
	Dodecylamine hydrochloride	7.45

[With permission from Bruckenstein, S., and Kolthoff, I. M., *J. Am. Chem. Soc.*, **78**, 2974 (1956).]

and, from (4-44),

$$K_B = \frac{[OAc^-]^2}{C_B} = \frac{[OAc^-]^2}{(C_B)_t - [OAc^-]} = \frac{[OAc^-]^2}{(C_B)_t} \tag{4-47}$$

The approximation $C_B = (C_B)_t$ in Eq. (4-47) is generally valid because of the low degree of dissociation in glacial acetic acid. Setting $[H_2OAc^+] = K_s/[OAc^-]$, we have

$$[H_2OAc^+] = \frac{K_s}{\sqrt{K_B(C_B)_t}} \tag{4-48}$$

The hydrogen ion concentration varies inversely as the square root of the concentration of base. Thus, for a hundredfold increase in base concentration, the pH increase is 1 unit.[1-3]

[1] Bruckenstein and Kolthoff, *J. Am. Chem. Soc.*, **78**, 2974 (1956).

[2] Hall, N. F., and Werner, T. H., *J. Am. Chem. Soc.*, **50**, 2367 (1928).

[3] Higuchi, T., Danguilan, M. L., and Cooper, A. D., *J. Phys. Chem.*, **58**, 1167 (1954).

Solution of Base B and Its Perchlorate. It is necessary to consider the dissociation equilibria of the salt $BH^+ClO_4^-$ and the acid as well as those of the weak base.

The dissociation of the salt is expressed by an equation analogous to (4-41) or (4-44):

$$K_{BHClO_4} = \frac{[BH^+][ClO_4^-]}{C_{BHClO_4}} \qquad (4\text{-}49)$$

The electroneutrality expression is

$$[H_2OAc^+] + [BH^+] = [OAc^-] + [ClO_4^-] \qquad (4\text{-}50)$$

And, to calculate $[H_2OAc^+]$, we can express the other concentrations in terms of the desired hydrogen ion concentration, as follows:

From Eqs. (4-44) and (4-45),

$$[BH^+] = \frac{K_B C_B}{[OAc^-]} = \frac{K_B C_B [H_2OAc^+]}{K_s} \qquad (4\text{-}51)$$

From Eqs. (4-49) and (4-51),

$$[ClO_4^-] = \frac{K_{BHClO_4} C_{BHClO_4}}{[BH^+]} = \frac{K_{BHClO_4} C_{BHClO_4} K_s}{K_B C_B [H_2OAc^+]} \qquad (4\text{-}52)$$

Combining Eqs. (4-45), (4-50), (4-51), and (4-52), we have

$$[H_2OAc^+] = \left\{ \frac{K_s(1 + K_{BHClO_4} C_{BHClO_4}/K_B C_B)}{1 + K_B C_B/K_s} \right\}^{\frac{1}{2}} \qquad (4\text{-}53)$$

If the base is strong enough to give a detectable end point, $K_B C_B/K_s$ is much greater than 1; so Eq. (4-53) becomes

$$[H_2OAc^+] = \frac{K_s}{K_B C_B} (K_{BHClO_4} C_{BHClO_4} + K_B C_B)^{\frac{1}{2}} \qquad (4\text{-}54)$$

Kolthoff and Bruckenstein[1] pointed out an interesting relationship for the case in which K_B and K_{BHClO_4} are approximately equal. Thus, for diethylaniline, both pK values are equal to 5.78 (Table 4-6). Now, if the titrant is relatively concentrated so that the sum of $C_B + C_{BHClO_4}$ remains sensibly constant and equal to C, Eq. (4-54) reduces to

$$[H_2OAc^+] = \frac{K_s}{C_B} \sqrt{\frac{C}{K_B}} = \frac{K'}{C_B} \qquad (4\text{-}55)$$

where $K' = K_s \sqrt{C/K_B} \cong$ constant during titration. Thus the hydrogen ion concentration is inversely proportional to the concentration of untitrated base. If X is the fraction titrated, a plot of $\log (1 - X)$ vs.

[1] Kolthoff and Bruckenstein, *J. Am. Chem. Soc.*, **79**, 1 (1957).

pH is a straight line, as is observed for a *strong acid–strong base* titration curve in water. Such a relationship was actually observed by Hall and Werner[1] for guanidine and for diethylaniline. It appeared paradoxical because the solution of the pure base behaved like a typical weak base upon dilution.

It will be noted that, for aqueous solution, the quantity $\log[(1 - X)/X]$ plotted against pH yields a straight line for the titration of a weak base with a strong acid. No relationship of this type exists in acetic acid. Therefore it is not possible to reason directly by analogy and use buffer formulas derived for aqueous solutions in acetic acid.

Ordinarily, Eq. (4-54) may be applied using stoichiometric concentrations instead of equilibrium concentrations for C_B and C_{BHClO_4}. This is analogous to applying the simple buffer formulas in water. For an equimolar mixture of base and its salt, such that $C_B = C_{BHClO_4} = C$, Eq. (4-54) becomes

$$[H_2OAc^+] = K_s \left(\frac{K_{BHClO_4} + K_B}{K_B^2 C} \right)^{\frac{1}{2}} \tag{4-56}$$

and, therefore, the hydrogen ion concentration increases tenfold for a hundredfold dilution. A similar result was observed also by Hall and Werner.[2]

If the base is very weak, K_{BHClO_4} is much greater than K_B, and Eq. (4-54) becomes

$$[H_2OAc^+] = \frac{K_s}{K_B C_B} \sqrt{K_{BHClO_4} C_{BHClO_4}} \tag{4-57}$$

If C_{BHClO_4} is set equal to X and C_B equal to $1 - X$, a plot of pH vs. $\log \{\sqrt{X}/(1 - X)\}$ should yield a straight line. Kolthoff and Bruckenstein[3] found this to be true for urea.

Solution of a Pure Salt. To calculate the acidity at the equivalence point, the equilibrium constant of the titration reaction is considered:

$$B + HClO_4 \rightleftharpoons BHClO_4 \qquad K_f^{BHClO_4} = \frac{C_{BHClO_4}}{C_B C_{HClO_4}} \tag{4-58}$$

where $K_f^{BHClO_4}$ is the formation constant of the salt $BHClO_4$. It follows from Eqs. (4-41), (4-44), and (4-45) that

$$K_f^{BHClO_4} = \frac{K_{HClO_4} K_B}{K_s K_{BHClO_4}} \tag{4-59}$$

Equation (4-54) can be simplified because, for most salts, $K_B C_B$ is

[1] Hall and Werner, *op. cit.*

[2] *Ibid.*

[3] *Op. cit.*

negligible in comparison to $K_{BHClO_4}C_{BHClO_4}$, so that

$$[H_2OAc^+] = \sqrt{\frac{K_s^2 K_{BHClO_4}C_{BHClO_4}}{K_B^2 C_B^2}} \qquad (4\text{-}60)$$

At the equivalence point $C_B = C_{HClO_4}$, and, from Eqs. (4-58) and (4-59),

$$C_B^2 = \frac{C_{BHClO_4}}{K_f^{BHClO_4}}$$

$$= \frac{C_{BHClO_4}K_s K_{BHClO_4}}{K_{HClO_4}K_B}$$

which, when substituted into Eq. (4-60), gives

$$[H_2OAc^+] = \sqrt{K_s K_{HClO_4}/K_B} \qquad (4\text{-}61)$$

Equation (4-61) yields the interesting conclusion that the hydrogen ion concentration of a pure salt solution is *independent of the concentration of salt*. On this basis Kolthoff and Bruckenstein suggested that titration to an equivalence potential should actually be more useful than determining the inflection point of a titration curve.

Solution of Salt plus Excess Acid. From Eqs. (4-58) and (4-59),

$$\frac{K_B C_B}{K_s} = \frac{K_{BHClO_4}}{K_{HClO_4}} \frac{C_{BHClO_4}}{C_{HClO_4}} \qquad (4\text{-}62)$$

Substituting into Eq. (4-53),

$$[H_2OAc^+]^2 = \frac{K_s + K_{HClO_4}C_{HClO_4}}{1 + K_{BHClO_4}C_{BHClO_4}/K_{HClO_4}C_{HClO_4}} \qquad (4\text{-}63)$$

which holds at all points of the titration. In the presence of an appreciable excess of acid, $K_{HClO_4}C_{HClO_4}$ is much greater than K_s, so that Eq. (4-63) becomes

$$[H_2OAc^+] = \frac{K_{HClO_4}C_{HClO_4}}{\sqrt{K_{HClO_4}C_{HClO_4} + K_{BHClO_4}C_{BHClO_4}}} \qquad (4\text{-}64)$$

In the vicinity of the end point, C_{BHClO_4} is much greater than C_{HClO_4}. Either of the two terms under the square-root sign may be negligible in certain cases, depending upon the relative magnitudes of K_{HClO_4} and K_{BHClO_4}.

Behavior of Acid-Base Indicators. In considering the behavior of an indicator, it should be borne in mind that the relative strength of two acids HX and HY, determined by their reactions with a base B, *depends upon the nature of the reference base* B.

From Eq. (4-59), the formation of salts BHX and BHY is described by the formation constants

$$K_f^{\text{BHX}} = \frac{K_{\text{HX}}K_{\text{B}}}{K_{\text{BHX}}K_s} \quad \text{and} \quad K_f^{\text{BHY}} = \frac{K_{\text{HY}}K_{\text{B}}}{K_{\text{BHY}}K_s}$$

The ratio R of the two formation constants is

$$R = \frac{K_f^{\text{BHX}}}{K_f^{\text{BHY}}} = \frac{K_{\text{HX}}K_{\text{BHY}}}{K_{\text{HY}}K_{\text{BHX}}} \tag{4-65}$$

and the right-hand side of Eq. (4-65) is not independent of the nature of B. For example, if the corresponding ratio for another base B′ is

$$R' = \frac{K_f^{\text{B'HX}}}{K_f^{\text{B'HY}}}$$

then

$$\frac{R}{R'} = \frac{K_{\text{BHY}}}{K_{\text{B'HY}}} \frac{K_{\text{B'HX}}}{K_{\text{BHX}}} \tag{4-66}$$

which is not necessarily unity. Two different indicators, therefore, might lead to different conclusions about the relative strengths of the two acids HX and HY.

The reaction between an indicator base In and an acid HX may be represented in its simplest form by

$$\text{In} + \text{HX} \rightleftharpoons \text{InH}^+\text{X}^- \rightleftharpoons \text{InH}^+ + \text{X}^- \tag{4-67}$$

where In represents the alkaline form and InH^+X^- and InH^+ represent the acid forms of the indicator. Kolthoff and Bruckenstein[1] found that the absorption spectra of the various acid forms (including higher ion aggregates) of p-naptholbenzein were identical irrespective of the nature of the anion X^-. Owing to the importance of ion pairs and higher aggregates, the color-change behavior of an indicator in glacial acetic acid is not analogous to its behavior in water.

The first equilibrium of Eq. (4-67) is described by the ionization constant

$$K_i^{\text{InHX}} = \frac{[\text{InH}^+\text{X}^-]}{[\text{In}][\text{HX}]} \tag{4-68}$$

and the second equilibrium is described by the dissociation constant

$$K_d^{\text{InHX}} = \frac{[\text{InH}^+][\text{X}^-]}{[\text{InH}^+\text{X}^-]} \tag{4-69}$$

The ratio of acid form to alkaline form is

$$\frac{\Sigma[\text{InH}^+]}{[\text{In}]} = \frac{[\text{InH}^+] + [\text{InH}^+\text{X}^-]}{[\text{In}]} \tag{4-70}$$

[1] Bruckenstein and Kolthoff, *J. Am. Chem. Soc.*, **78**, 1 (1956).

but no simple relationship exists between this ratio and the hydrogen ion concentration.

Kolthoff and Bruckenstein[1] found that, for perchloric acid solutions, the ratio of acid to alkaline forms of p-naphtholbenzein was proportional to the concentration of perchloric acid.   On the other hand, the hydrogen ion concentration varies with the square root of the perchloric acid concentration [see Eq. (4-41)].

For weak acids, such as hydrochloric acid, the relationship between indicator concentration and acid concentration is more complicated,[1] and will not be considered in detail here.   However, it is worthy of mention that the color varies with the concentration of anion.   Thus, with increasing chloride ion concentration, the dissociation of indicator salt InH^+Cl^- is repressed, and the ratio $\Sigma[InH^+]/[In]$ decreases with increasing chloride ion concentration.   However, when a certain chloride ion concentration is exceeded, higher ion aggregates such as $Cl^-InH^+Cl^-$ begin to form, and the color once more shifts toward the acidic form.

From the viewpoint of titrimetry, the behavior of indicators during the titration of weak bases with perchloric acid is most important. During the course of the titration, the salt $BH^+ClO_4^-$ is present in large excess and suppresses the dissociation of the indicator salt $InH^+ClO_4^-$. Therefore, the ratio of acid to alkaline forms is given by Eq. (4-68), as follows:

$$\frac{[InH^+ClO_4^-]}{[In]} = K_i^{InHClO_4}[HClO_4] \tag{4-71}$$

or by Eq. (4-58), as follows:

$$\frac{C_{InHClO_4}}{C_{In}} = K_f^{InHClO_4}C_{HClO_4} \tag{4-72}$$

where $K_i^{InHClO_4}/K_f^{InHClO_4} = 1 + K_i^{HClO_4}$.

Equation (4-71) is not an experimentally useful form, because the concentration $[HClO_4]$ of unionized perchloric acid is unknown.   However, Eq. (4-72) can be used by writing in place of C_{InHClO_4}/C_{In} the quantity $[InH^+ClO_4^-]/[In]$, because the indicator is a very weak base whose salt is essentially completely ionized (although not dissociated).

Thus
$$\frac{[InH^+ClO_4^-]}{[In]} = K_f^{InHClO_4}C_{HClO_4} \tag{4-73}$$

From Eq. (4-58), C_{HClO_4} is given by

$$C_{HClO_4} = \frac{C_{BHClO_4}}{C_B K_f^{BHClO_4}} \tag{4-74}$$

[1] *Ibid.*

and the color of the indicator is given by

$$\frac{[\text{InH}^+\text{ClO}_4^-]}{[\text{In}]} = \frac{K_f^{\text{InHClO}_4}}{K_f^{\text{BHClO}_4}} \frac{C_{\text{BHClO}_4}}{C_{\text{B}}} \tag{4-75}$$

From Eq. (4-75), it can be seen that the color ratio of the indicator is determined by the *ratio* of concentrations of salt to base and is, therefore, independent of dilution at a given point of the titration (neglecting solvolysis). When we recall that, by Eq. (4-56), the hydrogen ion concentration varies inversely with the square root of concentration, it is evident that the indicator color does not respond to changes of hydrogen ion concentration in fashion analogous to its response in water.

However, if the ratio $C_{\text{BHClO}_4}/C_{\text{B}}$ is replaced by $X/(1 - X)$, Eq. (4-75) becomes

$$\frac{[\text{InH}^+\text{ClO}_4^-]}{[\text{In}]} = \frac{K_f^{\text{InHClO}_4}}{K_f^{\text{BHClO}_4}} \frac{X}{1 - X} \tag{4-76}$$

which shows that the indicator color ratio changes during the course of the titration in the same way as it does in aqueous solution for a titration of a weak base with a strong acid. Thus, if an indicator is chosen such that $K_f^{\text{InHClO}_4}$ is of the same order of magnitude as $K_f^{\text{BHClO}_4}$, the spectrophotometric measurement of indicator color ratio is equivalent to a determination of the ratio $X/(1 - X)$, and a graphical method can be used to detect the end point.[1]

At the equivalence point, corresponding to a solution of the salt BHClO_4, $C_{\text{B}} = C_{\text{HClO}_4}$. And, from Eq. (4-58),

$$C_{\text{HClO}_4}^2 = \frac{C_{\text{BHClO}_4}}{K_f^{\text{BHClO}_4}} \tag{4-77}$$

which, with Eq. (4-73), gives

$$\frac{[\text{InH}^+\text{ClO}_4^-]}{[\text{In}]} = K_f^{\text{InHClO}_4} \left(\frac{C_{\text{BHClO}_4}}{K_f^{\text{BHClO}_4}} \right)^{\frac{1}{2}} \tag{4-78}$$

The color ratio of the indicator, therefore, varies with the square root of salt concentration. The hydrogen ion concentration was seen [Eq. (4-61)] to be independent of concentration.

Beyond the equivalence point, the ratio of acid to alkaline forms of the indicator is proportional to the concentration of excess perchloric acid. Thus, upon tenfold dilution, the color ratio decreases tenfold while the hydrogen ion concentration decreases by a factor of $\sqrt{10}$. Again, it is evident that the indicator color is not a straightforward index of acidity.

[1] Higuchi, T., Rehm, C., and Barstein, C., *Anal. Chem.*, **28**, 1506 (1956); Rehm and Higuchi, *ibid.*, **29**, 367 (1957).

4-6. The Hammett Acidity Function H_0 *

In order to be able to measure the strengths of very weak bases, Hammett used a succession of strongly acidic solvents, such as mixtures of hydrochloric, nitric, perchloric, or sulfuric acids with water. Suppose that a reference base B, for instance, an indicator, is chosen, such that the thermodynamic dissociation constant K_a of its conjugate acid BH^+ is known in water. Now, to measure the strength of a somewhat weaker base C, it might be necessary to use 10 per cent sulfuric acid as a solvent. The bases B and C and the solvent are chosen such that the ratios of concentration $[B]/[BH^+]$ and $[C]/[CH^+]$ can both be measured in the solvent. Then

$$(pK_a)_C - (pK_a)_B = - \log \frac{[C][BH^+]}{[B][CH^+]} - \log \frac{f_C f_{BH^+}}{f_B f_{CH^+}} \qquad (4\text{-}79)$$

There are, however, good theoretical grounds and ample experimental justification for neglecting the activity coefficient ratios given in the last term *for high-dielectric-constant solvents.* By choosing a series of successively weaker bases D, E, F, etc., and correspondingly more acidic solvents, values of pK_a were determined for the various bases, and these turned out to be internally consistent. Thus the values of pK_a were found to be essentially independent of the reference base and of the solvent used.

Now, to express the acidity of the *solvent,* Hammett defined the function

$$H_0 = pK_a + \log \frac{[B]}{[BH^+]} \qquad (4\text{-}80)$$

which is characteristic of a particular solvent, because the ratio f_B/f_{BH^+} was found to have the same value for all bases in the solvent. Clearly, for *dilute aqueous solutions,* the value of H_0 approaches pH as the ionic strength approaches zero. For all other solvents it is an empirical constant, which decreases with increasing acidity and which measures on a logarithmic scale the tendency for the solvent to donate protons to *uncharged base molecules.*

The function H_0 has proved to be of great value for expressing the acidity of aqueous solutions and of certain nonaqueous solutions of high dielectric constant. For example, consistent values of H_0 can be obtained with a variety of mineral acids up to concentrations of the order of 6 to 10 M (see Fig. 4-2). For sulfuric acid, useful values of H_0 are available even in fuming sulfuric acid containing up to 31 per cent sulfur trioxide. By means of the H_0 function, it has been possible to evaluate the pK

* Hammett, L. P., "Physical Organic Chemistry," chap. 9, McGraw-Hill Book Company, Inc., New York, 1940.

values of very weak uncharged bases and to interpret acid catalysis effects of numerous acid-water mixtures.[1]

It is interesting to consider why H_0 has proved to be so valuable although the analogous functions H_- for anionic bases and H_+ for cationic bases have been found in general not to be properties of the solvent alone but rather to depend upon the nature of the reference base. In Eq. (4-79), the f's may be regarded as activity coefficients in the usual sense *only if the solvent is essentially aqueous*, because the standard state of the

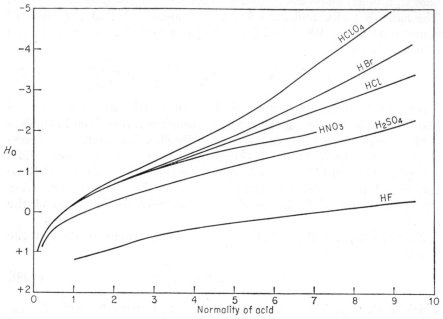

FIG. 4-2. Acidity function H_0 for aqueous solutions of acids. [*With permission from Paul, M. A., and Long, F. A., Chem. Revs.*, **57**, 1 (1957).]

hydrogen ion is unit activity in water. When the solvent deviates appreciably from water, the f's should be regarded as partition coefficients, and Eq. (4-25) should apply. Now if B is a molecular base, the ratio $PH^+ \cdot PB/PBH^+$ should be independent of the dielectric constant, as a first approximation [see Eq. (4-28)], *as long as the salts of the cation BH^+ are completely dissociated*. In solvents of very low dielectric constant such as glacial acetic acid,[2] ion association is so pronounced that H_0 is dependent on the nature of the reference base.

For the function H_- or H_+ to be independent of the dielectric constant, it would be necessary that the ratio $PH^+ \cdot PB^-/PBH$ or $PH^+ \cdot PB^+/PBH^{++}$

[1] Paul, M. A., and Long, F. A., *Chem. Revs.*, **57**, 1 (1957).

[2] Gutbezahl and Grunwald, *J. Am. Chem. Soc.*, **75**, 559, 565 (1953).

be independent of dielectric constant. This cannot be so; therefore, H_- and H_+ can be properties of the solvent only in essentially aqueous solutions. Of course, in dilute aqueous solutions all the quantities H_0, H_-, and H_+ approach the pH.

PROBLEMS

4-1. Using the data of Tables 4-2 and 4-3, calculate the dissociation constants of (a) acetic acid and (b) anilinium ion in 50 per cent ethanol. *Ans.* (a) 5.87; (b) 3.92.

4-2. Taking K_s for ethanol to be 3×10^{-20}, calculate pH ethanol for 0, 50, 90, 99, 99.9, 100, 100.1, and 101 per cent of the stoichiometric amount of reagent added for the titration of 10^{-3} M perchloric acid with 0.01 M sodium ethoxide in 100 per cent ethanol. Assume 100 per cent dissociation, and neglect dilution. *Ans.* 3.0, 3.3, 4.0, 5.0, 6.0, 9.75, 13.5, 14.5.

4-3. Calculate pH ethanol for the titration curve of 0.01 M acetic acid in 100 per cent ethanol with 0.1 M sodium ethoxide. Would phenolphthalein be suitable as an indicator?

Compare this curve with the titration curve of 0.01 M acetic acid with 0.1 M sodium hydroxide using 20 per cent ethanol for the solvent. *Ans.* At 0, 9, 50, 91, 99, 99.9, 100, 100.1, 101 per cent neutralization pH = 6.16, 9.32, 10.32, 11.32, 12.32, 13.32, 13.91, 14.5, 15.5, for 100 per cent ethanol and 3.56, 4.13, 5.13, 6.13, 7.13, 8.10, 8.66, 9.39, 10.33 for 20 per cent ethanol.

4-4. If pK_r is plotted against $1/D$ to give a straight line for a number of solvents, what is the significance of the slope of the line [see Eq. (4-32)]? What is the significance of the intercept corresponding to $1/D = 0$?

4-5. Compare the magnitude of the change in pH in going from 10^{-3} M strong acid to 10^{-3} M strong base in water, ethanol, ammonia, formic acid, and acetic acid. In acetic acid, consider that the strong acid and strong base are completely ionized but that the dissociation constants are both equal to 10^{-5}. *Ans.* pH = 8.0, 13.5, 27, 0.51, 6.4.

4-6. For the titration of N,N-diethylaniline with perchloric acid in glacial acetic acid, calculate the pH at the following percentages of the stoichiometric amount of $HClO_4$ added: 0, 50, 99, 100, 101. Take the initial concentration of base to be 0.01 N, and neglect dilution. *Ans.* 10.56, 10.26, 8.56, 6.77, 5.00.

5. Applications of Acid-Base Titrations

It is the purpose of this chapter to consider the preparation and standardization of standard acids and bases and to review some of the more important applications of acid-base titrations in aqueous and nonaqueous systems.

5-1. Preparation of Standard Acid

A standard solution of hydrochloric acid can be prepared determinately by weighing constant-boiling hydrochloric acid.[1-3] Shaw[4] has given directions for distillation that should ensure accuracy within 1 part per thousand. The procedure consists in distilling a diluted acid, discarding the first 75 per cent, and catching the next 10 to 15 per cent of the distillate. The barometric pressure is determined, and the composition of the acid is found from tabular values; a selection of these is listed in Table 5-1.

It is evident that the composition varies only slightly with barometric pressure, so that for ordinary purposes an accuracy of 1 mm Hg in reading the barometric pressure is adequate. A standard 0.1 M solution is readily prepared by weighing accurately 18 grams of standard boiling acid from a weight buret and diluting to 1 liter.

A determinate solution of hydrochloric acid can readily be prepared by using sodium chloride as a primary standard. The sodium chloride is dissolved in water and passed through a well-rinsed cation exchange column in the hydrogen form. The equivalent amount of hydrochloric

[1] Hulett, G. A., and Bonner, W. D., *J. Am. Chem. Soc.*, **31**, 390 (1903).

[2] Foulk, C. W., and Hollingsworth, M., *J. Am. Chem. Soc.*, **45**, 1220 (1923).

[3] Bonner, W. D., and Titus, A. C., *J. Am. Chem. Soc.*, **52**, 634 (1930).

[4] Shaw, J. A., *Ind. Eng. Chem.*, **18**, 1065 (1926).

Table 5-1. Composition of Constant-boiling Hydrochloric Acid

Pressure, mm Hg	HCl (vacuum-wt basis), %	Soln (air-wt basis), grams per mole HCl
760	20.221	180.193
750	20.245	179.979
740	20.269	179.766
730	20.293	179.555

[From Foulk, C. W., and Hollingsworth, M., *J. Am. Chem. Soc.*, **45**, 1220 (1923).]

acid is rinsed from the column into a volumetric flask and made up to volume.[1]

For some purposes standard sulfuric acid is suitable, although it has the disadvantage of having a relatively weak second step of ionization ($pK_a \cong 2.0$). Moreover, a number of metallic sulfates and basic sulfates are relatively insoluble. However, constant-boiling sulfuric acid has been shown to be readily attainable with a composition known to within 0.01 per cent.[2] The composition corresponds to 98.48 per cent sulfuric acid by weight at 750 mm pressure, and varies only very slightly with barometric pressure.

According to Smith and Koch,[3] perchloric acid can be distilled to produce an acid of definite composition (73.60 ± 0.03 per cent). However, the product is slightly hygroscopic and fumes faintly in the air, and special precautions must be taken in weighing.

In most analytical work, hydrochloric acid is used, although sulfuric and perchloric acids are advantageous if relatively concentrated solutions must be boiled. Kolthoff and Stenger[4] state that 0.1 N solutions of hydrochloric acid can be boiled for 1 hr without loss of acid if the evaporated water is continually replaced. Even 0.5 N acid can be boiled for 10 min without appreciable loss. Nitric acid is relatively unstable, but it finds use in special procedures such as the alkalimetric method for phosphorus. Kolthoff and Stenger[5] list tables of data[6] for the determinate preparation of solutions of standard acids and standard sodium hydroxide by weighing solutions of known density and diluting to volume.

[1] Schubert, J., *Anal. Chem.*, **22**, 1359 (1950).

[2] Kunzler, J. E., *Anal. Chem.*, **25**, 93 (1953).

[3] Smith, G. F., and Koch, W. W., *Ind. Eng. Chem., Anal. Ed.*, **3**, 52 (1931).

[4] Kolthoff, I. M., and Stenger, V. A., "Volumetric Analysis," 2d ed., vol. 2, p. 64, Interscience Publishers, Inc., New York, 1947.

[5] *Ibid.*, pp. 65–66.

[6] Data due to Schoorl, N., *Chem. Jaarboekje Ned. Chem. Ver.*, 15th ed., vol. 2, p. 94, Centen, Amsterdam, 1930.

Although the determinate preparation of standard acids may be strongly recommended, the use of a standardization method is common practice. In certain situations, for example, when the same indicator color change is observed in the standardization and in the application, it may be advantageous to carry out both procedures under parallel conditions.

5-2. Standardization of Acids

In any titrimetric standardization, the solution to be standardized must be compared directly or indirectly[1] against the weight of a *primary standard substance*. A primary standard is a *pure substance* (element or compound) which is stable enough to be stored indefinitely without decomposition, which can be weighed accurately without special precautions when exposed to laboratory air, and which will undergo an accurate stoichiometric reaction in a titration. It should be readily available in a state of high purity, and simple tests should be available to detect common impurities. Ideally, in order to minimize weighing errors, it should possess a high equivalent weight. Some chemists feel that the above definition is too rigid and would designate as a primary standard any material that can be weighed directly to prepare a solution of known concentration. Although such a definition may often serve in a practical way, it may lead to unsuspected errors. For example, impurities in the standard may just compensate for an error in the titration reaction, and the error may not be exactly the same in the determination as in the standardization. Again, a primary standard may be used in two entirely different reactions, and impurities that are inert in one reaction may be active in another. An example would be sodium oxalate contaminated with sodium carbonate. This would be inert in an oxidimetric reaction but active in an acid-base reaction. Such material, which fulfills the requirement that it be able to be weighed accurately to provide a known amount of reactant but which is not a pure substance, can properly be designated as a *secondary* standard; it must be compared ultimately with a primary standard. Constant-boiling hydrochloric acid is an example.

Sodium Carbonate as a Primary Standard. The most common method of standardizing a solution of acid is against sodium carbonate. For accurate results, several precautions are necessary.

To ensure complete decomposition of any bicarbonate, it is recommended[2] that the sample be ignited at 260 to 265°C. Smith and Croad[3] recommended heating at 290 to 300°C at 1 to 4 mm pressure, but

[1] Even in a coulometric standardization, the comparison is ultimately made against the weight of silver, which is the basis of the definition of the *coulomb*, or *ampere-second*.

[2] Ferguson, W. C., *J. Soc. Chem. Ind.*, **24**, 781 (1905).

[3] Smith, G. F., and Croad, G. F., *Ind. Eng. Chem., Anal. Ed.*, **9**, 141 (1937).

Carmody[1] found that for practical purposes 30 min of heating at 200°C sufficed to remove occluded moisture. Kolthoff[2] warned against storage of ignited samples in a desiccator, because moisture in amounts up to 0.1 per cent can be taken up during the opening and closing of the container. According to Richards and Hoover,[3] even a freshly ignited sample contains up to 0.05 per cent moisture. The last trace of moisture can be removed by fusing the sample in a stream of pure carbon dioxide, which is gradually displaced by air as the sample is cooled. A serious loss of carbon dioxide occurs above 300°C, 1 hr of heating at 310 to 315°C giving an error of more than 1 per cent.[4]

To carry out the titration, some procedures specify direct titration at room temperature to a methyl orange or modified methyl orange end point. It is difficult to get accurate results without special precautions, particularly in standardizing solutions that are 0.1 N or more dilute. In the first place, the concentration of carbon dioxide is not reproducible, because the solution becomes supersaturated as the titration proceeds, and variable amounts of carbon dioxide are lost near the end point, depending upon the amount of shaking. Secondly, the color of methyl orange in a saturated solution of carbon dioxide is sensitive to the concentration of sodium chloride. With increasing salt concentration, the color is shifted to the acid side. Therefore, for accurate results, a comparison solution, saturated with carbon dioxide and containing the same concentration of sodium chloride and indicator as the titrated solution at the end point, should be used.

These difficulties can be avoided by a back-titration method. Kolthoff and Stenger[5] recommend carrying the titration to a distinctly acid color of methyl orange (pH $\simeq$ 3), then adding a drop of freshly prepared bromine water to destroy the indicator. The solution is boiled to remove carbon dioxide, cooled, and titrated with 0.01 N sodium hydroxide to a methyl red or bromthymol blue end point.

However, a similar result can readily be obtained by direct titration, if a boiling step is introduced. The author prefers the two-indicator method described by Kolthoff and Sandell,[6] because it gives a preliminary estimate of the end point and an exceptionally sharp end point following the boiling step, yet avoids a back titration. First the titration is carried out in the cold to a colorless phenolphthalein end point (pH $\simeq$ 8), which lies a little past the first equivalence point of the titration (Fig. 5-1).

[1] Carmody, W. R., *Ind. Eng. Chem., Anal. Ed.*, **17**, 577 (1945).

[2] Kolthoff, *J. Am. Chem. Soc.*, **48**, 1448 (1926).

[3] Richards, T. W., and Hoover, C. R., *J. Am. Chem. Soc.*, **37**, 99 (1915).

[4] Smith and Croad, *op. cit.*

[5] Kolthoff and Stenger, *op. cit.*, p. 78.

[6] Kolthoff, I. M., and Sandell, E. B., "Textbook of Quantitative Inorganic Analysis," 3d ed., p. 523, The Macmillan Company, New York, 1952.

Then bromcresol green is added, and the titration is continued until the first indication of a green color (pH $\simeq$ 5), corresponding to the addition of about 98 per cent of the theoretical quantity of acid. At this point, the solution is boiled to eliminate carbon dioxide. If the titration is stopped noticeably before the end point, a purple color corresponding to the red of phenolphthalein and the blue of bromcresol green in a solution

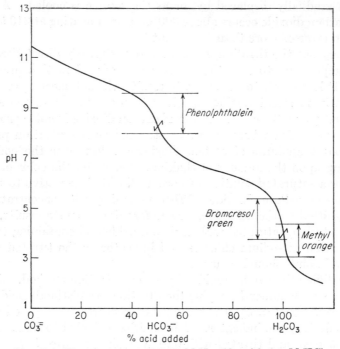

FIG. 5-1. Titration curve of 0.05 M Na$_2$CO$_3$ with 0.1 M HCl.

of bicarbonate (pH = 8.4) is observed after cooling. The titration is continued through the blue to a green end-point color of bromcresol green. We may estimate the titration error as follows.

For the usual standardization involving 5 milliequivalents of acid and an end point volume of 100 ml, the end point concentration of carbonic acid is 0.025 M, assuming no loss of carbon dioxide. At a pH of 5, we have $[HCO_3^-] = K_1[H_2CO_3]/[H^+] = 10^{-3}$, taking $K_1 = 4 \times 10^{-7}$, corresponding to 4 per cent of the carbonic acid concentration, or 2 per cent of the total equivalents of acid used. After boiling to remove carbon dioxide and performing a second titration to pH = 5, 4 per cent of the remaining bicarbonate would remain untitrated, corresponding to an error of 0.16 per cent based on the second end point, or 0.08 per cent on the entire titration.   Actually the error is smaller, because the second titration is carried more nearly to the equivalence point.

Borax as a Primary Standard.   The stoichiometry may be represented by

$$B_4O_7^= + 2H^+ + 5H_2O \rightarrow 4H_3BO_3 \tag{5-1}$$

and so the equivalent weight of borax, $Na_2B_4O_7 \cdot 10H_2O$, is one-half its molecular weight.

An aqueous solution of borax contains the tetraborate anion $B_4O_7^=$, which reacts with hydrogen ions

$$B_4O_7^= + H^+ \rightleftharpoons HB_4O_7^- \qquad \frac{1}{K_2} = 10^9 \tag{5-2}$$

$$HB_4O_7^- + H^+ \rightleftharpoons H_2B_4O_7 \qquad \frac{1}{K_1} = 10^4 \tag{5-3}$$

and undergoes depolymerization [1,2]

$$H_2B_4O_7 + 5H_2O \rightleftharpoons 4H_3BO_3 \qquad K = 2.7 \times 10^2 \tag{5-4}$$

A dilute aqueous solution of borax may be regarded[3] as a solution of boric acid $(K_a = 6.4 \times 10^{-10})$ half-titrated with a strong base.   The initial hydrogen ion concentration is about 6×10^{-10}, corresponding to a pH of 9.2.   The solution at the equivalence point corresponds to a dilute solution of boric acid.   The degree of polymerization is so low that the pH may be calculated as that of a monobasic weak acid of $pK_a - 9.2$, which at a concentration of 0.1 M is 5.1.   This corresponds nicely with the pK value of methyl red, which, therefore, serves as an excellent indicator.

Borax has the practical advantages (1) that it has a high equivalent weight, 190.72; (2) that it is readily prepared in a high state of purity; and (3) that a single and direct titration is possible with a convenient indicator.[4]   The principal disadvantage of borax is that special precautions must be taken to ensure exact composition with respect to its degree of hydration.   Hurley[5] recommends recrystallization under concentration conditions such that crystallization above 55°C is prevented, thus preventing the formation of the pentahydrate.   The decahydrate should be stored in a desiccator over a solution saturated with respect to sodium bromide dihydrate[4] or with respect to sodium chloride and sucrose.[5]

---

[1] Latimer, W. M., "Oxidation Potentials," 2d ed., pp. 278–279, Prentice-Hall, Inc., Englewood Cliffs, N.J., 1952.

[2] Ricci, J. E., "Hydrogen Ion Concentration," p. 294, Princeton University Press, Princeton, N.J., 1952.

[3] *Ibid.*

[4] Kolthoff, *J. Am. Chem. Soc.*, **48**, 1453 (1926).

[5] Hurley, F. H., Jr., *Ind. Eng. Chem., Anal. Ed.*, **8**, 220 (1936); **9**, 237 (1937).

Other Primary Standards. *Sodium oxalate* was first recommended as a primary standard for acidimetry by Sørensen.[1] The pure primary-standard material is converted to the carbonate by heating in a platinum crucible,[2,3] taking care to avoid mechanical loss. The method is capable of a high degree of accuracy but is relatively inconvenient.

Thallous carbonate is readily prepared in a pure state,[4,5] is practically nonhygroscopic, and is stable at 175°C.

Potassium bicarbonate, prepared by recrystallization from water at 65 to 70°C saturated with carbon dioxide[6] and dried over sulfuric acid in a carbon dioxide atmosphere, gives results agreeing within 0.02 per cent with those obtained using pure borax and sodium carbonate.[7]

Potassium iodate can be used for the standardization of strong acids[8,9] through the reaction

$$IO_3^- + 5I^- + 6H^+ \rightarrow 3I_2 + 3H_2O \qquad (5\text{-}5)$$

The neutral iodate solution is treated with an excess of potassium iodide and sodium thiosulfate (tested for neutrality). As the solution is titrated with strong acid, the iodine formed reacts with the excess thiosulfate. The first excess of acid causes an acid-base indicator such as methyl red to change color. The titration must be performed with adequate stirring to prevent decomposition of thiosulfate in a local excess of acid. Near the end point, adequate time must be allowed for the redox reactions to proceed to completion after the addition of each drop of acid.

Tris (hydroxymethyl) aminomethane, proposed by Fossum, Markunas, and Riddick,[10] has many favorable properties as a primary acidimetric standard. It is commercially available in a high state of purity; it can be dried at 100 to 103°C; it is stable in the air and also in solution. The equivalence-point pH is 4.7 when titrated with a strong acid, showing that the compound acts as a weak base.

5-3. Preparation of Standard Base

An important consideration in the preparation of standard solutions of strong bases is the desirability of avoiding carbonate in most applications.

[1] Sørensen, S. P. L., *Z. anal. Chem.*, **36**, 639 (1897); **42**, 333, 512 (1903).
[2] *Ibid.*
[3] Lunge, G., *Z. angew. Chem.*, **17**, 230 (1904).
[4] Hac, R., and Kamen, K., *Coll. Czech. Chem. Communs.*, **4**, 145 (1932).
[5] Jensen, E., and Nilssen, B., *Ind. Eng. Chem., Anal. Ed.*, **11**, 508 (1939).
[6] Schmitt, K. O., *Z. anal. Chem.*, **70**, 321 (1927).
[7] Kolthoff and Sandell, *Ind. Eng. Chem., Anal. Ed.*, **3**, 115 (1931).
[8] Kolthoff, *Pharm. Weekblad*, **63**, 37 (1926).
[9] Kolthoff and Stenger, *op. cit.*, p. 89.
[10] Fossum, J. H., Markunas, P. C., and Riddick, J. A., *Anal. Chem.*, **23**, 491 (1951).

Barium hydroxide has the advantage of being automatically free of carbonate. A storage bottle should be set up with a soda-lime protective tube and a siphon to deliver the clear supernatant liquid to the buret. The insolubility of barium sulfate and phosphate is a disadvantage for some applications.

Sodium hydroxide is the most commonly used standard base. The classical method of removing carbonate contamination is to prepare a concentrated solution (1:1 or 4:5 sodium hydroxide to water by weight), in which sodium carbonate is practically insoluble. After filtration through fritted glass[1-3] or centrifugation,[4] the solution is diluted with freshly boiled and cooled water or with distilled water in equilibrium with the carbon dioxide of the air. Such "equilibrium water" contains only 1.5×10^{-5} moles of carbon dioxide per liter[5] and is readily prepared by bubbling with air that has been passed successively through wash bottles containing dilute acid and water.

The analogous procedure is not successful with *potassium hydroxide*, because potassium carbonate is relatively soluble in concentrated potassium hydroxide.

An ion exchange method is convenient and efficient for the removal of carbonate from either sodium or potassium hydroxides.[6] The solution is passed through a "strong base" anion exchange column (cf. Sec. 25-7) in the chloride form. The first portions of hydroxide convert the resin to the hydroxide form, so the first portions of effluent contain chloride. If it is desired not to dilute the standard base and if chloride is objectionable, the first effluent is discarded until it shows no test for chloride. Carbonate is retained on the anion exchange column, and carbonate free base is collected. When the column becomes saturated with carbonate, it is readily reconverted to the chloride form by passing through it dilute hydrochloric acid, followed by water to remove the excess acid. Anion exchangers have also been used to prepare standard solutions of sodium hydroxide from weighed amounts of sodium chloride[7] or potassium chloride.[8]

Solutions of strong bases should be stored in polyethylene bottles, which are resistant even to concentrated solutions. If carbonate contamination is undesirable, protection from the carbon dioxide of the atmosphere should be provided.

[1] Cowles, H. W., Jr., *J. Am. Chem. Soc.*, **30**, 1192 (1908).

[2] Sørensen, *Biochem. Z.*, **21**, 168 (1909).

[3] Han, J. E. S., and Chao, T. Y., *Ind. Eng. Chem., Anal. Ed.*, **4**, 229 (1932).

[4] Allen, N., and Low, G. W., Jr., *Ind. Eng. Chem., Anal. Ed.*, **5**, 192 (1933).

[5] Kolthoff, *Biochem. Z.*, **176**, 101 (1926).

[6] Davies, C. W., and Naucollas, G. H., *Nature*, **165**, 237 (1950).

[7] Steinbach, J., and Freiser, H., *Anal. Chem.*, **24**, 1027 (1952).

[8] Grunbaum, B. W., Schöniger, W., and Kirk, P. L., *Anal. Chem.*, **24**, 1857 (1952).

5-4. Standardization of Bases

Potassium Biphthalate as a Primary Standard. Potassium acid phthalate, available from the Bureau of Standards as a primary standard, is the most common reagent for the standardization of strong bases. It is readily available in a pure form and is readily soluble in water. Since it is also used as a reference standard for the definition of the practical pH scale (see page 27), its use as a titrimetric standard is convenient. The pure product is stable upon heating up to 135°C[1] and is nonhygroscopic. Its only real disadvantage is that it is the salt of a weak acid ($K_2 = 4 \times 10^{-6}$), and the end point, therefore, occurs in the alkaline region. Consequently, the base solution must be free of carbonate contamination if a sharp end point with negligible titration error is to be achieved. Phenolphthalein is generally used as the indicator.

Benzoic Acid as a Primary Standard. Benzoic acid is available from the Bureau of Standards as a calorimetric standard, and can also be used to standardize strong bases. The fused product is free of water and is not appreciably hygroscopic.[2,3]

Like potassium biphthalate, benzoic acid is a weak acid. A further disadvantage is its relatively low solubility in water. The sample is, therefore, dissolved in alcohol and diluted with water before titration. Alcohol may contain acidic impurities; a blank should therefore be run using the same quantity of alcohol and indicator diluted to the end-point volume with water.

Other Standard Substances. *Potassium biiodate*, $KH(IO_3)_2$, has been recommended by Kolthoff and van Berk[4] as a primary standard for bases. It is a relatively strong acid and has a high equivalent weight.

Sulfamic acid, NH_2SO_3H, acts as a strong acid,[5] and can be titrated using a variety of indicators to an end-point pH of 4 to 9. It should be mentioned that sulfamic acid undergoes slow hydrolysis, forming an equivalent amount of bisulfate ion and ammonium ion. The latter, being weakly acidic, prevents the use of indicators that show a transition color in the alkaline range for solutions that have undergone hydrolysis. Wagner, Wuellner, and Feiler,[6] using indicators with transition colors in the acid range, found that the titer of a sulfamic acid solution remained constant within about 0.1 per cent after standing for 213 days, even though hydrolysis had occurred. Kolthoff and Stenger[7] do not recognize

[1] Caley, E. R., and Brundin, R. H., *Anal. Chem.*, **25**, 142 (1953).

[2] Morey, G. W., *J. Am. Chem. Soc.*, **34**, 1027 (1912).

[3] Weaver, E. R., *J. Am. Chem. Soc.*, **35**, 1309 (1913).

[4] Kolthoff, I. M., and van Berk, L. H., *J. Am. Chem. Soc.*, **48**, 2800 (1926).

[5] Butler, M. J., Smith, G. F., and Audrieth, L. F., *Ind. Eng. Chem., Anal. Ed.*, **10**, 690 (1938).

[6] Wagner, W. F., Wuellner, J. A., and Feiler, C. E., *Anal. Chem.*, **24**, 1491 (1952).

[7] Kolthoff and Stenger, *op. cit.*

sulfamic acid as a primary standard on the grounds that tests for purity are not available, but they consider it acceptable as a secondary standard.

Calcium acid malate hexahydrate, which was proposed as a primary standard by Shead,[1] has a high equivalent weight (207.14). The hydrate is stable under ordinary conditions of humidity but cannot be dried at 100°C.

2,4,6-*Trinitrobenzoic acid* is recommended by Smith and Wilkins[2] as a primary standard. It is strongly acidic ($pK_a = 2.38$), has a high equivalent weight (257.12), and is stable at 130°C. It can serve as its own indicator, but the end point comes a little late (pH = 8 to 8.5); so it is preferable to use such an indicator as bromthymol blue.

5-5. Applications of Aqueous Acid-Base Titrations

Determination of Weak Acids. From the titration curves of weak acids it is evident that, for accurate results, an indicator must be chosen that shows a transition color in the alkaline range coinciding as nearly as possible with the pH at the equivalence point. For best results, a comparison color of the indicator in a solution of the salt of the weak acid should be used. In some cases, for example, if the salt is not available, a buffer solution of the same pH may be convenient.

The theoretical precision of the titration may be estimated from the slope of the titration curve in the vicinity of the end point, as described in Sec. 3-8. In practice, however, the precision and accuracy are often limited by the presence of carbonate in the strong base.

The effect of carbonate is evident from the titration curve of carbonic acid, which is the reverse of the curve of a carbonate with a strong acid (Fig. 5-1). Starting with a solution of a weak acid, the presence of carbonate in the base results in the formation of a dilute solution of carbonic acid. Below a pH of about 4, the carbonic acid has no effect, but, between the pH values of 4 and 8.5, the carbonic acid present is titrated to bicarbonate by the further addition of strong base. However, the rate of the reaction between carbon dioxide and hydroxyl ion is slow;[3] so an indicator such as phenolphthalein or thymol blue exhibits its alkaline color temporarily and then fades back slowly to its acid color upon standing. To reach a permanent alkaline color of phenolphthalein it is necessary to titrate all the added carbonate to bicarbonate. Thus, the hydroxide that has been converted to carbonate in the reagent has lost half its effective normality as a reagent if the titration is carried to a phenolphthalein end point, whereas no error is caused if a methyl orange end point can be used. For the titration of strong acids of concentration

[1] Shead, A. C., *Anal. Chem.*, **24**, 1451 (1952).

[2] Smith, G. F., and Wilkins, D. H., *Anal. Chim. Acta*, **8**, 209 (1953).

[3] Vorländer, D., and Strube, W., *Ber. deut. chem. Ges.*, **46**, 172 (1913); Thiel, A., and Strohecker, R., *ibid.*, **47**, 945, 1061 (1914).

equal to 0.1 N or more, the error involved in titrating to a pH of 4 is negligible. For the titration of more dilute solutions, however, it is advisable to titrate to the first perceptible color change of methyl red (pH range 4.4 to 6.0), boil to remove carbon dioxide, cool, and continue to the yellow color of the indicator.

Determination of Boron. Boron is usually separated from interfering substances by distillation as methyl borate from a mixture of concentrated hydrochloric acid and calcium chloride containing methyl alcohol.[1-3] The ester is hydrolyzed by catching the distillate in excess alkali; the methanol is evaporated off. After it is neutralized to a methyl orange end point with hydrochloric acid, the solution is boiled to remove carbon dioxide, and titrated.

Boric acid is such a weak acid ($K_a = 6.4 \times 10^{-10}$) that it cannot be titrated directly in dilute solution. In the presence of polyhydroxy compounds such as glycerol or mannitol it acts as a much stronger acid and can be titrated to a phenolphthalein end point. Hermans[4] has explained this effect of polyhydroxy compounds on the basis of the formation of 1:1 and 1:2 mole ratio complexes between the hydrated borate ion and 1,2 or 1,3 diols. The effect of mannitol M on the ionization of boric acid HA may be represented by the equilibria[5]

$$HA \rightleftharpoons H^+ + A^- \qquad K_a = 6.4 \times 10^{-10} \qquad (5\text{-}6)$$
$$M + A^- \rightleftharpoons MA^- \qquad k_1 = 3 \times 10^2 \qquad (5\text{-}7)$$
$$M + MA^- \rightleftharpoons M_2A^- \qquad k_2 = 1.7 \times 10^2 \qquad (5\text{-}8)$$

where k_1, k_2 = successive formation constants of complexes between mannitol and borate ion. This gives an over-all equilibrium constant

$$HA + 2M \rightleftharpoons H^+ + M_2A^- \qquad k_1 k_2 K_a = 3.3 \times 10^{-5} \qquad (5\text{-}9)$$

which was evaluated by Ross and Catotti[6] at 1.0×10^{-4} and by Böeseken, Vermaas, and Küchlin[7] at 1.7×10^{-4}.

In the usual titration 0.5 to 0.7 gram of mannitol is added per 10 ml. In place of mannitol, various substances such as invert sugar[8] or glucose[9] can be used.

Determination of Bicarbonate and Carbonate in Mixtures. The classi-

[1] Wherry, E. T., and Chapin, W. H., *J. Am. Chem. Soc.*, **30**, 1687 (1908).
[2] Wilcox, L. V., *Ind. Eng. Chem., Anal. Ed.*, **2**, 358 (1930).
[3] Schulek, E., and Vastagh, G., *Z. anal. Chem.*, **84**, 167 (1931).
[4] Hermans, P. H., *Z. anorg. u. allgem. Chem.*, **142**, 83 (1925).
[5] Deutsch, A., and Osoling, S., *J. Am. Chem. Soc.*, **71**, 1637 (1949).
[6] Ross, S. O., and Catotti, A. J., *J. Am. Chem. Soc.*, **71**, 3563 (1949).
[7] Böeseken, J., Vermaas, N., and Küchlin, A. T., *Rec. trav. chim.*, **49**, 711 (1930).
[8] Mellon, M. G., and Morris, V. N., *Ind. Eng. Chem.*, **16**, 123 (1924).
[9] Weatherby, L. S., and Chesny, H. H., *Ind. Eng. Chem.*, **18**, 820 (1926).

cal method of determining carbonate in the presence of bicarbonate is to titrate in the cold to a bicarbonate end point. Since the pH of sodium bicarbonate is very nearly constant at 8.3 to 8.4 over a wide range of concentrations, this method is applicable in principle over a wide range of sample compositions.

However, from the titration curve (Fig. 5-1) it is evident that the slope of the curve is fairly shallow. The relative precision (Sec. 3-8) is $\sqrt{K_2/K_1} = 1.4 \times 10^{-2}$, indicating that, if an uncertainty of ± 0.1 pH is allowed, a relative error of ± 1.4 per cent is to be expected. To attain even this precision it is necessary to use a comparison standard of a pure bicarbonate solution containing the same concentration of indicator. Phenolphthalein, commonly used as the indicator, does not become decolorized until a pH of 8.0, corresponding to an error of 3 to 5 per cent. Therefore, a color comparison is essential. If thymol blue, a two-color indicator, is used, less attention need be paid to making the indicator concentration identical in the two solutions. By using a mixed indicator composed of thymol blue and cresol red, Simpson[1] showed that results accurate to within 0.5 per cent could be obtained without a comparison solution.

In the determination of bicarbonate or of total alkalinity, titration to a methyl orange end point is common practice,[2] with boiling to remove carbon dioxide just prior to the final end point. The two-indicator procedure outlined in connection with the standardization of acids using sodium carbonate may be used to advantage.

However, many practical determinations of total carbonates are based on direct titration procedures involving no boiling step. For example, official procedures for the determination of carbonates in water[3,4] call for the determination of the carbonic acid end point by using methyl orange or methyl orange-xylene cyanole.[5]

Such procedures may lead to serious errors in dilute solutions (below about 0.001 M) because the pH at the equivalence point varies with the concentration of carbonic acid. [Cf. Eq. (3-42), Sec. 3-4.]

Titration curves given by Cooper[6] (Fig. 5-2) show the constancy of pH at the bicarbonate end point and the variation of pH at the carbonic acid end point. The second-end-point pH, moreover, is distinctly higher in

[1] Simpson, S. G., *Ind. Eng. Chem.*, **16**, 709 (1924).

[2] Scott, W. W. (ed.), "Standard Methods of Chemical Analysis," 5th ed., Furman, N. H. (ed.), vol. 2, D. Van Nostrand, Inc., Princeton, N.J., 1939.

[3] "Standard Methods for Examination of Water and Sewerage," 8th ed., p. 65, American Public Health Association, New York, 1936.

[4] "Official and Tentative Methods of Analysis," 4th ed., p. 515, Association of Official Agricultural Chemists, Washington, D.C., 1936.

[5] Hickman, K. C. D., and Linstead, R. P., *J. Chem. Soc. London*, **121**, 2502 (1922).

[6] Cooper, S. S., *Ind. Eng. Chem., Anal. Ed.*, **13**, 466 (1941).

this dilute range than the pH corresponding to the transition color of methyl orange (pH 4.0) or methyl orange–xylene cyanol (pH 3.8). Cooper compared various indicators and recommended a mixture of bromcresol green and methyl red. To allow for the change in equivalence-point pH with concentration, different shades of color were selected for various total carbonate contents.

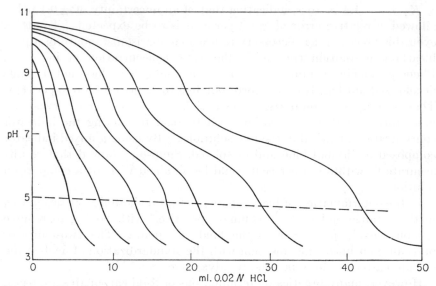

FIG. 5-2. Titration curves of mixed carbonates. 0.15 to 1.57 millimoles Na_2CO_3, 0.05 to 0.21 millimoles $NaHCO_3$ per liter. [*With permission from Cooper, S. S., Ind. Eng. Chem., Anal. Ed.*, **13**, 466 (1941).]

Determination of Hydroxyl Ion in Presence of Carbonate. Owing to the very weak second ionization of carbonic acid ($K_2 = 6 \times 10^{-11}$), the titration of hydroxyl ion is not feasible in the presence of an appreciable concentration of carbonate ion. For example, a 0.01 M solution of sodium carbonate has a pH of 11.2, so the total pH change in the titration of 0.01 M sodium hydroxide would be only about 0.8 pH unit.

Winkler[1] showed that, if the carbonate ion is precipitated by adding an excess of barium chloride, hydroxyl ion can be sucessfully titrated in the presence of precipitated carbonate.

Thus, if 0.1 M barium ion is added in excess, the concentration of carbonate is $K_{sp}/[Ba^{++}] = 5 \times 10^{-9}/0.1 = 5 \times 10^{-8}$. Actually, the situation is more complicated, because barium carbonate coprecipitates a little bicarbonate if an excess of barium chloride is added to a cold solution

[1] Winkler, C., "Praktische Übungen in der Massanalyse," 3d ed., Akademische Verlagsgesellschaft, Leipzig, 1902.

of sodium carbonate.[1] On the other hand, if alkali hydroxide is present, the barium carbonate is contaminated with hydroxide.[2] For the most accurate results, the excess hydroxide should be approximately neutralized by adding an amount of hydrochloric acid estimated from a preliminary test, and the barium carbonate should be precipitated from a warm solution.[1] Sulfate tends to cause error by occlusion of hydroxide with the precipitated barium sulfate.[3]

A two-indicator method may also be used, as in the determination of carbonate and bicarbonate. The method, originally due to Warder,[4] consists in titrating the hydroxide plus one-half the carbonate alkalinity to a phenolphthalein end point and then carrying out the usual total alkalinity determination.

Determination of Phosphoric Acid and Phosphates. Orthophosphoric acid can be titrated as a monobasic acid to a pH of 4.4 or as a dibasic acid to a pH of 9.6.[5] The pH values calculated from the expressions $(pK_1 + pK_2)/2$ and $(pK_2 + pK_3)/2$ are 4.35 and 9.57. Both are essentially independent of concentration, except for salt effects.

The low-pH end point corresponds to the transition color of bromcresol green, or to a color toward the alkaline end of the transition range of methyl orange. A comparison solution of sodium dihydrogen phosphate and indicator should be used.

The high-pH end point corresponds to phenolphthalein almost completely in its red form. Kolthoff[6] found that, by adding enough sodium chloride to half-saturate the solution, the titration can be carried out to a phenolphthalein end point with an accuracy of the order of 1 per cent. Alternatively, thymolphthalein can be used without salt.

Since two end points are available, it is obvious that any mixture of orthophosphoric acid and its sodium or potassium salts can be analyzed by two titrations. For instance, a mixture of phosphoric acid and trisodium phosphate would react to produce two adjoining members of the series H_3PO_4, $H_2PO_4^-$, $HPO_4^=$, PO_4^{3-} depending upon the relative amounts added. Likewise, a mixture of PO_4^{3-} and hydroxide can be analyzed by titrating separate aliquots to a phenolphthalein end point and a bromcresol green end point. Salt should not be present in the latter titration, because the salt effect causes the end point to be late.[6]

Calamari and Hubata[7] used saturated sodium chloride for both end

[1] Sørensen, S. P. L., and Anderson, A. C., Z. anal. Chem., **45,** 220 (1906); **47,** 279 (1908).

[2] Lindner, J., Z. anal. Chem., **72,** 135 (1927); **78,** 188 (1929).

[3] Partridge, E. P., and Schroeder, W. C., Ind. Eng. Chem., Anal. Ed., **4,** 271 (1932).

[4] Warder, R. B., Am. Chem. J., **3,** 55, 232 (1881).

[5] Kolthoff, Chem. Weekblad, **12,** 644, 1915.

[6] Ibid.

[7] Calamari, J. A., and Hubata, R., Ind. Eng. Chem., Anal. Ed., **14,** 55 (1942).

points, matching the colors of bromphenol blue and cresol red, respectively, with specially prepared comparison solutions. Verma and Agarwal[1] recommended a mixed screened indicator consisting of methyl orange, xylene cyanole FF and phenolphthalein. With this indicator, sodium chloride (half saturated) is needed only for the second end point.

Jones[2] has devised procedures for the analysis of mixtures of various phosphates, including ortho-, meta-, and pyrophosphates and various polyphosphates. The details are beyond the scope of this book.

Determination of Amino Acids. Sørensen[3] devised the important *formol titration* that is widely used for the determination of amino acids. By adding a relatively large excess of a neutral formaldehyde solution, the acid strengths of amino acids are greatly increased owing to the formation of very weakly basic Schiff's bases:

$$NH_2RCOOH + CH_2O \rightarrow H_2C{=}NRCOOH + H_2O \qquad (5\text{-}10)$$

According to Harris[4] the acid strengths of amino acids are increased by a factor of the order of 10^3 by the presence of 16 per cent formaldehyde at the end point.

Kjeldahl Method for Determination of Nitrogen in Organic Compounds. Various modifications of the Kjeldahl[5] method are used, depending upon the form of the combined nitrogen in the sample, but no modification is applicable to all nitrogenous compounds. In its simplest form, the Kjeldahl method consists in decomposing the sample by boiling with concentrated sulfuric acid, thus converting the nitrogen to ammonium sulfate. After the addition of an excess of sodium hydroxide, the ammonia is distilled into an excess of standard sulfuric acid, which is back-titrated to determine the excess.

Potassium sulfate[6] is usually added to raise the boiling point, and mercuric oxide or mercury are often used to hasten the decomposition of organic matter.[7,8] Mercury is precipitated by the addition of sodium sulfide prior to distillation to prevent the retention of nitrogen as ammine or imino complexes. The amount of sulfuric acid required for the digestion of various substances has been studied by Bradstreet.[9] According to this author, sodium sulfate is unsatisfactory, particularly for

[1] Verma, M. R., and Agarwal, K. C., *J. Sci. Ind. Research*, **15B**, 701 (1956).

[2] Jones, L. T., *Ind. Eng. Chem., Anal. Ed.*, **14**, 536 (1942).

[3] Sørensen, *Biochem. Z.*, **7**, 45 (1907); **25**, 1 (1910).

[4] Harris, L. J., *Proc. Roy. Soc. London*, **B95**, 500 (1923); **B104**, 412 (1939).

[5] Kjeldahl, J., *Z. anal. Chem.*, **22**, 366 (1883).

[6] Gunning, J. W., *Z. anal. Chem.*, **28**, 188 (1889).

[7] Phelps, I. K., and Daudt, H. W., *J. Assoc. Offic. Agr. Chemists*, **3**, 306 (1920); **4**, 72 (1921).

[8] Shedd, O. M., *J. Assoc. Offic. Agr. Chemists*, **10**, 507 (1927).

[9] Bradstreet, R. B., *Anal. Chem.*, **29**, 944 (1957).

samples requiring a high digestion temperature, because a solid digestion mass results unless a relatively large excess of sulfuric acid is used, with a consequent lowering of the temperature. Selenium and selenium oxychloride have both been used as catalysts.[1,2] Bradstreet[3] found that the digestion period could be shortened by adding both selenium and ferrous sulfate. The use of dipotassium phosphate, mercury, and iron(III) sulfate has been recommended by Stubblefield and DeTurk,[4] who have reviewed various digestion methods. In other procedures various oxidants have been used. A mixture of hydrogen peroxide and sulfuric acid is worthy of mention.[5] Reducing conditions are, however, generally required to avoid loss of elemental nitrogen.

The usual Kjeldahl procedure works for a large variety of nitrogen compounds such as amines, amino acids, and alkaloids, but fails for nitrates, nitrites, azo compounds, cyanides, and derivatives of hydrazine.

If nitrates are present, a method involving the addition of salicylic acid[6] may be used. Azo compounds give quantitative results if first reduced[7] by refluxing with stannous chloride and hydrochloric acid. Hydrazine derivatives are decomposed by heating with formaldehyde, zinc dust, and hydrochloric acid, followed by stannous chloride, prior to the usual Kjeldahl digestion.[7]

The ammonia is frequently absorbed in a boric acid solution rather than in a standard acid solution, in order to avoid a back-titration procedure.[8] A direct titration with standard acid, using bromphenol blue, with a blank determination gives excellent results.

Determination of Phosphorus through 12-Molybdiphosphate. A commonly used routine method for the determination of phosphorus consists in precipitating ammonium 12-molybdiphosphate, dissolving the precipitate in a small excess of standard sodium hydroxide, and determining the excess hydroxide.[9] Ideally the reaction of dissolution of the precipitate is

$$(NH_4)_3PO_4 \cdot 12MoO_3 + 27OH^- \rightarrow 12MoO_4^= + PO_4^{3-} + 3NH_4OH \quad (5\text{-}11)$$

[1] Lauro, M. F., *Ind. Eng. Chem., Anal. Ed.*, **3**, 401 (1931).

[2] Sreenivasan, A., and Sadasivan, V., *Ind. Eng. Chem., Anal. Ed.*, **11**, 314 (1939).

[3] Bradstreet, *Ind. Eng. Chem., Anal. Ed.*, **10**, 696 (1938).

[4] Stubblefield, F. M., and DeTurk, E. E., *Ind. Eng. Chem., Anal. Ed.*, **12**, 396 (1940).

[5] Koch, F. C., and McMeekin, T. L., *J. Am. Chem. Soc.*, **46**, 2066 (1924).

[6] Moore, H. C., *Ind. Eng. Chem.*, **12**, 669 (1920); *J. Assoc. Offic. Agr. Chemists*, **8**, 411 (1924–5).

[7] Phelps and Daudt, *op. cit.*

[8] Winkler, *Z. angew. Chem.*, **26**, 231 (1913); Scales, F. M., and Harrison, A. P., *Ind. Eng. Chem.*, **12**, 350 (1920); Spears, H. D., *J. Assoc. Offic. Agr. Chemists*, **5**, 105 (1921); Markley, K. S., and Hann, R. M., *ibid.*, **8**, 455 (1925).

[9] Hillebrand, W. F., Lundell, G. E. F., Bright, H. A., and Hoffman, J. I., "Applied Inorganic Analysis," 2d ed., p. 706, John Wiley & Sons, Inc., New York, 1953.

followed by addition of standard acid to the disappearance of the phenolphthalein color and then by titration with standard base to the reappearance of the indicator color. It is generally assumed that at the end point the species $HPO_4^=$ and NH_4^+ exist, corresponding to the consumption of four hydrogen ions per mole of phosphate in proceeding from the alkaline solution to the final end point. Thus a net consumption of 23 hydroxyl ions per mole of phosphate is assumed. However, in practice, the mole ratio is usually higher than 23 to 1.

There are several causes for the higher ratios,[1] among them (1) incomplete titration of ammonia at the pH corresponding to the phenolphthalein end point, (2) loss of ammonia by volatilization from the alkaline solution, (3) incorrect composition of precipitate owing to precipitation at too high a temperature [at temperatures above 45°C an excess of molybdenum(VI) oxide is precipitated], (4) retention of nitric acid by the precipitate owing to incomplete washing, and (5) absorption of carbon dioxide by the alkaline solution.

By adding an excess of formaldehyde, as in the Sørensen formol titration of amino acids (page 98), the ammonia can be tied up, thus leading to a mole ratio of 26 hydroxyl ions[2] per mole of phosphate. Thereby, of the causes and of error listed above, the first two can be avoided.

Determination of Metals. Kolthoff and Stenger[3] have reviewed various acid-base methods used for determination of metals. Most such methods are based on the precipitation of a hydroxide or salt of a weak acid or on the formation of a complex with the anion of a weak acid, taking advantage of the acid-base properties of the anion. Usually, acid-base methods are not widely applicable, because of the interference of other metals and because of inexact composition of precipitates. For example, if heavy metal salts are titrated with a strong base, basic salts are usually precipitated. If an excess of hydroxide is added, the composition of a hydroxide or hydrous oxide is approached, but other metals are apt to interfere. Coprecipitation of foreign metals limits the use of selective precipitation by regulation of the pH. The nature of the anions is often important in determining whether basic salts or normal salts will precipitate in preference to the hydroxide at a given pH value.

Since about 1945, the development of complex formation titrations for metals (cf. Chap. 13) has rendered obsolete many of the older procedures. For example, the classical Blacker[4] method for determining hardness in water, based on the titration of alkaline earth ions with potassium

[1] *Ibid.*

[2] Kolthoff and Stenger, *op. cit.*, p. 145.

[3] *Ibid.*, pp. 176–208.

[4] Blacker, C., Grünberg, P., and Kissa, M., *Chemiker Ztg.*, **37**, 56 (1913).

palmitate, has been largely replaced by the ethylenediaminetetraacetate (EDTA) method.

5-6. Applications of Nonaqueous Acid-Base Titrations

In contrast with the relatively meager amount of fundamental work that has been done in nonaqueous titrimetry, a great many practical applications have been made. Much of the work has been devoted to establishing the stoichiometry of acid-base reactions that cannot be carried out conveniently or accurately in water and to comparing the results obtained with various indicators and electrometric end-point detection methods. Even though quantitative equilibrium data are often lacking, particularly in mixed solvents, a qualitative understanding of acid-base principles is generally valuable as a guide to the application of solvents and titrants in a given problem.

The applications of nonaqueous titrations are so numerous and are developing so rapidly that an exhaustive listing is far beyond the scope of this book. The reader is referred to appropriate review papers[1] for numerous references.

Nonaqueous solvents can be classified broadly into three groups, which will be considered in turn: acidic, basic, and neutral. In each group, mixed solvents are often used to modify the acidic or basic strength of the solvent or, what is often more important, to change the dielectric constant and hydrogen-bonding characteristics of the parent solvent. In this way, its solvent properties for the sample can be enhanced, and the titration reaction can be promoted by decreasing the degree of dissociation and the solubilities of ionic products.

As an empirical guide to the applicability of various solvents, the method of van der Heidje and Dahmen[2] deserves mention. These experimenters measured the available potential range in each solvent under extreme conditions of acidity and basicity, using glass and calomel electrodes. Included in their experiments were acidic solvents (acetic and trifluoroacetic acids), neutral solvents (chlorobenzene, acetonitride, acetone, methanol, isopropyl alcohol, water) and basic solvents (n-butylamine, ethylenediamine, pyridine, dimethylformamide). The feasibility of a titration was expressed in terms of the "half-neutralization potential" of an acid or base in relation to the limiting values of the available potentials in the solvent. For mixtures, a difference of 200 to 300 mv in half-neutralization potential was found in most instances to be sufficient to permit selective titration. From the consideration of acid-base equilibria in acetic acid (Sec. 4-5) it is evident that, in solvents of very

---

[1] Riddick, J. A., *Anal. Chem.*, **24**, 41 (1952); **26**, 77 (1954); **28**, 679 (1956); **30**, 793 (1958).

[2] Van der Heijde, H. B., and Dahmen, E. A. M. F., *Anal. Chim. Acta*, **16**, 378 (1957).

low dielectric constant, the half-neutralization potential must be a function of concentration. Moreover, the apparent strength of a base depends upon the strength of the acid used for its neutralization, and vice versa.[1] Therefore, the concept of half-neutralization potential is of limited applicability.

Acidic Solvents. Acidic solvents are used primarily to enhance the basic properties of very weak bases. To take full advantage of the solvent effect it is necessary to use as the titrating reagent as strong an acid as possible.

By far the most important acidic solvent is acetic acid, with perchloric acid as a titrant. In the pioneering work of Hall, Conant, and Werner,[2] the chloranil (tetrachloroquinone-tetrachlorohydroquinone) electrode was introduced as an indicator electrode for acidity. Various bases too weak to be titrated in water gave excellent inflection points when titrated with perchloric acid in anhydrous acetic acid.

To illustrate the advantage of an acidic solvent, consider the amino group of an amino acid so weakly basic that aqueous titrations are possible only by special means (such as conductometric titrations). The carboxyl group of an amino acid is essentially inert in glacial acetic acid, which itself is a carboxylic acid, so an amino acid such as glycine behaves like an aliphatic amine.[3] Potentiometric and indicator end points are suitable.[4,5]

The use of the glass electrode in anhydrous acetic acid was introduced by Blumrich and Bandel.[6] Many applications of the glass electrode, as well as acid-base indicators, have been made by later workers. To summarize some of the observations, it may be noted that, as a rule, bases of ionization constant greater than about 10^{-12} in water can be titrated in acetic acid. Urea shows a relatively poor titration curve, and acetamide and acetanilide are too weakly basic to give end points.

Primary and secondary aliphatic amines can be titrated if care is taken to avoid an excess of acetic anhydride, which is used to remove water from the solvent and from the 70 to 72 per cent perchloric acid used to prepare the reagent. Tertiary amines, which do not undergo acetylation, can be titrated even in the presence of acetic anhydride. Advantage is taken of this behavior to determine tertiary amines in the presence of primary and secondary amines. Aromatic amines and heterocyclic

[1] Higuchi, T., Danguilan, M. L., and Cooper, A. D., *J. Phys. Chem.*, **58**, 1167 (1954).

[2] Hall, N. F., and Conant, J. B., *J. Am. Chem. Soc.*, **49**, 3047 (1927); Conant and Hall, *ibid.*, **49**, 3062 (1927); Hall, N. F., and Werner, T. H., *ibid.*, **50**, 2367 (1928); Conant and Werner, *ibid.*, **52**, 4436 (1930); Hall, *ibid.*, **52**, 5115 (1930).

[3] Kolthoff, I. M., and Willman, A., *J. Chem. Soc.*, **56**, 1014 (1934).

[4] Nadeau, G. F., and Branchen, L. E., *J. Am. Chem. Soc.*, **57**, 1363 (1935).

[5] Toennies, G., and Kolb, J., *J. Biol. Chem.*, **144**, 219 (1942).

[6] Blumrich, K., and Bandel, G., *Angew. Chem.*, **54**, 374 (1941).

nitrogen compounds such as pyridine and the alkaloids can be titrated readily.

Salts of carboxylic acids, e.g., acetates, citrates, benzoates, etc. are of course strongly basic and show good titration behavior. It should be borne in mind that varying degrees of ion association render the effective basic strengths different even for a closely related series such as the alkali metal acetates.

An important trend in the application of acetic acid as a solvent has been to add various "neutral" solvents to the sample solvent, the reagent, or both. Fritz[1] dissolved weakly basic samples in a variety of solvents such as chloroform, nitrobenzene, ethyl acetate, and acetonitrile and then titrated with perchloric acid in acetic acid using a glass electrode or with methyl violet as the indicator.

In many of the more recent applications, dioxane has been substituted for acetic acid as a solvent for perchloric acid.[2,3] It should be noted that such a reagent is no longer strictly anhydrous, because no provision is made to remove water from the 72 per cent perchloric acid used to prepare the reagent. A small amount of water seems to have relatively little effect, and sharper titration curves are often observed in practice when dioxane is present.[4]

Pifer and Wollish[5] titrated hydrohalides of weak bases by adding mercury(II) acetate before titrating with perchloric acid in dioxane. The reaction

$$BH^+ + 2X^- + Hg(OAc)_2 \rightarrow BH^+ + 2OAc^- + HgX_2 \qquad (5\text{-}12)$$

takes advantage of the weak electrolyte properties of mercury(II) salts to convert the original halides to the acetates, which can readily be titrated even in the presence of excess mercury(II) acetate.

Relatively few applications have been made of solvents of greater acidity than anhydrous acetic acid. Gremillion[6] titrated very weakly basic amines dissolved in acetic anhydride with perchloric acid in acetic acid. De Vries and coworkers[7] used trifluoroacetic acid as a titration medium for nitroguanidines and thiourea, which are too weakly basic to be titrated in acetic acid.

Basic Solvents. A basic solvent can be used to enhance the acidic properties of very weak acids. To gain the full advantage of a basic solvent, a very strongly basic titrant should be chosen.

[1] Fritz, J. S., *Anal. Chem.*, **22**, 1028 (1950).
[2] *Ibid.*, p. 578.
[3] Pifer, C. W., Wollish, E. G., and Schmall, M., *Anal. Chem.*, **25**, 310 (1953).
[4] *Ibid.*
[5] Pifer and Wollish, *Anal. Chem.*, **24**, 300 (1952).
[6] Gremillion, A. F., *Anal. Chem.*, **27**, 133 (1955).
[7] De Vries, J. E., Schiff, S., and Gantz, E. St. C., *Anal. Chem.*, **27**, 1814 (1955).

Moss, Elliott, and Hall[1] were able to observe separate end points for carboxylic acids and phenols using sodium aminoethoxide as a titrant in ethylenediamine as the solvent. Antimony electrodes were used in the end-point detection, one electrode being placed in the solution being titrated and another in the buret below the stopcock. This method has also been applied to phenolic esters.[2]

Deal and Wyld[3] noted that the glass electrode behaved properly in ethylenediamine in the presence of potassium salts but that it was insensitive to hydrogen ion in the presence of sodium salts. They explained this behavior as similar to the well-known sodium ion error of a glass electrode in strongly alkaline aqueous solutions, where the ratio of concentrations of sodium ion to hydrogen ion becomes very large. The glass electrode evidently is not permeable to potassium ion, which, therefore, does not exert a "buffering" action. Similar effects may be expected in other solvents that are strongly basic in character.

Sodium methoxide in a benzene-methanol mixture was introduced as a titrant by Fritz and Lisicki.[4] Various applications have since been made in a number of basic solvents, notably ethylenediamine, butylamine, and dimethylformamide. Acid-base indicators have been chosen empirically to give the best results.

Other titrants that have found use in basic solvents are potassium methoxide in benzene-methanol, potassium hydroxide in ethanol or isopropyl alcohol, and tetrabutylammonium hydroxide in ethanol, isopropyl alcohol, or benzene-methanol mixtures. The last reagent has been especially recommended[5] for selective titrations of mixtures of acids in pyridine as the solvent.

Neutral Solvents. The term "neutral solvent" as used here applies to any solvents not primarily acidic or basic in character. These include solvents that are amphiprotic (ethanol, methanol); very weakly basic but not appreciably acidic (ethers, dioxane, acetone, acetonitrile, esters, etc.); or aprotic (benzene, carbon tetrachloride, 1,2-dichloroethane, etc.).

Although acid-base reactions can be carried out in aprotic solvents and indicator color changes can be observed, few such reactions have found use in analytical chemistry.[6,7] Aprotic solvents are used mainly in mixed solvents to alter the solubility characteristics of the reactants. Presumably, the main effect is that of lowering the dielectric constant.

[1] Moss, M. L., Elliott, J. H., and Hall, R. T., *Anal. Chem.*, **20,** 784 (1948).

[2] Glenn, R. A., and Peake, J. T., *Anal. Chem.*, **27,** 205 (1955).

[3] Deal, V. Z., and Wyld, G. E. A., *Anal. Chem.*, **27,** 47 (1955).

[4] Fritz, J. S., and Lisicki, N. M., *Anal. Chem.*, **23,** 589 (1951).

[5] Cundiff, R. H., and Markunas, P. C., *Anal. Chem.*, **30,** 1447, 1450 (1958).

[6] Rice, R. V., Zuffanti, S., and Luder, W. F., *Anal. Chem.*, **24,** 1022 (1952).

[7] Garber, E. B., Pease, E. D., Jr., and Luder, W. F., *ibid.*, **25,** 581 (1953).

Many titrations have been made in such solvents as mixtures of alcohol or acetone with water. As has already been pointed out in Chap. 4, the main effect of adding alcohol to water is to weaken molecular and anionic acids. Only as the composition approaches anhydrous alcohol does the autoprotolysis constant show a large decrease. Therefore, the main advantage of avoiding the leveling effect of water and permitting the use of acids stronger than hydronium ion or bases stronger than hydroxyl ion is to be gained *only by using essentially anhydrous solvents.*

Many years ago, Folin and Flanders,[1] using sodium ethoxide in absolute ethanol and sodium amylate in amyl alcohol, titrated various weak acids in benzene, toluene, chloroform, and carbon tetrachloride with phenolphthalein as the indicator.

More recently, Palit[2] found that solvents which he called "G-H mixtures," where G is a glycol and H is a hydrocarbon solvent such as a hydrocarbon, alcohol, or chlorinated hydrocarbon, are exceptionally effective as solvents for alkali metal salts of organic acids. Such alkali metal salts could be titrated with perchloric acid in the same solvent, using either a visual indicator or a glass electrode.

Recent applications have been made of solvents such as dioxane, benzene-methanol mixtures, acetone, acetonitrile, chloroform, and ethyl acetate. Perchloric acid in dioxane or sodium or potassium methoxides in methanol or benzene-methanol have usually been used as titrants. Tetrabutylammonium hydroxide has occasionally been found advantageous because of favorable solubility characteristics of its salts.

Special mention should be made of lithium aluminum hydride, which was introduced by Higuchi, Lintner, and Schleif[3] in a method of determining alcohols by titration of active hydrogen. Tetrahydrofuran served as a solvent. The same reagent was applied by Higuchi and Zuck[4] for the determinations of various functional groups (alcohols, esters, phenols, ketones, aldehydes, etc.) that react with lithium aluminum hydride. The excess reagent was determined by titration with alcohol. To avoid the strongly reducing properties of lithium aluminum hydride, Higuchi, Concha, and Kuramoto[5] introduced lithium aluminum amides, prepared by the reaction of amines with lithium aluminum hydride. Such reagents should be of use for special purposes where extremely basic conditions are desired.

[1] Folin, O., and Flanders, F. F., *J. Am. Chem. Soc.*, **34**, 774 (1912).
[2] Palit, S. R., *Ind. Eng. Chem.*, *Anal. Ed.*, **18**, 246 (1946).
[3] Higuchi, T., Lintner, C. J., and Schleif, R. H., *Science*, **111**, 63 (1950); Lintner, Schleif, and Higuchi, *Anal. Chem.*, **22**, 534 (1950).
[4] Higuchi, T., and Zuck, D. A., *J. Am. Chem. Soc.*, **73**, 2676 (1951).
[5] Higuchi, T., Concha, J., and Kuramoto, R., *Anal. Chem.*, **24**, 685 (1952).

PROBLEMS

5-1. If 25 ml 0.4 M H_3PO_4 and 30 ml 0.5 M Na_3PO_4 are mixed and diluted to 100 ml, calculate the ml of 0.1 N acid or base required to titrate 25 ml of the solution to (a) a methyl orange end point, (b) a phenolphthalein end point. Calculate (c) the ionic strength, (d) the pH, and (e) the buffer capacity of the solution. $pK_1 = 2.16$; $pK_2 = 7.13$; $pK_3 = 12.30$. *Ans.* (a) 50 ml H^+; (b) 12.5 ml OH^-; (c) 0.65; (d) 7.73; (e) 0.092 mole liter^{-1}.

5-2. A sample of orthophosphates required 10 ml of standard acid to reach a phenolphthalein end point and 40 ml more to reach a methyl orange end point. What was the pH of the original sample? *Ans.* 11.82.

5-3. A sample containing orthophosphate, made up to 250 ml, required 15 ml of 0.1 N NaOH to titrate a 20-ml aliquot to a methyl orange end point. An equal aliquot required 50 ml to reach a phenolphthalein end point. Calculate the phosphate content of the original sample. *Ans.* 25 millimoles $H_2PO_4^-$, 18.75 millimoles H_3PO_4.

5-4. A solution of 0.01 M boric acid is treated with enough mannitol (mol. wt = 182) to give a final concentration of 50 g liter^{-1}. What is (a) the initial pH, and (b) the pH after the addition of an equivalent amount of strong base? Neglect dilution. *Ans.* (a) 3.80; (b) 8.30.

5-5. A standard NaOH solution is contaminated with Na_2CO_3. With phenolphthalein in the cold, 30.50 ml is required to titrate 50.00 ml of 0.5010 N HCl. With methyl orange boiling just before the end point, 30.00 ml is required for the same amount of acid. Calculate the moles (a) of NaOH, and (b) of Na_2CO_3 per liter. *Ans.* (a) 0.807; (b) 0.0137.

6. Solubility of Precipitates

In Chap. 2, it was seen that the solubility product of a precipitate in a given solvent at a given temperature is a function of the ionic strength. This activity effect or *diverse ion effect* is evidently a nonspecific electrolyte effect.

It is our purpose here to examine the specific chemical and physical factors that affect the solubility of a particular precipitate in a given solvent. The effects of activity coefficients will be neglected for the sake of simplicity. A rough correction for these effects could be made by estimating activity coefficients at the prevailing ionic strength and calculating the corresponding solubility product. Often, however, these effects are small in comparison with the uncertainties arising from disregarded or unknown side reactions and from the fact that the solubility product of a precipitate can depend on the crystalline state, the state of hydration, and even the state of perfection (aging) of the precipitate.

6-1. The Common Ion Effect

The solubility of a precipitate can be calculated in a straightforward way from the solubility product at a given ionic strength *provided that the precipitated substance is a strong electrolyte in solution and that its ions undergo no secondary reactions*. These complicating factors will be considered separately in later sections.

For the simple case, the solubility in water of a precipitate M_mA_n is represented by

$$M_mA_n \rightleftharpoons mM + nA \qquad (6\text{-}1)$$

(for simplicity of notation, the charges are omitted). If the molar solubility is S, the concentrations of M and A are mS and nS, respectively, and the solubility-product expression

$$K_{sp} = [M]^m[A]^n = (mS)^m(nS)^n \qquad (6\text{-}2)$$

can readily be solved for the solubility.

Example 6-1. The solubility product of calcium fluoride is 4×10^{-11}. Calculate its solubility S, neglecting hydrolysis of fluoride.

Answer. $[Ca^{++}] = S$; $[F^-] = 2S$; $4S^3 = 4 \times 10^{-11}$; $S = 2.1 \times 10^{-4}$ mole liter^{-1}.

In the presence of a common ion of the precipitate, the contribution from the solubility may often be neglected. If excess M^{n+} is present to the extent C_M, the solubility S may be calculated from

$$K_{sp} = (C_M + mS)^m (nS)^n \cong (C_M)^m (nS)^n \qquad (6-3)$$

Example 6-2. Calculate the solubility of calcium fluoride in 0.01 M CaCl$_2$.

Answer. If S = solubility, $[F^-] = 2S$. Then $(0.01 + S)(2S)^2 = 4 \times 10^{-11}$; this is a cubic equation. Solving it, we have, approximately, $0.01 \times 4S^2 = 4 \times 10^{-11}$; $S = 3.2 \times 10^{-5}$ mole liter^{-1}.

Note that, in accurate calculations, the total ionic strength, including that contributed by the precipitate, determines the value of K_{sp}. Cf. Example 2-4, Sec. 2-7.

6-2. Effect of Hydrogen Ion Concentration

If the anion of the precipitate is that of a weak acid, the solubility will vary with acidity.

Consider first the salt of a monobasic weak acid HA:

$$MA_n \rightleftharpoons M^{n+} + nA^- \qquad (6-4)$$
$$nA^- + nH^+ \rightleftharpoons nHA \qquad (6-5)$$

If C_A is the total concentration of A, or $C_A = [A^-] + [HA]$, and if α_1 is the fraction of the total A in the ionized form [cf. Eq. (3-61)], then

$$K_{sp} = [M^{n+}][A^-]^n = [M^{n+}]\alpha_1^n C_A^n \qquad (6-6)$$

where $$\alpha_1 = \frac{K_a}{[H^+] + K_a} \qquad (6-7)$$

If $[H^+]$ is known, α_1 may be calculated from (6-7) and substituted in (6-6) to give an apparent, or *conditional*[1] *solubility product* K'_{sp}, given by

$$K'_{sp} = [M^{n+}]C_A^n = \frac{K_{sp}}{\alpha_1^n} \qquad (6-8)$$

which varies with pH and which is used conveniently to calculate solubility.

Example 6-3. Calculate the solubility S of CaF$_2$ in 0.01 N HCl, if the K_a of HF is 6×10^{-4} and if $K_{sp} = 4 \times 10^{-11}$.

Answer. $\alpha_1 = 6 \times 10^{-4}/0.01 = 0.06$
$\qquad S = [Ca^{++}]$
$\qquad 2S = C_F = [HF] + [F^-]$
$\qquad S(2S)^2 = 4 \times 10^{-11}/(0.06)^2$
$\qquad S = 1.4 \times 10^{-3}$ mole liter^{-1}

[1] The term "conditional solubility product" was suggested to the author by Professor I. M. Kolthoff and has also been used at his suggestion by A. Ringbom, *J. Chem. Educ.*, **35**, 282 (1958).

Consider now the salt of a dibasic acid. The procedure is the same, except that the divalent anion concentration $[A^=]$ is given by $\alpha_2 C_A$ where α_2 is the fraction of the total anion in the $A^=$ form, or

$$\alpha_2 = \frac{K_1 K_2}{[H^+]^2 + K_1[H^+] + K_1 K_2} \tag{6-9}$$

[Cf. Eq. (3-64c).]

Example 6-4. Calculate the solubility of calcium oxalate at pH = 4, if $K_{sp} = 2 \times 10^{-9}$, $K_1 = 6 \times 10^{-2}$, and $K_2 = 6 \times 10^{-5}$ for oxalic acid.

Answer. $K_{sp} = [Ca^{++}][C_2O_4^-] = [Ca^{++}]\alpha_2 C_{ox}$
where $\quad C_{ox} = [H_2C_2O_4] + [HC_2O_4^-] + [C_2O_4^-]$
$\quad\quad S = [Ca^{++}] = C_{ox}$
$\quad\quad \alpha_2 = 0.375$
$\quad\quad S^2 = K_{sp}/\alpha_2$
$\quad\quad S = 7.4 \times 10^{-5}$ mole liter^{-1}

Example 6-5. Calculate the solubility of calcium oxalate in a solution of pH = 3.0 that contains a total oxalate excess of 0.01 M.

Answer. $\alpha_2 = 0.056$
$\quad\quad S = [Ca^{++}]$
$\quad\quad C_{ox} = S + 0.01$
$\quad\quad S(S + 0.01) = K_{sp}/\alpha_2 = 3.6 \times 10^{-8}$
$\quad\quad S = 3.6 \times 10^{-6}$ mole liter^{-1}

Example 6-6. Calculate the solubility of Ag_2S in 0.1 N HCl. For H_2S, $K_1 = 9 \times 10^{-8}$, $K_2 = 1.2 \times 10^{-15}$. For Ag_2S, $K_{sp} - 10^{-50}$.

Answer. $\alpha_2 \cong K_1K_2/[H^+]^2 = 1.1 \times 10^{-20}$
$\quad\quad S = C_S = [H_2S] + [HS^-] + [S^=]$
$\quad\quad 2S = [Ag^+]$
$\quad\quad (2S)^2 S = K_{sp}/\alpha_2 = 9 \times 10^{-31}$
$\quad\quad S = 6 \times 10^{-11}$ mole liter^{-1}

Example 6-7. Calculate the solubility of Ag_2S in 0.1 N HCl saturated with H_2S. Solubility of H_2S = 0.1 M.

Answer. $\alpha_2 = 1.1 \times 10^{-20}$
$\quad\quad C_S = 0.1$
$\quad\quad [S^=] = \alpha_2 C_S = 1.1 \times 10^{-21}$
$\quad\quad 2S = [Ag^+]$
$\quad\quad (2S)^2 \times 0.1 = 10^{-50}/1.1 \times 10^{-20}$
$\quad\quad S = 1.5 \times 10^{-15}$ mole liter^{-1}

6-3. Effect of Hydrolysis of Anion

If the anion of a sparingly soluble salt undergoes hydrolysis in water, for example, if

$$MA \rightleftharpoons M^+ + A^- \quad\quad\quad K_{sp} \tag{6-10}$$

$$A^- + H_2O \rightleftharpoons HA + OH^- \quad\quad \frac{K_w}{K_a} \tag{6-11}$$

$$H_2O \rightleftharpoons H^+ + OH^- \quad\quad\quad K_w \tag{6-12}$$

the problem could be handled generally by use of the electroneutrality relation

$$[M^+] + [H^+] = [A^-] + [OH^-] \tag{6-13}$$

giving four equations in four unknowns. The relationship is even more complex if two or more stages of hydrolysis of a polyvalent anion must be considered.

However, a simplification is usually possible at the outset. If K_{sp} is very small, the hydroxyl ion contribution from (6-11) is negligible compared to that already present in the water, and the pH is 7. Corresponding to this pH, the fraction of anion in the unhydrolyzed form is readily calculated.

Example 6-8. *Hydroxyl ion concentration from hydrolysis is negligible.*
Calculate the solubility S of Ag_2S in water, considering hydrolysis of sulfide ion.
Answer. From the very low K_{sp}, we deduce that $[OH^-]$ from hydrolysis is negligible in comparison with 10^{-7}. Therefore, pH = 7, and $\alpha_2 = 5.8 \times 10^{-9}$.

$$S = [H_2S] + [HS^-] + [S^-] = [S^-]/\alpha_2$$
$$2S = [Ag^+]$$
$$4S^3 = K_{sp}/\alpha_2 = 10^{-50}/5.8 \times 10^{-9}$$
$$S = 7.5 \times 10^{-15} \text{ mole liter}^{-1}$$

From the low solubility, we confirm that the hydroxyl concentration is indeed 10^{-7}.

On the other hand, the contribution of hydroxyl from water may be negligible compared to that from the hydrolysis.

Example 6-9. *Hydroxyl ion concentration from water is negligible.*
Calculate the solubility S of Ag_2CO_3 in water, considering hydrolysis of the carbonate ion. The K_{sp} of Ag_2CO_3 is 8×10^{-12}; for H_2CO_3 $K_1 = 4 \times 10^{-7}$, $K_2 = 5 \times 10^{-11}$.
Answer. From relatively large K_{sp} and small K_2, we conclude that the reaction is best represented by

$$Ag_2CO_3 + H_2O \rightleftharpoons 2Ag^+ + HCO_3^- + OH^- \qquad K = \frac{K_{sp}K_w}{K_2}$$

Then, $[HCO_3^-] = [OH^-] = S$; $[Ag^+] = 2S$; $4S^4 = 8 \times 10^{-12} \times 10^{-14}/5 \times 10^{-11}$; and $S = 1.4 \times 10^{-4}$ mole liter^{-1}.

More exactly,

$$[Ag^+] = 2([CO_3^-] + [HCO_3^-] + [H_2CO_3]) = 2[CO_3^-]/\alpha_2$$

But we calculate at $[OH^-] = 1.4 \times 10^{-4}$,

$$\alpha_2 = 0.71$$

From K_{sp},

$$4S^3 = K_{sp}/\alpha_2$$
$$S = 1.4 \times 10^{-4} \text{ mole liter}^{-1}$$

6-4. Effect of Hydrolysis of Cation

Many heavy metal cations undergo appreciable hydrolysis, with a corresponding effect on the solubility of their precipitates.

In the simplest type of hydrolysis reactions, the steps

$$M^{n+} + H_2O \rightleftharpoons MOH^{(n-1)+} + H^+ \qquad\qquad K_1 \qquad (6\text{-}14)$$
$$MOH^{(n-1)+} + H_2O \rightleftharpoons M(OH)_2^{(n-2)+} + H^+ \qquad K_2$$
$$\cdots$$

may be regarded as the successive acid dissociation constants of the aquated cation M^{n+}. Correspondingly, the fraction β of metal in the aquated form may be calculated from equations of the type

$$\beta = \frac{[H^+]^n}{[H^+]^n + K_1[H^+]^{n-1} + K_1K_2[H^+]^{n-2} + \cdots + K_1K_2 \cdots K_n} \qquad (6\text{-}15)$$

which is identical with Eq. (3-66a) for the fraction of undissociated acid in a solution of a polybasic acid and its salts.

Recent work, however, has indicated that the hydrolysis reactions of many cations are much more complicated than is implied by Eq. (6-14). Particularly with metal ions of charge greater than 2 but also for some dipositive ions, there is a pronounced tendency to form ionic species containing more than one metal atom.

Thus Hedström[1] deduced that the hydrolysis of Fe(II) could be represented by the single reaction

$$Fe^{++} + H_2O \rightleftharpoons FeOH^+ + H^+ \qquad\qquad K = 3 \times 10^{-10}$$

whereas that of Fe(III) involves the following reactions:

$$Fe^{3+} + H_2O \rightleftharpoons FeOH^{++} + H^+ \qquad\qquad K_1 = 9 \times 10^{-4}$$
$$FeOH^{++} + H_2O \rightleftharpoons Fe(OH)_2^+ + H^+ \qquad\quad K_2 = 5 \times 10^{-7} \qquad (6\text{-}16)$$
$$2Fe^{3+} + 2H_2O \rightleftharpoons Fe_2(OH)_2^{4+} + 2H^+ \qquad K = 1.2 \times 10^{-3}$$

The equilibrium constants of reactions (6-16) are such that, under certain conditions, the dimeric species $Fe_2(OH)_2^{4+}$ is the major form of Fe(III) present.

The hydrolysis of Al(III) is much more complicated.[2] The mononuclear species $Al(OH)^{++}$ and $Al(OH)_2^+$ and the polynuclear species $Al_2(OH)_2^{4+}$ and $Al_3(OH)_6^{3+}$, if they exist, are not the main products. The experimental data can be explained on the assumption of either a series of complexes $Al\{(OH)_5Al_2\}_n^{(n+3)+}$ or a single large complex $Al_6(OH)_{15}^{3+}$.

Similarly, the hydrolysis of Th(IV) could be accounted for only on the assumption of a series of polynuclear complexes $Th\{(OOH)Th\}_n^{(n+4)+}$ where n has various values, certainly exceeding 6 in certain cases.[3]

[1] Hedström, B. O. A., *Arkiv Kemi*, **5**, 457 (1952); **6**, 1 (1952).
[2] Brosset, C., Biedermann, G., and Sillén, L. G., *Acta Chem. Scand.* **8**, 1917 (1954).
[3] Hietanen, S., *Acta Chem. Scand.*, **8**, 1626 (1954).

With cadmium ion only the simple product $CdOH^+$ is formed,[1] but with $Cu(II)$ the binuclear reaction predominates[2]

$$2Cu^{++} + 2H_2O \rightleftharpoons Cu_2(OH)_2^{++} + 2H^+ \qquad K = 2.5 \times 10^{-11}$$

It is apparent that, if accurate calculations are to be carried out on the solubilities of heavy metal salts, careful attention must be paid to the nature of the hydrolytic species present. However, as the following example illustrates, the effect of cation hydrolysis is often of minor importance.

Example 6-10. Calculate the solubility of CdS in water, considering hydrolysis of Cd^{++} and $S^=$. $K_{sp} = 10^{-28}$; the first hydrolysis constant of $Cd^{++} = 10^{-9}$.

Answer. From the small value of K_{sp}, we conclude that $[H^+] = 10^{-7}$ and, therefore, that $\alpha_2 = 5.8 \times 10^{-9}$ (Example 6-8) and that $\beta = [H^+]/([H^+] + K_h) = 0.99$. If S = solubility, $[Cd^{++}] = \beta S$, $[S^=] = \alpha_2 S$, and $S = 1.3 \times 10^{-10}$ mole liter^{-1}.

6-5. Effect of Foreign Complexing Agents

If a slightly soluble salt MA is treated with a complexing agent X, we have the following equilibria:

$$MA \rightleftharpoons M + A \qquad K_{sp} \qquad (6\text{-}17)$$

$$M + X \rightleftharpoons MX \qquad k_1 = \frac{[MX]}{[M][X]} \qquad (6\text{-}18)$$

$$MX + X \rightleftharpoons MX_2 \qquad k_2 = \frac{[MX_2]}{[MX][X]} = \frac{[MX_2]}{k_1[M][X]^2} \qquad (6\text{-}19)$$

$$MX_{n-1} + X \rightleftharpoons MX_n \qquad k_n = \frac{[MX_n]}{[MX_{n-1}][X]} \qquad (6\text{-}20)$$

where M and A may both be univalent or divalent, etc., and X may be molecular or ionic; therefore, we omit the charges for the sake of simplicity. The constants $k_1, k_2, \ldots, k_n$ are the *successive formation constants* or *stepwise formation constants* of the complexes MX, $MX_2, \ldots, MX_n$.

It is convenient to calculate the fraction β of metal ion in the uncomplexed form M. Evidently the total metal ion concentration C_M is given by

$$C_M = [M] + [MX] + [MX_2] + \cdots + [MX_n]$$

$$= [M] \left(1 + k_1[X] + k_1k_2[X]^2 + \cdots + \prod_{i=1}^{i=n} k_i[X]^n \right) \quad (6\text{-}21)$$

The products of the successive formation constants are the *over-all*

[1] Marcus, Y., *Acta Chem. Scand.*, **11**, 690 (1957).
[2] Berecki-Biedermann, C., *Arkiv Kemi*, **9**, 175 (1956).

formation constants, or

$$K_i = k_1 k_2 \cdots k_i = \prod_{i=1}^{i=i} k_i \tag{6-22}$$

and $\dfrac{1}{\beta} = \dfrac{C_M}{[M]} = 1 + K_1[X] + K_2[X]^2 + K_3[X]^3 + \cdots + K_n[X]^n$

$$\tag{6-23}$$

$$= \sum_{i=0}^{i=n} K_i[X]^i \tag{6-24}$$

where, by definition, $K_0 = 1$. From the solubility-product expression,

$$K_{sp} = [M][A] = \beta C_M[A] \tag{6-25}$$

In the absence of common ion, the solubility S is given by

$$S = C_M = [A] = \sqrt{K_{sp}/\beta} \tag{6-26}$$

The effect of complex formation has been to increase the value of the solubility product in proportion to the decreasing fraction of metal ion in the uncomplexed form. Similar considerations may readily be applied to the more involved types of precipitates.

Example 6-11. Calculate the solubility of AgI in 0.01 M NH$_3$, if the solubility product of AgI is 9×10^{-17} and if the logarithms of the successive formation constants of the silver ammonia complexes are 3.2 and 3.8.

Answer. From (6-24), $1/\beta = 1 + 10^{3.2} \times 10^{-2} + 10^{7.0} \times 10^{-4} = 10^3$. From (6-26),

$$S = \sqrt{9 \times 10^{-17} \times 10^3} = 3 \times 10^{-7} \text{ mole liter}^{-1}$$

Note from (6-24) that the intermediate formation of Ag(NH$_3$)$^+$ is negligible in comparison with Ag(NH$_3$)$_2^+$.

Example 6-12. Calculate the solubility of AgCl in 0.01 M NH$_4$Cl, 0.001 M NH$_3$ buffer. $K_{sp} = 2 \times 10^{-10}$.

Answer. From (6-24), $1/\beta = 1 + 10^{3.2} \times 10^{-3} + 10^{7.0} \times 10^{-6} = 12.7$.

$$S = C_{Ag} = K_{sp}/0.01\beta = 2.5 \times 10^{-7} \text{ mole liter}^{-1}$$

Note that Ag(NH$_3$)$^+$ makes an appreciable contribution.

Example 6-13. Calculate the solubility of AgI in 0.01 M KCN, if log $k_1 k_2 = 20.9$.

Answer:

$$1/\beta = 1 + 10^{20.9} \times 10^{-4} = 8 \times 10^{16}$$
$$S = \sqrt{9 \times 10^{-17} \times 8 \times 10^{16}} = \sqrt{7.2} = 2.7$$

Since the calculated solubility is greater than that possible from stoichiometry, we conclude that $S = 0.005$ mole liter^{-1}.

6-6. Effect of Complex Formation with Precipitating Anion : Amphoterism

If a metal ion forms a sparingly soluble salt with an anion, it frequently forms a complex with excess anion. The solubility passes through a minimum as the suppressing effect of the common ion is balanced by the increasing solubility due to complex formation.

Consider first a 1:1 salt MA, which dissolves in excess reagent A to form a series of complexes. M and A may both be univalent or divalent, etc.; therefore, we omit the charges. The precipitation reaction may be written

$$M + A \rightleftharpoons MA(\text{solid}) \qquad K_{eq} = \frac{1}{K_{sp}} \qquad (6\text{-}27)$$

The solution concentration of undissociated MA, which may be called the *intrinsic solubility* of MA, is a constant at a given temperature and may be represented by

$$[MA]_{soln} = S^\circ \qquad (6\text{-}28)$$

The successive complexes are formed by the reactions:

$$MA(\text{soln}) + A \rightleftharpoons MA_2 \qquad k_2 = \frac{[MA_2]}{[MA]_{soln}[A]} \qquad (6\text{-}29)$$

$$MA_2 + A \rightleftharpoons MA_3 \qquad k_3 = \frac{[MA_3]}{[MA_2][A]} \qquad (6\text{-}30)$$

$$MA_{n-1} + A \rightleftharpoons MA_n \qquad k_n = \frac{[MA_n]}{[MA_{n-1}][A]} \qquad (6\text{-}31)$$

where the constants k_2, k_3 . . . , k_n are again the successive formation constants.

The first formation constant k_1 is defined by the equation

$$M + A \rightleftharpoons MA(\text{soln}) \qquad k_1 = \frac{[MA]_{soln}}{[M][A]} = \frac{S^\circ}{[M][A]} = \frac{S^\circ}{K_{sp}} \qquad (6\text{-}32)$$

The solubility of the precipitate is given by the total concentration of all forms of M, or

$$S = [M] + [MA] + [MA_2] + [MA_3] + \cdots + [MA_n]$$

Substituting from Eq. (6-27) to (6-31),

$$S = \frac{K_{sp}}{[A]} + S^\circ + S^\circ k_2[A] + S^\circ k_2 k_3[A]^2 + \cdots + S^\circ k_2 k_3 \cdots k_n[A]^{n-1}$$

and, from (6-32),

$$S = \frac{K_{sp}}{[A]} + k_1 K_{sp} + k_1 k_2 K_{sp}[A] + k_1 k_2 k_3 K_{sp}[A]^2 + \cdots \qquad (6\text{-}33)$$

In terms of the over-all formation constants [Eq. (6-22)],

$$S = K_{sp}\left(\frac{1}{[A]} + K_1 + K_2[A] + K_3[A]^2 + \cdots + K_n[A]^{n-1}\right) \quad (6\text{-}34)$$

or
$$S = K_{sp} \sum_{i=0}^{i=n} K_i[A]^{i-1} \quad (6\text{-}35)$$

where $K_0 = 1$, by definition.

The solubility given by the polynomial (6-34) or (6-35) passes through a minimum at some value of [A] and, beyond that concentration, increases with increasing concentration of A.

If no higher complexes than MA_2 are formed, Eq. (6-34) or (6-35) becomes

$$S = K_{sp}\left(\frac{1}{[A]} + K_1 + K_2[A]\right)$$

or
$$S = \frac{K_{sp}}{[A]} + S^\circ + K_2 K_{sp}[A] \quad (6\text{-}36)$$

showing that the solubility increases linearly with [A] at sufficiently high values of [A]. The minimum solubility is determined by setting $dS/d[A]$ equal to zero. For the case described by Eq. (6-36), this corresponds to

$$\frac{K_{sp}}{[A]^2_{min}} = K_2 K_{sp} \quad \text{or} \quad [A]_{min} = \frac{1}{\sqrt{K_2}} \quad \text{and} \quad S_{min} = S^\circ + 2K_{sp}\sqrt{K_2}$$
$$(6\text{-}37)$$

Example 6-14. Johnston, Cuta, and Garrett[1] found that the solubility of silver oxide in sodium hydroxide solutions could be expressed by the equation $S = 5 \times 10^{-8}/[OH^-] + 1.95 \times 10^{-4}[OH^-]$. Comparing this equation with Eq. (6-36), we find $S^\circ = 0$; $K_{sp} = 5 \times 10^{-8}$; $K_2 K_{sp} = 1.95 \times 10^{-4}$, or $K_2 = 3.9 \times 10^3$. From (6-37), the condition of minimum solubility corresponds to $[OH^-]_{min} = 0.016$ M, $S_{min} = 6.2 \times 10^{-6}$ M.

If a succession of complexes is formed, it is necessary to add a corresponding number of terms from Eq. (6-34). For example, Forbes and Cole[2] expressed the solubility of silver chloride by the expression

$$S = \frac{2 \times 10^{-10}}{[Cl^-]} + b + 3.4 \times 10^{-5}[Cl^-]$$

where the constant 2×10^{-10} is the solubility product and where the constant b was ascribed to undissociated silver chloride plus any colloidally dispersed solid. From the reproducible character of b (6.3×10^{-7} M for NaCl solutions, 6.1×10^{-7} M for HCl solutions), b appears to

[1] Johnston, H. L., Cuta, F., and Garrett, A. B., *J. Am. Chem. Soc.*, **55**, 2311 (1933); see also Reynolds, C. A., and Argersinger, W. J., Jr., *J. Phys. Chem.*, **56**, 417 (1952).

[2] Forbes, G. S., and Cole, H. I., *J. Am. Chem. Soc.*, **43**, 2492 (1921).

represent the intrinsic solubility $S°$. From $S° = K_1 K_{sp}$, we calculate the first formation constant $K_1 = 3 \times 10^3$, and from $K_2 K_{sp} = 3.4 \times 10^{-5}$ we estimate the second formation constant $K_2 = 1.7 \times 10^5$.

Previously, Forbes[1] had expressed the solubility of silver chloride at chloride concentrations above 2.5 M by the expression

$$S = 10^{-4}[Cl^-]^2 + 4.5 \times 10^{-5}[Cl^-]^3$$

from which we deduce $K_3 = 10^{-4}/K_{sp} = 5 \times 10^5$ and

$$K_4 = 4.5 \times \frac{10^{-5}}{K_{sp}} = 2 \times 10^5$$

Example 6-15. From the above equilibrium constants, estimate the solubility of AgCl in solutions containing chloride at the following concentrations: 10^{-3}, 10^{-2}, 10^{-1}, 1, 2 M. What is the minimum solubility, and at what chloride ion concentration does it occur?

Answer. From Eq. (6-34) we calculate the following solubilities at the specified chloride concentrations: 8.2×10^{-7}, 9.8×10^{-7}, 5×10^{-6}, 1.8×10^{-4}, 8×10^{-4} M. Taking only the first three terms, we calculate that the minimum solubility of 7.8×10^{-7} M occurs at a chloride ion concentration of 2.4×10^{-3} M.

Consider now a 1:2 type precipitate, such as MA_2 where M^{++} is a divalent cation and A^- is a univalent anion. By considerations similar to those above, the solubility is given by

$$S = [M^{++}] + [MA^+] + [MA_2] + [MA_3^-] + \cdots \qquad (6\text{-}38)$$

and

$$M^{++} + A^- \rightleftharpoons MA^+ \qquad k_1 = \frac{[MA^+]}{[M^{++}][A^-]}; \ [MA^+] = \frac{k_1 K_{sp}}{[A]}$$

$$MA^+ + A^- \rightleftharpoons MA_2 \qquad k_2 = \frac{[MA_2]}{[MA^+][A^-]}; \ [MA_2] = k_1 k_2 K_{sp} = S°$$

$$MA_2 + A^- \rightleftharpoons MA_3^- \qquad k_3 = \frac{[MA_3^-]}{[MA_2][A^-]}; \ [MA_3] = k_1 k_2 k_3 K_{sp} = K_3 K_{sp}$$

so that

$$S = K_{sp}\left(\frac{1}{[A^-]^2} + \frac{K_1}{[A^-]} + K_2 + K_3[A^-] + \cdots + K_n[A^-]^{n-2}\right) \qquad (6\text{-}39)$$

For the more general case of a precipitate MA_q, evidently

$$S = K_{sp}\left(\frac{1}{[A^-]^q} + \frac{K_1}{[A^-]^{q-1}} + \cdots + K_q + K_{q+1}[A^-] + \cdots \right.$$
$$\left. + K_n[A^-]^{n-q}\right) \qquad (6\text{-}40)$$

and once more the solubility passes through a minimum at some value of $[A^-]$. Unfortunately, experimental data are often lacking, especially

[1] Forbes, *J. Am. Chem. Soc.*, **33**, 1937 (1911).

with respect to the intrinsic solubility $S° = K_q K_{sp}$; so we cannot make as many applications of Eq. (6-40) as would be desirable.

Example 6-16. For the reaction of Th^{4+} with F^-, the logarithms of the successive formation constants are log $k_1 = 7.8$, log $k_2 = 6.1$, log $k_3 = 4.7$; and $K_{sp} = 4 \times 10^{-28}$. Calculate the solubility at a fluoride ion concentration of 10^{-2} M. Ignore the intrinsic solubility.

Answer:

$$S = \frac{10^{-27.4}}{10^{-8}} + \frac{10^{7.8} \times 10^{-27.4}}{10^{-6}} + \frac{10^{13.9} \times 10^{-27.4}}{10^{-4}} + \frac{10^{18.6} \times 10^{-27.4}}{10^{-2}}$$

$$= 10^{-6.8} = 1.6 \times 10^{-7} \text{ mole liter}^{-1}$$

due mainly to ThF_3^+.

6-7. Solubility of Metastable Form

A precipitate often comes down initially in a metastable form, which gradually reverts to a stable form upon standing. Hydrous oxides, for example, are often precipitated in an amorphous form or in the form of exceedingly small crystallites that adsorb enormous quantities of water. In the older literature, there are many references to "ortho" and "meta" modifications of hydrous oxides, such as ortho- and metastannic acids, silicic acids, and titania. Such modifications, however, are generally distinguished only by the particle size and degree of adsorption of water.[1]

Calcium oxalate, precipitated at room temperature, comes down as a mixture of di- and trihydrates, which are metastable with respect to the monohydrate[2] at temperatures above 50°C. Mercuric sulfide, precipitated from acid solution as the black cubic form, is gradually transformed upon aging to the red trigonal cinnabar.[3]

It is of interest that, under any given set of conditions, the *metastable form is more soluble than the stable form*, as is evident from the following argument. Imagine a container in the shape of an inverted Y, with the metastable form of a precipitate in one leg and the stable form in the other. If water is added, so that the two forms come to equilibrium each with the solution in its own compartment, the metastable form must be the more soluble, in order that, through dissolution and precipitation, it may be able to be transformed into the stable form. Through a similar argument, removing the solvent, it can be demonstrated that the vapor pressure of the metastable form is greater than that of the stable form.

6-8. Solubility and Particle Size

Already in 1878 J. Willard Gibbs had considered the problem of the relationship between the particle size of a solid and its solubility, and had

---

[1] Weiser, H. B., and Milligan, W. O., *Chem. Revs.*, **25**, 1 (1939); "Advances in Colloid Science," vol. 1, p. 227, Interscience Publishers, Inc., New York, 1942.

[2] Sandell, E. B., and Kolthoff, I. M., *J. Phys. Chem.*, **37**, 153 (1933).

[3] Moltzau, R., and Kolthoff, I. M., *J. Phys. Chem*, **40**, 637 (1936).

warned that the breakdown or growth of a crystal could not be considered a completely continuous transformation, as the gas-liquid transition could be. Thomson[1] derived the relationship, which has come to be known as the Gibbs-Thomson equation, relating the vapor pressure of liquid droplets to the size of the droplets.

Ostwald[2] extended the concept to the problem of solubility, but made a numerical error later corrected by Freundlich.[3] This led to the Ostwald-Freundlich equation:

$$\frac{RT}{M} \ln \frac{S_2}{S_1} = \frac{2\sigma}{\rho} \left(\frac{1}{r_2} - \frac{1}{r_1} \right) \tag{6-41}$$

an equation similar to the Gibbs-Thomson equation, in which S_2 and S_1 are the solubilities of the spherical particles of radii r_2 and r_1, respectively, M is the molecular weight, σ is the surface tension of the solid-liquid interface, and ρ is the density of the solid. The quantity RT has its usual significance.

According to this equation, a substance of large surface tension σ should show a pronounced dependence of solubility on particle size. A noticeable increase in solubility occurs only for particles of small radius (of the order of 1 μ or less). The surface tension (or surface free energy) is a measure of the tendency of a finely divided solid to decrease its total surface area by growing to a larger particle size. This tendency is reflected in an increased solubility for particles of small size.

If r_1 is very large, $1/r_1$ is negligible and S_1 may be replaced by S, the solubility of large crystals. Equation (6-41) becomes

$$\frac{RT}{M} \ln \frac{S_r}{S} = \frac{2\sigma}{\rho r} \tag{6-42}$$

where S_r is the solubility of particles of radius r. This equation, however, is valid only for a nonionic solid. The effect of ionization was considered by Jones[4] and by Dundon and Mack,[5] who introduced the van't Hoff factor $1 - \alpha + \nu\alpha$ on the left-hand side of Eq. (6-42). The degree of ionization is α, and ν is the number of ions resulting from the dissociation of one "molecule" of solute. May and Kolthoff[6] have presented a modern thermodynamic derivation, assuming that the solute is a strong electrolyte. The result is identical with (6-42) except that the solubility

[1] Thomson, W., *Phil. Mag.*, [4], **42**, 448 (1881).
[2] Ostwald, W., *Z. physik. Chem. Leipzig*, **34**, 495 (1900).
[3] Freundlich, H., "Kapillarchemie," Akademische Verlagsgesellschaft, Leipzig, 1909.
[4] Jones, W. J., *Z. physik. Chem. Leipzig*, **82**, 448 (1913).
[5] Dundon, M. L., and Mack, E., Jr., *J. Am. Chem. Soc.*, **45**, 2479, 2658 (1923).
[6] May, D. R., and Kolthoff, I. M., *J. Phys. Colloid Chem.*, **52**, 836 (1948).

S is replaced by the activity product, as follows:

$$\frac{RT}{M} \ln \frac{(K_{ap})_r}{K_{ap}} = \frac{2\sigma}{\rho r} \tag{6-43}$$

It has proved to be extraordinarily difficult to obtain experimental verification of Eqs. (6-42) and (6-43).

Hulett[1] attempted to measure the solubility of barium sulfate, mercuric oxide, and gypsum ($CaSO_4 \cdot 2H_2O$) of various particle sizes, by grinding the crystalline solid to a fine powder and measuring the conductivity. All these substances exhibited greater solubility when finely ground. The solubility of gypsum was 19 per cent in excess of the normal value for particles of 0.4-μ radius. When barium sulfate was freshly precipitated, its concentration decreased gradually from an initial value of 4.6 to a final value of 2.9 mg liter^{-1}.

Dundon and Mack[2] made measurements of the solubilities of several substances in a fine state of subdivision and calculated the surface tension from the solubility. The calculated surface-tension values showed a rough correlation with the hardness, as would be expected since a hard substance would have a high surface free energy. Dundon and Mack criticized the Hulett's data for gypsum on the basis that a dehydration probably occurred during the grinding, yielding some anhydrous calcium sulfate, which is more soluble than gypsum. Their data for barium sulfate agreed with Hulett's findings.

Balarew,[3] on the other hand, found that the conductance of finely ground barium sulfate decreased rapidly to a value about equal to that of a coarse powder. He believed that grinding exposed impurities (such as occluded barium chloride) that were adsorbed by the barium sulfate upon standing.

The use of conductivity measurements for determining the solubility of very finely divided solids was criticized by Cohen and Blekkingh[4] on the grounds that the suspended material could contribute to the conductance, both by motion of charged particles and by motion of ions in the double layer at the surface of the particles. These authors found no evidence for increased solubility of fine particles, but did not actually measure the particle size. Balarew[5] likewise found no increase in the solubility of barium sulfate particles of 0.1-μ diameter.

The most conclusive evidence for abnormal solubility of small particles

[1] Hulett, G. A., *Z. physik. Chem. Leipzig,* **37,** 385 (1901).

[2] Dundon and Mack, *op. cit.*

[3] Balarew, D., *Z. anorg. u. allgem. Chem.,* **145,** 122 (1925); **151,** 68 (1926); **154,** 170 (1926).

[4] Cohen, E., and Blekkingh, J. J. A., *Z. physik. Chem. Leipzig,* **A186,** 257 (1940).

[5] Balarew, *Kolloid-Z.,* **96,** 19 (1941).

is that of May and Kolthoff,[1] who measured the solubilities of various preparations of lead chromate. To avoid the questionable features of conductance measurements, they carried out a chemical analysis of the solution. To show that impurities had no important effect, they determined both lead and chromate ions and also measured the solubilities with varying amounts of solid present. They showed that supersaturation was relieved very rapidly (within 20 sec) by shaking the supersaturated solution with aged lead chromate. The solubility determinations were carried out with three different preparations: an aged precipitate, a fresh acid-precipitated product, and a fresh precipitate composed of very small particles. The particle radii were calculated from the specific surface (area per gram) measured by dye adsorption and by radioactive-isotope exchange methods. It is apparent from Table 6-1 that all three preparations gave the same final solubility but that the fresh precipitate showed considerable abnormal solubility for the first few minutes. During this time, a growth of particles was taking place; so the excess solubility was a temporary phenomenon.

TABLE 6-1. SOLUBILITY OF LEAD CHROMATE AS A FUNCTION OF PARTICLE SIZE

Preparation	Time of shaking, min	Calculated particle radius, μ	Molar solubility, $\times 10^4$
Aged	1	–	1.30
	6	–	1.28
	1,440	0.45	1.28
Fresh acid-precipitated	1	–	1.35
	6	–	1.24
	1,440	0.26	1.26
Fresh, small particles	1	0.086	2.10
	5	–	1.85
	20	0.28	1.41
	1,440	0.30	1.24

[With permission from May, D. R., and Kolthoff, I. M., *J. Phys. Colloid Chem.*, **52**, 836 (1948).]

Actually, an abnormal solubility of small particles could not be expected to be an equilibrium condition. Even if all the particles were uniform in size, the system would be metastable; for, if a slight dissolution of any particle occurred, the solution would become supersaturated with respect to all the other particles and unsaturated with respect to the particle that had decreased in size, so that ultimately this particle would dissolve.

[1] May and Kolthoff, *op. cit.*

Conversely, if any particle grew slightly larger than the others, its growth would continue.

Besides this experimental problem, there remain several important theoretical questions that lack adequate answers. First, is the surface tension independent of particle size for very small crystals? Harbury,[1] in attempting to apply the Ostwald-Freundlich equation to explain the limiting supersaturation of several relatively soluble salts, concluded that to fit the data the surface tension should be replaced by a quantity σ', smaller than the actual surface tension and decreasing with decreasing particle size. In the light of more recent evidence, to be presented in Chap. 7, it is doubtful that the quantity σ' has any physical significance. If anything, the most recent theoretical evidence points to a slight *increase* of surface tension with curvature.

Another problem is created by the nonspherical shapes of crystallites. As early as 1913, Jones[2] concluded that departure from spherical shape could cause considerable departure from the theory. Harbury[3] has pointed out that crystals separating from supersaturated solutions tend to be needlelike, dendritic growths, even when crystals grown at more normal rates are regular. If solubility increases with curvature, the ends of needles would be unlikely growth sites. The role of crystal imperfections may be decisive here, as will be brought out later.

Finally, the effect of electrical surface charge was considered by Knapp[4] and by May and Kolthoff,[5] who concluded that, with decreasing particle size, the solubility would pass through a maximum and decrease again. The surface charge is known to vary with conditions of precipitation and even with the state of perfection of the crystals, and so the maximum solubility cannot be regarded as corresponding to a particular particle size for a given precipitate.

In conclusion, it may be stated that precipitates of high surface free energy (like barium sulfate) show *qualitatively* a greater trend of solubility with particle size than precipitates of low surface tension (such as silver chloride). Evidence for this behavior is found, for example, in the much greater tendency toward stability of slightly supersaturated solutions of barium sulfate. However, it does not appear valid to apply the Ostwald-Freundlich equation quantitatively in comparing the behaviors of different precipitates. A type of aging (Sec. 9-4) known as "Ostwald ripening" is ascribed to the dissolution of small particles and the growth of large ones. Although this process has been proved to exist, it is less important than had been thought at the time of Ostwald.

[1] Harbury, L., *J. Phys. Chem.*, **50**, 190 (1946).
[2] Jones, *Ann. Physik*, [4], **41**, 441 (1913).
[3] Harbury, *J. Phys. Colloid Chem.*, **51**, 382 (1947).
[4] Knapp, L. F., *Trans. Faraday Soc.*, **17**, 457 (1922).
[5] May and Kolthoff, *op. cit.*

PROBLEMS

6-1. The solubility product of $CaCO_3$ is 1×10^{-8}. Considering hydrolysis of the carbonate ion, calculate (a) the solubility of $CaCO_3$ in water, (b) the pH of a saturated solution of $CaCO_3$, (c) the solubility of $CaCO_3$ at a pH of 7.00. *Ans.* (a) $1.1 \times 10^{-4} M$; (b) 10.04; (c) 0.005 M.

6-2. How would you proceed to determine whether the increase of solubility of magnesium oxalate in excess ammonium oxalate is due primarily to an activity effect or to complex formation?

6-3. The solubility product of CdS is 10^{-28}. The successive stepwise formation constants of $Cd(NH_3)_4^{++}$ are $k_1 = 300$, $k_2 = 100$, $k_3 = 20$, $k_4 = 6$. Taking the base dissociation constant of ammonia to be 2×10^{-5} and the acid dissociation constants of H_2S to be $K_1 = 10^{-7}$, $K_2 = 10^{-15}$, calculate the molar solubility of CdS in (a) 0.1 M NH_3, (b) a buffer of pH = 9 containing a total concentration of $NH_3 + NH_4Cl$ equal to 0.1 M. *Ans.* (a) 2.9×10^{-11}; (b) 8.4×10^{-11}.

6-4. The solubility product of calcium oxalate is 2×10^{-9}. For oxalic acid $K_1 = 6 \times 10^{-2}$, $K_2 = 6 \times 10^{-5}$. Calculate the solubility of calcium oxalate at pH values of 1, 2, 3, 4, 5, 6, and depict the results graphically. *Ans.* $S = 3.0 \times 10^{-3}$, 6.2×10^{-4}, 1.9×10^{-4}, 7.3×10^{-5}, 4.8×10^{-5}, 4.5×10^{-5}.

6-5. The solubility product of $MgNH_4PO_4$ is 2.5×10^{-12}. Calculate its solubility in buffers of pH 8, 9, and 10 containing $NH_4^+ + NH_3$ at a total concentration of 0.20 M and phosphate at a total concentration of 0.01 M. The formation constant of $Mg(OH)^+$ is 300; K_a of NH_4^+ is 5×10^{-10}; pK values of H_3PO_4 are 2.2, 7.2, 12.3. *Ans.* $S = 3.1 \times 10^{-5}$; 3.7×10^{-6}; 1.5×10^{-6} M.

6-6. According to Ahrland and Grenthe,[1] the value of pK_{sp} is 18.09 for BiI_3. The over-all formation constants of the higher complexes between Bi^{3+} and I^- are as follows: $\log K_4 = 14.95$; $\log K_5 = 16.8$; $\log K_6 = 18.8$. The lower complexes make a negligible contribution. From these data calculate the solubility of BiI_3 in 0.1 M KI. *Ans.* 5.6×10^{-3} M.

6-7. The solubility of mercurous chloride at chloride ion concentrations of 0.1 to 1.0 M follows the empirical equation $S = 5.9 \times 10^{-6} + 7.9 \times 10^{-5}[Cl^-]$. Taking $K_{sp} = 1.1 \times 10^{-18}$, evaluate the formation constants of the complexes Hg_2Cl_2 and $Hg_2Cl_3^-$. *Ans.* $K_2 = 5.4 \times 10^{12}$; $K_3 = 7.2 \times 10^{13}$.

6-8. The formation constant of $Zn(OH)^+$ is 2×10^4. The solubility product of $Zn(OH)_2$ is 1.3×10^{-17}. The equilibrium constant of the reaction $Zn(OH)_2(solid) \rightleftharpoons HZnO_2^- + H^+$ is 3×10^{-17}, and that of the reaction $Zn(OH)_2(solid) \rightleftharpoons ZnO_2^- + 2H^+$ is 10^{-29}. (a) Evaluate K_3 and K_4, the formation constants of $HZnO_2^-$ and ZnO_2^-; (b) Calculate the solubility of $Zn(OH)_2$ at pH = 6, 7, 8, 9, 10, 11, 12, 13. *Ans.* $K_3 = 2.3 \times 10^{14}$; $K_4 = 7.7 \times 10^{15}$; $S = 0.13$, 1.3×10^{-3}, 1.3×10^{-5}, 1.9×10^{-7}, 3×10^{-7}, 3.1×10^{-6}, 4×10^{-5}, 1.3×10^{-3}.

6-9. Taking the surface tensions of AgCl and $BaSO_4$ to be 150 and 1,500 erg cm^{-2}, respectively,[2] calculate from Eq. (6-42) the factor by which the normal solubility product would be exceeded for particles of radius 10^{-4} and 10^{-6} cm. The densities are 5.56 and 4.50 g cm^{-3}; the molecular weights are 143.3 and 233.4, for AgCl and $BaSO_4$, respectively. *Ans.* AgCl: 1.003, 1.37; $BaSO_4$: 1.065, 525.

[1] Ahrland, S., and Grenthe, I., *Acta Chim. Scand.*, **11**, 1111 (1957).

[2] La Mer, V. K., and Dinegar, R. H., *J. Am. Chem. Soc.*, **73**, 380 (1951).

7. The Formation of Precipitates

The mechanism of the formation of precipitates has been a controversial subject for many years. Even today, strong differences of opinion exist. We shall, therefore, consider first a number of experimental observations and then some alternative theoretical explanations.

7-1. Experimental Studies of Precipitate Formation

Perhaps the most striking, and rather general, phenomenon is the induction period that occurs after the mixing of the reagents and before the appearance of a visible precipitate. The duration of the induction period varies greatly for different precipitates; it is especially long for barium sulfate and short for silver chloride. These two salts have been studied extensively, and represent interesting cases for comparison because they have about the same molar solubility.

Nielsen[1] has compared the induction periods for several precipitates, as observed by various investigators and expressed by the empirical equation

$$t_i C_0^n = k \tag{7-1}$$

where t_i = induction period

C_0 = initial concentration just after mixing

n, k = empirical constants

For $AgCl$, Ag_2CrO_4, CaF_2, CaC_2O_4, and $KClO_4$, the values of n obtained by various investigators appear to be in reasonable agreement and are 5, 4.7, 9, 3.3, and 2.6, respectively. For barium sulfate, on the other hand, a variety of discordant values have been reported.

The duration of the induction period seems to be independent of the method of observation, whether by direct visual observation, by sensitive optical means, or by measurement of electrical conductance. According to Johnson and O'Rourke,[2] the conductivity remains very nearly constant

---

[1] Nielsen, A. E., *J. Colloid Sci.*, **10**, 576 (1955).

[2] Johnson, R. A., and O'Rourke, J. D., *J. Am. Chem. Soc.*, **76**, 2124 (1954).

during the induction period, which indicates that during this period only a small fraction of the solute exists as ion pairs or higher aggregates.

For barium sulfate, the length of the induction period varies with the method of mixing. Examination of the data of La Mer and Dinegar[1] reveals that, if sulfate ion is generated in homogeneous solution by the reaction

$$S_2O_8^= + S_2O_3^= \rightarrow 2SO_4^= + S_4O_6^= \qquad (7\text{-}2)$$

in the presence of barium ion, a solution of given supersaturation ratio persists without precipitation for a longer time than if the same solution is prepared by direct mixing. Using the homogeneous method, La Mer and Dinegar concluded that precipitation occurred at a specific limiting supersaturation ratio $(a_{Ba^{++}} \cdot a_{SO_4^-}/K_{sp})^{1/2} = 21.5$ regardless of the barium ion concentration or the rate of generation of sulfate. More recent work by Collins and Leineweber,[2] however, has indicated that the critical supersaturation ratio is dependent on the purity of the reagents. By repeated recrystallization and filtration of the reagents they observed critical supersaturation ratios as high as 32. It was concluded that homogeneous nucleation probably did not occur in these experiments but that crystallization began on foreign nuclei, perhaps elemental sulfur present in the thiosulfate solution. Nielsen[3] found that, if the walls of the precipitation vessel were thoroughly cleaned by prolonged steaming, the number of barium sulfate crystals per unit volume could be decreased by a factor of 10 or more. From this behavior he concluded that under normal precipitation conditions most of the nucleation occurs on the walls of the glass vessel.

There is also good evidence that foreign nuclei occur in freshly prepared barium chloride solutions,[4-6] as shown by the decreasing number and increased size of barium sulfate particles formed when aged and filtered barium chloride solutions are used.

Another significant type of observation is concerned with the variation in size and number of precipitate particles with the concentration of precipitating reagents. Von Weimarn,[7] in his classic studies of precipitate formation, measured the size of barium sulfate crystals obtained by rapid mixing of equimolar solutions of barium thiocyanate and manganous sulfate. At very high dilution ($\sim 10^{-4}\ M$) he observed no precipitate at

[1] La Mer, V. K., and Dinegar, R. H., *J. Am. Chem. Soc.*, **73**, 380 (1951).

[2] Collins, F. C., and Leineweber, J. P., *J. Phys. Chem.*, **60**, 389 (1956).

[3] Nielsen, *Acta Chem. Scand.*, **11**, 1512 (1957).

[4] Fischer, R. B., and Rhinehammer, T. B., *Anal. Chem.*, **25**, 1544 (1953); **26**, 244 (1954).

[5] Bogan, E. J., and Moyer, H. V., *Anal. Chem.*, **28**, 473 (1956).

[6] O'Rourke, J. D., and Johnson, R. A., *Anal. Chem.*, **27**, 1699 (1955).

[7] Von Weimarn, P. P., *Chem. Revs.*, **2**, 217 (1926).

all, but, with increasing concentration (in the range 10^{-3} to 10^{-4} M), the initial precipitate, described as "amorphous" grains, gradually transformed into well-formed crystals. The changes, however, were very slow, taking up to 6 months for perfection of the crystals. The size of the initially formed particles increased with increasing concentration, whereas the size of the final crystals decreased with increasing initial concentration.

The behavior typical of many precipitates is depicted graphically in Fig. 7-1, for various times increasing from t_1 to t_5. As the initial concentration was increased from 10^{-3} to 1 M, the freshly formed crystals

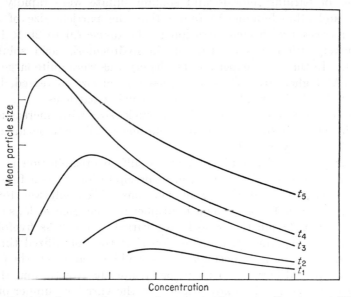

Fig. 7-1. Particle size as a function of concentration, according to von Weimarn.

became less perfect, and more needles and skeletal crystals appeared. Above 1 M, jellylike masses were formed first, and these changed gradually to voluminous, fine-grained precipitates. It is interesting that von Weimarn believed early in the present century that the "amorphous" precipitates were actually crystalline but composed of extremely small and imperfect particles. This view has been confirmed by later X-ray investigations, which generally show that freshly formed precipitates have the same powder diffraction patterns as the aged products but with more diffuse lines.[1] Von Weimarn did not distinguish clearly between the formation of the precipitate particles and the later changes that are now classified as "aging phenomena" (see Chap. 9).

[1] Weiser, H. B., and Milligan, W. O., *Chem. Revs.*, **25**, 1 (1939); "Advances in Colloid Science," vol. I, p. 227, Interscience Publishers, Inc., New York, 1942.

Odén and Werner[1] measured the particle size of barium sulfate crystals, using a sedimentation procedure, and concluded that the particle size became larger and more uniform with increasing dilution, in the concentration range 10^{-3} to 0.1 M.

On the other hand, under certain conditions, the particle size increases with increasing concentration. It has already been mentioned that von Weimarn found this to be true for many precipitations from very dilute solutions. O'Rourke and Johnson[2] found that the total number of barium sulfate particles formed was independent of initial concentration of barium sulfate over the range 2.5 to 25 $\times$ 10^{-4} M, when well-aged solutions of barium chloride and sodium sulfate were rapidly mixed. Fischer and Rhinehammer,[3,4] found that the particle size of barium sulfate increased with concentration in the range 2.6 to 26 $\times$ 10^{-3} M, when precipitation was carried out in hydrochloric acid solution at pH = 1. In the latter experiments, the crystals were quite large (4.3 to 16 μ). At higher pH values, the gross crystal size increased, but the crystals were fluffy, fragile aggregates of smaller particles.

Other observations of increasing particle size with increasing concentrations have been made for silver chromate,[5] silver thiocyanate,[6] and nickel dimethylglyoxime.[7]

Another noteworthy study of barium sulfate precipitation is that of Turnbull,[8] who studied the fraction of precipitation X as a function of time t, after the rapid mixing of solutions. Turnbull was forced to introduce a "scale factor" f as a multiplier for the time scale, such that $X = F(ft)$. Although the scale factor varied as much as fivefold from experiment to experiment, the function F of the normalized time scale became the same for all experiments. As will be seen below, the function F was interpreted entirely in terms of precipitate growth, and the scale factor f was considered an adjustment for the variable number of nuclei formed from one experiment to the next.

In contrast with barium sulfate, even moderately supersaturated solutions of silver chloride precipitate rapidly. Davies and Jones[9] claimed to have found a lower limit of supersaturation below which

[1] Odén, S., and Werner, D., *Arkiv Kemi Mineral. Geol.*, **7**, no. 26 (1920); **9**, no. 23 (1925); **9**, no. 32 (1926).

[2] O'Rourke and Johnson, *op. cit.*

[3] Fischer and Rhinehammer, *op. cit.*

[4] Fischer, *Anal. Chem.*, **23**, 1667 (1951).

[5] Gulbransen, E. A., Phelps, R. T., and Langer, A., *Ind. Eng. Chem., Anal. Ed.*, **17**, 646 (1945).

[6] Fischer, *J. Chem. Ed.*, **24**, 484 (1947).

[7] Fischer, R. B., and Simonsen, S. H., *Anal. Chem.*, **20**, 1107 (1948).

[8] Turnbull, D., *Acta Met.*, **1**, 684 (1953).

[9] Davies, C. W., and Jones, A. L., *Discussions Faraday Soc.*, **5**, 103 (1949).

nucleation presumably would not occur at all. Their method involved an observation of the rate of change of conductivity with time as a function of solution concentration, and extrapolation to zero rate of change. The limiting supersaturation was found to vary with the ratio of silver ion to chloride ion concentration and to reach a minimum value of 1.32 for a ratio of unity. The validity of the extrapolation procedure is questionable, because the rate of change of conductivity has to do more with crystal growth than with the nucleation process.

Silver chloride and other silver halides are usually described as "curdy precipitates" and are composed of aggregates of colloidal particles, in contrast with barium sulfate, which is composed of discrete crystals, at least when precipitated from dilute solutions.

7-2. The Classical Concept of Nucleation

It is clear that the particle-size distribution of a precipitate must be determined by the relative rates of two processes: (1) the formation of nuclei, and (2) the growth of nuclei. According to Ostwald,[1] a supersaturated solution may be metastable; i.e., it can remain indefinitely in a homogeneous state unless suitably inoculated with nuclei for crystal formation. Beyond a certain degree of supersaturation (the metastable limit) the solution was regarded as *labile*, or subject to spontaneous crystallization.

A number of early workers, notably Miers,[2] plotted "supersolubility" curves, which separated the metastable and labile regions as a function of temperature. Two such plots are presented in Figs. 7-2 and 7-3; these differ with respect to the magnitude of the metastable region.

According to this view, the formation of a precipitate may be described as follows. If, at temperature A, the concentration of solute is gradually increased, for example, by the slow addition of precipitating reagent with efficient stirring (or by gradual formation of a precipitating reagent by a homogeneous reaction), no precipitate will form until point C on the supersolubility curve is reached. If at this point the addition of reagent is halted, the concentration will drop to point B on the solubility curve. Further addition of reagent can not cause formation of new nuclei if the instantaneous concentration is not allowed to reach point C. Consequently, a precipitate formed under these conditions must be relatively coarse and uniform in particle size.

If, because of rapid addition or insufficient stirring, the local instantaneous concentration exceeds C, new crystal nuclei can form throughout the course of the precipitation, with the result that a larger number of

[1] Ostwald, W., *Z. physik. Chem. Leipzig*, **22,** 289 (1897).

[2] Miers, H. A., and Isaac, F., *J. Chem. Soc.*, **89,** 413 (1906); *Proc. Roy. Soc. London*, **A79,** 322 (1907).

particles, smaller and less uniform, will be formed. Obviously, if the solubility and "supersolubility" curves lie close together, as in Fig. 7-3, it will be more difficult to achieve a precipitate of large and uniform particle size.

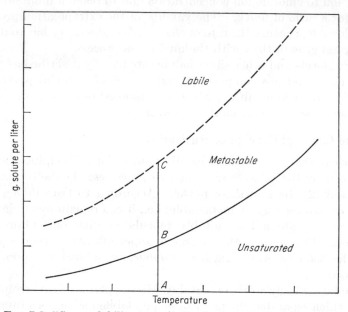

FIG. 7-2. "Supersolubility curve" showing large metastable region.

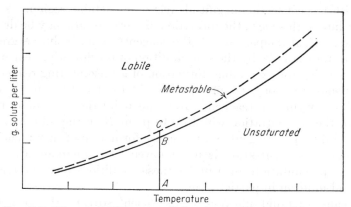

FIG. 7-3. "Supersolubility curve" showing small metastable region.

In a general way, the behavior of barium sulfate corresponds to that predicted from Fig. 7-2. As was seen above, relatively highly supersaturated solutions can be maintained for appreciable periods of time before the appearance of a precipitate, and barium sulfate prepared from very dilute solution does tend to form as relatively coarse, uniform particles. On the other hand, silver chloride, which has about the same molar solubility as barium sulfate, has much less tendency to exist as a supersaturated solution, and its primary particles are accordingly very finely divided, even when precipitated from dilute solutions.

7-3. The Becker-Döring Theory of Nucleation

The nucleation process may be treated thermodynamically or kinetically. The thermodynamic treatment, originally due to Gibbs, has been applied by Rodebush[1] to the nucleation of water droplets from water vapor. The tendency for a molecular cluster to grow (to decrease the surface free energy) is counterbalanced by the tendency for nuclei to dissociate (to gain entropy) when the size of the cluster is of the order of 100 molecules. There is a maximum free energy per mole for this size of cluster (the critical nucleus); consequently, smaller clusters will tend to dissociate, and larger ones will tend to grow.

An analogous situation, but a more complicated one, can be considered to prevail in the formation of a crystal nucleus. If a given size of crystal nucleus is to grow, it can do so only by partial dehydration of added ions or of ions already in the nucleus. This involves a loss in energy (by the system) corresponding to a lattice energy term and a gain in energy (nonspontaneous process) corresponding to dehydration. In addition, a decrease in entropy accompanies the increasing degree of order upon crystallization, together with an increase in entropy due to increasing disorder of the solvent molecules. Thus we may consider that there are an energy term and an entropy term tending to favor growth and a similar pair of terms favoring dissociation. At some critical size, the free energy is a maximum.

Nucleation has also been considered from a kinetic viewpoint. The nucleation process for the condensation of a liquid from its vapor was considered by Volmer and Weber[2] and by Becker and Döring[3] to consist of a series of bimolecular steps to form clusters, which can also shrink by loss of individual molecules. The nucleation frequency, then, is the rate at which clusters form critical nuclei by collision with single molecules. Volmer and Weber assumed that the concentration of clusters corresponds to an equilibrium situation, whereas Becker and Döring refined the theory by assuming that a steady state, rather than equilibrium, exists. Thus critical nuclei grow rapidly to form droplets, and the steady-state concentration is much lower than the concentration that would correspond to equilibrium.

[1] Rodebush, W. H., *Ind. Eng. Chem.*, **44**, 1289 (1952).
[2] Volmer, M., and Weber, A., *Z. physik. Chem. Leipzig*, **119**, 277 (1926).
[3] Becker, R., and Döring, W., *Ann. Physik*, [5], **24**, 719 (1935).

The Becker-Döring theory predicts a high-order dependence of nucleation rate on concentration and, therefore, a critical supersaturation. The size of a critical nucleus for condensation of liquids turns out to be essentially the same for various liquids, and is of the order of 50 to 100 molecules.

In making comparisons between theory and experiment, the critical supersaturation ratio is determined and used with the Gibbs-Thomson equation to calculate the surface tension of critical nuclei, a value which can be compared with the bulk surface tension. Turnbull,[1] in a recent comparison of experimental results with theory, concludes that the agreement is not so good as was once thought on the basis of the classical work of Volmer and Flood[2] on the nucleation of water droplets, but that no other theory works nearly so well.

An important difficulty is the lack of an adequate theory for the possible variation of surface tension with curvature. The theoretical difficulty of applying Gibb's theory of surfaces to particles containing no more than 100 molecules has been discussed, for example, by Reiss[3] and by Buff.[4]

Becker[5] used a "nearest neighbor hypothesis" in which the difference in coordination number between surface molecules and interior molecules is considered. Even for small clusters, the coordination number of surface molecules was regarded as the same as for ions in a plane. According to Benson and Shuttleworth,[6] who considered second-nearest-neighbor interactions, the surface tension of small clusters may be as much as 15 per cent lower than that of plane surfaces.

For solid particles, the question of surface tension is even more difficult because of the difficulty of measurement, even for large crystals. Nevertheless, similar theoretical approaches have been used,[7] with results once more indicating critical nuclei of the order of magnitude of 100 ions, with the necessary consequence that nucleation rate is a high-order function of concentration.

Consistent with this theory is Turnbull's[8] view that the induction period for barium sulfate precipitation is apparent rather than real and that it corresponds to a very slow growth period limited by the small area. The nuclei are considered to be formed at the instant of mixing, in locali-

[1] Turnbull, "Solid State Physics," vol. 4, Academic Press, Inc., New York, 1957.

[2] Volmer, M., and Flood, H., Z. physik. Chem. Leipzig, 170A, 273 (1934).

[3] Reiss, H., Ind. Eng. Chem., 44, 1284 (1952); J. Chem. Phys., 20, 1216 (1952); 21, 1312 (1953).

[4] Buff, F. P., J. Chem. Phys., 23, 419 (1955).

[5] Becker, Ann. Physik, 32, 128 (1938).

[6] Benson, G. C., and Shuttleworth, R., J. Chem. Phys., 19, 130 (1951).

[7] Becker, op. cit.

[8] Turnbull, op. cit.

ties where the critical concentration for nucleation has been exceeded. The variable scale factor mentioned above is explained by the lack of reproducibility of mixing. The relatively long apparent induction period, with homogeneous generation of precipitant, is explained on the theory that growth then occurs only on foreign nuclei. To explain the constant number of precipitate particles, observed by O'Rourke and Johnson, it seems necessary to assume that there is present a constant number of foreign nuclei per unit volume of solution, independent of solute concentration in the very dilute range. The variation in results among various investigators must be due to variation in numbers of foreign nuclei.

7-4. The Christiansen-Nielsen Theory of Nucleation

Christiansen and Nielsen[1] developed a theory of nucleation based on an interpretation of the length of the induction period, which is presumed to be closely related to the order of the nucleation reaction. As in the Becker-Döring theory, ion clusters are considered to be formed by bimolecular steps leading to a critical nucleus, which then grows spontaneously. However, since the induction period is a relatively low-order function (3d to 9th power) of concentration, an inevitable conclusion is that the critical nucleus contains a relatively small number of ions.

Johnson and O'Rourke[2] refined the theory by considering the fact that the concentration is constant during the induction period and that the nucleation rate should, therefore, be constant during this interval. Only at the end of the induction period, according to this view, is growth alone to be considered; both nucleation and growth must be considered during the induction period. An interesting conclusion was that the total number of nuclei of barium sulfate should be independent of concentration if the precipitation is carried out at great dilution; this is because it was found that the nucleation rate varies with the fourth power of the concentration and remains constant during the induction period. The length of the induction period varied *inversely* with the fourth power of concentration. Thus, the observed constancy of the number of particles appears to be readily explained.

According to Christiansen and Nielsen, the number of ions in the critical nucleus is 8, 6, and 9, respectively, for $BaSO_4$, Ag_2CrO_4, and CaF_2 of the salt. Similarly, Peisach and Brescia[3] considered the critical nucleus of magnesium oxalate to be $(MgC_2O_4)_2$. It is not clear, however, why such a unit should correspond to a *maximum* of free energy, and in

[1] Christiansen, J. A., and Nielsen, A. E., *Z. Elektrochem.*, **56**, 465 (1952); *Acta Chem. Scand.*, **5**, 673, 674 (1951).

[2] Johnson and O'Rourke, *J. Am. Chem. Soc.*, **76**, 2124 (1954).

[3] Peisach, J., and Brescia, F., *J. Am. Chem. Soc.*, **76**, 5946 (1954).

any case there is an uncertainty of at least 1 in the number of ions. Johnson and O'Rourke prefer a critical nucleus of four ions for barium sulfate.

Duke and Brown[1] counted the number of precipitate particles as a function of initial concentrations of precipitating ions. Considering the final number of particles to be determined by the interaction of nucleation rate and growth rate, they derived the size of the critical nucleus by assuming a growth law. Once again, a small critical nucleus is the logical conclusion to be drawn from a low-order dependence of the number of particles on reactant concentrations. Assuming a first-order growth law, the critical nucleus of tetraphenylarsonium perchlorate would consist of three ion pairs, or, assuming a second-order growth law, it would consist of four ion pairs. Interestingly, for nickel nioxime the nature of the critical nucleus would depend on whether an excess of nioxime or of nickel ion were present. With an excess of nioxime the critical nucleus would be $(NiNiox)_3$ and with an excess of nickel ion $Ni(Niox)_3$, assuming a first-order growth law. It should be noted that in the theory of Duke and Brown it is assumed that no new nuclei are formed after the initial nucleation burst.

The concept of a small critical nucleus is intuitively satisfying, for the nucleus then requires only a small number of steps for its formation. However, the fundamental assumption underlying the Christiansen-Nielsen theory is rejected by Turnbull, on the grounds that there is no theoretical justification for assuming the existence of a small critical nucleus of size independent of the supersaturation ratio.

The disagreement between the "large nucleus" and "small nucleus" schools involves the question of a high-order or low-order dependence of nucleation rate on supersaturation. If nucleation is a high-order process (proportional, say, to C^{100}), it will occur only if a critical local concentration is exceeded. Otherwise, foreign nuclei may serve as growth sites. To emphasize the importance of foreign nuclei, Turnbull cites the fact that certain small droplets of liquid or aqueous solutions can be undercooled extraordinarily as compared with bulk liquids, because of the smaller probability of finding a single foreign nucleation site in a small droplet.[2] It might be supposed that a clear-cut decision could be made on the basis of careful observation of the shape of the curve of electrical conductance during the growth period. However, in both theories a slow growth process is considered to exist during the induction period, the end of which is marked by the disappearance of an appreciable fraction of free ions from solution.

[1] Duke, F. R., and Brown, L. M., J. Am. Chem. Soc., 71, 1443 (1954).

[2] Turnbull, J. Appl. Phys., 20, 817 (1949); 21, 1022 (1950); Acta Met., 1, 8 (1953); Newkirk, J. B., and Turnbull, D., J. Appl. Phys., 26, 579 (1955).

In formulating a growth law, it is necessary to assume either a particular geometry (such as spherical particles) or the law that area is proportional to the $\frac{2}{3}$ power of volume, which implies a constant geometry. Moreover, all elements of area must be assumed to be equally efficient as growth sites. It will be pointed out in the next section that the growth law is sensitive to the shapes of crystal particles and there is no *a priori* reason to suppose that a given shape persists throughout the growth period. On the contrary, from aging studies (Chap. 9) it appears that rapid recrystallization is going on, particularly in the first seconds or minutes after precipitate formation.

At the present time, it does not appear possible to make a clear choice between the two viewpoints. The Becker-Döring theory appears reasonably adequate for nucleation of liquids from vapor, but it cannot be tested rigorously for crystallization of ionic precipitates. The Christiansen-Nielsen theory accounts for the reproducible induction periods observed with several precipitates, but involves a perhaps unwarranted assumption about the existence of a small critical nucleus.

7-5. The Growth of Precipitate Particles

Noyes and Whitney[1] interpreted rates of dissolution of crystals on the basis of diffusion from a region of saturation at the surface to the bulk of the solution. Various attempts to explain the rate of crystal growth in terms of a reverse diffusion mechanism have not in general been successful. Marc,[2] in an extensive series of investigations, found that most growth processes were of second order instead of first order, as required by the diffusion mechanism. Beyond a certain stirring rate, the rate of crystallization became independent of stirring rate. Crystal growth was often retarded or inhibited by adsorbed dyes that did not appreciably influence the rate of dissolution. These observations point to some factor other than diffusion as contributing to the rate.

Rate laws for the growth of precipitate particles governed simultaneously by surface-reaction rate and by diffusion have been developed by Wert and Zener,[3] by Frisch and Collins,[4] and by Turnbull.[5] For the simplest case of spherical particles, where the number of particles is independent of time, the diffusional flux is greatest when the particles are smallest and decreases with time as the particles grow. Consequently, surface reaction rate is apt to be rate-controlling at the beginning

[1] Noyes, A. A., and Whitney, W. R., *Z. physik. Chem. Leipzig*, **23**, 689 (1897).

[2] Marc, R., *Z. physik. Chem. Leipzig*, **79**, 71 (1912); *Z. Elektrochem.*, **18**, 161 (1912); and earlier papers.

[3] Wert, C., *J. Appl. Phys.*, **20**, 943 (1949); Zener, C., *ibid.*, 950; Wert and Zener, *ibid.*, **21**, 5 (1950).

[4] Frisch, H. L., and Collins, F. C., *J. Chem. Phys.*, **21**, 2158 (1953).

[5] Turnbull, *Acta Met.*, **1**, 684 (1953).

of growth.   According to Turnbull, the growth of barium sulfate particles is controlled by surface reaction when the fraction of precipitation, X, is less than 0.04 and by diffusion for X between 0.04 and 0.5.   Beyond $X = 0.5$, the growth rate was slower than expected, presumably because of aggregation of the crystals.

Collins and Leineweber[1] derived equations that take into account the moving boundary of spherical particles and competition between crystallites for the solute.   To consider surface reaction rate, they introduce an "adsorption probability" representing the fraction of collisions effective in the growth process.   For barium sulfate they estimated the adsorption probability to be only 5×10^{-5}.

Turnbull[2] has concluded that the growth law is sensitive to the shapes of the particles and even to the growth habit and, therefore, that determination of the exponent of time in the growth law is not in itself sufficient to establish the growth mechanism.

Nielsen,[3] in studying the growth of barium sulfate particles as a function of concentration, concluded that, in very dilute solutions (below 4×10^{-4} M initial concentration of barium and sulfate ions), the growth process is kinetically controlled by a surface reaction of the fourth order with respect to barium sulfate concentration.   At higher concentrations, however, a diffusion-controlled mechanism prevails, the rate of growth being proportional to the first power of concentration.   By microscopic observation, the growth in very dilute solutions appeared to be uniform over the entire surface of the crystals, so that the particles retained essentially a constant prismatic shape during their growth.   On the other hand, at higher concentrations (above about 5×10^{-4} M) the growth rate at corners became noticeably faster than at the plane faces.   At initial concentrations above 1.5×10^{-3} M, the growth at corners became so predominant that star-shaped crystals were formed.   According to Nielsen, the preferred growth at corners is due simply to the more rapid diffusion rate at these points and not to any inherently greater reactivity at the corners.

An aspect of crystal growth that has received insufficient study is the effect of an excess of one of the lattice ions in solution.   The state of the surface with respect to adsorbed potential-determining ions is known to influence the rate of aging by recrystallization (see Chap. 9).   From the work of Lucchesi[4] it appears qualitatively that the rate of precipitation of lead sulfate and barium sulfate depends upon which ion is present in

[1] Collins and Leineweber, *J. Phys. Chem.*, **60**, 389 (1956).

[2] Turnbull, "Solid State Physics," Academic Press, 1957.

[3] Nielsen, *Acta Chem. Scand.*, **12**, 951 (1958).

[4] Lucchesi, P. J., *J. Colloid Sci.*, **11**, 113 (1956).

excess. But, since the adsorption of lattice ion depends greatly upon the state of perfection of the surface (see Chap. 8), it cannot be expected in general that any simple growth law could hold throughout the growth history of a precipitate particle.

Another interesting question about crystal growth, particularly for larger crystals, is whether a two-dimensional nucleation on a perfect crystal plane requires a higher supersaturation than is required for the growth of a partially completed crystal plane. As early as 1878, Gibbs[1] suggested that crystal growth proceeds by nucleation on a crystal face, forming monolayer islands, which then grow rapidly to the boundaries of the crystal face. The theoretical rate expressions for mechanisms involving two-dimensional nucleation have been derived by Volmer,[2] Kossel,[3] and Stranski.[4] These expressions predict that, for nucleation of a new crystal plane of a metal from its vapor, a vapor pressure of at least 25 to 50 per cent higher than saturation would be required. Volmer and Schultz,[5] however, found that, at a supersaturation of only 1 per cent, crystals of naphthalene, mercury, and phosphorus could be grown from the vapor. Theoretically, at this supersaturation, growth could occur only adjacent to atoms brought out of the plane surface by thermal agitation, at a rate 10^{1000} times lower than the rate actually observed! This enormous discrepancy[6] was finally explained by Frank[7] in terms of growth at a screw dislocation, which is represented schematically in Fig. 7-4. It is apparent that a crystal with such an imperfection can grow with a spirally advancing face and that no nucleation on a plane surface is required. Many direct observations have been made in which spiral growth patterns are visually evident. Many substances show whisker formation upon condensation from a supersaturated vapor. For example zinc, cadmium, silver, and cadmium sulfide form whiskers[8] if the supersaturation is kept below some critical value, presumably that necessary for nucleation on a plane surface. Likewise, crystals grown from melts and from solution clearly show spiral growth patterns. Evidently, crystal imperfections play a profound role in the growth of crystalline

[1] Gibbs, J. W., "Collected Works," p. 325, Longmans, Green & Co., Inc., New York, 1928.

[2] Volmer, Z. physik. Chem. Leipzig, **102**, 267 (1922); Z. Elektrochem., **35**, 555 (1929).

[3] Kossel, W., Nachr. Ges. Wiss. Göttingen Jahresber. Math.-physik. Kl., **1927**, 135.

[4] Stranski, I. N., Z. physik. Chem. Leipzig, **136**, 259 (1928).

[5] Volmer, M., and Schultz, W., Z. physik. Chem. Leipzig, **156A**, 1 (1931).

[6] Described by R. L. Fullman, Sci. American, March, 1955, as perhaps the all-time record for discrepancy between theory and experiment.

[7] Frank, F. C., Discussions Faraday Soc., **5**, 48 (1949).

[8] Sears, G. W., Acta Met., **3**, 361, 367 (1955); J. Chem. Phys., **23**, 1630 (1955); **25**, 637 (1956); **26**, 1549 (1957).

precipitates. In view of the highly imperfect state of most freshly formed precipitates, two-dimensional nucleation does not appear to make a significant contribution to the growth process.

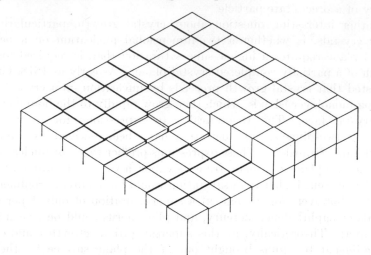

FIG. 7-4. Schematic drawing of a screw dislocation. [*After Frank, F. C., Discussions Faraday Soc.*, **5**, 48 (1949).]

7-6. Conditions of Analytical Precipitation

Von Weimarn[1] summarized his observations on precipitate formation in the form of three precipitation laws:

1. If the mean size of crystals, as determined after a given time interval after mixing, is plotted against concentration, a curve with a maximum is observed. As the time interval selected becomes greater, the concentration corresponding to the maximum size of crystals becomes smaller and the maximum size increases. This behavior is represented in curves t_1 to t_4 in Fig. 7-1.

2. After the crystals have completed their growth, the size varies with concentration according to an equation of the form $Cd^n = $ const, where C is the concentration and d is the size. This is illustrated by curve t_5 in Fig. 7-1.

3. For various media in which a given solid has varying solubility, the particle size will be the smallest for the medium in which the solubility is lowest at any given value of concentration.

As a corollary to the second and third laws, von Weimarn postulated that the average size of particles is determined by $(Q - S)/S$, where Q is $C/2$ if C is the initial concentration of each of the reactants (that is, Q is the concentration that would prevail if no precipitation occurred), and

[1] Von Weimarn, *Chem. Revs.*, **2**, 215 (1926).

S is the solubility. $(Q - S)/S$ is the *relative supersaturation*. According to von Weimarn, the particle size of a given precipitate increases with increasing solubility and with decreasing concentration of reactants. Although this is qualitatively true of many precipitates (though not of those formed at extreme dilution), it should not be inferred that two different precipitates formed at the same relative supersaturation will necessarily have the same particle size.

Odén and Werner[1] studied the particle size of barium sulfate, strontium sulfate, and calcium sulfate as a function of the concentrations of added reagents, by washing and peptizing the precipitates and measuring the sedimentation rate. They concluded that the number of particles was proportional to the product of the initial concentrations of the two reagents. As expected from von Weimarn's rules, the particle size of the three sulfates increased in order of increasing solubility when they were precipitated at equal concentration. However, Odén and Werner did not find the same particle size at the same relative supersaturation for the three salts. For example, at a relative supersaturation of 166, the peak of the particle-size distribution curve occurred at a particle radius of 6 μ for strontium sulfate, but for barium sulfate the most probable particle radius was only 0.9 μ at a relative supersaturation of 100.

Fischer and Rhinehammer[2] found that various organic addition agents, when added to a barium chloride solution that was added rapidly to an acidic potassium sulfate solution, caused a marked increase in crystal size. However, when the addition agents were added to the sulfate solution, no effects on particle size were observed. Evidently the addition agents rendered ineffective the crystal nuclei present in fresh barium chloride solutions, because similar effects could be obtained by filtration through a fine fritted glass filter. Addition agents did not noticeably affect the particle size of silver chloride but markedly increased the rate of flocculation. This effect, the sensitization of a sol, will be considered in the next chapter.

An elevated temperature is frequently beneficial in promoting a well-formed precipitate. However, the increased solubility appears to be a relatively minor factor compared with the increased reaction rate at the interface during the growth process. The influence of temperature on crystallization rates will become more evident in the discussion of aging phenomena (Chap. 9).

Factors that decrease the local concentration of precipitated species include the concentration and rate of addition of reagent and the stirring. For ideal analytical precipitation, the slow addition of dilute reagents with adequate stirring will permit the maximum growth of nuclei with a

[1] Odén and Werner, *Arkiv Kemi*, **7**, no. 26 (1920); **9**, no. 23 (1925); **9**, no. 32 (1926).
[2] Fischer and Rhinehammer, *Anal. Chem.*, **26**, 244 (1954).

minimum of nucleation at regions of local supersaturation. Under some conditions, rapid mixing may actually be favorable to the formation of a coarse precipitate. For example, as seen above, barium sulfate has a tendency to remain in supersaturated solution without nucleation. If, by increasing the acidity, say, to pH = 1, the sulfate ion is converted largely to bisulfate ion ($pK_a = 2$), the nucleation rate may be so greatly decreased that growth of large particles is favored. Rapid mixing would favor the instantaneous formation of nuclei, which grow uniformly to a relatively coarse product, whereas slow mixing may permit continuous nucleation at local regions of high concentration, with the formation of a heterodisperse precipitate.

A method that effectively encourages crystal growth rather than nucleation is to form the precipitate from an initially unsaturated homogeneous solution. This method is so important that it will be discussed in a separate section.

7-7. Precipitation from Homogeneous Solution[1]

Two general methods are employed for bringing down a precipitate from an initially unsaturated, homogeneous solution. (1) The solubility may be gradually decreased, usually by gradually raising the pH by means of a slow chemical reaction that consumes hydrogen ions. (2) The concentration of precipitating ion may be gradually increased by means of a reaction that gradually forms or liberates the precipitating ions.

Willard[2] has reviewed the early methods used for gradually increasing the pH. These methods include the decomposition of sodium thiosulfate, the reaction between iodide and iodate, the reaction between nitrite and urea, the decomposition of ammonium nitrite or sodium nitrite, and the hydrolysis of hexamethylenetetramine. Moser,[3] apparently, was the first to recognize the advantage of this technique in forming a denser precipitate.

However, Willard and Tang[4] made the important observation that the nature of the anion is important in the formation of compact precipitates and that certain basic salts are more effective than hydroxides in the precipitation of aluminum. Another noteworthy contribution was the introduction of the hydrolysis of urea

$$CO(NH_2)_2 + H_2O \rightarrow CO_2 + 2NH_3 \tag{7-3}$$

[1] Gordon, L., Salutsky, M. L., and Willard, H. H., "Precipitation from Homogeneous Solution," John Wiley & Sons, Inc., New York, 1959.

[2] Willard, *Anal. Chem.*, **22**, 1372 (1950).

[3] Moser, L., *Monatsh. Chem.*, **53**, 39 (1929).

[4] Willard, H. H., and Tang, N. K., *J. Am. Chem. Soc.*, **59**, 1190 (1937).

as a method of gradual neutralization of acid. Urea has the advantage of being a very weak base ($K_b = 1.5 \times 10^{-14}$) which does not hydrolyze at an appreciable rate at room temperature but which does hydrolyze at a convenient rate at 90 to 100°C. The final pH that can be attained depends upon the initial concentration of ammonium ion, but is about 9.3 in its absence.

The use of basic salt separations has proved advantageous for many metals. For aluminum, Willard[1] recommends the basic succinate, for iron and thorium the basic formates, and for titanium and gallium the basic sulfates. The anions of organic acids are useful because they regulate the gradual change of pH by buffer action and also because the basic salts are readily ignited to the oxides. In this connection it is interesting that Dupuis and Duval[2] found that basic aluminum succinate precipitated from homogeneous solution reached constant weight at 611°C, whereas hydrous aluminum oxide normally requires an ignition temperature of 1100°C. In some cases, it is advantageous to bring down the main portion of the precipitate at a very low pH to ensure optimum purity and to finish at a higher pH value to complete the precipitation quantitatively. For example, in the basic formate procedure for iron, the recommended procedure is to boil the urea solution until the pH has reached 1.8, then filter off the main portion of the precipitate, and continue the boiling until the pH has reached 3. The small additional precipitate can be added to the same filter.

Gordon[3] has compared the compactness of several basic salt precipitates prepared from homogeneous solution with the usual hydrous oxides prepared by addition of ammonia. The apparent volume of basic ferric formate, for example, was 20 times smaller than that of hydrous ferric oxide that had settled for 2 months. Similarly, basic tin(IV) sulfate was 20 times more compact, and basic thorium(IV) formate was 9 times more compact than the hydrous oxide.

Usually the efficiency of separation is also markedly improved. For example, in the usual ammonia precipitation of aluminum hydroxide, a rather narrow pH limit must be maintained to get quantitative precipitation, because of the amphoteric nature of aluminum. Consequently it is not possible to regulate the ratio of ammonium ion and ammonia to minimize coprecipitation. Copper, when present to the extent of 50 mg in the presence of 0.1 g aluminum, was coprecipitated to the extent of 21 mg by the usual ammonia method. With the urea-succinate method,[4] only 0.05 mg was coprecipitated from 1.0 g of copper initially present.

[1] Willard, *op. cit.*
[2] Dupuis, T., and Duval, C., *Anal. Chim. Acta*, **3**, 201 (1949).
[3] Gordon, *Anal. Chem.*, **24**, 459 (1952).
[4] Willard and Tang, *Ind. Eng. Chem., Anal. Ed.*, **9**, 357 (1937).

On the other hand, basic tin(IV) sulfate is unsuitable as an analytical precipitate even when brought down from homogeneous solution, because of extensive coprecipitation.[1,2]

Other precipitations based on the urea hydrolysis method are the precipitation of calcium as the oxalate[3] and of barium as the chromate.[4] In both cases, the crystals are large and readily filtered. However, the calcium oxalate prepared by homogeneous precipitation is not so free from magnesium as that prepared by the method of Kolthoff and Sandell,[5] which involves a room-temperature precipitation followed by digestion at a higher temperature. This is a special case of unusually drastic aging, involving transformation of hydrates, which evidently is especially effective.

The second general method of precipitation from homogeneous solution involves the generation of precipitating ion. Examples of the hydrolysis of esters are the use of triethyl phosphate for the fractionation of zirconium and hafnium;[6] methyl oxalate for thorium, the rare earths,[7] and calcium;[8] ethyl oxalate for magnesium,[9] zinc,[10] and calcium;[11] and dimethyl sulfate for calcium, strontium, and barium.[12]

Other types of hydrolytic reactions for the generation of precipitants include the formation of sulfate by the hydrolysis of sulfamic acid[13] and the hydrolysis of thioacetamide to form hydrogen sulfide.[14] This latter reaction is of considerable interest because thioacetamide has been used as a substitute for hydrogen sulfide in qualitative-analysis schemes on the assumption that the hydrolysis rate is rapid in both acid and alkaline solutions and that a direct substitution is, therefore, permissible.[15]

Swift and coworkers[16,17] showed that, in acid solution, thioacetamide

[1] Willard, op. cit.

[2] Gordon, L., Teicher, H., and Burtt, B. P., Anal. Chem., **26**, 992 (1954).

[3] Willard, H. H., Furman, N. H., and Bricker, C. E., "Elements of Quantitative Analysis," 4th ed., p. 389, D. Van Nostrand Company, Inc., Princeton, N.J., 1956.

[4] Gordon, L., and Firsching, F. H., Anal. Chem., **26**, 759 (1954).

[5] Kolthoff, I. M., and Sandell, E. B., J. Phys. Chem., **37**, 443 (1937).

[6] Willard, H. H., and Freund, H., Ind. Eng. Chem., Anal. Ed., **18**, 195 (1946).

[7] Willard and Gordon, Anal. Chem., **20**, 165 (1948).

[8] Gordon, L., and Wroczynski, A. F., Anal. Chem., **24**, 896 (1952).

[9] Gordon, L., and Caley, E. R., Anal. Chem., **20**, 560 (1948).

[10] Caley, E. R., Gordon, L., and Simmons, G. A., Jr., Anal. Chem., **22**, 1060 (1950).

[11] Elving, P. J., and Chao, P. C., Anal. Chem., **21**, 507 (1949).

[12] Elving, P. J., and Van Atta, R. E., Anal. Chem., **22**, 1375 (1950).

[13] Wagner, W. F., and Wuellner, J. A., Anal. Chem., **24**, 1031 (1952).

[14] Swift, E. H., and Butler, E. A., Anal. Chem., **28**, 146 (1956).

[15] Barber, H. H., and Taylor, T. I., "Semimicro Qualitative Analysis," revised ed., Harper & Brothers, New York, 1953.

[16] Swift and Butler, op. cit.

[17] Butler, E. A., Peters, D. G., and Swift, E. H., Anal. Chem., **30**, 1379 (1958).

hydrolyzes relatively slowly, even at 90°C, to give acetamide and hydrogen sulfide.

$$CH_3CSNH_2 + H_2O \rightarrow CH_3CONH_2 + H_2S \qquad (7\text{-}4)$$

The further hydrolysis of acetamide is negligible in acid solution. In alkaline solution, on the other hand, the hydrolysis of the amide group is faster than that of the thiocarbonyl group by a factor of about 3 or 4.[*,†] This results in the formation of a mixture of acetamide and thioacetate, both of which hydrolyze much more slowly than thioacetamide. Sulfide is, therefore, formed in two reactions in alkaline medium, namely, from the hydrolysis of the thiocarbonyl group [reaction (7-4)], and from the slower hydrolysis of thioacetate. Ammonia accelerates the hydrolysis of the thiocarbonyl group but does not affect the rate of hydrolysis of thioacetate. In carbonate-bicarbonate buffers, the rate of formation of sulfide increases with the first power of thioacetamide and carbonate ion concentrations but varies inversely with the square root of the bicarbonate ion concentration. A plausible mechanism could be postulated for the effect of ammonia but not for the effect of bicarbonate.[1]

The rate of formation of lead sulfide[2] and cadmium sulfide[3] in acid solution (pH-2) is controlled by the rate of formation of hydrogen sulfide according to Eq. (7-4). At higher pH values, a "direct reaction" increases the rate of sulfide precipitation beyond what would be predicted from the hydrolysis rate. The rate of the direct reaction increases with metal ion and thioacetamide concentrations and varies inversely with the square root of the hydrogen ion concentration. From these observations it is evident that only at pH-2 can the hydrolysis rate be used in predicting the precipitation rate of sulfides with thioacetamide. At higher pH values, a detailed study of each particular system must be made. It would be desirable to have more information about the mechanism of the direct reaction, as well as about the mechanism of the peculiar effects of bicarbonate and carbonate.

Oxidation-reduction reactions that have been used for the production of a precipitant include the oxidation of arsenite to arsenate with nitric acid for the precipitation of zirconium,[4] the oxidation of iodine to iodate with chlorate for the precipitation of thorium,[5] and the reduction of peroxydisulfate by thiosulfate for the precipitation of barium.[6]

* *Ibid.*
† Peters and Swift, *Talanta*, **1**, 30 (1958).
[1] *Ibid.*
[2] Swift and Butler, *op. cit.*
[3] Bowersox, D. F., and Swift, E. H., *Anal. Chem.*, **30**, 1288 (1958).
[4] Gump, J. R., and Sherwood, G. R., *Anal. Chem.*, **22**, 496 (1950).
[5] Gordon, dissertation, University of Michigan, Ann Arbor, 1947.
[6] La Mer and Dinegar, *op. cit.*

8. Colloidal Properties
of Precipitates

In the filtration of certain precipitates, a vexing problem is how to coagulate or flocculate a colloidal dispersion of a finely divided solid to permit its filtration and to prevent its repeptization upon washing the precipitate. At other times, for example, in titrimetric operations, it may be desirable to keep a precipitate in suspension. An understanding of the basic principles of the colloid chemistry of precipitates is, therefore, desirable.

8-1. Classification of Colloidal Systems

The region of colloids is generally considered to include particles having diameters in the range 10^{-7} to 10^{-4} cm. Staudinger[1] has suggested that it is preferable to consider that colloidal particles contain 10^3 to 10^9 atoms per particle, because some colloidal particles are single macromolecules and others are needle-shaped, disc-shaped, or spherical aggregates for which a single linear dimension has little meaning.

A useful classification is to distinguish *lyophobic* colloids (which have also been called suspensoids and hydrophobic, inorganic, irreversible, and irresoluble colloids) from *lyophilic* colloids (also called emulsoids or hydrophilic, organic, reversible, or resoluble colloids).

Lyophobic colloids are generally dispersions of insoluble inorganic substances in a liquid medium, usually an aqueous solution. They are characterized by being relatively sensitive to coagulation by electrolytes and by the fact that the flocculation process usually cannot be reversed completely upon dilution. The dispersions (*sols*) are of relatively low viscosity, and the flocculated solid contains relatively little water. Typical examples are colloidal sulfur, gold, silver iodide, and arsenious sulfide.

[1] Staudinger, H., "Organischer Kolloidchemie," F. Vieweg u. Sohn, Braunschweig, 1941.

Lyophilic colloids, on the other hand, are relatively viscous and insensitive to electrolytes. Upon addition of high concentrations of salts, the system tends to break into two liquid layers (coacervation). The process is readily reversed upon dilution. The suspended solid is highly hydrated and hygroscopic if dried. Typical examples are proteins and starches.

Most precipitates of analytical interest are lyophobic in character, although certain precipitates, such as freshly formed silicic acid, behave like lyophilic colloids. Other highly hydrated oxides also exhibit lyophilic behavior but to a lesser degree.

8-2. Source of Surface Charge : Primary Stability

Colloidal dispersions owe their stability to electrical repulsion of charged particles. It is our purpose here to examine the origin of the charge and to consider the variables that determine its magnitude.

If an ionic precipitate such as silver iodide is placed in pure water, it will, of course, reach solubility equilibrium as determined by its solubility product. However, the solid does not necessarily have the same attraction for both of its ions. In the case of silver iodide, Verwey and Kruyt[1] found that the solid has a much greater attraction for iodide than for silver ions, so that the zero point of charge corresponds to $[Ag^+] = 10^{-6}$ and $[I^-] = 10^{-10}$ rather than to equal concentrations of the two ions. Van Laar[2] has compared various methods for determination of the zero point of charge of silver iodide and has given $pAg = 5.52$ as the most probable value.

The zero points of the three silver halides are as follows:[3-5] AgCl, $pAg = 4$, $pCl = 5.7$; AgBr, $pAg = 5.4$, $pBr = 6.9$; AgI, $pAg = 5.5$, $pI = 10.6$. For hydrous ferric oxide, the isoelectric point[6] lies at about $pH = 8$. For barium sulfate, the point of zero charge seems to be dependent upon the source of the product and its degree of perfection.[7]

Lange and Berger[8] studied the adsorption of *potential-determining ions*, or ions that carry a charge *to the solid phase*. For many cases, including that of silver iodide, they found that the adsorption follows the equation

$$\Delta X = k \, \Delta \ln C \qquad (8\text{-}1)$$

where ΔX is the change in the amount of adsorbed ion brought about by

[1] Verwey, E. J. W. and Kruyt, H. R., *Z. physik. Chem. Leipzig*, **A167**, 149 (1934).

[2] Van Laar, J. A. W., quoted in Kruyt, H. R. (ed.), "Colloid Science," vol. 1, p. 161, Elsevier Publishing Company, Amsterdam, 1952.

[3] Verwey and Kruyt, *op. cit.*; Basinski, A., *Rec. trav. chim.*, **60**, 267 (1941).

[4] Jonker, G. H., thesis, University of Utrecht, 1943.

[5] Lange, E., and Crane, P. W., *Z. physik. Chem. Leipzig*, **A141**, 225 (1929).

[6] Troelstra, S. A., thesis, University of Utrecht, 1941.

[7] Ruyssen, R., and Loos, R., *Nature*, **162**, 741 (1948).

[8] Lange, E., and Berger, R., *Z. Elektrochem.*, **36**, 171 (1930).

a change $\Delta \ln C$ in the concentration of potential-determining ion in solution. They gave the following equation for the resulting potential difference ΔE between solid and solution:

$$\Delta E = \frac{RT}{ZF} \Delta \ln C \tag{8-2}$$

where Z is the charge of the potential-determining ion.

If Eq. (8-2) is applied between two concentrations C and $C°$, the concentration at the point of zero charge, we have, using the solubility-product relationship,

$$E = \frac{RT}{Z_+F} \ln \frac{C_+}{C_+°} = \frac{RT}{Z_-F} \ln \frac{C_-°}{C_-} \tag{8-3}$$

where C_+ and C_- refer to the concentrations of cation and anion. E has the value zero at $C_+ = C_+°$ or $C_- = C_-°$, and corresponds to the potential of the solid with respect to the solution, ignoring any residual boundary potential for a neutral solid.

Although it is, of course, impossible to measure the potential difference between solid and solution directly, it is interesting that Kolthoff and Sanders[1] found that the potentials of silver halide membrane electrodes varied with halide ion (or silver ion) activity very nearly as expected from Eq. (8-3). In this connection, the "precipitate membranes" of Fischer and Babcock,[2] composed of particles of precipitate imbedded in a paraffin matrix, do not behave as lattice ion membranes at all but instead respond to the counter ions in solution (see Sec. 8-3), because the transfer of electricity through the membrane occurs through a water layer rather than through the solid phase. The measured potential, therefore, is more nearly an electrokinetic potential (Sec. 8-4) than a thermodynamic potential.

Actually, as Overbeek[3] has pointed out, Eq. (8-2) states that the potential across the double layer is proportional to the charge transferred across it and, therefore, implies that the electrical capacity of the double layer is a constant. More recent and accurate adsorption experiments[4] are not strictly in accord with Eq. (8-1) and indicate that the capacity of the double layer does not remain constant with varying amounts of adsorbed lattice ion (varying potential of the solid). It is interesting also that a small amount of acetone shifts the point of zero charge of silver iodide far toward the higher silver ion concentrations,[5] probably because of the

[1] Kolthoff, I. M., and Sanders, H. L., *J. Am. Chem. Soc.*, **59**, 416 (1937).

[2] Fischer, R. B., and Babcock, R. F., *Anal. Chem.*, **30**, 1732 (1958).

[3] Overbeek, J. Th. G., in Kruyt, "Colloid Science."

[4] Mackor, E. L., *Rec. trav. chim.*, **70**, 747, 763 (1951).

[5] Overbeek, *loc. cit.*

effect of an oriented adsorbed layer of acetone, which changes the phase-boundary potential. Therefore, the colloidal behavior of precipitates may be influenced strongly by the presence of organic solvents.

Another complication in attempts to calculate the potential change of the solid is that foreign ions other than lattice ions can act as potential-determining ions to a greater or lesser extent. For example, Reyerson, Kolthoff, and Coad[1] found that lead ions as well as barium ions act as potential-determining ions for barium sulfate. Citrate ion was actually much more effective than sulfate ion in causing the precipitate to assume a negative charge. Similarly, silver iodide is peptized as a negative colloid by various ions other than iodide, such as bromide, chloride, cyanide, thiocyanate, and phosphate.[2]

There is also evidence that the adsorption of lattice ions depends on the state of subdivision of the solid, or perhaps on the state of perfection of the crystal faces. Thus it was reported by Julien[3] for silver bromide, by Verwey[4] for the oxides of titanium and zirconium, and by Buchanan and Heymann[5] for barium sulfate, that coarse material has a more negative character than fine crystals.

8-3. The Electrical Double Layer

If lattice ions or other potential-determining ions are adsorbed on a solid surface, they may be regarded as belonging to the solid and imparting an electrical charge to it. An equivalent amount of oppositely charged ions (counter ions) exist in solution, drawn to the charged surface by electrical attraction.

The rudimentary picture of a charged surface and a rigid layer of counter ions is often called the "Helmholtz double layer." Helmholtz, however, actually left the question of double-layer structure completely open, and the rigid layer concept seems to have been postulated first by Perrin.[6]

This simple picture is inadequate to account for the flocculation of colloids by electrolytes. Gouy[7] and Chapman,[8] independently, developed the theory of the diffuse double layer, which takes into account the effect of thermal agitation. The theory is similar in principle to the

[1] Reyerson, L. H., Kolthoff, I. M., and Coad, K., *J. Phys. Colloid Chem.* **51**, 321 (1947).

[2] Weiser, H. B., "Inorganic Colloid Chemistry," vol. 3, pp. 27 *et seq.*, John Wiley & Sons, Inc., New York, 1938.

[3] Julien, P. F. J. A., thesis, University of Utrecht, 1933.

[4] Verwey, *Rec. trav. chim.*, **60**, 625 (1941).

[5] Buchanan, A. S., and Heymann, E., *J. Colloid Sci.*, **4**, 137 (1949).

[6] Perrin, J., *J. chim. phys.*, **2**, 607 (1904).

[7] Gouy, G., *J. phys.*, [4], **9**, 457 (1910); *Ann. phys.*, [9], **7**, 129 (1917).

[8] Chapman, D. L., *Phil. Mag.*, [6], **25**, 475 (1913).

calculation of the ionic atmosphere in the Debye-Hückel theory, which it antedated by a decade. In fact, the quantity $1/\kappa$, which, in the Debye-Hückel theory, has the significance of the radius of the ionic atmosphere (see Sec. 2-3), is a measure of the thickness of the double layer in the Gouy-Chapman theory.

The Gouy-Chapman theory predicts a double-layer capacity about 10 times larger than the capacity actually observed,[1] because it does not take into account the finite sizes of the ions. Also, Overbeek[2] has shown that an impossibly high concentration of counter ions is calculated adjacent to the wall for moderately high surface potentials. For example, for a $0.1\ N$ univalent electrolyte, a surface concentration of $300\ N$ is calculated for a potential difference between solid and solution of 200 mv.

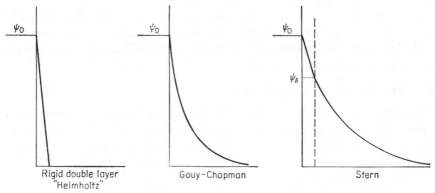

Rigid double layer "Helmholtz"   Gouy-Chapman   Stern

FIG. 8-1. Representation of the double layer according to three theories.

Stern[3] applied a correction for the finite dimensions of the first layer of ions by assuming that the ions cannot come closer to the wall than a finite distance δ. Stern also considered the possibility that the counter ions might be specifically adsorbed and would be located in the plane, also at distance δ from the surface. According to this theory, the potential falls linearly from a value ψ_0 at the surface to ψ_δ at the boundary of the "Stern layer," and then exponentially to zero, as in the Gouy-Chapman theory.

The potential gradient in the vicinity of the solid-solution interface is depicted schematically in Fig. 8-1 for the three historically important concepts of the double layer. Stern's theory is regarded as essentially correct today, although Grahame[4] has found it advantageous to distin-

[1] Overbeek, in Kruyt, "Colloid Science," pp. 131–132.

[2] Ibid.

[3] Stern, O., Z. Elektrochem., **30**, 508 (1924).

[4] Grahame, D. C., Chem. Revs., **41**, 441 (1947).

guish between the "outer Helmholtz plane," representing the closest approach of ions that are not adsorbed, and the "inner Helmholtz plane," representing the closest approach of adsorbed ions. In the inner region, according to Grahame,[1] there is a strongly oriented layer of solvent molecules firmly attached to the surface. This "icelike" but not hydrogen-bonded layer is considered to have the property of excluding anions from a positively charged surface. At higher temperatures, such small anions as the fluoride ion can penetrate the gradually "melting" layer.

Qualitatively, then, the double layer should be regarded as being composed of a layer of potential-determining ions on the solid phase together with a layer of oppositely charged counter ions in the solution phase. The first layer of counter ions may or may not be adsorbed, but in any case a relatively compact inner layer of counter ions exists together with a diffuse "ionic atmosphere." The extent of the diffuse ion layer varies (approximately) inversely with the square root of the concentration of a particular electrolyte. For a counter ion of high charge, the double layer is much more compressed than for a counter ion of low charge, because the electrical force of attraction increases with the square of the ionic charge.

8-4. The Electrokinetic Potential (Zeta Potential)

The rate of motion of colloidal particles in an electric field (electrophoresis) is proportional not to the total potential difference between the solid and the solution, but to a part of it, the *electrokinetic potential*. Several other properties (electroosmosis, streaming potential, migration potential) are also determined by the same quantity, often called the *zeta potential*. The zeta potential is sensitive to the total concentration of electrolyte, particularly to counter ions of high charge, whereas the total potential across the double layer is determined by the adsorption of specific types of potential-determining ions.

The relationship becomes qualitatively clear at once when it is recognized that the zeta potential is the electrical potential between the boundary of a firmly attached water layer (the slipping plane) and the bulk of the solution. As far as electrokinetic phenomena are concerned, the water sheath a few molecules in thickness acts as though it were a part of the solid phase.[2] The magnitude of the zeta potential is determined both by the surface potential ψ_0 and by the steepness of the poten-

[1] Grahame, *J. Am. Chem. Soc.*, **79**, 2093 (1957).

[2] Wallace, C. H., and Willard, J. E., *J. Am. Chem. Soc.*, **72**, 5275 (1950), have shown that silver chloride particles retain a surface layer of moisture even after heating for 4 hr in a vacuum system at 160°C. Upon vacuum fusion, the moisture disappears completely. The surface moisture may be regarded as residual hydration of surface ions.

tial gradient (Fig. 8-2). For a given surface potential, the double layer can be increasingly compressed by increasing the electrolyte concentration. Counter ions of higher charge are especially effective in compressing the double layer.

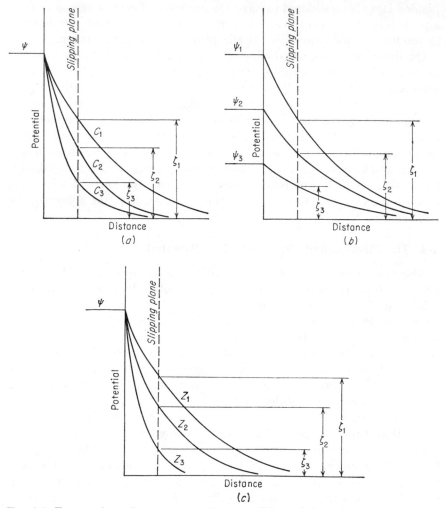

FIG. 8-2. Factors that affect zeta potential. (*a*) Effect of electrolyte concentration; (*b*) effect of surface potential; (*c*) effect of charge of counter ion.

It is possible in some instances to reverse the sign of the zeta potential, especially with electrolytes containing counter ions of high charge (Fig. 8-3). Strongly adsorbed substances, such as dyes of charge opposite to that of the solid, often cause a reversal of sign. This effect is due to adsorption of more than an equivalent amount of oppositely charged material, so that a triple layer of charge is present. The diffuse layer of counter ions is now of the same charge as the original surface. It is not clear whether multivalent cations are adsorbed as such (thereby more

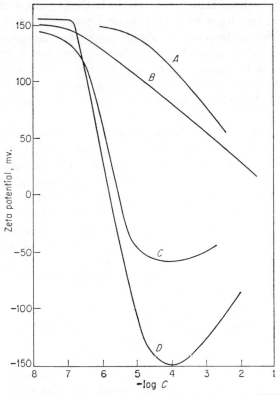

FIG. 8-3. Effect of electrolytes upon zeta potential of glass. *A*, KCl; *B*, Ca(NO₃)₂; *C*, Al(NO₃)₃; *D*, Th(NO₃)₄. [*With permission from Rutgers, A. J., and de Smet, M., Trans. Faraday Soc.*, **41**, 758 (1945).]

than neutralizing the local charge of the negative site on which the adsorption occurred) or whether a positively charged colloidal hydrous oxide is adsorbed. As will be seen below, the reversal of sign of the zeta potential is responsible for the peculiar "irregular series" in the coagulation of colloids.

8-5. Coagulation of Lyophobic Colloids: Secondary Stability

Verwey[1] has made a useful distinction between *primary stability* of colloids, imparted by the surface charge, and *secondary stability*, which

[1] Verwey, *Chem. Revs.*, **16**, 363 (1935).

pertains to the effective repulsion of colloidal particles. The primary stability is governed by the total (thermodynamic) potential of the solid, whereas the secondary stability is determined primarily by the electrokinetic potential.

The distinction between primary and secondary stability becomes clear when it is realized that two particles, both carrying a surface charge, can approach each other with very little repulsion to a distance corresponding to the coalescence of their water sheaths, *provided that the double layer is so compressed that the counter ions are largely within the firmly attached water layers.* Thus, for the existence of a stable sol, it is necessary to have not only a primary charge on the solid phase but also a diffuse double layer of thickness large compared to the thickness of the water sheath.

Schulze[1] first showed that inorganic colloids are especially sensitive to electrolytes of high charge, and Hardy[2] pointed out that their stability is closely related to electrophoretic mobility. The Schulze-Hardy rule states that the sensitivity of lyophobic colloids to coagulating electrolytes is governed by the charge of the ion opposite to that of the colloid and that the sensitivity increases far more rapidly than the charge of the ion.

The effects of various electrolytes are usually compared in terms of the "flocculation values," or minimal concentrations, expressed in millimoles per liter, required to bring about coagulation. Typical values, as listed by Overbeek, are given in Table 8-1. The values listed were chosen as being typical of electrolytes that are not specifically adsorbed. Organic salts, and potential-determining ions generally, have specific effects that are not considered here. It should be noted that flocculation is not an instantaneous process and that the flocculation values are determined by setting up a "flocculation series" of increasing concentrations. After each suspension is allowed to stand for a period up to an hour or so, the concentration corresponding to the flocculation value can be selected. The process can usually be hastened materially by shaking.

The theoretical ratios were derived by Verwey and Overbeek[3] by calculating the potential energy of interaction of colloidal particles as a function of the distance of separation. The potential energy is the resultant of two opposite terms: a repulsion due to the electrostatic interaction of the diffuse double layers, and a van der Waals attraction of the particles. The repulsion term is essentially determined by the zeta potential and is sensitive, therefore, to the charge of the counter ion. The potential energy of attraction varies with the sizes and shapes of the particles and

---

[1] Schulze, H., *J. prakt. Chem.*, [2], **25**, 431 (1882); **27**, 320 (1883).

[2] Hardy, W. B., *Proc. Roy. Soc. London*, **66**, 110 (1900).

[3] Verwey and Overbeek, "Theory of the Stability of Lyophobic Colloids," Elsevier Publishing Company, Amsterdam, 1948; *Trans. Faraday Soc.*, **42B**, 117 (1946).

with the distance of separation. For single atoms the potential energy of attraction varies inversely as the sixth power of the distance,[1] but for infinite plates the attraction summed over all the atoms turns out to decay only as the square of the distance. This is important to the theory, for it results in attractive forces between colloidal particles at distances of the order of magnitude of their own sizes.[2]

TABLE 8-1. MEAN FLOCCULATION VALUES FOR VARIOUS SOLS
(millimoles liter^{-1})

Counter ion / Sol	Monovalent	Bivalent	Tervalent	Quadrivalent
Negative:				
As_2S_3, flocc. value	55	0.69	0.091	0.090
Ratio	1	0.013	0.0017	0.0017
Au, flocc. value	24	0.38	0.006	0.0009
Ratio	1	0.016	0.0003	0.00004
AgI, flocc. value	142	2.43	0.068	0.013
Ratio	1	0.017	0.0005	0.0001
Positive:				
Fe_2O_3, flocc. value	11.8	0.21	–	–
Ratio	1	0.018	–	–
Al_2O_3, flocc. value	52	0.63	0.080	0.053
Ratio	1	0.012	0.0015	0.0010
Theoretical ratio	1.00	0.016	0.0013	0.00024

[By permission from Overbeek, J. Th. G., in Kruyt, H. R. (ed.), "Colloid Science," vol. 1, pp. 308–309, Elsevier Publishing Company, Amsterdam, 1952.]

In Fig. 8-4, a family of curves, calculated by Verwey and Overbeek, shows the potential energy of interaction of two colloidal particles as a function of their distance of separation, for reasonable assumed values of the surface potential and the van der Waals attraction. At increasing concentrations of electrolyte, corresponding to increasing values of κ, the repulsion gradually changes to an attraction at sufficiently small distances of separation.

At very small distances the attractive force should change once more to a repulsion (Born repulsion, due to deformation of electron shells). This type of repulsion, however, is of no consequence for colloid flocculation, because flocculation corresponds to the sharing of the firmly bound water layers of adjacent particles. Qualitatively, flocculation occurs when the counter ions are largely within the attached water layer. When

[1] London, F., Z. Physik, **63**, 245 (1930).
[2] Overbeek, in Kruyt, "Colloid Science," p. 264.

this is true, the surface charge has been effectively neutralized by an equivalent amount of counter ion charge held close to the surface.

Actually, for flocculation to occur, it is not necessary to lower the zeta potential to zero, but only to some small critical value. At this point the small repulsion is counteracted by the van der Waals attraction. The

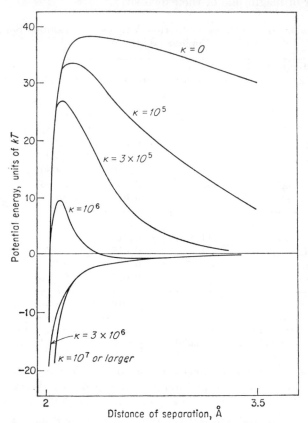

FIG. 8-4. Potential energy of interaction of colloidal particles. (*With permission from Verwey, E. J. W., and Overbeek, J. Th. G., "Theory of the Stability of Lyophobic Colloids," p. 161, Elsevier Publishing Company, Amsterdam, 1948.*)

calculated flocculation values for counter ions of charge 1, 2, 3, and 4 are in the ratio $1:(\frac{1}{2})^6:(\frac{1}{3})^6:(\frac{1}{4})^6$, and correspond—at least in order of magnitude—to the observed values (Table 8-1).

Some care should be exercised in interpreting flocculation values for ions of high charge, because there is tendency for such ions to undergo hydrolysis and, therefore, actually to exist as lower-charged species. For example, Fe^{3+} would undergo extensive hydrolysis, whereas an ion such as $Co(NH_3)_6^{3+}$ would not. Thorium ion, which is often used as a quadrivalent ion, is undoubtedly present to some extent as various hydrolyzed species (cf. Chap. 6). For negative ions of high charge, ferricyanide and ferrocyanide are commonly used. The ferrocyanide ion undergoes hydrolysis in acid solution (cf. Chap. 15) and so it exists as an ion of -3 or -2 charge under these conditions. For this reason, the observed flocculation values of highly charged ions are often erroneously high.

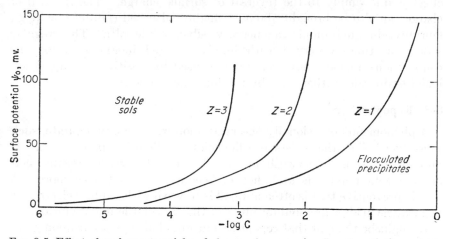

FIG. 8-5. Effect of surface potential and charge of counter ion Z on flocculation values. [*With permission from Overbeek, J. Th. G., "Theory of the Stability of Lyophobic Colloids," in Kruyt, H. R. (ed.), "Colloid Science," vol. 1, p. 304, Elsevier Publishing Company, Amsterdam, 1952.*]

If the van der Waals attraction is not taken into account, the concentrations of electrolyte required to cause the same compression of the double layer are in the approximate ratio $1 : \frac{1}{5} : (\frac{1}{5})^2 : (\frac{1}{5})^3$, according to the calculations of Verwey.[1] These ratios do not show so large a dependence on the charge of the counter ion as that actually observed.

The flocculation value for a given type of sol depends to some extent on the magnitude of the surface potential, as is evident from the curves of Fig. 8-2b. The flocculation values calculated for various surface potentials, assuming a given reasonable van der Waals attraction, are shown in Fig. 8-5. If the surface potential ψ_0 exceeds 50 to 100 mv, the curves separating the region of stable sols from that of flocculated precipitates are very steep, particularly for counter ions of charge greater than 1. The flocculation values under these conditions become independent of surface potential. On the other hand, for colloids of surface potential less than 50 mv and particularly for monovalent counter ions, the flocculation value depends greatly on the surface potential.

[1] Verwey, *Chem. Revs.*, **16**, 363 (1935).

In some cases a peculiar "irregular series" of flocculation is observed as increasing concentrations of electrolyte are added. A small concentration of electrolyte brings about coagulation; a higher concentration causes peptization to a colloid of opposite charge; this is finally flocculated by a still higher electrolyte concentration. When potential-determining ions are added (silver ions to negatively charged silver halide or hydroxide ions to a positively charged hydrous ferric oxide sol) the effect is due simply to the reversal of surface charge. The reversal of charge can also be brought about by highly adsorbed counter ions (e.g., laurylpyridinium bromide on a negative silver iodide sol[1]). The irregular series sometimes observed with highly charged inorganic cations as counter ions appears, however, to be caused by positively charged colloidal hydroxides rather than by the ions themselves.[2]

8-6. Repeptization

A phenomenon occasionally observed upon washing a precipitate, such as a silver halide, that exists as a flocculated colloid is repeptization. If pure water is used for washing, the flocculated particles regain their original zeta potentials and, hence, become dispersed once more. A simple preventive that is often applied is to wash with a dilute electrolyte (e.g., nitric acid or ammonium nitrate) that is volatile upon ignition.

It might be thought that repeptization would always occur upon great dilution. However, several effects work toward preventing it. In the first place, recrystallization of the primary particles (cf. Sec. 9-2) causes a diminution and perfection of the surface, with the result that adsorbed potential-determining ions are released. In fact, Kolthoff and Lingane[3] located the point of zero charge of silver iodide by finding the composition at which no adsorbed silver or iodide ions were released upon aging. Another effect, especially observed with salts of appreciable solubility, is that of *Ostwald ripening*, or growth of coarse particles at the expense of fine ones. Also, it is possible for colloidal particles in the coagulated state to merge by recrystallization. Multivalent cations, if used for causing flocculation, are not easily desorbed upon dilution. All these effects tend to lower the surface potential of the solid and, therefore, to discourage repeptization.

8-7. Influence of Lyophilic Colloids on Lyophobic Sols

Lyophilic colloids such as gelatin or dextrin exert a "protective action" to lessen the tendency of a lyophobic sol to be flocculated by electrolytes. It is found from electrophoresis experiments that the electrokinetic

[1] Lottermoser, A., and Stendel, R., *Kolloid-Z.*, **82**, 319 (1938); **83**, 37 (1938).

[2] Kruyt, H. R., and Troelstra, S. A., *Kolloid-Beih.*, **54**, 277, 284 (1943).

[3] Kolthoff, I. M., and Lingane, J. J., *J. Am. Chem. Soc.*, **58**, 1528 (1936).

behavior of the protected system is characteristic of the lyophilic colloid. The inference is clear that the hydrophobic particles are coated by an adsorbed layer of hydrophilic substance.

To measure protective action, Zsigmondy[1] defined the *gold number*, which is the number of milligrams of hydrophilic colloid required just to prevent the flocculation of 10 ml of a gold sol by the addition of 1 ml of a 10 per cent solution of sodium chloride. The gold number, which may vary from 0.01 or less for a well-protecting colloid to 25 or more for a poorly protecting colloid, is found to be a good measure of the protection against flocculation of various lyophobic sols. The gold number of gelatin is 0.01 as compared with 20 for dextrin. An analogous "iron oxide number" for gelatin is 5 and for dextrin 20, showing that for different sols the protective action lies in the same order, but that the ratios are quantitatively different. This behavior is typical of various protective colloids.[2]

Another effect which is more mysterious is that of *sensitization;* this is just the opposite effect and is observed upon the addition of very small amounts of lyophilic colloids. When the lyophilic and lyophobic colloids are oppositely charged, e.g., in the addition of positively charged gelatin to negatively charged silver iodide, the effect is simply a mutual coagulation.[3] However, sensitization occurs even when an exclusively negative colloid like gum arabic or starch is added to a negative silver iodide sol.[4] The sol particles are not affected in their Brownian motion or in their electrophoretic velocity by the sensitizing colloid alone, but coagulation occurs at a lower electrolyte concentration. It appears that, when the repulsion of the two colloids is lowered by addition of electrolyte, an agglomeration occurs in which a lyophilic particle is attached to two or more lyophobic ones. If enough lyophilic colloid is added, the agglomerates are unstable, because the entire surfaces of the lyophobic particles are covered.

[1] Zsigmondy, R., *Z. anal. Chem.*, **40**, 697 (1901).

[2] Freundlich, H., "Kapillarchemie," vol. 2, Akademische Verlagsgesellschaft, Leipzig, 1932.

[3] Such an effect is readily demonstrated by the following experiment, suggested to the author by Professor I. M. Kolthoff. A positively charged sol of barium sulfate is prepared by rapid addition of a slight deficiency of potassium sulfate to barium chloride at room temperature. If, after acidification to pH 2 to 2.5, a trace of gelatin is added, there is no effect, because the gelatin is positively charged at these pH values. If, on the other hand, the sol is treated with ammonia to bring the pH to 8.5, the addition of a few drops of 0.01 per cent gelatin solution to 100 ml of sol will cause flocculation.

[4] Kruyt, H. R., and Horsting, C. W., *Rec. trav. chim.*, **57**, 737 (1938); Overbeek, *Chem. Weekblad*, **35**, 117 (1938).

9. Aging of Precipitates

Aging has been defined by Kolthoff[1,2] to include "all irreversible, structural changes that occur in a precipitate after it has been formed." These changes may include (1) recrystallization of primary particles; (2) cementing of primary particles by recrystallization in an agglomerated state; (3) Ostwald ripening, or growth of large particles by dissolution of small ones; (4) thermal aging, or perfection by thermal agitation of ions to form a more perfect structure; (5) couple action in perfection of metallic precipitates; (6) transformation of a metastable modification into another, more stable form; and (7) chemical aging, including processes involving changes in composition.

9-1. Experimental Methods

Experimental studies of aging usually involve the use of radioactive tracer techniques for observation of exchange of ions between precipitate and solution, adsorption of suitable dyes on the surface of a precipitate to measure the extent of the surface, microscopic or X-ray observation of the precipitate, or combinations of these methods.

Paneth[3,4] studied the exchange of thorium B (naturally occurring isotope of lead) with lead sulfate as a method of measurement of the specific surface. Kolthoff and Rosenblum,[5] in an extensive series of papers, compared the use of dye adsorption with radioactive isotope exchange and observed the process of aging of lead sulfate under a variety of conditions.

The use of gas adsorption is applicable only to materials that can be

[1] Kolthoff, I. M., *Suomen Kemistilehti*, **16A**, 89 (1943).

[2] Kolthoff, *Analyst*, **77**, 1000 (1952).

[3] Paneth, F., *Physik Z.*, **15**, 924 (1914); *Z. Elektrochem.*, **28**, 113 (1922).

[4] Paneth, F., and Vorwerk, W., *Z. physik. Chem. Leipzig*, **101**, 445 (1922).

[5] Kolthoff, I. M., and Rosenblum, C., *J. Am. Chem. Soc.*, **55**, 2656, 2664 (1933); **56**, 1264, 1658 (1934); **57**, 597, 607, 2573, 2577 (1935); **58**, 116, 121 (1936).

placed in a vacuum system,[1,2] An unusual method for measuring the specific surface of silica was described recently by Sears,[3] who suspended the silica particles in 20 per cent sodium chloride solution and titrated the surface with sodium hydroxide. The consumption of hydroxyl ions in going from pH 4 to 9 was found to be proportional to the specific surface, and the titration procedure, once it was calibrated by nitrogen adsorption, proved to be a simple and convenient method of comparing surface areas.

The amount of adsorption of dye may also be used for the measurement of specific surface if the surface is covered with a monolayer of dye. The area covered by a dye molecule is established by comparison with isotope exchange or by direct measurement of particle sizes of well-developed crystals. For example, it has been shown that the dye wool violet 4BN is adsorbed on lead sulfate to the extent of one dye anion per 1.5 surface lead ions.[4] For lead chromate, one dye anion is adsorbed for two surface lead ions.[5] Care must be exercised, because the area covered by a dye molecule sometimes depends upon the surface charge. For example, silver bromide adsorbs twice as much wool violet or methylene blue from a solution containing excess silver ion than from one containing an excess of bromide.[6]

Another method of determining specific surface is by studying the distribution of ions capable of replacing lattice ions between the surface and the solution. This method has been applied to the distribution of lead ions[7] or chromate ions[8] between the surface of barium sulfate and the solution. The rate of penetration of bromide ions into silver chloride has been used to study aging of silver chloride.[9] The adsorption of lead acetate on lead chromate[10] and of water on barium sulfate[11] have been used to measure specific surface.

9-2. Recrystallization of Primary Particles

It was thought in the early work that a fresh precipitate might have fine capillary cracks not penetrated by the large dye molecules. Thus, a precipitate would have an "external surface," which would be measured

[1] Brunauer, S., Emmett, P. H., and Teller, E., *J. Am. Chem. Soc.*, **60**, 309 (1938).
[2] Harkins, W. D., and Jura, G., *J. Am. Chem. Soc.*, **66**, 919, 1356 (1944).
[3] Sears, G. W., *Anal. Chem.*, **28**, 1981 (1956).
[4] Kolthoff and Rosenblum, *op. cit.*
[5] Kolthoff, I. M., and Eggertsen, F. T., *J. Am. Chem. Soc.*, **62**, 2125 (1940).
[6] Kolthoff, I. M., and O'Brien, A. S., *J. Am. Chem. Soc.*, **61**, 3409 (1939).
[7] Kolthoff and Eggertsen, *op. cit.*
[8] Kolthoff, I. M., and MacNevin, W. M., *J. Am. Chem. Soc.*, **58**, 499, 725 (1936).
[9] Kolthoff and O'Brien, *op. cit.*
[10] Kolthoff, I. M., and Noponen, G. E., *J. Am. Chem. Soc.*, **60**, 39 (1938).
[11] Kolthoff and MacNevin, *J. Phys. Chem.*, **44**, 921 (1940).

by dye adsorption, and an "internal surface," which would be measured as a part of the total surface by isotope exchange. However, it was found, upon shaking lead sulfate with lead nitrate containing thorium B, that eventually the entire precipitate reached a homogeneous composition. This is illustrated in Fig. 9-1, in which the rate of penetration of thorium B into lead sulfate of varying age is shown. The mechanism of the penetration is a recrystallization of primary particles of precipitate. The rate of recrystallization is very large for a fresh precipitate, but

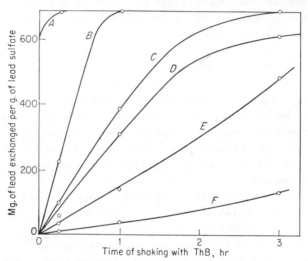

Fig. 9-1. Exchange of lead ions between lead sulfate and solution at 25°C. *A*, fresh; *B*, aged 13 min; *C*, aged 20 min; *D*, aged 45 min; *E*, aged 57 min; *F*, aged 3 hr. [*With permission from Kolthoff, I. M., and von Fischer, W., J. Am. Chem. Soc.*, **61**, 191 (1939).]

diminishes gradually as the particles become perfected. A 3-hr-old product is recrystallizing relatively slowly but still at a distinctly measurable rate.

In a similar study with lead chromate,[1] it was found that under certain conditions the amount of radioactive lead taken up by the solid greatly exceeded the equilibrium amount corresponding to a uniform distribution between solid and solution (Fig. 9-2). A very fresh product (15 sec old) reaches the homogeneous composition rapidly through recrystallization. A product 10 min old is recrystallizing more slowly and extracts temporarily a relatively large quantity of radioactive lead, because the surface originally exposed to rich radioactive solution is buried by recrystallization, so that the precipitate in effect performs a multiple extraction. Eventually the abnormally rich solid approaches equilibrium by continued recrystallization. These experiments provide

[1] Kolthoff and Eggertsen, *J. Am. Chem. Soc.*, **63**, 1412 (1941).

striking evidence for a *several-fold* recrystallization process, occurring with a gradually diminishing rate as the aging proceeds.

It is interesting that the rate of aging is decreased practically to zero by the presence of an adsorbed layer of dye on lead sulfate,[1,2] silver chloride,[3] barium sulfate,[4] silver bromide,[5] or lead chromate.[6] The rate

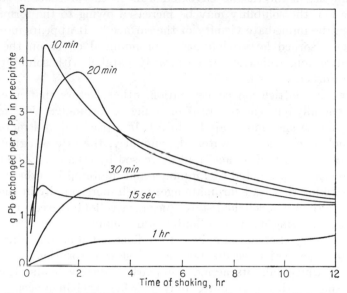

Fig. 9-2. Penetration of ThB into lead chromate. Age of precipitate before adding ThB given on curves. [*With permission from Kolthoff, I. M., and Eggertsen, F. T., J. Am. Chem. Soc.*, **63**, 1412 (1941).]

of exchange of radioactive isotopes can thus be used for measuring the specific surface after inhibiting recrystallization by adsorbed dye.[5,6]

The rate of aging is influenced greatly by the presence of excess lattice ions in solution. Lead sulfate ages more slowly in excess lead nitrate than in water,[1,7] and barium sulfate ages more slowly in barium ion solution than in sulfate but faster in sulfate than in water.[4] The aging of

[1] Kolthoff and Rosenblum, *op. cit.*

[2] Kolthoff, I. M., von Fischer, W., and Rosenblum, C., *J. Am. Chem. Soc.*, **56**, 832 (1934).

[3] Kolthoff, I. M., and Yutzy, H. C., *J. Am. Chem. Soc.*, **59**, 1215 (1937).

[4] Kolthoff and Noponen, *J. Am. Chem. Soc.*, **60**, 499, 505 (1938).

[5] Kolthoff and O'Brien, *op. cit.*

[6] Kolthoff and Eggertsen, *J. Am. Chem. Soc.*, **62**, 2125 (1940).

[7] Kolthoff, I. M., and Halversen, R. A., *J. Phys. Chem.*, **43**, 605 (1939).

silver chloride is impeded by silver ion but speeded by chloride ion,[1] and a similar effect exists for silver bromide.[2] For lead chromate no particular lattice ion effect was noticed.[3] Apparently the rate of aging is not parallel with solubility, which is decreased by the common ion effect. Kolthoff *et al.* postulated that the solubility in the adsorbed water layer actually may be quite different from that in the bulk of the solution. For example, in the case of silver chloride in the presence of adsorbed chloride ion, the solubility may be increased owing to the formation of $AgCl_2^-$ in the immediate vicinity of the surface.[1] It appears more likely that the adsorbed lattice ion has a pronounced effect on the *rate* of recrystallization, which is not necessarily parallel with solubility, even in the adsorbed water layer.

Apart from lattice ion concentration, other factors that affect solubility generally change the rate of aging accordingly. For example, barium sulfate ages more rapidly in 0.1 M nitric acid and more slowly in ethanol than it does in water.[4,5] Similarly, the rate of aging of lead chromate[6] is increased by acid and decreased by ethanol. The aging of silver chloride is promoted by ammonia and inhibited by ethanol.[1]

It is striking that lead chromate ages much more rapidly in the flocculated state than in a colloidal state[7] (negative colloid in excess chromate). However, preaging in the colloidal state eliminates an "incubation period" or very slow initial aging in the flocculated state. Presumably the incubation period occurs because of slow desorption of adsorbed chromate, which inhibits aging. Similarly, when colloidal lead chromate is shaken with molybdate,[8] only a surface exchange occurs. After flocculation, a rapid interaction to form a solid solution indicates a rapid recrystallization. In contrast, a colloidal dispersion of silver bromide forms homogeneous solid solutions almost instantaneously with added chloride ion.[9]

9-3. Thermal Aging

Thermal aging may be defined as a process in which a perfection of particles occurs through thermal agitation rather than through recrystallization. The rate of such a process increases rapidly with rising temperature, but at any temperature it is independent of the presence or

[1] Kolthoff and Yutzy, *op. cit.*

[2] Kolthoff and O'Brien, *J. Am. Chem. Soc.*, **61**, 3414 (1939).

[3] Kolthoff and Eggertsen, *J. Am. Chem. Soc.*, **63**, 1412 (1941).

[4] Kolthoff and MacNevin, *J. Am. Chem. Soc.*, **58**, 499, 725 (1936).

[5] Kolthoff and Noponen, *op. cit.*

[6] Kolthoff and Eggertsen, *op. cit.*

[7] Kolthoff and Eggertsen, *J. Phys. Chem.*, **46**, 458 (1942).

[8] Kolthoff and Eggertsen, *J. Phys. Chem.*, **46**, 616 (1942).

[9] Kolthoff and Eggertsen, *J. Am. Chem. Soc.*, **61**, 1036 (1939).

absence of solvent and of the nature of the solvent. Of course, the rate of recrystallization processes also increases rapidly with rising temperature; so the temperature dependence is *not* the criterion of thermal aging.

To illustrate the phenomena involved, let us examine the behavior of lead sulfate, as observed by Kolthoff and Rosenblum.[1] An air-dried product of lead sulfate undergoes no appreciable aging at room temperature, unless it is stored in an atmosphere of relative humidity 0.85. Under these conditions, it takes up 2 per cent by weight of moisture and undergoes slow aging by recrystallization in the film of moisture. At higher temperatures, the recrystallization is greatly speeded up, but eventually the occluded or adsorbed moisture is lost and the rate of aging decreases again. Thus the rate of perfection is greater at 250 than at 300°C. As the temperature exceeds 300°C the rate of thermal aging increases, and a pronounced sintering occurs at 400°C.

Silver bromide apparently undergoes appreciable thermal aging even at room temperature.[2,3] Silver bromide undergoes complete homogeneous exchange with radioactive bromide within a few seconds,[4] a behavior that is attributed to the exceptional thermal aging properties of silver bromide. The rapid recrystallization was attributed to lattice defects that give rise to a high mobility of ions, at least in the layers near the surface. Compressed pellets of freshly precipitated silver bromide have considerable electrical conductivity, an effect that is also attributed to highly mobile surface ions.[5,6]

Lead chromate undergoes no thermal aging at room temperature but shows a pronounced effect upon heating at 355°C.[7] Barium sulfate shows no thermal aging in 24 hr at 300°C or in 1 hr at 400°C, but shows a marked sintering at 500°C. Thermal aging becomes very rapid above 700°C, and occluded sodium chloride is volatilized at temperatures above 800°C.[8] Silica gel particles undergo two types of aging upon heating: a low temperature perfection of individual particles below 700°C and a sintering process above 700°C with a pronounced decrease in porosity.[9] In general, the critical temperature at which thermal aging becomes appreciable corresponds to Tammann's "relaxation temperature,"[10] the temperature at which thermal agitation begins to overcome lattice forces

[1] Kolthoff and Rosenblum, *op. cit.*
[2] Kolthoff and O'Brien, *op. cit.*
[3] Kolthoff and O'Brien, *J. Chem. Phys.*, **7**, 401 (1939).
[4] Kolthoff, I. M., and Bowers, R. C., *J. Am. Chem. Soc.*, **76**, 1503 (1954).
[5] Shapiro, I., and Kolthoff, I. M., *J. Chem. Phys.*, **15**, 41 (1947).
[6] Shapiro and Kolthoff, *J. Phys. Colloid Chem.*, **52**, 1319 (1948).
[7] Kolthoff and Eggertsen, *J. Phys. Chem.*, **46**, 458 (1942).
[8] Kolthoff and MacNevin, *J. Phys. Chem.*, **44**, 921 (1940).
[9] Shapiro and Kolthoff, *J. Am. Chem. Soc.*, **72**, 776 (1950).
[10] Tammann, G., and Sworykin, A., *Z. anorg. u. allgem. Chem.*, **176**, 46 (1928).

appreciably; this occurs at about half the melting point on the absolute temperature scale.

9-4. Ostwald Ripening

At the time of Ostwald, when it first became generally realized that the solubility of very small particles should be abnormally large (cf. Sec. 6-8) compared with the normal solubility, it was a logical deduction that a freshly formed precipitate should undergo a process of "ripening" by dissolution of small particles and growth of large ones.

A great deal of evidence, however, indicates that Ostwald ripening is of subordinate importance in aging,[1-4] at least during the early stages when recrystallization is very rapid and under conditions of low solubility of the solid. For example, the rate of aging is not increased by increased agitation for lead sulfate,[5] lead chromate,[1] or barium sulfate,[6] although with silver bromide[7] in excess bromide appreciable Ostwald ripening occurs. Generally, it may be expected to be noticeable under conditions of increased solubility.[1,3,4]

Colloidal silver bromide undergoes extensive Ostwald ripening,[8] as shown by the decreasing surface measured by dye adsorption and by the decrease in number of particles observed by electron microscopy. Adsorbed wool violet prevents Ostwald ripening and limits radioactive exchange to the surface layer. Flocculated silver bromide shows no Ostwald ripening.[9]

9-5. Other Aging Effects

Aging due to cementing of primary particles is difficult to observe directly because of other changes that occur simultaneously, but it may be inferred that such processes going on in the flocculated state render impossible the subsequent peptization of an aged product. Kolthoff et al. have discussed the cementing process for barium sulfate,[6] lead chromate,[1] and silver bromide.[10]

A special type of aging occurs in the case of calcium oxalate,[11] which

---

[1] Kolthoff and Eggertsen, J. Am. Chem. Soc., **63**, 1412 (1941).

[2] Kolthoff, von Fischer, and Rosenblum, op. cit.

[3] Kolthoff and Yutzy, op. cit.

[4] Kolthoff and Yutzy, J. Am. Chem. Soc., **59**, 1634 (1937).

[5] Kolthoff and Rosenblum, op. cit.

[6] Kolthoff and Noponen, J. Am. Chem. Soc., **60**, 499, 505 (1938).

[7] Kolthoff and O'Brien, J. Am. Chem. Soc., **61**, 3414 (1939).

[8] Kolthoff and Bowers, op. cit.

[9] Kolthoff and Bowers, J. Am. Chem. Soc., **76**, 1510 (1954).

[10] Ibid.

[11] Kolthoff and Sandell, J. Phys. Chem., **37**, 448 (1933).

at room temperature is precipitated as a mixture of dihydrate and tri-hydrate. Upon digestion at higher temperatures, these products become metastable with respect to the monohydrate. As a result of the drastic recrystallization, coprecipitated impurities are largely removed by digestion.

Another type of aging occurs with hydrous oxides. Krause[1] has explained the aging of hydrous ferric oxide as a polymerization, involving a dehydration and formation of Fe—O—Fe linkages, with chain structures containing 40 to 50 atoms of iron. However, Weiser and Milligan[2] showed by X-ray and phase-rule studies that hydrous ferric oxide prepared by precipitation from hot solutions shows only a band diffraction pattern of α-Fe_2O_3, or hematite. A product precipitated at room temperature is at first amorphous to X rays but, after standing at room temperature for several weeks, it shows a band diffraction pattern of hematite. After several months the pattern has changed to give sharp lines. A similar sharp pattern is observed after a few hours at the boiling point. The X-ray results indicate the absence of hydrates such as α-$Fe_2O_3 \cdot H_2O$, or göthite, a yellow product that can be prepared by slow hydrolysis of ferric sulfate, nitrate, or acetate. Likewise, isothermal or isobaric dehydration studies show no evidence of hydrates if care is taken to reach equilibrium. The yellow precipitate obtained from ferric chloride does not show the α-Fe_2O_3 structure, but it contains a variable amount of chloride and was postulated by Kolthoff and Moskovitz[3] to be a solid solution of FeOOH and FeOCl.

The rate of aging was found to be negligible at room temperature in water or dilute acid but to increase markedly with hydroxyl ion concentration (ammoniacal or sodium hydroxide solution),[4,5] even though the solubility decreases with increasing alkalinity. Digestion at 98°C greatly speeded the aging process. A striking observation was made that the aging process was inhibited by adsorbed divalent metal ions, such as zinc, nickel, cobalt, or magnesium, but not by calcium. The inhibiting effect was attributed to the replacement of hydroxyl hydrogen by metals (ferrite formation) to prevent the polymerization process. In support of this view was the finding that the precipitate removed *increased* amounts of zinc, nickel, or cobalt from solution upon digestion at 98°C and (slowly) even upon standing at room temperature. However, the X-ray evidence[6] indicates that the aging process should be regarded as a

[1] Krause, A., *Kolloid-Z.*, **72**, 18 (1935).

[2] Weiser, H. B., and Milligan, W. O., *Chem. Revs.*, **25**, 1 (1939).

[3] Kolthoff, I. M., and Moskovitz, B., *J. Phys. Chem.*, **41**, 629 (1937).

[4] *Ibid.*

[5] Kolthoff, I. M., and Overholser, L. G., *J. Phys. Chem.*, **43**, 909 (1939).

[6] Weiser and Milligan, *op. cit.*

growth of very fine crystallites of Fe_2O_3 to form crystals large enough to give a sharp diffraction pattern.

Similar conclusions appear valid for other hydrous oxides.[1] Hydrous aluminum(III) oxide brought down in a highly gelatinous form at room temperature shows the X-ray diffraction pattern of γ-$Al_2O_3 \cdot H_2O$ (böhmite). Upon aging, böhmite is transformed into α-$Al_2O_3 \cdot 3H_2O$ (bayerite), a metastable hydrate which is very slowly converted to γ-$Al_2O_3 \cdot 3H_2O$ (gibbsite), the stable form. As gibbsite is dehydrated under equilibrium conditions, it shows no intermediate formation of γ-$Al_2O_3 \cdot H_2O$. The dehydration step is not well defined, because γ-Al_2O_3 is highly adsorptive to water vapor. Eventually, at high temperatures, α-Al_2O_3 (alundum), which is not hygroscopic, is formed.

The dioxides of the tetravalent metals (Sn, Ti, Zr, and Th) have long been characterized as alpha (ortho) and beta (meta) modifications. The two forms in each case show identical X-ray patterns, characteristic of the anhydrous oxides and differ, therefore, only in the amount of adsorbed water. Aging is characterized by a sharpening of the X-ray lines, a decrease in dye adsorption, and a decrease in tendency toward peptization.[1]

[1] *Ibid.*

10. Contamination of Precipitates

The literature of analytical chemistry is more confused on the subject of precipitate contamination than on any other major topic. Much of the difficulty lies in the definition of terms and specifically in the lack of uniform interpretation of definitions. The term "occlusion," for example, has been variously used to cover (1) broadly, all modes of the carrying down of impurities, (2) inclusion of pockets of mother liquor in crystals, and (3) creation of crystal imperfections by inclusion of ions or molecules of foreign solute (perhaps also water of solvation). The term "mixed crystal" formation is often used to describe the *isomorphous* replacement of ions to form solid solutions. It appears more accurate to speak of "solid solution" formation, particularly when distinguishing between homogeneous and heterogeneous solid solutions, in order to avoid the implication that two types of crystals have been "mixed." Some terms, such as "isodimorphism" (Hahn) and "adsorption on inner surfaces" (Balarew), have been introduced with a particular theoretical concept in mind, but have not come into accepted usage because of the lack of proof (or even later disproof) of the validity of the concept.

It appears necessary, therefore, to adopt a clear set of definitions, based as far as possible on phenomenological rather than theoretical concepts. Kolthoff[1] has distinguished between two broad classes of contamination phenomena, *coprecipitation* and *postprecipitation;* in coprecipitation the main precipitate and the impurity come down together, whereas in postprecipitation the main precipitate is initially pure and the impurity comes down later.

It should be noted that coprecipitation includes only the carrying down of impurities from *unsaturated* solutions. Thus the fact that two substances are carried down together does not classify the phenomenon as coprecipitation. If a trace of beryllium hydroxide is brought down

[1] Kolthoff, I. M., *J. Phys. Chem.*, **36**, 860 (1932).

quantitatively with a large quantity of hydrous aluminum oxide under conditions such that both are insoluble, we should speak of *gathering* rather than coprecipitation. Postprecipitation, as will be seen below, usually occurs from supersaturated solutions.

As types of coprecipitation we can distinguish two classes. (1) *Adsorption* is the carrying down of impurities on the surface of particles. It should be noted that the surfaces of primary colloidal particles become a sort of internal surface of coagulated colloids (Chap. 8), but the phenomenon is still an adsorption process. (2) *Occlusion* will be used here to denote the carrying down of impurities in the interior of primary particles, by whatever mechanism it may occur. Solid solution formation and ion entrapment (growth of precipitate around adsorbed ions) are two such mechanisms. *Inclusion* of pockets of mother liquor is a form of entrainment that occurs frequently in the crystallization of soluble salts, but it is of relatively little importance in analytical precipitates. Inclusion of mother liquor in the interstices of colloidal precipitates is another type of gross entrainment that can be minimized by proper choice of precipitation conditions to yield a compact form of precipitate.

10-1. Adsorption

Kolthoff[1] has classified several types of adsorption processes occurring at the surface of crystalline precipitates.

Adsorption of Potential-determining Ions. Ideally, as seen in Chap. 8, lattice ions held at the surface of a precipitate[2] containing the same ions are adsorbed in accordance with an equation of the type

$$d\frac{X}{m} = kd \ln C_i$$

or, in the integrated form,

$$\frac{X}{m} = k \ln \frac{C_i}{C_i^\circ} \tag{10-1}$$

where X = amount adsorbed (mg, g, or moles)
    m = weight of precipitate
    C_i = concentration of lattice ion in solution
    C_i° = isoelectric concentration, corresponding to $X = 0$ when $C_i = C_i^\circ$
    k = constant

Actually, the adsorption of lattice ions is far from ideal, as mentioned previously (Sec. 8-2), because of the nonequivalence of perfect and

[1] Kolthoff, *J. Phys. Chem.*, **40**, 1027 (1936).
[2] Fajans, K., and Frankenburger, W., *Z. physik. Chem. Leipzig*, **105**, 255 (1933).

imperfect crystal surfaces and because of the interference of nonlattice ions that may also be potential-determining.

Adsorption by Ion Exchange. Kolthoff[1] has distinguished between two types of exchange adsorption:

1. *Exchange of lattice ion with foreign ion,* as in the equation[2]

$$\underset{\text{Surf}}{\text{BaSO}_4} + \underset{\text{Soln}}{\text{Pb}^{++}} \rightleftharpoons \underset{\text{Surf}}{\text{PbSO}_4} + \underset{\text{Soln}}{\text{Ba}^{++}} \qquad (10\text{-}2)$$

which is described by the equilibrium constant

$$K = \frac{[\text{Ba}^{++}]_{\text{soln}}\,[\text{PbSO}_4]_{\text{surf}}}{[\text{BaSO}_4]_{\text{surf}}\,[\text{Pb}^{++}]_{\text{soln}}} \qquad (10\text{-}3)$$

or

$$\frac{X}{m} = K'\,\frac{[\text{Pb}^{++}]}{[\text{Ba}^{++}]}$$

2. *Exchange of counter ions,* as in the equation

$$\text{AgI}\cdot\text{I}^-|\text{Na}^+ + \text{NH}_4^+ \rightleftharpoons \text{AgI}\cdot\text{I}^-|\text{NH}_4^+ + \text{Na}^+$$

which is described by the same type of equilibrium expression.

To predict which of several ions in solution will be preferentially adsorbed as counter ions, we may set forth the following rules:

1. Of two ions present at equal concentrations, the ion of higher charge is preferentially adsorbed (see Sec. 8-5).

2. Of two ions of equal charge, the ion present at higher concentration is preferentially adsorbed.

3. Of two ions of equal charge at the same concentration, the ion most strongly attracted by the lattice ions is preferentially adsorbed (Paneth-Fajans-Hahn adsorption rule).[3-7] Stronger interionic attraction between adsorbed lattice ions and counter ions is indicated by (a) lower solubility, (b) lesser degree of dissociation, (c) greater covalency, or (d) greater electrical polarizability of the anion and greater polarizing character of the cation.

To illustrate, calcium ion is adsorbed preferentially over magnesium ion on negatively charged barium sulfate, as is to be expected because calcium sulfate is less soluble than magnesium sulfate. Silver acetate is more strongly adsorbed on silver iodide than is silver nitrate, which is

[1] Kolthoff, *loc. cit.*

[2] Kolthoff, I. M., and MacNevin, W. M., *J. Am. Chem. Soc.,* **58**, 499 (1936).

[3] Paneth, F., *Physik. Z.,* **15**, 924 (1914); Horowitz, K., and Paneth, F., *Z. physik. Chem. Leipzig,* **89**, 513 (1915).

[4] Fajans, K., and von Beckerath, K., *Z. physik. Chem. Leipzig,* **97**, 478 (1921).

[5] Fajans, K., and Joos, G., *Z. Physik,* **23**, 1 (1924).

[6] Hahn, O., *Ber. deut. chem. Ges.,* **59**, 2014 (1926); *Naturwissenschaften,* **14**, 1196 (1926).

[7] Hahn, "Applied Radiochemistry," Cornell University Press, Ithaca, N.Y., 1936.

consistent with the lower solubility and greater covalency of silver acetate. Dye anions are strongly adsorbed on positively charged silver halides, in line with the covalency of the silver dye salt. Hydrogen sulfide is strongly adsorbed on metal sulfides, as expected from its weakly ionized character. It should be mentioned here that the Paneth-Fajans-Hahn rule is often applied erroneously to situations involving solid solution formation rather than adsorption. Thus barium nitrate is more strongly coprecipitated with barium sulfate than is barium chloride, a fact in line with the lower solubility of the nitrate. However, both the chloride and the nitrate are quite soluble; in fact, barium nitrate has been shown to form solid solutions with barium sulfate.[1] Similarly, sodium and potassium are coprecipitated as solid solutions of the bisulfates[2] in barium sulfate, and the adsorption rules do not apply.

Molecular or Ion-pair Adsorption. The adsorption of potassium bromate on the surface of barium sulfate, called an *equivalent adsorption*,[3] appears to involve the simultaneous occupation of adjacent sites on the crystal surface by potassium ions and bromate ions, because the amounts of the two ions adsorbed are equivalent. Such an adsorption follows an empirical equation known as the *Freundlich adsorption isotherm* (and, in fact so do many molecular adsorption processes); this equation is

$$\frac{X}{m} = kC^{1/n} \tag{10-4}$$

where k and n are constants. The constant n is usually of the order of 2 to 4. Equation (10-4) represents a parabola of order n, and does not describe those saturation processes in which X/m reaches a limiting value at high concentrations.

Monolayer Adsorption. If the adsorbed substance can occupy only a limited number of surface sites and if the process does not continue to form several molecular layers, a condition of saturation is reached at sufficiently high concentrations of adsorbed substance. This behavior is described by the *Langmuir adsorption isotherm*:

$$\frac{X}{m} = \frac{k_1 C}{1 + k_2 C} \tag{10-5}$$

where X/m reaches the saturation value k_1/k_2 as C approaches infinity. For very small values of C, $(k_2 C \ll 1)$, $X/m \cong k_1 C$; that is, the amount adsorbed is proportional to concentration. For intermediate values of

[1] Walden, G. H., Jr., and Cohen, M. A., *J. Am. Chem. Soc.*, **57**, 2591 (1935); Averell, P. R., and Walden, G. H., Jr., *J. Am. Chem. Soc.*, **59**, 906 (1937).

[2] Walton, G., and Walden, G. H., Jr., *J. Am. Chem. Soc.*, **68**, 1742 (1946).

[3] Reyerson, L. H., Kolthoff, I. M., and Coad, K., *J. Phys. Colloid Chem.*, **51**, 321 (1947).

C, the Langmuir isotherm expresses variation of X/m with a fractional power of concentration, and, over a limited range, the adsorption can equally well be described by the Freundlich isotherm.

A good example of monolayer adsorption is the adsorption of dyes, which reaches a saturation value at low concentrations and is, therefore, useful in measuring the specific surface of precipitates.

Contamination by Adsorption. Adsorption is the principal source of contamination of precipitates that have an exceptionally large surface development, as is the case when the precipitate is a flocculated colloid (e.g., metal sulfides, silver halides, hydrous oxides). The extent of adsorption may be relatively small, as it usually is with silver halides, or severe, as it often is with hydrous oxides.

A silver halide precipitate brought down with excess alkali halide will carry down halide ion adsorbed as lattice ions and alkali metal ions as counter ions. By washing with dilute nitric acid, the alkali metal ions can be largely displaced by counter ion exchange. The adsorbed hydrogen halide volatilizes upon ignition of the precipitate. If silver ion is the adsorbed lattice ion, washing is not effective in removing the adsorbed silver salt, which of course does not volatilize upon ignition. The amount of adsorbed material can be materially decreased by aging during digestion, when recrystallization causes a marked decrease in total surface and also creates a more nearly perfect surface which has a smaller tendency to adsorb lattice ions.

Hydrous oxides, such as Al_2O_3 and Fe_2O_3, that come down in an amorphous or finely crystalline form containing large quantities of adsorbed water, have a great tendency to adsorb hydroxide ions as potential-determining ions and heavy metal ions as counter ions. A systematic investigation of the coprecipitation of divalent metals with hydrous iron(III) oxide was made by Kolthoff et al.[1,2] The Freundlich isotherm was found to hold for copper, nickel, and zinc ion adsorption over a wide range of concentrations. By comparative experiments in which the precipitate was formed (1) in the presence of the contaminant, and (2) in the absence of the contaminant, which was then added to the liquid, it was found that a substantial fraction of the foreign ion was carried down even if it was added after the precipitate formation had been completed. This indicates clearly that adsorption, rather than occlusion, is the principal cause of contamination.

It is interesting to consider the effects of varying the concentrations of ammonium chloride and ammonium hydroxide on the amount of coprecipitation with hydrous iron(III) oxide. If the concentration of ammonium chloride is increased at a constant ammonia concentration (Fig.

[1] Kolthoff, I. M., and Moskovitz, B., *J. Phys. Chem.*, **41**, 629 (1937).
[2] Kolthoff, I. M., and Overholser, L. G., *J. Phys. Chem.*, **43**, 767, 909 (1939).

10-1), the adsorption is decreased (1) because the primary hydroxyl ion adsorption is less at the lower pH value, and (2) because ammonium ion competes with the foreign metal ions for counter ion adsorption. If the concentration of ammonia is increased at a constant ammonium chloride

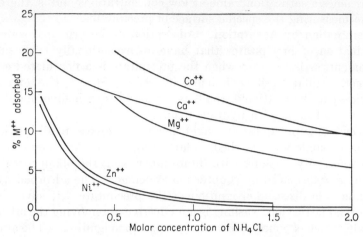

FIG. 10-1. Effect of NH_4Cl concentration on adsorption of divalent metals on hydrous ferric oxide. NH_3 concentration, 0.90 M, except 0.73 M for Zn^{++}.

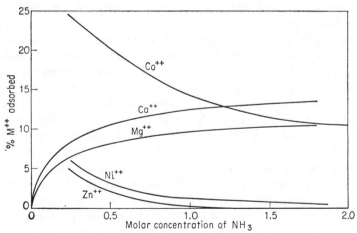

FIG. 10-2. Effect of NH_3 concentration on adsorption of divalent metals on hydrous ferric oxide. NH_4Cl concentration, 1.00 M.

level (Fig. 10-2), adsorption of calcium and magnesium is increased because of greater primary adsorption of hydroxyl ion at the higher pH. On the other hand, the adsorption of cobalt, nickel, and zinc ions is decreased, because these metals form complexes with ammonia. It was shown experimentally that zinc did not carry down an appreciable amount of ammonia and was, therefore, adsorbed as the aquated ion. The adsorption of Co(II) was unusually severe, perhaps because its coordination sphere is not completely occupied by ammonia at the concentrations used.

Evidently, a low ammonia concentration (0.003 M) and a high ammonium chloride concentration (1.5 to 2 M) are favorable for efficient separation of metal ions (Ca^{++}, Mg^{++}) that do not form ammine complexes. In fact, a single precipitation was found to be effective under these conditions.[1] A very low pH separation using ammonia would seem even more effective, but in physical character the hydrous oxide is very gelatinous; so it is better to use a basic salt method instead. To separate Fe(III) from copper, zinc, and nickel, high concentrations of both ammonia and ammonium chloride led to good results in a single precipitation. However, Co(II) and Mn(II) could not be satisfactorily separated by the ammonia method, and a basic salt method was recommended.[2]

It has already been mentioned (page 163) that the coprecipitation of copper, zinc, nickel, or cobalt is actually increased upon digestion at 98°C.

10-2. Solid Solution Formation

One of the ions of a precipitate can be replaced by a foreign ion of the same charge, provided the ions do not differ in size by more than 10 to 15 per cent and provided the two salts crystallize in the same system.[3] Thus silver chloride and silver bromide form a complete series of solid solutions[4] by isomorphous replacement of bromide by chloride.

If pure silver bromide is shaken with a solution containing chloride ions, an equilibrium is set up:

$$Ag(Br,Cl) \rightleftharpoons Ag^+ + Br^- + Cl^- \qquad (10\text{-}6)$$

which may be regarded as a distribution equilibrium of the two halide ions between solid and solution:

$$AgBr + Cl^- \rightleftharpoons AgCl + Br^-$$
$$\text{Solid} \quad \text{Soln} \quad \text{Solid} \quad \text{Soln}$$

described by a distribution coefficient

$$D = \frac{[Br^-]_{soln}}{[Cl^-]_{soln}} \frac{N_{AgCl}}{N_{AgBr}} \qquad (10\text{-}7)$$

[1] Kolthoff and Overholser, *op. cit.*

[2] *Ibid.*

[3] Grimm, H. G., *Z. physik. Chem. Leipzig*, **98**, 353 (1921); *Z. Elektrochem.*, **28**, 75 (1922); **30**, 467 (1924).

[4] Wilsey, R. B., *J. Franklin Inst.*, **200**, 739 (1925).

where the composition of the solid is expressed conveniently in terms of mole fraction N. Several experimentally determined values of distribution coefficients[1] are listed in Table 10-1.

TABLE 10-1. SOLID SOLUTION DISTRIBUTION COEFFICIENTS

Precipitate A	Precipitate B	$K = \dfrac{A_{solid}\,[B_{soln}]}{B_{solid}\,[A_{soln}]} = \dfrac{1}{D}$	Mole % B in solid	Ref.
AgBr	AgCl	450	92	1
		374	50	1
		265	15	1
		393 (colloidal)	85–99	2
		211	99.9–99.99	3
$PbMoO_4$	$PbCrO_4$	250	6–8	4
$BaCrO_4$	$BaSO_4$	1.1	5–33	5
$RaSO_4$	$BaSO_4$	1.8	–	6
$BaSO_4$	$PbSO_4$	8	–	7
$Pb(IO_3)_2$	$Ba(IO_3)_2$	25	–	8
$Ra(IO_3)_2$	$Ba(IO_3)_2$	1.42	–	9
$MgNH_4PO_4$	$MgNH_4AsO_4$	5.6	1–60	10

1. Kolthoff, I. M., and Yutzy, H. C., *J. Am. Chem. Soc.*, **59**, 916 (1937).
2. Kolthoff, I. M., and Eggertsen, F. T., *ibid.*, **61**, 1036 (1939).
3. Vaslow, F., and Boyd, G. E., *ibid.*, **74**, 4691 (1952).
4. Kolthoff and Eggertsen, *J. Phys. Chem.*, **46**, 616 (1942).
5. Kolthoff, I. M., and Noponen, G. E., *J. Am. Chem. Soc.*, **60**, 39 (1938).
6. Hahn, O., "Applied Radiochemistry," p. 88, Cornell University Press, Ithaca, N.Y., 1936.
7. Kolthoff and Noponen, *J. Am. Chem. Soc.*, **60**, 197 (1938).
8. Polessitsky, A., *Acta Physichochim. U.R.S.S.*, **8**, 864 (1938).
9. Polessitsky, A., and Karataewa, A., *ibid.*, **8**, 251 (1938).
10. Kolthoff, I. M., and Carr, C. W., *J. Phys. Chem.*, **47**, 148 (1943).

To express theoretically the relationships involved, we shall follow the simple treatment given by Flood[2] and by Flood and Bruun.[3] A more complete thermodynamic consideration of silver chloride–silver bromide equilibria has been presented by Vaslow and Boyd.[4]

Consider the equilibrium given by Eq. (10-6), which may first be considered from the viewpoint that the solid is impure silver bromide, with

[1] The values of $K(= 1/D)$ listed are taken in such a direction as to be greater than unity. We shall find it more convenient in writing Eqs. (10-7) to (10-12) and in Chap. 12 to define the distribution coefficients in such a way as to make D less than unity.

[2] Flood, H., *Z. anorg. u. allgem. Chem.*, **229**, 76 (1936).

[3] Flood, H., and Bruun, B., *Z. anorg. u. allgem. Chem.*, **229**, 85 (1936).

[4] Vaslow, F., and Boyd, G. E., *J. Am. Chem. Soc.*, **74**, 4691 (1952).

chloride as a foreign ion. Thus

$$\frac{a_{Ag^+}a_{Br^-}}{a_{AgBr}} = \mathbf{K}_{eq,1} \quad \text{or} \quad a_{Ag^+}a_{Br^-} = \mathbf{K}_{eq,1}a_{AgBr} \tag{10-8}$$

but, since in the limit this equation should hold for pure silver bromide ($a_{AgBr} = 1$), we see that $\mathbf{K}_{eq,1} = \mathbf{K}_{ap,AgBr}$. Similarly, considering the precipitate to be an impure silver chloride,

$$a_{Ag^+}a_{Cl^-} = \mathbf{K}_{eq,2}a_{AgCl} \tag{10-9}$$

where $\mathbf{K}_{eq,2} = \mathbf{K}_{ap,AgCl}$. Dividing Eq. (10-8) by (10-9) to eliminate the silver ion activity, we have

$$\frac{a_{Br^-}}{a_{Cl^-}} = \frac{\mathbf{K}_{ap,AgBr}}{\mathbf{K}_{ap,AgCl}} \frac{a_{AgBr}}{a_{AgCl}} \tag{10-10}$$

The activities of the solids may be replaced by mole fractions multiplied by activity coefficients:

$$\frac{a_{Br^-}}{a_{Cl^-}} = \frac{\mathbf{K}_{ap,AgBr}}{\mathbf{K}_{ap,AgCl}} \frac{N_{AgBr}}{N_{AgCl}} \frac{\gamma_{AgBr}}{\gamma_{AgCl}} \tag{10-11}$$

The activity ratio in solution may be replaced to a close approximation by the concentration ratio, because the activity coefficients of two ions of the same charge and similar size will be nearly equal.[1]

Thus, *for an ideal solid solution*, in which the activity coefficient ratio $\gamma_{AgBr}/\gamma_{AgCl}$ is unity, Eq. (10-11) may be replaced by

$$\frac{[Br^-]}{[Cl^-]} = \frac{\mathbf{K}_{ap,AgBr}}{\mathbf{K}_{ap,AgCl}} \frac{N_{AgBr}}{N_{AgCl}} \tag{10-12}$$

which is identical with the distribution-coefficient expression (10-7), provided that the distribution coefficient D is equal to the ratio of activity products.

Although the experimental distribution coefficients are sometimes of the same order of magnitude as the ratio of activity products, there is often a wide discrepancy; moreover, D usually varies with the composition of the solid phase, indicating a nonideal solid-solution behavior. Nevertheless, in the absence of experimental data, an expression similar to (10-12) serves as a useful guide in estimating the possible extent of coprecipitation due to solid solution formation.

Another important factor that governs the extent of contamination is the rate of attainment of solid solution equilibrium. Consider two extreme situations that might be encountered in the addition of silver

[1] For a discussion of activity effects in the liquid solution, see Ratner, A. P., *J. Chem. Phys.*, 1, 789 (1933).

nitrate to a mixture of bromide and chloride. At the one extreme, the precipitate could undergo recrystallization so rapidly that, as the solution composition changes during the titration, the precipitate is at all times homogeneous and in equilibrium with the particular composition at that instant. At the other extreme, it could be imagined that every infinitesimal increment of solid is in equilibrium with the composition at the instant of its formation and that it does not undergo recrystallization. The composition of the solid solution would be heterogeneous because of the continually changing solution composition. Clearly, the first bit of precipitate in this situation would be relatively pure silver bromide, because it came down from a solution rich in bromide. Therefore, the average composition of the heterogeneous precipitate would be purer in silver bromide than the homogeneous precipitate.

The quantitative relationships involved in the case of heterogeneous solid solution formation were considered by Doerner and Hoskins,[1] who derived the equilibrium expression.

For the case of silver bromide and chloride, the two extreme situations are represented by

$$\frac{[Br^-]_f}{[Cl^-]_f} = D\,\frac{N_{AgBr}}{N_{AgCl}} \qquad \text{homogeneous} \qquad (10\text{-}13)$$

$$\log\frac{[Br^-]_f}{[Br^-]_i} = \lambda\,\log\frac{[Cl^-]_f}{[Cl^-]_i} \qquad \text{heterogeneous} \qquad (10\text{-}14)$$

where the subscripts f and i refer to final and initial concentrations in solution. The coefficient λ is identical with D; the different symbols are commonly used in order to distinguish between the two extreme types of equilibrium.

In Table 10-2 are shown the experimental results for precipitation of bromide from equimolar mixtures of bromide and chloride determined by Kolthoff and Eggertsen and compared with the values calculated assuming homogeneous and heterogeneous solid solutions. It is evident that, in the absence of aluminum, when the precipitate remained colloidally dispersed, homogeneous distribution equilibrium was reached, whereas, in the presence of aluminum ions added as a coagulant, the theoretical heterogeneous composition was approached. Actually this limit could never be reached because finite rather than infinitesimal increments of precipitate are involved. Recrystallization (aging) of the precipitate also prevents its isolation from the solution. It is interesting that, when the precipitation was carried out in the presence of a dye that inhibited aging, the coprecipitation of chloride was more pronounced, because local excesses of silver carried down chloride, which was trapped because dye adsorption inhibited recrystallization.

[1] Doerner, H. A., and Hoskins, W. M., *J. Am. Chem. Soc.*, **47,** 662 (1925).

TABLE 10-2. EFFECT OF SOLID SOLUTION FORMATION ON PRECIPITATION OF BROMIDE FROM EQUIMOLAR BROMIDE-CHLORIDE SOLUTION

Ag^+ added, %*	Bromide left in solution, %			
	Calc†	Calc‡	Found, no Al^{3+}	Found, Al^{3+} present§
98	5.90	–	5.82	–
99	5.33	1.99	5.30	–
100	4.80	1.13	4.81	2.18
101	4.33	0.39	4.26	1.52
102	3.90	0.03	3.87	1.19

[With permission from Kolthoff, I. M., and Eggertsen, F. T., *J. Am. Chem. Soc.*, **61**, 1036 (1939). For calculated quantities, compare Kolthoff, I. M., and Stenger, V. A., "Volumetric Analysis," 2d ed., vol. I, p. 203, Interscience Publishers, Inc., New York, 1942.]

* Based on bromide equivalence point.
† From homogeneous distribution, $D = 393$.
‡ From heterogeneous distribution, $\lambda = 393$.
§ In 3 min, 40 sec.

TABLE 10-3. DEPENDENCE OF COPRECIPITATION OF LEAD ON DIRECTION OF MIXING BARIUM AND SULFATE

Time, hr	Pb coprecipitated, %	
	Addition of sulfate	Addition of barium
0	4.82	31.7
1	4.96	30.0
24	5.52	29.5

In contrast with this rapid attainment of equilibrium, Kolthoff and Noponen[1] found a slow equilibrium between solid solutions of barium and lead sulfates and the aqueous solution. Therefore, the amount of contamination depended greatly on the order of mixing of the reagents if the mixing was slow (Table 10-3). Two modes of precipitation were compared: (1) addition of sulfate to an equimolar mixture of barium and lead ions (in the presence of acetate to increase the solubility of lead sulfate), (2) addition of barium to a mixture of lead and sulfate in the presence of acetate. With method (1) the concentration of barium in solution is relatively high and the coprecipitation is relatively low; with method (2) the ratio of barium to lead in solution is low. Apparently,

[1] Kolthoff, I. M., and Noponen, G. E., *J. Am. Chem. Soc.*, **60**, 508 (1938).

the two precipitates were approaching the same composition very slowly from either side.

Hahn[1] has discussed numerous examples of slow solid-solution equilibrium in connection with the separation of barium and radium by fractional crystallization.

Other examples of solid solution formation of analytical interest are $MgNH_4PO_4$ and $MgKPO_4$; $MnNH_4PO_4$ and $ZnNH_4PO_4$; $ZnHg(SCN)_4$ and $CuHg(SCN)_4$; HgS and ZnS, MnS, CdS, or PbS; $BaSO_4$ and $SrSO_4$; etc.

Another type of solid solution formation is encountered when two ions as a pair can replace two other ions in a crystal lattice. Grimm[2] pointed out that such a twofold replacement can occur if the two salts have the same type of chemical structure and crystallize in the same type of crystal with lattice dimensions not too dissimilar. A good example is barium sulfate, which can form solid solutions with potassium permanganate. X-ray diffraction has revealed that solid solution formation actually occurs.[3] It has also been shown that solid solution equilibrium can be reached from both directions.[4] Other examples of ion pair replacements are $BaSeO_4 + KMnO_4$, $BaCrO_4 + KMnO_4$, and $BaSO_4 + KBF_4$.

Some controversy has arisen in the interpretation of the coprecipitation of rare earths when precipitated as the oxalates. Weaver[5] at first interpreted his data on fractional separation of rare earth oxalates in terms of a homogeneous distribution coefficient D and, later, after criticism by Salutsky and Gordon,[6] recalculated his data, to find that a heterogeneous distribution coefficient λ was more nearly independent of composition. More recently, Feibush, Rowley, and Gordon[7] compared the values of λ for various rare earth oxalate pairs with the value calculated from solubility products by an equation analogous to Eq. (10-12). Once again λ turns out to be more nearly independent of composition than D, but the experimental values of λ do not agree with the ratios of the square roots of solubility products that would be expected to hold.[8] There is also some evidence[9] that the value of λ depends on the rate of precipitation. Feibush, Rowley, and Gordon conclude that λ may be determined by a ratio of *rate* rather than *equilibrium* constants for the rare earth oxalates.

---

[1] Hahn, "Applied Radiochemistry."

[2] Grimm, H. G., and Wagner, G., *Z. physik. Chem. Leipzig*, **132**, 131 (1928).

[3] Wagner, *Z. physik. Chem. Leipzig*, **B2**, 27 (1929).

[4] Kolthoff and Noponen, *J. Phys. Chem.*, **42**, 237 (1938).

[5] Weaver, B., *Anal. Chem.*, **26**, 479 (1954); **28**, 138 (1956).

[6] Salutsky, M. L., and Gordon, L., *Anal. Chem.*, **28**, 138 (1956).

[7] Feibush, A. M., Rowley, K., and Gordon, L., *Anal. Chem.*, **30**, 1605 (1958).

[8] The derivation of this relationship is left as an exercise for the student.

[9] Hermann, J. A., Ph.D. thesis, University of New Mexico, Albuquerque, 1955.

Walden *et al.*[1-3] have made the interesting observation that barium sulfate forms solid solutions with a surprising variety of substances, such as barium nitrate,[4] ammonium, sodium, and potassium bisulfates,[1] lithium bisulfate, lithium sulfate dihydrate,[4] H_3OMnO_4, and water.[2]   In the case of the alkali metal bisulfate, the addition of a proton relieves the charge discrepancy between barium and alkali metal ions, thus permitting an ion-pair substitution.   Hydronium permanganate is another example.   A group of three water molecules apparently replaces a barium sulfate ion pair in the lattice.

In conclusion, it may be stated that solid solution formation represents an exceptionally troublesome situation, because substantial contamination may be present even at equilibrium.   Aging can only help to reach homogeneous equilibrium; whether the state of purity is better or worse after aging depends on the direction from which equilibrium is approached.

10-3. Ion Entrapment

Kolthoff[5] proposed the concept that foreign ion entrapment, involving the growth of precipitate around adsorbed ions, is an important source of contamination, particularly of crystalline precipitates such as barium sulfate, calcium oxalate, and the like.   It is important to this concept that such ion entrapment is not an equilibrium process and that recrystallization during aging should effect a purification.   The foreign ions represent *lattice imperfections* unless they are actually held in solid solution. Whether solid solution formation is involved or not, the order of mixing of the reagents will be an important factor in determining the nature and extent of contamination.

If a barium ion solution is added slowly to a slightly acidified solution of sulfate, the precipitate is formed in the presence of an excess of sulfate, and cation occlusion would be expected to predominate.   On the other hand, if the sulfate is added to the barium ion solution, anion occlusion should predominate.

The effect of the order of mixing on anion occlusion is illustrated by the data of Weiser and Sherrick,[6] who found that the occlusion of chloride was decreased from 15.8 to 1.25 milliequivalents per mole of barium sulfate by adding barium to sulfate rather than the reverse.   Nitrate and chlorate are much more seriously coprecipitated than is chloride,

[1] Walton and Walden, *J. Am. Chem. Soc.*, **68**, 1742 (1946).
[2] Walton and Walden, *J. Am. Chem. Soc.*, **68**, 1750 (1946).
[3] Walden and Cohen, *op. cit.*
[4] *Ibid.*
[5] Kolthoff, *J. Phys. Chem.*, **36**, 860 (1932).
[6] Weiser, H. B., and Sherrick, J. L., *J. Phys. Chem.*, **23**, 205 (1919).

and should be destroyed by evaporation with concentrated hydrochloric acid.

Cation occlusion can be decreased by reverse precipitation, i.e., by adding the sulfate to the acidified barium chloride solution,[1] thereby increasing the occlusion of barium chloride. The occluded barium chloride tends to compensate for the negative error in the sulfate determination caused by occlusion of alkali metal (lower equivalent weight of alkali metal than barium). Occlusion of sulfuric acid, or bisulfate, causes low results which are accentuated by volatilization.

Careful studies of the contamination of barium sulfate brought down from sulfuric acid and barium chloride have been made by Richards and Parker.[2] The coprecipitation of alkali metals and heavy metals has been studied by Allen and Johnston[3] and Johnston and Adams.[4] It may be concluded that under no conditions is the precipitate free of contamination and that, on the contrary, both anion and cation occlusion usually occur. A compensation of errors may yield deceptively accurate-looking results.

Rieman and Hagen[5] made a comparison of various methods of precipitating barium sulfate and concluded that the method of Hintz and Weber,[6] involving the rapid addition of barium chloride to the sulfate solution, gave the best results for sulfate, particularly in the presence of sodium chloride. Kolthoff and Sandell[7] believe that the good results obtained by this method may be due to a compensation of errors, but they recommend this procedure for the determination of sulfur in a soluble sulfate. Voth[8] has recently found by spectrographic analysis that the amount of sodium coprecipitation can be halved by sudden addition of barium chloride. Contrary to the findings of Johnston and Adams,[9] the presence of high concentrations of sodium chloride was found to increase relatively slightly its coprecipitation. Variation of pH over the range 2 to 6 caused no significant change in sodium coprecipitation.

Another precipitate showing pronounced tendency toward foreign ion entrapment is calcium oxalate monohydrate.[10] The occlusion of sodium oxalate was found to be more pronounced than that of potassium oxalate

[1] Popoff, S., and Neuman, E. W., Ind. Eng. Chem., Anal. Ed., 2, 45 (1930).

[2] Richards, T. W., and Parker, H. G., Z. anorg. Chem., 8, 413, 419, 420, 421 (1895).

[3] Allen, E. T., and Johnston, J., J. Am. Chem. Soc., 32, 588 (1910).

[4] Johnston, J., and Adams, L. H., J. Am. Chem. Soc., 33, 829, (1911).

[5] Riemann, W., III, and Hagen, G., Ind. Eng. Chem., Anal. Ed., 14, 450 (1942).

[6] Hintz, E., and Weber, H., Z. anal. Chem., 45, 31 (1906).

[7] Kolthoff, I. M., and Sandell, E. B., "Textbook of Quantitative Inorganic Analysis," 3d ed., p. 329, The Macmillan Company, New York, 1952.

[8] Voth, J. L., Anal. Chem., 31, 1094 (1959).

[9] Johnston and Adams, loc. cit.

[10] Kolthoff and Sandell, J. Phys. Chem., 37, 443, 459 (1933).

but about equal to that of ammonium oxalate, in correspondence with the adsorbabilities of these compounds on calcium oxalate. As expected, the amount of occlusion of alkali metals was greater when an excess of oxalate was present during precipitation. The results given in Table 10-4 were obtained in precipitations at room temperature and at 100°C. The coprecipitation of chloride, bromide, and iodide with calcium oxalate was found to be very small, as expected from the high solubilities of the calcium halides.

The amount of occlusion generally increases with the speed of formation of a precipitate. The rapidly formed crystals produced from relatively concentrated solutions are generally less pure, but the rate of aging of the highly imperfect crystals is greater than that of more perfect crystals. For this reason, some procedures call for rapid precipitation at room temperature followed by high-temperature aging.

TABLE 10-4. COPRECIPITATION WITH CALCIUM OXALATE

	Millimoles contaminant per mole of calcium oxalate			
Contaminant	Room temperature		100°C	
	Ca^{++} excess	Oxalate excess	Ca^{++} excess	Oxalate excess
$Na_2C_2O_4$	26	20	5.4	9.3
$K_2C_2O_4$	17	12	0.74	1.05
$(NH_4)_2C_2O_4$	6.4	9.3	0.93	1.2
$Ca(IO_3)_2$	2.5	1.6	6.4	4.1
$CaSO_4$	7.8	4.1	19.8	8.0

[Adapted from Kolthoff, I. M., and Sandell, E. B., *J. Phys. Chem.*, **37**, 443 (1933).]

One instance in which this procedure is especially successful is in the precipitation of calcium oxalate.[1] The best results were obtained by forming relatively small crystals by room-temperature precipitation, followed by digestion at a higher temperature. The success of this procedure is no doubt enhanced by the transformation of hydrates during aging (page 163), but small particles precipitated at 100°C also proved to undergo more effective purification upon aging than larger particles formed by slow precipitation.

10-4. Postprecipitation

The phenomenon of postprecipitation has been reviewed by Kolthoff and Moltzau.[2]

[1] *Ibid.*

[2] Kolthoff, I. M., and Moltzau, R., *Chem. Revs.*, **17**, 293 (1935).

In the separation of calcium from magnesium by the oxalate method, the solubility of magnesium oxalate may be exceeded. However, magnesium oxalate has a pronounced tendency to form supersaturated solutions[1,2] and slowly postprecipitates upon calcium oxalate. The solubility of $MgC_2O_4 \cdot 2H_2O$ at 22°C is only 0.036 g per 100 ml of solution,[3] but increases due to complex formation with oxalate to 0.187 g per 100 ml in the presence of 4 g ammonium oxalate monohydrate per 100 ml. The postprecipitation of magnesium is prevented by a sufficiently large excess of ammonium oxalate, but, because of the inconvenience of destroying large amounts of oxalate, an excessive amount should be avoided if magnesium is to be determined in the filtrate.

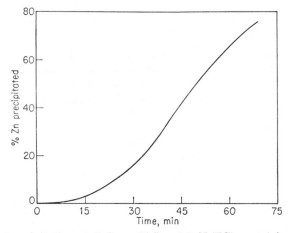

Fig. 10-3. Postprecipitation of ZnS on Bi_2S_3. 0.2 N HCl containing tartaric acid. [From Kolthoff, I. M., and Griffith, F. S., J. Phys. Chem., **42**, 531 (1938).]

Especially pronounced postprecipitation has been observed in the separation of metals by sulfide precipitation. Zinc sulfide, for example, which belongs in the ammonium sulfide group in qualitative analysis, has a pronounced tendency to postprecipitate on the sulfides of the hydrogen sulfide group. In dilute mineral acids (0.1 to 0.3 N), zinc sulfide is actually insoluble, but will remain indefinitely in supersaturated solution unless nuclei are present for crystallization,[4] evidently because of the very low concentration of sulfide and even of bisulfide ion present in acidic solution. Crystals of another sulfide, such as copper or bismuth sulfide, induce the postprecipitation of zinc sulfide,[5] because hydrogen

[1] Fischer, W., Z. anorg. u. allgem. Chem., **153**, 62 (1926).

[2] Holth, T., Anal. Chem. **21**, 1221 (1949).

[3] Kolthoff and Sandell, "Textbook of Quantitative Inorganic Analysis," p. 347, Macmillan, 1952.

[4] Kolthoff, I. M., and Pearson, E. A., J. Phys. Chem., **36**, 549 (1932).

[5] Kolthoff, I. M., and Griffith, F. S., J. Phys. Chem., **42**, 531 (1938)

sulfide is adsorbed in a more ionic form than usual owing to the strong attraction of the metal sulfide lattice for sulfide ions.   The postprecipitation begins slowly on copper(II) or bismuth(III) sulfides (Fig. 10-3), evidently because these sulfides are not efficient crystallization surfaces. On the other hand, on mercury(II) sulfide[1] (Fig. 10-4), which is isomorphous with zinc sulfide, no induction period exists, and the postprecipitation curves begin steeply from the origin.   That no coprecipitation is taking place is shown by the fact that, if not quite all of the mercury is

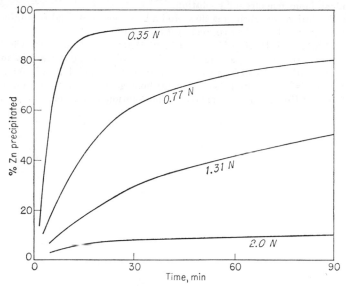

Fig. 10-4. Postprecipitation of ZnS on HgS.   Normality of H_2SO_4 given on curves. [*From Kolthoff, I. M., and Moltzau, R. J., Phys. Chem.,* **40,** 779 (1936).]

precipitated, the mercuric sulfide contains no appreciable zinc.   Nevertheless, the postprecipitated zinc sulfide appears to enter solid solution with the mercury(II) sulfide, as evidenced by the fact that it could not be extracted completely by continuous extraction with 3 N hydrochloric acid, whereas the zinc sulfide was extracted readily from bismuth(III) sulfide or copper(II) sulfide.

PROBLEMS

10-1. If $BaCO_3$ $(K_{sp} = 8 \times 10^{-9})$ and $SrCO_3$ $(K_{sp} = 2 \times 10^{-9})$ form an ideal, homogeneous solid solution, what is the theoretical mole fraction of $BaCO_3$ in the precipitate if half the Sr^{++} is precipitated from a solution initially equimolar in Ba^{++} and Sr^{++}?   *Ans.* 0.286.

10-2. Use the distribution coefficient given in Table 10-1 for the system $MgNH_4PO_4$, $MgNH_4AsO_4$ to answer the following:

a. Which of the two *pure* solids is more soluble?

[1] Kolthoff and Moltzau, *J. Phys. Chem.*, **40,** 779 (1936).

  b. If a liter of 10^{-7} M arsenate is treated with phosphate to bring its concentration to 0.1 M and if 99.9 per cent of the phosphate is then precipitated as $MgNH_4PO_4 \cdot 6H_2O$, what percentage of the arsenate remains in solution?   *Ans.* 0.56 per cent.

  10-3. The solubility products of calcium oxalate and strontium oxalate are, respectively, 1.8×10^{-9} and 5.4×10^{-8}. A liter of solution containing 0.1 mole of Ca^{++} and 10^{-6} mole of Sr^{++} is treated with 0.11 mole of oxalate ion.

  a. Calculate the concentrations of Ca^{++} and Sr^{++} remaining in solution, assuming no interaction between solid calcium and strontium oxalates and no coprecipitation by ion entrapment.

  b. Calculate the concentration of Sr^{++} remaining if calcium and strontium oxalates form an ideal, homogeneous solid solution.

  c. If solid solution equilibrium is slow, and a heterogeneous solid is obtained, which order of mixing would give less coprecipitation of Sr^{++}?

  Ans. (a) 1.8×10^{-7} M, 10^{-6} M; (b) 5.4×10^{-11} M; (c) add oxalate to $Ca^{++} + Sr^{++}$.

  10-4. A liter of solution containing 10^{-6} mole of chromate and 0.2 mole of molybdate is treated with sufficient lead ions to precipitate half the molybdate.   What fraction of the chromate is precipitated, assuming (a) homogeneous solid solution formation, and (b) Doerner-Hoskins heterogeneous solid solution formation.   *Ans.* (a) 0.004; (b) $1 - 10^{-63}$.

11. Thermal Decomposition and Volatilization

It is our purpose in this chapter to consider the principles involved in several types of analytical operations involving the separation of a gas from a solid or, less often, from a liquid sample. Distillation methods are treated not here but in Chap. 25, under Multistage Separation Techniques, because a single separation stage is seldom useful for quantitative purposes. Combustion analysis methods, such as those commonly carried out in elementary analysis of organic compounds, are arbitrarily omitted here in spite of their practical importance, because of limitations of space. Many modifications of reaction conditions, combustion catalysts, and apparatus have been made to suit the requirements of particular classes of organic compounds. For such details the reader is referred to the excellent monographs that are available.[1,2] Special mention should be made, however, of the oxyhydrogen flame combustion technique introduced by Wickbold[3] for quantitative conversion of organic halogen compounds to hydrogen halides, which are absorbed in NaOH. Sweetser[4] has applied this technique to various organic fluorine compounds.

We are here concerned principally with methods that involve a chemical change, e.g., a thermal decomposition or dehydration reaction or a reaction between the sample and a carrier gas that sweeps the gaseous product from the sample. Indirect determination can be based upon the change in weight, or direct determination of the gaseous product can be

[1] Niederl, J. B., and Niederl, V., "Micromethods of Quantitative Organic Analysis," 2d ed., John Wiley & Sons, Inc., New York, 1942.

[2] Grant, J., "Quantitative Organic Microanalysis Based on the Methods of Fritz Pregl," 5th English ed., J. and A. Churchill, London, 1951.

[3] Wickbold, R., *Angew. Chem.*, **64**, 133 (1952); **66**, 173 (1954).

[4] Sweetser, P. B., *Anal. Chem.*, **28**, 1766 (1956).

carried out by measurement of its volume or weight, by titration, or by instrumental means.

In dealing with thermal decomposition and volatilization reactions it is necessary to consider not only the equilibria involved in reversible reactions but also the rates of both reversible and irreversible reactions. From thermodynamic data it is often possible to deduce rather accurately the effects of conditions such as temperature and pressure on the equilibrium behavior. The kinetic aspects, however, are much more difficult to predict, and it is in general necessary to determine by experiment the experimental conditions for carrying out the desired reaction.

11-1. Thermodynamic Relationships

The effect of temperature on chemical equilibria is expressed by the familiar thermodynamic equations:

$$\Delta F^\circ = \Delta H^\circ - T \Delta S^\circ = -RT \ln \mathbf{K}_p \tag{11-1}$$

$$\frac{d \ln \mathbf{K}_p}{dT} = \frac{\Delta H^\circ}{RT^2} \tag{11-2}$$

$$\left(\frac{\partial \Delta F^\circ}{\partial T}\right)_p = -\Delta S^\circ \tag{11-3}$$

where ΔF° = standard free energy change
ΔH° = standard enthalpy change
ΔS° = standard entropy change
$\mathbf{K}_p$ = equilibrium constant expressed in terms of pressure
R = gas constant
T = absolute temperature

To carry out accurate calculations of $\mathbf{K}_p$ or ΔF° as a function of temperature, it is necessary to consider the variation of ΔH° and of ΔS° and, therefore, of the temperature coefficients given by Eqs. (11-2) and (11-3), with changes in temperature. To do this, it is necessary first to consider the heat of formation ΔH_T° of each substance at the desired temperature T; this is done by carrying out the integration

$$\Delta H_T^\circ = \Delta H_{298}^\circ + \int_{298}^{T} \Delta C_p \, dT$$

where ΔC_p is the difference in heat capacities between the substance and its constituent elements. Similarly, the entropy of each substance is determined by means of the equation

$$S_T^\circ = S_{298}^\circ + \int_{298}^{T} \frac{\Delta C_p}{T} \, dT$$

The integrations can be carried out graphically or else by expressing ΔC_p

as a polynomial function of temperature and integrating the polynomial.[1] From the values of ΔH_T° and ΔS_T° for the reaction, the values of ΔF° and $\mathbf{K}_p$ can then be calculated by Eq. (11-1).

However, as a first approximation, it often suffices to assume that ΔH° and ΔS° for the *reaction* are independent of the temperature, even though the heats and entropies of formation of the individual reactants vary with temperature. This amounts to setting equal to zero the temperature coefficients $(\partial \Delta H^\circ / \partial T)_p = \Delta C_p$ and $(\partial \Delta S^\circ / \partial T)_p = \Delta C_p / T$, where ΔC_p is the difference in heat capacities between products and reactants, averaged over the desired temperature interval.[2]

Thus we use the values of ΔH° and ΔS° at 25°C, and we write

$$\ln \mathbf{K}_p = \frac{-\Delta H^\circ}{RT} + \frac{\Delta S^\circ}{R} \tag{11-4}$$

which shows that, if the variations of ΔH° and ΔS° with temperature are neglected, the logarithm of the equilibrium constant is a linear function of the reciprocal of the absolute temperature. From the slope and intercept, the values of ΔH° and ΔS° can be calculated.

Example 11-1. Trautzl and Treadwell[3] investigated the selective oxidation of tin from copper-tin alloys by means of a stream of dry hydrogen chloride. They determined the equilibrium constants $\mathbf{K}_p = p_{H_2}/p_{HCl}^2$ for the reactions:

$$2Cu + 2HCl(gas) \rightleftharpoons 2CuCl + H_2 \tag{11-5}$$
$$Sn + 2HCl \rightleftharpoons SnCl_2 + H_2 \tag{11-6}$$

and expressed them in the form of the equation

$$\log \mathbf{K}_p = \frac{A}{T} + B \tag{11-7}$$

where A and B are constants.

The constant A was evaluated at 3,489 and 7,359 and the constant B at -4.74 and -7.60 for reactions (11-5) and (11-6), respectively. From the values of A and B, we calculate $\Delta H^\circ = -2.3RA = -16.0$ and -33.6 kcal; $\Delta S^\circ = 2.3RB = -21.6$ and -34.8 cal mole^{-1} deg^{-1}; $\Delta F^\circ = -2.3RT \log \mathbf{K}_p = -9.5$ and -23.3 kcal at 25°C and $\Delta F^\circ = -1.38$ and -10.3 kcal at 400°C for reaction (11-5) and reaction (11-6), respectively.

The empirical equation (11-7) is plotted in Fig. 11-1 for both reactions. The plots represent extrapolation to room temperature of data obtained in the temperature

[1] Lewis, G. N., and Randall, M., "Thermodynamics and the Free Energy of Chemical Substances," McGraw-Hill Book Company, Inc., New York, 1923.

[2] For an interesting comparison of calculations carried out neglecting and considering specific-heat corrections, see Rutgers, A. J., "Physical Chemistry," p. 324, Interscience Publishers, Inc., New York, 1954. For the following reactions the exact values of $\log \mathbf{K}_p$ at 3,000°C are given, followed by the approximate values (shown in parentheses): $C + O_2 \rightleftharpoons CO_2$, 6.84 (6.8); $2C + O_2 \rightleftharpoons 2CO$, 12.90 (13.0); $C + CO_2 \rightleftharpoons 2CO$, 6.06 (6.1).

[3] Trautzl, P., and Treadwell, W. D., *Helv. Chim. Acta*, **34**, 1723 (1951).

range 360 to 665°C for copper and 210 to 605°C for tin. The reaction rates at room temperature are too slow to attain equilibrium in a flowing system. It is evident that a greater selectivity of reaction exists at *low* temperatures than at high temperatures. However, it is desired to vaporize the stannous chloride formed in reaction (11-6),

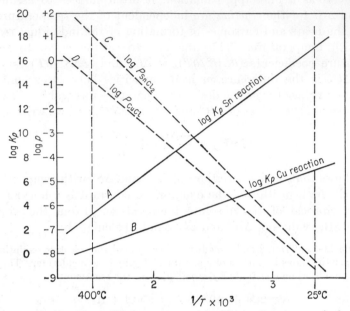

Fig. 11-1. Variation of equilibrium constants with temperature. A, log $\mathbf{K}_p$ for $Sn + 2HCl \rightleftharpoons SnCl_2 + H_2$; B, log $\mathbf{K}_p$ for $2Cu + 2HCl \rightleftharpoons 2CuCl + H_2$; C, log vapor pressure $SnCl_2$ (mm Hg); D, log vapor pressure CuCl (mm Hg). [*Trautzl, P., and Treadwell, W. D., Helv. Chim. Acta*, **34**, 1723 (1951).]

and, it is necessary, therefore, to consider the vapor pressures of the salts that are given by equations of the form

$$\log p = \frac{C}{T} + D \qquad (11\text{-}8)$$

where p is measured in millimeters of mercury and where C has the values $-4,220$ and $-4,490$ and D the values 5.45 and 7.73, respectively, for CuCl and $SnCl_2$.

From Fig. 11-1, it appears that greater selectivity with respect to vaporization exists at *high* temperatures. A high temperature is, of course, also favorable with respect to the rate of the desired reaction. Trautzl and Treadwell chose a temperature of 400°C and showed that $SnCl_2$ could be vaporized quantitatively from copper-tin alloys containing 8.8 to 47.6 per cent tin, leaving essentially pure copper as the residue.

For a decomposition reaction of the type

$$M(\text{liquid or solid}) \rightleftharpoons N(\text{liquid or solid}) + Q(\text{gas}) \qquad (11\text{-}9)$$

the standard entropy change $\Delta S°$ is a relatively large positive quantity, because the standard entropy values of gases are, in general, much larger than those of liquids or solids (see Table 11-1).[1]   Therefore, the standard negative free energy change $-\Delta F°$ increases with rising temperature [Eq. (11-3)].   Equation (11-4) contains two terms on the right-hand side. The first, or enthalpy term, becomes increasingly important at low temperatures, whereas the second, or entropy term, is practically independent

TABLE 11-1. THERMODYNAMIC CONSTANTS AT 25°C

Substance	$H°$, kcal	$F°$, kcal	$S°$, cal mole^{-1} deg^{-1}
H_2	0.0	0.0	31.211
H_2O (liquid)	-68.317	-56.690	16.716
H_2O (gas)	-57.798	-54.635	45.106
CO_2	-94.052	-94.260	51.061
HCl (gas)	-22.063	-22.769	44.617
BaO	-133.4	-126.3	16.8
$BaCO_3$	-291.3	-272.2	26.8
CaO	-151.9	-144.4	9.5
$CaCO_3$	-288.5	-269.5	21.2
$CaCl_2$	-190.0	-179.3	27.2
SiO_2	-205.4	-192.4	10.00
$CaSiO_3$	-378.6	-358.2	19.6

[With permission from Latimer, W. M., "The Oxidation States of the Elements and Their Potentials in Aqueous Solutions," 2d ed., Prentice-Hall, Inc., Englewood Cliffs, N.J., 1952.   The values are Bureau of Standards data.]

of temperature and, therefore, increases in relative importance at higher temperatures.   For reactions such as (11-9), with positive $\Delta S°$, the reaction must become spontaneous at sufficiently high temperatures regardless of $\Delta H°$ unless vaporization of the other reactants intervenes; so there is no longer a net formation of gaseous products.   Of course, some other reaction may also intervene.

Example 11-2.   The following thermodynamic data are given for the dissociation of calcium carbonate at 25°C: $\Delta H° = 42.5$ kcal; $\Delta F° = 31.1$ kcal; $\Delta S° = 38.4$ cal mole^{-1} deg^{-1}.   Estimate the temperature at which the dissociation pressure is 1 atm, ignoring the heat capacity correction.

Answer.   From Eq. (11-1), $\ln K_p = 0$ when $\Delta H° = T \Delta S°$; $T = 1,108°K$ or 835°C. The actual temperature for $\ln K_p = 0$ is 882°C; the deviation of the estimated value was caused by assuming $\Delta H°$ and $\Delta S°$ to be independent of temperature.

[1] According to Trouton's rule, the entropy of vaporization for an unassociated liquid is 21.5 cal mol^{-1} deg^{-1} at the normal boiling point.   For excellent discussions of the entropy of gases, see Giaque, W. F., *J. Am. Chem. Soc.*, **52**, 4808 (1930), and Eastman, E. D., *Chem. Revs.*, **18**, 257 (1936).

11-2. The Phase Rule

The phase rule of Gibbs is often a useful guide to the understanding of heterogeneous equilibria. The phase rule is

$$F = C - P + 2 \tag{11-10}$$

where F = number of degrees of freedom, i.e., number of intensive variables that are *independently* variable. The intensive variables include temperature, pressure, and as many variables as are necessary to define the compositions of the phases at equilibrium.

C = number of components, i.e., the minimum number of substances that must be specified to characterize the system. The number of components is given by the number of substances present minus the number of chemical reactions involved.

P = number of phases

In the system represented by Eq. (11-9) there are two components. If M and N form two phases (either pure substances or solutions), $P = 3$ and $F = 2 - 3 + 2 = 1$. The single degree of freedom corresponds to either the temperature or the pressure, one of which can be varied independently, the other being a dependent variable. On the other hand, if M and N interact to form a single phase, $P = 2$ and

$$F = 2 - 2 + 2 = 2$$

Of the three variables: temperature, pressure, and composition, two are independently variable.

It is interesting to contrast the reactions

$$CaCO_3 \rightleftharpoons CaO + CO_2 \tag{11-11}$$

and
$$6Fe_2O_3 \rightleftharpoons 4Fe_3O_4 + O_2 \tag{11-12}$$

which are discussed in more detail below. In (11-11), the two solids do not interact, so only a single degree of freedom (either temperature or pressure) exists. In (11-12), the solids interact to form a solid solution, so the equilibrium pressure is a function not only of temperature but also of composition.

Suppose we consider the possibility of the coexistence of two equilibria of the type (11-9) with a common gas phase, for example, the dissociation of $CaCO_3$ and $BaCO_3$. From the phase rule, if both equilibria exist and if the solids do not interact, $C = 3$, $P = 5$, and $F = 3 - 5 + 2 = 0$. The invariant system would correspond to the specific temperature at which the dissociation pressures are equal, or

$$\Delta H_1^\circ - T \, \Delta S_1^\circ = \Delta H_2^\circ - T \, \Delta S_2^\circ$$

Example 11-3.   Given that the values of $\Delta H°$ are 63.9 and 42.5 kcal at 25°C for the dissociation reactions of $BaCO_3$ and $CaCO_3$, respectively.   For the same reactions the values of $\Delta S°$ are 41.1 and 38.4 cal mole^{-1} deg^{-1}.   If the temperature dependences of $\Delta H°$ and $\Delta S°$ are neglected, the invariant temperature T_i can be estimated roughly from the room-temperature values of $\Delta H°$ and $\Delta S°$, using the equation

$$T_i = \frac{\Delta H_1° - \Delta H_2°}{\Delta S_1° - \Delta S_2°}$$

We estimate $T_i = 21.4/0.0027 = 7{,}930°K$.   This temperature has no quantitative significance because of the crudeness of our simplifying assumption, but the mere fact that it is very high indicates that the two equilibria cannot actually coexist under ordinary experimental conditions.   The dissociation of $BaCO_3$ can, therefore, be completely prevented by keeping the pressure of CO_2 below the equilibrium pressure for the dissociation of $BaCO_3$ (assuming that none of the solids interact).

11-3. Vapor Pressure of Hydrates

The hydrate system

$$M{\cdot}xH_2O \rightleftharpoons M{\cdot}yH_2O + (x - y)H_2O(\text{gas}) \qquad (11\text{-}13)$$

corresponds to a two-component, three-phase system, that has a single degree of freedom.   Therefore at a particular temperature, the equilibrium vapor pressure is independent of the relative amounts of the two hydrates.

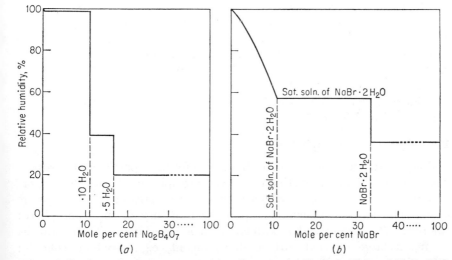

Fig. 11-2. Isothermal pressure: composition diagrams for $Na_2B_4O_7$-H_2O and $NaBr$-H_2O systems.   (a) $Na_2B_4O_7$; (b) $NaBr$.

In Fig. 11-2 the vapor pressure–composition diagrams are plotted for the systems $Na_2B_4O_7$-H_2O and $NaBr$-H_2O at 25°C.   The vapor pressure is plotted in terms of relative humidity.   Suppose that a very dilute solution of each salt is evaporated isothermally, for example, by drawing dry air through it at room temperature. The vapor pressure gradually decreases as the solution concentration increases, until a saturated solution of the salt is formed. When the solid phase appears, it follows from the phase rule that the vapor pressure must remain invariant as long as any liquid phase remains. The vapor pressure of the saturated solution is determined largely by the solubility of the solid that forms; in the above example it corresponds to 99 and 57 per cent relative humidity for borax and sodium bromide, respectively. If a salt is exposed to an atmosphere of relative humidity greater than that corresponding to its saturated solution, the system cannot reach equilibrium until an unsaturated solution is formed, and the salt is, therefore, deliquescent under these conditions.

Now, if the evaporation process is continued beyond the point at which the liquid phase has disappeared, the hydrate loses water, and the pressure must remain invariant as long as two solids remain. For example, the equilibrium vapor pressure for the reaction

$$Na_2B_4O_7 \cdot 10H_2O \rightleftharpoons Na_2B_4O_7 \cdot 5H_2O + 5H_2O \qquad (11\text{-}14)$$

corresponds to 39 per cent relative humidity. Therefore, the decahydrate is stable over the relative humidity range 39 to 99 per cent. If the surrounding atmosphere has a relative humidity less than 39 per cent, the decahydrate is efflorescent. This property of borax represents the main disadvantage to its use as a primary standard for acidimetry (Sec. 5-2). Figure 11-2 also illustrates the use of a hygrostat[1] in the form of a desiccator containing a saturated solution of $NaBr \cdot 2H_2O$, which automatically maintains a relative humidity of 57 per cent, nicely in the range of stability of $Na_2B_4O_7 \cdot 10H_2O$. A solution saturated with both sodium chloride and sucrose, which maintains a relative humidity of 70 per cent, is preferred by Menzel.[2]

11-4. Ignition of Precipitates

Precipitates may contain water in several forms,[3] apart from the superficially adherent water clinging to a moist precipitate: (1) *adsorbed* water, or water of hygroscopicity, which is present to a greater or lesser extent on all solid surfaces depending upon the humidity of the atmosphere; (2) *imbibed* water, or *sorbed* water, which is associated with substances having a large internal surface development, e.g., lyophilic colloids; (3) *occluded* water, present in solid solution or as cavities within crystals;

[1] Kolthoff, I. M., and Sandell, E. B., "Textbook of Quantitative Inorganic Analysis," 3d ed., chap. 9, The Macmillan Company, New York, 1952.

[2] Menzel, H., Z. anorg. u. allgem. Chem., **224**, 1 (1935).

[3] Koltzoff and Sandell, op. cit.

(4) *essential* water, present either as water of hydration (molecular water) or as water of constitution. In the last case, water molecules are not present as such but are formed when the solid is heated. The behavior of these various forms of water will be illustrated by examples important in gravimetric analysis.

In addition to the evolution of water, ignition of precipitates often involves thermal decomposition reactions involving the dissociation of salts into acidic and basic components. As common examples we may cite the decomposition of carbonates or sulfates to give a basic oxide and an acidic oxide. Knowing that the decomposition temperature must be related to the acidic and basic properties of the oxides thus produced, we can predict some important trends in the stabilities of related compounds. Thus, since the basicity of alkali and alkaline earth oxides increases in moving downward in a periodic group, the stabilities of alkali metal carbonates and sulfates also increase in the same order. Likewise, since sulfur trioxide is more acidic than carbon dioxide, the thermal stability of a particular metal sulfate is generally greater than that of the carbonate. Predictions such as these are generally valid if more deep-seated changes, such as changes in oxidation state, are not involved. Other acid-base reactions, such as combination or displacement reactions, can also occur during ignition, as will be mentioned in examples given below.

Silver chloride is very easily dried. Upon heating to 130 to 150°C, only about 0.01 per cent of adsorbed water remains.[1] The last traces are lost only upon fusion, which occurs at 455°C.

Barium sulfate contains not only adsorbed water, which is readily given off at 115°C, but also occluded water, in solid solution.[2] Fales and Thompson[3] found, for example, that, in the ignition of relatively uncontaminated barium sulfate which had been dried at 115°C, further weight losses of 0.1 and 0.3 per cent occurred upon heating for two 2-hr periods at 300 and 600°C, respectively. An additional weight loss of 0.05 per cent occurred in 1 hr of heating at 800°C. Ordinarily, an ignition temperature of 800 to 900°C is used. The upper temperature limit is imposed by the decomposition

$$BaSO_4 \rightleftharpoons BaO + SO_3$$

which does not become appreciable in rate until a temperature of 1400°C is reached,[4] unless impurities such as iron oxide or silica are present. In this case, a loss of sulfur trioxide may begin at 1000°C, no doubt because

[1] Baxter, G. P., and Hilton, F. A., Jr., *J. Am. Chem. Soc.*, **45**, 694 (1923).

[2] Walton, G., and Walden, G. H., Jr., *J. Am. Chem. Soc.*, **68**, 1750 (1946).

[3] Fales, H. A., and Thompson, W. S., *Ind. Eng. Chem., Anal. Ed.*, **11**, 206 (1939).

[4] Mostowitsch, W., *Metallurgie*, **6**, 450 (1909).

the iron oxide or silica acts as an acidic oxide and reacts with the strongly basic barium oxide to favor the loss of volatile sulfur trioxide. If filter paper is used, it should be burned off at a temperature not exceeding 600°C and in an oxidizing atmosphere, as a precaution against reduction of barium sulfate by carbon to give barium sulfide.

Hydrous oxides contain relatively large quantities of adsorbed and imbibed water and, in some instances, water of constitution (hydroxide) as well.[1] Although claims have been made for the existence of a whole series of hydrates of oxides such as Fe_2O_3, SnO_2, and SiO_2,[2,3] Weiser and Milligan found no constant-pressure plateaus on the dehydration isotherms and concluded that the water was present as adsorbed or entrained water. On the other hand, X-ray diffraction and dehydration evidence points to existence of the hydrates $Al_2O_3 \cdot H_2O$, $Al_2O_3 \cdot 3H_2O$, $Sc_2O_3 \cdot H_2O$, $Nd_2O_3 \cdot 3H_2O$, and $Cr_2O_3 \cdot H_2O$.

Duval[4,5] and his coworkers made the interesting observation that the minimum temperature necessary for quantitative dehydration of hydrous oxides often depends greatly upon the method of precipitation. Thus, alumina precipitated by gaseous ammonia was dried completely at 475°C, a product precipitated by the urea-succinate method was dried at 611°C, and material precipitated with aqueous ammonia required 1031°C. These temperature limits were determined by registering the weight automatically as a function of temperature while heating to give a continuously rising temperature. The resulting "thermolysis" curves have horizontal regions corresponding to the attainment of constant weight (see Fig. 11-3). It should be borne in mind that the results of such continuous-heating experiments are not necessarily valid for the ordinary conditions of gravimetric analysis.

Since the temperature is continuously increased at an arbitrary rate, equilibrium is not necessarily achieved. Moreover, the precipitate is not exposed to a cool and humid atmosphere, because the weighing is carried out at elevated temperatures. For example, alumina that has been ignited to 900 to 1000°C is hygroscopic[6] and, during the first few minutes of exposure to moist air, takes up a large proportion of the water that it will absorb in 24 hr. On the other hand, if alumina is ignited to

[1] Weiser, H. B., and Milligan, W. O., in "Advances in Colloid Science," vol. 1, p. 227, Interscience Publishers, Inc., New York, 1942.

[2] Thiessen, P. A., and Körner, O., *Z. anorg. u. allgem. Chem.*, **189**, 168, 174 (1930).

[3] Thiessen, P. A., and Köppen, R., *Z. anorg. u. allgem. Chem.*, **189**, 113 (1930); **228**, 57 (1936).

[4] Duval, C., *Anal. Chem.*, **23**, 1271 (1951).

[5] Duval, "Inorganic Thermogravimetric Analysis," Elsevier Press, Inc., Houston, Tex., 1953.

[6] Hillebrand, W. F., Lundell, G. E. F., Bright, H. A., and Hoffman, J. I., "Applied Inorganic Analysis," 2d ed., p. 503, John Wiley & Sons, Inc., New York, 1953.

1200°C, the hygroscopic γ-Al_2O_3 is transformed into α-Al_2O_3 (alundum) which is not hygroscopic and which can be weighed at leisure.[1]

Similarly, silica reaches its final constant weight at 358°C in the recording thermobalance,[2] but in ordinary gravimetry it is ignited at high temperatures to lower its hygroscopicity. Miehr, Koch, and Kratzert[3] found the following percentages of water in silica that had been heated for 1 hr at the indicated temperature and cooled for $\frac{1}{2}$ hr in a desiccator. 900°C, 0.9 per cent; 1000°, 0.5; 1,100°, 0.2; 1200°, 0.1 per cent.

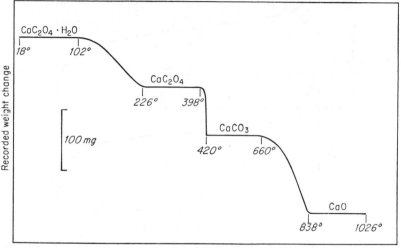

Fig. 11-3. Thermolysis curve of calcium oxalate temperatures as marked. [*With permission from Peltier, S., and Duval, C., Anal. Chim. Acta,* **1**, 346 (1947).]

Iron(III) oxide prepared by ignition of precipitates obtained with aqueous ammonia, ammonium formate, and cupferron reached constant weight at 470, 296, and 610°C, respectively, in the recording thermobalance.[2] Usually much higher temperatures (1000 to 1100°C) are recommended. Baxter and Hoover[4] found that pure Fe_2O_3 lost only 0.004 per cent of its weight upon heating to 1100°C. This weight loss evidently corresponds to an *equilibrium* composition of the solid, because Sosman and Hostetter[5] showed that Fe_2O_3 and Fe_3O_4 form solid solutions over practically, if not completely, the whole composition range. The equilibrium pressure of oxygen falls off very rapidly as Fe_3O_4 is added to

[1] Frers, J. N., *Z. anal. Chem.*, **95**, 113 (1933).

[2] Duval, *op. cit.*

[3] Miehr, W., Koch, P., and Kratzert, J., *Z. angew. Chem.*, **43**, 250 (1930).

[4] Baxter, G. P., and Hoover, C. R., *J. Am. Chem. Soc.*, **34**, 1657 (1912).

[5] Sosman, R. B., and Hostetter, J. C., *J. Am. Chem. Soc.*, **38**, 807, 1188 (1916).

Fe_2O_3 (Fig. 11-4); so the decomposition due to the reaction

$$6Fe_2O_3 \rightleftharpoons 4Fe_3O_4 + O_2$$

does not, theoretically, proceed to completion once the dissociation pressure exceeds the partial pressure of oxygen in the atmosphere, as it would if the two solids did not interact.[1]

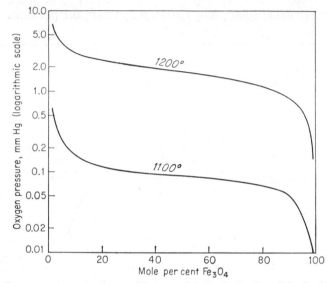

FIG. 11-4. Pressure of oxygen in equilibrium with Fe_2O_3-Fe_3O_4 solid solutions.   [*From Sosman, R. B., and Hostetter, J. C., J. Am. Chem. Soc.*, **38**, 807 (1916).]

Calcium oxalate is normally precipitated as the monohydrate from hot solution. The thermolysis curve[2] shows several plateaus corresponding to the monohydrate from room temperature to 100°C, anhydrous calcium oxalate from 226 to 398°C, calcium carbonate from 420 to 660°C, and calcium oxide above 840 to 850°C. Sandell and Kolthoff[3] concluded that the monohydrate is not a reliable weighing form because of its tendency to retain excess moisture. Coprecipitated ammonium oxalate also remains undecomposed, so the results are usually 0.5 to 1.0 per cent high if the precipitate is dried at 105 to 110°C. Anhydrous calcium oxalate is also unsuitable as a weighing form because of its hygroscopicity.

Willard and Boldyreff[4] investigated calcium carbonate as a weighing form and concluded that it is excellent if the oxalate is ignited at a tem-

---

[1] For an excellent discussion, see Smith, T. B., "Analytical Processes," 2d ed., p. 107 *et seq.*, Edward Arnold & Co., London, 1940.

[2] Duval, *op. cit.*

[3] Sandell and Kolthoff, *Ind. Eng. Chem., Anal. Ed.*, **11**, 90 (1939).

[4] Willard, H. H., and Boldyreff, A. W., *J. Am. Chem. Soc.*, **52**, 1888 (1930).

perature of $500 \pm 25°C$. That this closeness of temperature control is necessary becomes evident from the following consideration. The minimum temperature is determined by the *rate* of the irreversible decomposition

$$CaC_2O_4 \rightarrow CaCO_3 + CO \qquad (11\text{-}15)$$

which is too slow to reach completion in a reasonable time at 450°C but becomes rapid at 475°C. The maximum temperature limit is determined by the *equilibrium* pressure of carbon dioxide at a given temperature, regardless of the ratio of $CaCO_3$ to CaO. Therefore, if the equilibrium pressure exceeds the partial pressure of carbon dioxide in the atmosphere, the carbonate should decompose *completely*. The dissociation pressure at 500°C is 0.15 mm,* compared with a partial pressure of 0.23 mm in normal atmospheric air. The dissociation pressure reaches 0.23 mm at 509°C, but the dissociation rate does not become appreciable until the temperature is above 525°C.

Two alternative schemes of ignition are suggested by the fact that the dissociation pressure of calcium carbonate reaches 760 mm at 882°C.† Either the oxalate can be ignited to calcium carbonate in an atmosphere of carbon dioxide[1] at a convenient temperature *below* 882°C, or else it can be ignited to calcium oxide at a temperature *above* 882°C. In the latter case, removal of the carbon dioxide is necessary to prevent reversal of the reaction upon cooling. Calcium oxide, of course, is hygroscopic. It may be concluded that calcium carbonate is the ideal weighing form, provided that means are available either to control the temperature at a value near 500°C or to ignite in an atmosphere of carbon dioxide. Calcium sulfate and calcium fluoride are good weighing forms,[2] but are seldom used because of the inconvenience of converting calcium oxalate to either of them.

Magnesium ammonium phosphate is converted quantitatively to magnesium pyrophosphate at temperatures above 477°C, according to the pyrolysis curves of Duval.[3] Depending, however, upon the conditions of precipitation, various coprecipitation processes occur, and much higher ignition temperatures are usually beneficial. For example, in the presence of high concentrations of ammonium salts, $(NH_4)_2HPO_4$ or $NH_4H_2PO_4$ are coprecipitated.[4] They yield ammonia and metaphosphoric acid upon gentle ignition, but the latter decomposes only slowly upon strong ignition to yield P_2O_5. Primary magnesium phosphate,

* Andrussow, L., *Z. physik. Chem. Leipzig*, **116**, 95 (1925).
† *Ibid.*
[1] Foote, H. W., and Bradley, W. M., *J. Am. Chem. Soc.*, **48**, 676 (1926).
[2] Brunck, O., *Z. anal. Chem.*, **45**, 77 (1906).
[3] Duval, *op. cit.*
[4] Epperson, A. W., *J. Am. Chem. Soc.*, **50**, 321 (1928).

$Mg(H_2PO_4)_2$, is often coprecipitated, particularly when the ratio of ammonium ion concentration to ammonia is relatively high.[1] Upon ignition, magnesium metaphosphate, $Mg(PO_3)_2$, is formed. This product loses P_2O_5 only slowly, even at 1,150 to 1,200°C,

$$2Mg(PO_3)_2 \rightleftharpoons Mg_2P_2O_7 + P_2O_5 \qquad (11\text{-}16)$$

A magnesium ammonium phosphate precipitate that is contaminated by foreign phosphates, e.g., calcium phosphate, may give trouble by forming a fused mass at temperatures as low as 1,000°C. It is usually necessary to reprecipitate magnesium ammonium phosphate by dissolving the initial precipitate in a minimum of hydrochloric acid and adding only a slight excess of precipitant to minimize the concentration of ammonium salts and of foreign ions. Even so, a temperature of 1050 to 1100°C is usually used for the ignition.

At temperatures above 1100°C, the precipitate gradually loses weight, probably because of a slow decomposition of the pyrophosphate to give $Mg_3(PO_4)_2$ and P_2O_5.* Care must be exercised in burning off the carbon of the filter paper, in order to avoid loss of phosphorus by reduction[2] and inclusion of carbon in the precipitate. This inclusion appears to be associated with a conversion of amorphous magnesium pyrophosphate into a crystalline form at 550 to 600°C.†

Ammonium 12-molybdiphosphate, the familiar yellow precipitate formed upon the addition of excess ammonium molybdate to a phosphate solution containing nitric acid and ammonium nitrate, is said to have the ideal composition $(NH_4)_3PO_4 \cdot 12MoO_3 \cdot 2HNO_3 \cdot H_2O$.‡ For the most accurate results, the precipitate should be dissolved in ammonium hydroxide, and the phosphate should be determined by precipitation as magnesium ammonium phosphate and ignition to the pyrophosphate.[3]

To take advantage of the high equivalent weight of ammonium 12-molybdiphosphate, various workers have recommended weighing it as $(NH_4)_3PO_4 \cdot 12MoO_3$ after drying the precipitate at 300 to 500°C.§ According to the thermolysis curves of Duval,[4] the best weighing form is the compound $P_2O_5 \cdot 24MoO_3$, which is obtained by ignition at 812 to 850°C.

[1] Sandell and Kolthoff, *op. cit.*

* Hoffman, J. I., and Lundell, G. E. F., *J. Research Natl. Bur. Standards,* **5**, 279 (1930).

[2] Jacob, K. D., and Reynolds, D. S., *J. Assoc. Offic. Agr. Chemists,* **11**, 128 (1928).

† Kiehl, S. J., and Hardt, H. B., *J. Am. Chem. Soc.,* **55**, 3555 (1933); cf. Kolthoff and Sandell, "Textbook of Quantitative Inorganic Analysis," p. 359.

‡ Hundeshagen, F., *Z. anal. Chem.,* **28**, 141 (1889).

[3] Lundell and Hoffman, *Ind. Eng. Chem.,* **15**, 44, 171 (1923); *J. Assoc. Offic. Agr. Chemists,* **8**, 188 (1924).

§ Baxter, *Am. Chem. J.,* **28**, 298 (1902).

[4] Duval, *op. cit.*

According to Lundell and Hoffman,[1] gravimetric procedures based on weighing the molybdiphosphate are slower and no more accurate than the alkalimetric procedure.   From the thermolysis curve[2] it appears that the anhydrous compound $(NH_4)_3PO_4 \cdot 12MoO_3$ is formed at temperatures of 180 to 410°C, in accord with the findings of Baxter,[3] who recommended drying at 300°C, a temperature at which ammonium nitrate is readily decomposed.   The product formed at 100 to 110° is hygroscopic and somewhat variable in composition.   Ignition at 400 to 500°C to yield the blue-black anhydride $P_2O_5 \cdot 24MoO_3$ is commonly recommended.   The thermolysis curve[4] shows a reasonably constant weight over the temperature range 600 to 850°C, the flattest portion being at 812 to 850°C. Caution should be exercised, however, in heating to such temperatures for the prolonged periods usually used in ordinary ignitions, because molybdenum(VI) oxide is sublimed rapidly at temperatures above 850°C* and slowly at much lower temperatures.

Potassium tetraphenylborate, which is normally dried at 105 to 120°C, is stable up to 265°C, according to the thermolysis curve of Wendlandt.[5] At 715 to 825°C, the metaborate KBO_2 is formed.   The ammonium salt, however, begins to sublime at about 130°C and leaves only a small residue of boric oxide upon stronger ignition.

Metallic copper or nickel, prepared by electrode position, is subject to ready oxidation.   According to Duval,[6] the ignition temperature should not exceed 67 for copper or 93°C for nickel.   *Silver*, on the other hand, is stable to 950°C.   *Lead dioxide*, prepared by anodic deposition,[7] is usually dried at 125°C, but, judging by the thermolysis curve, it is stable up to 340°C.

11-5. Thermogravimetric Analysis

Duval[6] has examined the thermolysis curves of a large number of analytical precipitates from the viewpoint of direct application of the curves to automatic or semiautomatic determinations.   He has also determined the thermal stabilities of many analytical standards.[8]   Duval listed the following requirements for rapid determinations: (1) quantitative and immediate precipitation, (2) immediate filterability, (3) immedi-

---

[1] Lundell and Hoffmann, *J. Assoc. Offic. Agr. Chemists*, **8**, 184 (1924).

[2] Dupuis, T., and Duval, C., *Compt. rend.*, **229**, 51 (1949).

[3] Baxter, *op. cit.*

[4] Dupuis and Duval, *op. cit.*

* *Ibid.*

[5] Wendlandt, W. W., *Anal. Chem.*, **28**, 1001 (1956).

[6] Duval, *op. cit.*

[7] Hillebrand, Lundell, Bright, and Hoffman, "Applied Inorganic Analysis," p. 228.

[8] Duval, *Anal. Chim. Acta*, **13**, 32, 427 (1955); **15**, 223 (1956); **16**, 221, 545 (1957); **20**, 20 (1959).

ate drying, (4) occurrence of a horizontal region on the thermolysis curve at the lowest possible temperature.   On the basis of these requirements, he has ruled out inorganic hydroxides and sulfides, not only because of their slow aging and their tendencies toward coprecipitation but also because of the inconveniently high ignition temperatures that are often necessary.   On the other hand, he has favored the use of organic precipitants, which often yield precipitates that can be dried rapidly at low temperatures.

For the determination of single constituents, thermogravimetric methods are of interest mainly as rapid control methods in which the weighing operation has been rendered automatic.   The accuracy is limited to about 1 part in 300.   Determinations of more than one component are also possible if sufficient constant-weight regions are available. For example, a mixture of calcium oxalate and magnesium oxalate can be analyzed by weighing $CaCO_3$ + MgO at 500°C and CaO + MgO at 900°.*   Similarly, a mixture of silver nitrate and cupric nitrate yields $AgNO_3$ + CuO at 280 to 400°C and Ag + CuO at temperatures above 529°C.   Hagan, Gordon, and Campbell[1] determined potassium perchlorate in the presence of barium nitrate, taking advantage of the fact that barium nitrate catalyzes the thermal decomposition of potassium perchlorate.

Another procedure that has been proposed is to record the temperature as a function of time at a constant temperature or at a gradually rising temperature.   Griffith[2] was able to determine water of hydration in salts to an accuracy of the order of ±1 per cent and to determine the composition of certain hydrate mixtures by determining the weight loss in appropriate dehydration steps.   It should be kept in mind that such a procedure as this is carried out under nonequilibrium conditions and that the experimental procedure must be followed faithfully to get reproducible results.   Nevertheless, it appears that, if the temperature schedule is properly selected, the halts or breaks in the weight-loss curves can be made to correspond to stoichiometric losses of water of hydration.

11-6. Pyrohydrolytic Determination of Halides

A high-temperature hydrolytic reaction of the type

$$MX_{2n} + nH_2O(gas) \rightleftharpoons MO_n + 2nHX(gas)$$

where HX is a hydrogen halide, has a positive standard entropy change because the standard entropy of 2 moles of hydrogen halide is much larger than that of 1 mole of water vapor (Table 11-1).   Therefore, the forward reaction is favored at high temperatures.

* Peltier, S., and Duval, C., *Anal. Chim. Acta*, **1**, 408 (1947).

[1] Hagan, V. D., Gordon, S., and Campbell, C., *Anal. Chem.*, **29**, 306 (1957).

[2] Griffith, E. J., *Anal. Chem.*, **29**, 198 (1957).

Briner and Gagnaux[1] have considered the thermodynamics of the reactions:

$$CaCl_2 + H_2O \rightleftharpoons CaO + 2HCl \tag{11-17}$$
$$CaCl_2 + H_2O + SiO_2 \rightleftharpoons CaSiO_3 + 2HCl \tag{11-18}$$

For each reaction, $K_p = P^2_{HCl}/P_{H_2O}$, and the equilibrium pressure of hydrogen chloride for $P_{H_2O} = 1$ atm is given by $P_{HCl} = \sqrt{K_p}$. From the data in Table 11-2 it is evident that the equilibrium constants of both reactions increase with rising temperature and that the hydrolytic reaction is greatly promoted by the presence of silica, with the consequent formation of calcium silicate. Aluminum oxide and kaolin were also found to favor the hydrolytic reaction, through the formation of calcium aluminate and calcium aluminum silicate.

These are all examples of acid-displacement reactions in which a nonvolatile, acidic component promotes the evolution of gaseous hydrogen chloride.

TABLE 11-2. PYROHYDROLYTIC EQUILIBRIUM DATA FOR $CaCl_2$

T, °K	Reaction (11-17)		Reaction (11-18)	
	K_p, atm	P_{HCl}, atm	K_p, atm	P_{HCl}, atm
300	4.5×10^{-37}	6.7×10^{-19}	9×10^{-17}	9.9×10^{-9}
900	4.1×10^{-9}	6.3×10^{-5}	2.0×10^{-2}	0.16
1,000	3.9×10^{-7}	6.2×10^{-4}	0.12	0.35
1,100	1.8×10^{-6}	1.3×10^{-3}	0.46	0.67
1,200	1.1×10^{-5}	3.3×10^{-3}	1.65	1.28

Similar reactions of alkali metal chlorides were studied by Briner and Roth.[2] As early as 1937, Domange[3] had determined the equilibrium constants for the high-temperature hydrolysis of a variety of metal fluorides. Hydrolytic reactions of rare earth chlorides

$$RCl_3 + H_2O(gas) \rightleftharpoons ROCl + 2HCl(gas)$$

have also been studied in some detail for lanthanum, samarium, and gadolinium chlorides.[4] All these equilibrium studies were carried out for the purpose of determining thermodynamic constants, and no suggestions of analytical applications were made.

[1] Briner, E., and Gagnaux, N., *Helv. Chim. Acta*, **31**, 556 (1948).

[2] Briner, E., and Roth, P., *Helv. Chim. Acta*, **31**, 1352 (1948).

[3] Domange, L., *Ann. Chim.*, **7**, 225 (1937); Domange, L., and Wohlhuter, **M.**, *Compt. rend.*, **228**, 1591 (1949).

[4] Koch, C. W., Broido, A., and Cunningham, B. B., *J. Am. Chem. Soc.*, **74**, 2349 (1952); Koch and Cunningham, *ibid.*, **75**, 796 (1953).

The first systematic studies of such reactions for analytical purposes were made by Warf and coworkers,[1] who introduced the term "pyrohydrolysis." They studied the evolution of hydrogen fluoride upon passage of steam at 1000°C over various metal fluorides in a platinum apparatus. Haff, Butler, and Bisso[2] used a similar method for the analysis of aluminum fluoride. Later, it was found[3] that nickel could be substituted for platinum, and, more recently,[4] a platinum boat in a fused silica tube has been found to be satisfactory at 600 to 900°C.

In the original work[5] it was found that the various metal fluorides fell into two rather distinct groups. The first group, consisting of the fluorides of the heavy metals and magnesium, was completely hydrolyzed in 20 min; the second group, consisting of the fluorides of the alkali metals, the alkaline earth metals, and beryllium, was hydrolyzed very slowly. Even the slowly hydrolyzed fluorides evolved hydrogen fluoride rapidly if they were mixed with uranium oxide, U_3O_8, and heated in a stream of air and steam. The reaction was presumed to be of the type

$$6NaF + 2U_3O_8 + 3H_2O + O_2 \rightleftharpoons 6HF + 3Na_2U_2O_7 \quad (11\text{-}19)$$

Hibbits[6] studied the precision of the reactions of uranyl fluoride and uranium tetrafluoride:

$$3UO_2F_2 + 3H_2O \rightleftharpoons U_3O_8 + 6HF + \tfrac{1}{2}O_2 \qquad (11\text{-}20)$$
$$3UF_4 + 6H_2O + O_2 \rightleftharpoons U_3O_8 + 12HF \qquad (11\text{-}21)$$

in which the hydrogen fluoride was collected and titrated with sodium hydroxide. The standard deviations for the fluoride determination were 0.08 and 0.07 per cent (relative) for reactions (11-20) and (11-21), respectively.

More recently,[7] it has been shown that other substances, notably tungsten(VI) oxide, vanadium(V) oxide and sodium metavanadate, are superior to uranium oxide as accelerators. Metavanadate acts also as a flux to aid the evolution of fluoride from refractory materials. A stream of moist oxygen has been found to be superior to steam and more convenient.

Gahler and Porter[8] applied the pyrohydrolytic method to the determination of chloride in titanium sponge. Using a nickel apparatus, they found that substantial fractions of the chloride evolved as nickel chloride

---

[1] Warf, J. C., Cline, W. O., and Tevebaugh, R. D., *Anal. Chem.*, **26**, 342 (1954).

[2] Haff, L. V., Butler, C. P., and Bisso, J. D., *Anal. Chem.*, **30**, 984 (1958).

[3] Susano, C. D., White, J. C., and Lee, J. E., Jr., *Anal. Chem.*, **27**, 453 (1955).

[4] Powell, R. H., and Menis, O., *Anal. Chem.*, **30**, 1546 (1958).

[5] Warf, Cline, and Tevebaugh, *op. cit.*

[6] Hibbits, J. O., *Anal. Chem.* **29**, 1760 (1957).

[7] Powell and Menis, *op. cit.*

[8] Gahler, A. R., and Porter, G., *Anal. Chem.*, **29**, 296 (1957).

rather than hydrogen chloride. The chloride was, therefore, determined by the Volhard method (Sec. 12-5) rather than by titration with sodium hydroxide.

The pyrohydrolytic method appears to offer considerable promise, particularly in the analysis of refractory materials. It may prove to be an important competitor of the Willard and Winter distillation method for fluoride (Sec. 12-6), although much work remains to be done to establish its validity, particularly on a micro scale.

11-7. Pyrolytic Determination of Sulfur

Interesting examples of high-temperature acid-base reactions are represented by the use of vanadium pentoxide for the quantitative evolution of sulfur dioxide and trioxide from a variety of refractory materials.[1] A mixture of sulfur trioxide and sulfur dioxide is evolved by heating a mixture of the powdered sample and V_2O_5 in a stream of air at 900 to 950°C. The SO_2 probably is formed by thermal decomposition of SO_3, because it is found even when the sample contains sulfur only as sulfate. The evolved gases are absorbed in neutral hydrogen peroxide and titrated as sulfuric acid.

PROBLEMS

11-1. Confirm the calculations of $\Delta H°$, $\Delta S°$, and $\Delta F°$ for reactions (11-5) and (11-6) as described in Example 11-1.

11-2. Estimate the heats and entropies of vaporization of CuCl and $SnCl_2$ from the constants of Eq. (11-8). *Ans.* $\Delta H° = -19.3$, -20.5 kcal; $\Delta S° = 12.1$, 27.1 cal mole^{-1} deg^{-1}.

11-3. Apply the phase rule to reactions (11-5) and (11-6) occurring together, assuming (a) that Cu, Sn, CuCl, and $SnCl_2$ do not interact; (b) that Cu and Sn do not interact, but CuCl and $SnCl_2$ form a liquid solution; (c) that a pure compound of Sn and Cu is in equilibrium with a single liquid phase of CuCl and $SnCl_2$ and a gas phase. Interpret the degrees of freedom that are calculated.

11-4. From the data of Table 11-1, estimate the equilibrium constant K_p of Eq. (11-18) for the temperatures listed in Table 11-2, neglecting the heat-capacity corrections and taking the 25°C values of $\Delta H°$ and $\Delta S°$ to be independent of temperature. Compare your values with those listed in Table 11-2, which were calculated using the proper corrections. *Note:* Owing to a discrepancy in the value of $\Delta H°$ for CaO, the values of K_p for Eq. (11-17) calculated by the approximate method do not agree with those in Table 11-2. A similar comparison can be made using $\Delta H° = -146.8$ kcal for CaO at 25°C, as was done by Briner and Gagnaux.[2] *Ans.* log $K_p = -16.45$, -1.62, -0.87, -0.26, $+0.24$.

11-5. The vapor pressures of the systems $Na_2CO_3 \cdot 10H_2O - Na_2CO_3 \cdot H_2O$ and $Na_2CO_3 \cdot H_2O - Na_2CO_3$ in equilibrium with water vapor are 17.7 mm and 4.7 mm, respectively, at 25°C. A saturated solution of the decahydrate has a vapor pressure of 21.8 mm. Draw a vapor pressure–composition diagram for the system

---

[1] Hagerman, D. B., and Faust, R. A., *Anal. Chem.*, **27**, 1970 (1955).
[2] Briner and Gagnaux, *op. cit.*

Na_2CO_3–H_2O. **Over what range of humidities is the monohydrate stable?** *Ans.* 19.8 to 74.7 per cent.

11-6. A mixed precipitate of calcium oxalate and magnesium oxalate is to be analyzed by the thermogravimetric method. After heating to form $CaCO_3$ and MgO, the precipitate weighed 0.4123 g, and after ignition to CaO and MgO it weighed 0.2943 g. Calculate the weight of CaO in the sample. *Ans.* 0.1502 g.

11-7. A sample weighing 0.9876 g and containing only $CaCO_3$ and $MgCO_3$ is ignited to a mixture of CaO and MgO weighing 0.5123 g.

a. Calculate the weight of $CaCO_3$ in the mixture.

b. Calculate the weight of the residue if the sample is ignited to MgO and $CaCO_3$. *Ans.* (*a*) 0.4878 g; (*b*) 0.7268 g.

11-8. A 0.4987-g sample containing only ZnS and CdS is dissolved, and the metals are quantitatively precipitated as $MNH_4PO_4 \cdot 6H_2O$, which is ignited to yield 0.6987 g of mixed pyrophosphates. Calculate the weight of ZnS in the sample. *Ans.* 0.0562 g.

12. Precipitation Titrations

Many precipitation reactions that are useful as separation techniques or for gravimetric analysis fail to meet one or both of two requirements for titrimetry.

1. For titrimetry, the reaction rate must be sufficiently rapid. Particularly in the titration of dilute solutions and in the immediate vicinity of the end point, the rate of precipitation may be impracticably slow. To increase the precipitation rate, it is sometimes beneficial to change solvents, e.g., by adding alcohol, or to raise the temperature. By adding an excess of reagent and back-titrating, it may be possible to take advantage of a more rapid precipitation in the reverse direction. By choosing an end-point detection method that does not require equilibrium to be reached in the immediate vicinity of the end point, e.g., a conductometric, amperometric, or photometric method, one may be able to take advantage of a faster reaction rate at points removed from the end point.

2. For titrimetry, the stoichiometry must be exact. In direct titrations it is not, in general, possible to take advantage of the beneficial effects of aging on the purity of precipitates. It is, therefore, necessary that, under the conditions of titration, coprecipitation be negligible. Coprecipitation by solid solution formation, foreign ion entrapment, and adsorption must be considered possible sources of error. The nature of the solvent, the pH, the concentration of reactants, the nature and concentrations of foreign substances, the temperature, and the order and speed of addition of reagent are all conditions that may be of importance in determining the exactness of stoichiometry.

Considering these limitations, it is not surprising that the applications of titration methods based on precipitation reactions are less important than those based on acid-base, complex formation, or redox reactions.

12-1. Titration Curves

It is customary, by analogy with pH titration curves of acids and bases, to plot the quantity pM (defined either as $- \log [M^{n+}]$ or as $- \log a_{M^{n+}}$)

against titration volume or fraction of the stoichiometric quantity of reagent added. For certain metals that form reversible electrodes with their ions, the measured electrode potential is a linear function of the ion activity, so the titration curve can be realized experimentally in a potentiometric titration. In any case, the curve gives a useful indication of the sharpness of a titration.

As for acid-base titrations, the "relative precision" is a useful concept for comparing the steepness of titration curves in the immediate vicinity of the end point.[1] For the formation of a precipitate of symmetrical charge type

$$M^{n+} + A^{n-} \rightleftharpoons MA \qquad K_{sp} = [M^{n+}][A^{n-}] \qquad (12\text{-}1)$$

the titration curve is closely analogous to that of a strong acid–strong base titration. The relative precision, which is the fraction of the stoichiometric quantity of reagent required to traverse the region ± 0.1 pM unit on either side of the end point (cf. Sec. 3-8), is given approximately by $\sqrt{K_{sp}}/C$, where C is the hypothetical end-point concentration of MA that would exist if no precipitation had occurred. Thus the steepness of the titration curve in the end-point region decreases in proportion to the ratio of the solubility of precipitate to the hypothetical end-point concentration.

Example 12-1. Calculate the theoretical relative precision for the titration of 10^{-4} M NaI with 10^{-4} M AgNO$_3$, given that $K_{sp,AgI} = 10^{-16}$.

Answer. rp $= \sqrt{10^{-16}}/5 \times 10^{-5} = 2 \times 10^{-4}$, or 0.02 per cent.

For precipitates of unsymmetrical charge types, such as MA_2, M_2A, etc., the titration curve is unsymmetrical and the expressions for the relative precision are much more complicated. Qualitatively, it should be borne in mind that the point of maximum slope (inflection point) is not coincident with the equivalence point of an unsymmetrical titration curve. Therefore, if the inflection point is taken as the end point, as is common practice in potentiometric titrations, a theoretical titration error will in general exist. The magnitude of the error increases with increasing solubility and with increasing dilution.

It can be shown that, for a precipitate of the type M_2A, the inflection point of the titration of M with A corresponds to

$$1 - X_i = \frac{3}{4} \frac{\sqrt[3]{K_{sp}}}{C} \qquad (12\text{-}2)$$

where C is the hypothetical molar concentration of M_2A at the equivalence point, and X_i is the fraction of the stoichiometric quantity of

[1] Benedetti-Pichler, A. A., "Essentials of Quantitative Analysis," The Ronald Press Company, New York, 1956.

reagent that has been added up to the inflection point. The quantity $100(X_i - 1)$ represents the theoretical percentage error.

Example 12-2. Calculate the theoretical titration error in the titration of 0.1 M AgNO$_3$ with 0.05 M K$_2$CrO$_4$, given that the solubility product of Ag$_2$CrO$_4$ is 2×10^{-12}.
Answer. From Eq. (12-2), $1 - X_i = \frac{3}{4} \sqrt[3]{2 \times 10^{-12}}/2.5 \times 10^{-2} = 3.8 \times 10^{-3}$. Theoretical percentage error $= -0.38$ per cent.

12-2. Titration of Mixtures : Ideal Case

It is a simple matter to calculate the titration curve for the successive titration of several constituents that form precipitates of widely differing

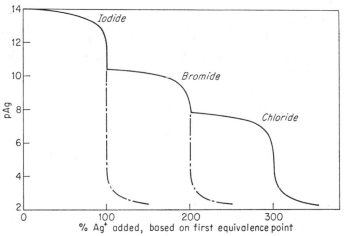

FIG. 12-1. Titration curves for 0.01 M halides. Solid line, calculated curve for mixtures; dashed line, calculated curves for iodide and bromide alone.

solubility with the reagent, if secondary effects such as adsorption and solid solution formation can be ignored. As an example, the titration curve for a solution 0.01 M in iodide, bromide, and chloride with silver ion, calculated neglecting dilution, is shown in Fig. 12-1. It is considered that silver iodide is being precipitated alone until the solubility product of silver bromide is reached. A small quantity of iodide is left untitrated at the "break point," which corresponds to the first precipitation of silver bromide.

If C_A and C_B are the initial concentrations of two anions A and B, which form 1:1-charge-type precipitates MA and MB with solubility products of K_{MA} and K_{MB}, at the break point we have

$$[A] = \frac{K_{MA}}{K_{MB}} C_B \qquad (12\text{-}3)$$

Therefore, the theoretical percentage error ϵ for the determination of A, which forms the less soluble salt, is approximately

$$\epsilon_A = -100 \frac{K_{MA} C_B}{K_{MB} C_A} \qquad (12\text{-}4)$$

if the break point is taken as the end point. Dilution need not be considered during the titration, because the relative error depends upon the concentration ratio C_B/C_A. The error increases as K_{MA}/K_{MB}, which is always less than unity, approaches unity. For the determination of B, the error is given approximately by

$$\epsilon_B = 100 \frac{[A]}{C_B} = 100 \frac{K_{MA}}{K_{MB}} \qquad (12\text{-}5)$$

In Eqs. (12-4) and (12-5) it is assumed that [A] as given by Eq. (12-3) is large compared with the solubility of MA. It is interesting that the relative error for the more soluble component turns out to be independent of the concentrations.

Example 12-3. For a mixture of $10^{-3}\ M$ iodide and $10^{-1}\ M$ bromide, calculate the theoretical percentage error in titration of the iodide and the bromide with silver nitrate, neglecting dilution. Take 10^{-16} and 4×10^{-13} as K_{sp} values of AgI and AgBr.

Answer. From Eqs. (12-4) and (12-5), $\epsilon_I = -2.5$ per cent, $\epsilon_{Br} = 0.025$ per cent.

Obviously, for a three-component mixture, the error for the middle component is made up of a positive and a negative part, which tend to cancel somewhat, depending upon the concentration.

Example 12-4. Calculate the theoretical titration error for the determination of $0.1\ M$ Br$^-$ in the presence of $0.01\ M$ I$^-$ and Cl$^-$, neglecting coprecipitation. Take $K_{sp,AgCl} = 2 \times 10^{-10}$.

Answer. From Eqs. (12-4) and (12-5), $\epsilon_{Br} = 0.025 - 0.020 = 0.005$ per cent.

It is of interest to note that, even in this ideal case of a two- or three-component mixture, only the first precipitate is really pure until a fraction of it equal to $1 - K_{MA} C_B / K_{MB} C_A$ has been precipitated. From that point on, the second component MB carries down with it a *constant* fraction, equal to K_{MA}/K_{MB}, of the first precipitate MA. Likewise, if a third component MC is precipitated, it is contaminated by a constant fraction of MA, equal to K_{MA}/K_{MC}, and also by a constant fraction of MB, equal to K_{MB}/K_{MC}.

12-3. Effect of Adsorption

In the above calculations we have neglected the adsorption of the ions of the precipitate (lattice ions) upon its surface.

From the discussion in Chap. 10, Sec. 10-1, it is apparent that the amount of lattice-ion adsorption varies widely with the nature of the precipitate and even with the state of perfection of its surface.

For silver iodide the effects are much more pronounced than for the bromide or the chloride, and they represent an interesting example for detailed study. Kolthoff and Lingane[1] made a careful potentiometric study of the behavior of silver iodide in the immediate vicinity of the equivalence point. Their results, together with the curve calculated without taking adsorption into account, are shown in Fig. 12-2.

The experimental curve was actually observed in the presence of a relatively large amount of solid silver iodide, so the effects of adsorption

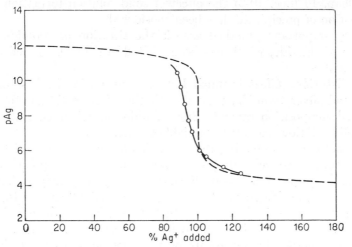

FIG. 12-2. Effect of adsorption in titration of iodide. 10^{-4} M I^- in presence of excess AgI, titrated with Ag^+. Solid line, observed; dashed line, calculated. [*Experimental curve plotted from results of Kolthoff, I. M., and Lingane, J. J., J. Am. Chem. Soc., 58, 1524, 1528 (1936).*]

are exaggerated. From data given by Shiner and Smith[2] for the titration of 2×10^{-4} M halides with 0.02 M silver ion it is possible to plot titration curves which show qualitatively similar distortions and which decrease in magnitude in the order: iodide, bromide, chloride, corresponding to decreased adsorption of lattice ions. At the isoelectric point (pAg = 6) the two curves of Fig. 12-2 cross, because neither lattice ion is adsorbed. On either side of the isoelectric point, adsorption acts to decrease the solution concentration of the ion present in excess. However, because of the asymmetry of the isoelectric point, the steepest portion of the experimental titration curve occurs slightly before the equivalence point. Theoretically, titration to a pAg value of 6 would be a more accurate procedure than titration to an inflection point. Shiner and Smith[3] obtained good results for individual halides by titrating to

[1] Kolthoff, I. M., and Lingane, J. J., *J. Am. Chem. Soc.*, **58**, 1524, 1528 (1936).
[2] Shiner, V. J., and Smith, M. L., *Anal. Chem.*, **28**, 1043 (1956).
[3] *Ibid.*

an equivalence potential (taken as the point of steepest slope) in the presence of a nonionic detergent. They also obtained good results for equimolar mixtures of the three halides. In view of the complications, due principally to adsorption of iodide at the first end point and to solid solution formation at the second end point, discussed below, uniformly good results cannot be expected from this method for all compositions.

12-4. Effect of Solid Solution Formation

In Chap. 10 (Sec. 10-2) the effect of solid solution formation on the composition of precipitates has been considered.

A very important practical case is the titration of bromide in the presence of chloride, which has been treated in detail by Flood and his coworkers.[1-3]

The disturbing effect is much less pronounced in the case of silver iodide and silver bromide, even though they form solid solutions over a limited composition range.[4] Silver iodide and silver chloride do not form solid solutions to any appreciable extent.

Two methods of detecting the end point of an experimental titration curve should be considered: (1) the use of the inflection point, or point of maximum slope of the titration curve, and (2) the extrapolation of the bromide and chloride curves to give a "break point" similar to that in the idealized curve in Fig. 12-1. In both methods, the magnitude of the error depends not only upon the initial concentration ratio C_A/C_B but also upon whether homogeneous or heterogeneous solid solution (see page 174) occurs.

Considering first the inflection-point method of end-point detection and assuming that homogeneous solid solution formation occurs, the following expression can readily be derived:[5]

$$\epsilon_A = 100 \left(\frac{C_B}{C_A} - 1 \right) \frac{K_{MA}\gamma_{MA}}{K_{MA}\gamma_{MA} + K_{MB}\gamma_{MB}} \qquad (12\text{-}6)$$

where ϵ_A = relative percentage error in determining less soluble component

     C_A, C_B = initial concentrations of A and B

K_{MA}, K_{MB} = activity products of MA and MB

     γ_A, γ_B = activity coefficients of MA and MB in solid

If K_{MB} is large compared with K_{MA}, Eq. (12-6) becomes, approximately,

$$\epsilon_A \cong 100 \left(\frac{C_B}{C_A} - 1 \right) \frac{K_{MA}\gamma_{MA}}{K_{MB}\gamma_{MB}} = 100 \left(\frac{C_B}{C_A} - 1 \right) D \qquad (12\text{-}7)$$

[1] Flood, H., *Z. anorg. u. allgem. Chem.*, **229**, 76 (1936).
[2] Flood, H., and Bruun, B., *Z. anorg. u. allgem. Chem.*, **229**, 85 (1936).
[3] Flood, H., and Sletten, E., *Z. anal. Chem.*, **115**, 30 (1938).
[4] Thiel, A., *Z. anorg. u. allgem. Chem.*, **24**, 1 (1900).
[5] Flood, *op. cit.*

The last factor of Eq. (12-7) is the distribution coefficient D [see Eqs. (10-7) and (10-11), Sec. 10-2] for solid solution formation, written in such a direction that $D < 1$. For *ideal* solid solutions, γ_{MA} and γ_{MB} are both equal to unity and $D = K_{MA}/K_{MB}$.

It is interesting that, according to Eq. (12-7), the *inflection point theoretically coincides with the equivalence point if equal concentrations of A and B are titrated and if homogeneous solid solutions are formed*. The error for component A is negative for $C_A > C_B$ and, for large ratio C_A/C_B, approaches the limiting value $-100D$. For $C_B > C_A$ the theoretical error is positive and increases without limit with increasing ratio C_B/C_A.

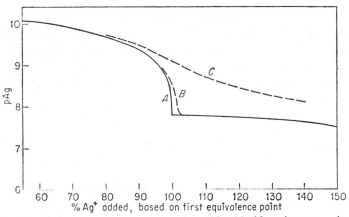

FIG. 12-3. Titration curves for equimolar bromide-chloride mixtures. *A*, no solid solution; *B*, ideal heterogeneous solid solution; *C*, homogeneous solid solution.

Equation (12-7) is of interest in view of the findings of Kolthoff and Eggertsen[1] that homogeneous solid solution formation can be closely approached for silver bromide and chloride if the precipitate is maintained in the colloidal state. For this case, $D = 0.0025$ and the limiting percentage error is -0.25 per cent for large ratios of bromide to chloride. This conclusion is particularly interesting in view of the fact that the most favorable condition for gravimetric determinations is in approaching the Doerner-Hoskins heterogeneous solid solution by continuous coagulation of the colloid. However, it should be kept in mind that the *magnitude* of the change of potential in the vicinity of the bromide equivalence point is greatly decreased by the formation of homogeneous solid solutions (see Fig. 12-3), so that the sensitivity of end-point detection is correspondingly decreased. Moreover, any departure from homogeneous composition due to slowness in adjustment of the solid composition to the rapidly changing solution composition will lead to an asymmetrical

[1] Kolthoff, I. M., and Eggertsen, F. T., *J. Am. Chem. Soc.*, **61**, 1036 (1939).

titration curve and a shift of the inflection point. Slow attainment of equilibrium is more the rule than the exception, in most precipitations, and the more practical case is that of heterogeneous solid composition.

Turning now to the case of "ideal heterogeneous" or Doerner-Hoskins solid solution formation, in which each infinitesimal increment of precipitate retains its original composition, Flood[1] wrote the following approximate expression for the deviation between the inflection point and the first equivalence point:

$$\epsilon_A \cong 100 \frac{C_B}{C_A} \left\{ 1 - \left(\frac{C_B}{DC_A} \right)^D - D \right\} \tag{12-8}$$

where we use the same notation as above.

For the case of bromide and chloride mixtures, taking $D = 0.0025$, the calculated correction factors for various bromide-chloride mixtures as listed by Flood and Sletten are given in Table 12-1. The bromide end point tends to come late; for an equimolar mixture the relative error is 1.2 per cent for both halides. In general, *the shift of the inflection point is very nearly the same as the percentage coprecipitation at the equivalence point* for ideal heterogeneous solid solution formation and for any initial ratio of concentrations.

The second method of end-point detection, the extrapolation or intersection-point method, was recommended by Flood and Sletten[2] for

TABLE 12-1. CORRECTION FACTORS FOR BROMIDE-CHLORIDE MIXTURES

Mole fraction bromide	Correction for:		Mole fraction bromide	Correction for:	
	Bromide	Chloride		Bromide	Chloride
0.05	0.913	1.005	0.6	0.991	1.013
0.1	0.940	1.007	0.7	0.994	1.014
0.2	0.965	1.009	0.8	0.996	1.016
0.3	0.977	1.010	0.9	0.998	1.018
0.4	0.983	1.011	0.95	0.999	1.020
0.5	0.988	1.012			

[From Flood, H., and Sletten, E., *Z. anal. Chem.*, **115**, 30 (1938).]

bromide in the presence of chloride. More recently, its use has been advocated by Martin[3] for both intermediate end points in the titration of mixtures of all three halides. It is evident from inspection of Fig. 12-3 that the extrapolation method could not be successful if homogeneous

[1] Flood, *op. cit.*
[2] Flood and Sletten, *op. cit.*
[3] Martin, A. J., *Anal. Chem.*, **30**, 233 (1958).

solid solutions of chloride and bromide were formed. On the other hand, if heterogeneous solid solutions are formed, high results should be obtained for bromide and low results for chloride. Martin[1] found that the results for iodide also tended to be high, as might be expected from the shape of the experimental curve in Fig. 12-2. Thus the error in the bromide determination tends to be compensated for, and the most serious errors occur in the iodide and chloride end points if all three halides are present in about equal concentrations. By applying empirical correction factors Martin was able to make corrections for the end-point errors. The corrections became less successful as the ratios of halide concentrations deviated greatly from unity.

From what has been said about the effects of adsorption and solid solution formation, it is clear that any empirical correction procedure must be applied with caution. All conditions should be controlled so as to be as nearly as possible the same in running standard samples and in titrating unknowns.

12-5. Indicator Methods for Halide Determination

The Mohr method, based on the formation of orange-red silver chromate at the end point, dates back to 1856.[2] Many studies of the optimum titration conditions and the effects of interferences have been made, the latest as recently as 1957.[3] Although good results are possible both with bromide and with chloride, the method is especially widely used for chloride. The usual titration is carried out in the presence of about 0.005 M chromate.[4] Since the solubility product of silver chromate is approximately 2×10^{-12}, precipitation of silver chromate theoretically begins at pAg = 4.7. However, the experimental end point corresponds to pAg = 4.4 to 4.5 because an appreciable amount of silver chromate must be formed to give a visual end point.[5] The solubility product of silver chromate increases with rising temperature; to get good results the titrations should be performed at room temperature.

Corresponding to pAg = 4.4, the titration error is readily estimated for various concentrations of chloride. If $K_{sp,AgCl}$ is taken as 1.6×10^{-10}, the silver ion concentration at the end point is 4×10^{-5} M; the chloride ion concentration is 4×10^{-6}. The excess silver ion (3.6×10^{-5} M) corresponds to a percentage error of $3.6 \times 10^{-3}/C$, where C is the concentration of chloride, corrected for dilution to the end point. Thus, for

[1] *Ibid.*

[2] Mohr, F., *Ann. Chem. Liebigs*, **97**, 335 (1856).

[3] Belcher, R., MacDonald, A. M. G., and Parry, E., *Anal. Chim. Acta*, **16**, 524 (1957).

[4] Kolthoff, I. M., and Stenger, V. A., "Volumetric Analysis," 2d ed., vol. 2, p. 242, Interscience Publishers, Inc., New York, 1947.

[5] Kolthoff, *Z. anal. Chem.*, **56**, 498 (1917).

$C = 0.1$ M, the error is 0.036 per cent; for $C = 0.01$ M, the error is 0.36 per cent. For 0.1 M and 0.01 M bromide, the errors are 0.04 and 0.4 per cent, respectively.

Titration of thiocyanate and iodide is not successful because excessive adsorption of chromate gives a false end point.

A serious limitation of the Mohr method is that the pH should be in the range 6.5 to 10.3.[*] Below pH 6.5, the solubility of silver chromate becomes excessive, and above pH 10.3 coprecipitation of silver hydroxide occurs. Borax or sodium bicarbonate can be used conveniently to neutralize excess acid. By using a mixture of potassium chromate and dichromate in proportions such as to give a neutral solution, the danger of accidentally raising the pH of an unbuffered solution beyond the acceptable limits is minimized.[1] Particularly in the presence of ammonium salts, the pH should not exceed 7.2 because of the effect of appreciable concentrations of ammonia on the solubility of silver salts.

The Fajans Adsorption Indicator Method.[2] Fajans and his coworkers introduced an interesting class of indicators for precipitation reactions, in which the color change depends upon the adsorption of dye either on a positively or a negatively charged precipitate surface. For example, fluorescein is adsorbed as an anion on positively charged silver chloride, but rhodamine 6G is adsorbed as a cation on negatively charged silver bromide.[3] The adsorbed indicator exhibits a different color from that of the indicator in solution and, therefore, acts essentially as an indicator for *adsorbed lattice ions* (Sec. 10-2).

To illustrate the principle, consider the use of fluorescein, abbreviated HFl, as an indicator for the titration of chloride with silver nitrate. In the early part of the titration, the precipitate is negatively charged owing to adsorption of chloride ions. When the isoelectric point is passed, the charge changes sign because silver ions are adsorbed.

In a neutral solution, fluorescein is present largely in solution as the neutral molecule. The indicator reaction then is

$$\text{AgCl·Ag}^+ \mid \text{NO}_3^- + \text{HFl} \rightleftharpoons \text{AgCl·Ag}^+ \mid \text{Fl}^- + \text{NO}_3^- + \text{H}^+ \quad (12\text{-}9)$$

Essentially, the counter ions are displaced by indicator anions, with the formation of an adsorbed silver salt of the dye. It should be carefully noted that the silver salt of the dye does not form from silver ions in solution, but only on the surface of the solid. The change in color was attributed

[*] Belcher, MacDonald, and Parry, *op. cit.*

[1] *Ibid.*

[2] Fajans, K., in Brennecke, E. (ed.), "Neuere massanalytische Methoden," p. 161, Ferd. Enke Verlag, Stuttgart, 1935.

[3] Fajans, K., and Wolff, H., *Z. anorg. u. allgem. Chem.*, **137,** 221 (1924).

by Fajans and Hassel[1] to the strong deformation of the dye anion by the adsorbed silver ion.

Ideally, the color change should occur just at the isoelectric point, when the charge of the precipitate changes sign. However, it is necessary to consider the fact that the dye anion can compete with lattice anion for adsorption even when the lattice ion is present in excess. Also, the pH is an important variable, because the dye anion is in equilibrium with hydrogen ions in the solution. In fact, reaction (12-9) is reversed if the solution is only slightly acidic (pH < 6.5).* The upper pH limit (pH < 10) is imposed by the coprecipitation of silver hydroxide.

Kolthoff, Lauer, and Sunde[2] showed that dichlorofluorescein is useful in slightly acidic solutions (pH > 4) because it is a stronger acid than fluorescein.

Eosin (tetrabromofluorescein) is a much stronger acid than fluorescein[3] and can, therefore, be used for the titration of bromide, iodide, and thiocyanate in moderately acidic solution (pH > 2). In fact Kolthoff and van Berk[4] recommended acidification with acetic acid to enhance the color change. Chloride, however, cannot be titrated with eosin as the indicator because the eosinate ion displaces chloride ion from the surface of silver chloride, so the color change occurs at the beginning of the titration. Bromide, iodide, and thiocyanate, being more strongly adsorbed on their silver salts, are not displaced before the isoelectric point.

A disadvantage of adsorption indicators is that silver halides are sensitized to the action of light by a layer of adsorbed dye. For best results, the titrations should be carried out with minimum exposure to light.

Another factor to be considered in the application of adsorption indicators is that at least a portion of the precipitate must remain dispersed as a sol. Particularly with higher concentrations of halides, the precipitate tends to flocculate about 1 per cent before the end point. If the titration is continued slowly with vigorous shaking, the end point is marked by a sudden change to a reddish color. Kolthoff found the addition of dextrin as a protective colloid to be beneficial in the titration of chloride, but not of bromide or iodide. In the titration of more dilute solutions, coagulation is less of a problem, but the total amount of precipitate becomes so small that the color change becomes less pro-

[1] Fajans, K., and Hassel, O., Z. Elektrochem., **29**, 495 (1923).

* Kolthoff, Chem. Revs., **16**, 87 (1935).

[2] Kolthoff, I. M., Lauer, W. M., and Sunde, C. J., J. Am. Chem. Soc., **51**, 3273 (1929).

[3] Fajans and Wolff, op. cit.

[4] Kolthoff, I. M., and van Berk, L. H., Z. anal. Chem., **70**, 369 (1927).

nounced. The optimum concentration range is from 0.005 to 0.025 N halide.

Electrolytes, especially multivalent cations, cause difficulties due to coagulation of the precipitate. This limitation is more severe with eosin than with fluorescein or dichlorofluorescein.

A somewhat different mechanism prevails in the operation of p-ethoxy-chrysoidin, $C_2H_5OC_6H_4N{=}NC_6H_4(NH_2)_2$, which has been used by Schulek and Pungor[1] as an adsorption indicator in the titration of iodide with silver. The indicator is adsorbed on both sides of the isoelectric point. In the presence of excess silver, the indicator is adsorbed as neutral molecules, which exhibit a yellow color. In the presence of excess iodide, the red cationic form is adsorbed. The pK_{In} value in water solution is 4.5, but is considerably shifted on the precipitate surface owing to preferential adsorption of one form of the indicator. On a positively charged surface pK_{In} is decreased; on a negatively charged surface it is increased, as compared with water, the total shift being of the order of 4 pK units. The pH must be held between 4 and 7 to observe an end point. A limitation is that only iodide can be titrated directly because the adsorptive tendencies of the other halides are insufficient.

Iodide cannot be titrated in the presence of chloride or bromide because these ions are adsorbed on the silver iodide surface and interfere by giving high results.[2] Schulek and Pungor[3] determined chloride, bromide, and thiocyanate by an indirect procedure involving the addition of excess silver followed by back-titration with iodide. The procedure involves coagulation of the initial precipitate to prevent its interaction with iodide. It does not appear to possess appreciable advantages over the conventional Volhard procedure, which is also an indirect one.

The Volhard Method. The original procedure of Volhard[4] involves the addition of an excess of silver ion to a solution of halide, followed by the back-titration of the excess silver ion with thiocyanate, using ferric ion as the indicator. The end point is marked by the appearance of a red color due to the formation of $FeSCN^{++}$:

$$SCN^- + Fe^{3+} \rightleftharpoons FeSCN^{++} \qquad K = 138 \qquad \text{at } \mu = 0.50 \quad (12\text{-}10)^*$$

Higher complexes, $Fe(SCN)_2^+$, etc., are important only at higher concentrations of thiocyanate.

No particular difficulties are experienced in the determination of bromide or thiocyanate, and the advantage is gained over the Mohr and

[1] Schulek, E., and Pungor, E., *Anal. Chim. Acta*, **4**, 109, 213 (1950).

[2] Pungor, *Acta Chim. Acad. Sci. Hung.*, **12**, 265 (1957).

[3] Schulek and Pungor, *op. cit.*

[4] Volhard, J., *J. prakt. Chem.*, **9**, 217 (1874); *Ann. Chem. Liebigs*, **190**, 1 (1878).

* Frank, H. S., and Oswalt, R. L., *J. Am. Chem. Soc.*, **69**, 1321 (1947).

Fajans procedures that even relatively strongly acid solutions can be titrated. Indeed, acid must be added, if it is not already present, to prevent hydrolysis of ferric iron. The precipitated thiocyanate adsorbs silver ions, thereby causing a false end point, which, however, disappears with vigorous shaking. The final end point gives accurate results, even in dilute solutions (10^{-3} N). In the determination of iodide, care must be taken to add excess silver ion before adding the ferric iron, to avoid the oxidation of iodide by the reaction

$$2Fe^{3+} + 2I^- \rightleftharpoons 2Fe^{++} + I_2 \tag{12-11}$$

In the determination of chloride, precautions must be taken to avoid the interaction of silver chloride and thiocyanate ion. From the equilibrium constant of the reaction

$$AgCl(solid) + SCN^- \rightleftharpoons AgSCN(solid) + Cl^-$$

$$K = \frac{K_{sp,AgCl}}{K_{sp,AgSCN}} \cong \frac{10^{-10}}{10^{-12}} = 100 \tag{12-12}$$

it follows that thiocyanate has a pronounced tendency to react with solid silver chloride and that a considerable excess must be added to give a red color with ferric iron. Kolthoff[1] found that 2.5 ml of 0.1 N thiocyanate had to be added to 100 ml of a suspension of silver chloride to produce a permanent color with ferric iron.

To avoid the interaction of solid silver chloride, Rosanoff and Hill[2] recommended that the precipitate be filtered after the suspension had been boiled for a few minutes to coagulate the silver chloride and thus remove most of the adsorbed silver ion from its surface before filtration. Schulek and coworkers[3] have found the addition of potassium nitrate as a coagulant, followed by 3 min of boiling, to be very effective.

Various immiscible liquids have been used to coat the silver chloride particles and thereby protect them from interaction with thiocyanate. The most successful is nitrobenzene,[4] which gives good results when the chloride concentration is above about 0.02 M.

Swift and coworkers[5] showed that the error can in principle be avoided by increasing the concentration of ferric ion. To avoid error, the end-point condition is that the total moles of silver must be equal to the sum

[1] Kolthoff, Z. anal. Chem., **56**, 568 (1917).

[2] Rosanoff, M. A., and Hill, A. E., J. Am. Chem. Soc., **29**, 269 (1907).

[3] Schulek, E., Pungor, E., and Kéthelyi, J., Anal. Chim. Acta, **8**, 229 (1953).

[4] Caldwell, J. R., and Moyer, H. V., Ind. Eng. Chem., Anal. Ed., **7**, 38 (1935).

[5] Swift, E. H., Arcand, G. M., Lutwack, R., and Meier, D. J., Anal. Chem. **22**, 306 (1950).

of the moles of chloride plus thiocyanate. If n represents numbers of moles, then

$$n_{Ag^+} + n_{AgCl} + n_{AgSCN} = n_{AgCl} + n_{Cl^-} + n_{AgSCN} + n_{SCN^-} + n_{FeSCN^{++}}$$

or

$$n_{Ag^+} = n_{Cl^-} + n_{SCN^-} + n_{FeSCN^{++}}$$

or, in terms of concentrations,

$$[Ag^+] = [Cl^-] + [SCN^-] + [FeSCN^{++}] \qquad (12\text{-}13)$$

The concentration of $FeSCN^{++}$ necessary to give a detectable red color was estimated by experiment to be 6.4×10^{-6} M. From Eq. (12-12), $[SCN^-] = 0.01[Cl^-]$, and $[Ag^+] = 10^{-10}/[Cl^-]$. From the quadratic solution of Eq. (12-13), $[Cl^-] = 7.2 \times 10^{-6}$, and

$$[SCN^-] = 7.2 \times 10^{-8}$$

From Eq. (12-10), $[Fe^{3+}] = 0.64$ M.

The calculated concentration of ferric iron, 0.64 M, is so high that the solution would be too highly colored to permit the sensitive detection of the end point. However, it was estimated by calculation and confirmed by experiment that, for a final concentration of 0.025 M, an error of only 0.1 per cent is caused by lowering the ferric ion concentration to 0.2 M, which is not so intensely colored as to interfere seriously. A direct titration of chloride was proposed, in which a solution containing 0.2 M ferric iron and a small amount of thiocyanate is titrated with silver nitrate to the disappearance of the red color.

12-6. Titration of Fluoride with Thorium(IV)

The most important method of determination of fluoride is its titration with thorium nitrate. Various modifications of a procedure originally devised by Willard and Winter[1] are widely used.

The first step is a distillation of fluoride as hexafluorosilicic acid, which is usually necessary because of many interferences in the titration. Clifford[2] has made a critical study of the distillation procedure, which is best carried out using perchloric acid and regulating the addition of water to maintain a temperature of 135 to 140°C.

Murty and coworkers[3] have claimed that phosphoric or sulfuric acid is superior to perchloric acid in the distillation in overcoming the retarding effects of large amounts of alumina, silica, or iron oxide which tend to prevent the complete volatilization of fluoride. Their procedure, how-

[1] Willard, H. H., and Winter, O. B., *Ind. Eng. Chem., Anal. Ed.,* **5,** 7 (1933).

[2] Clifford, P. A., *J. Assoc. Offic. Agr. Chemists,* **24,** 350 (1941).

[3] Murty, G. V. L. N., Viswanathan, T. S., and Ramakrishna, V., *Anal. Chim. Acta,* **16,** 213 (1953).

ever, requires a cumbersome precipitation and filtration scheme to remove the interfering phosphate and sulfate from the distillate.

In the original Willard and Winter procedure a lake of Zr(IV) and sodium alizarin 3-sulfonate (alizarin red S) was used as the indicator. Later, Armstrong[1] found that the Zr(IV) could be omitted, the end point being detected by observing the formation of a red thorium alizarin lake. Sodium alizarin sulfonate is an acid-base indicator, exhibiting a yellow color in acid solution and a red color in alkaline solution. It is, therefore, beneficial to buffer the solution with a monochloroacetic acid buffer, at pH 3.5 in 50 per cent ethanol or at pH 3.0 in water.[2-4]

Milton, Liddell, and Chivers[5] recommended solochrome brilliant blue (color index 723) over alizarin since it has a more rapid and sensitive color-change reaction.

12-7. Titration of Sulfate with Barium Ion

On the basis of solubility considerations, barium ion is the most favorable precipitant for sulfate. Unfortunately, the complications due to coprecipitation are so severe that highly accurate results cannot be expected. If other precipitants, e.g., lead ion or benzidine, are chosen, the solubility is so high that special methods, such as determining the excess reagent after filtration, or extrapolation methods of end-point detection are necessary. Nevertheless, for control work a titrimetric procedure is often sufficiently accurate and is much more rapid than the gravimetric method.

Sodium rhodizonate serves as an indicator for barium ion, but the color change is satisfactory only in a back-titration procedure involving the addition of excess barium ion.[6,7] Tetrahydroxyquinone can be used for the forward titration,[8] but the accuracy is only of the order of 3 per cent.[9]

Fritz and Freeland[10] introduced sodium alizarin 3-sulfonate (alizarin red S) as an indicator for the direct titration, using 30 to 40 per cent alcohol as the solvent. By using a cation exchange column to remove interfering cations, a rapid titrimetric procedure was evolved. Errors

[1] Armstrong, W. D., J. Am. Chem. Soc., 55, 1741 (1933).

[2] Hoskins, W. M., and Ferris, C. A., Ind. Eng. Chem., Anal. Ed., 8, 6 (1936).

[3] Armstrong, Ind. Eng. Chem., Anal. Ed., 8, 384 (1936).

[4] Rawley, R. J., and Churchill, H. V., Ind. Eng. Chem., Anal. Ed., 9, 551 (1937).

[5] Milton, R. F., Liddell, H. F., and Chivers, J. E., Analyst, 72, 43 (1947).

[6] Mutschin, A., and Pollack, R., Z. anal. Chem., 108, 8 (1937).

[7] Miller, C. C., J. Chem. Soc., 1940, 401.

[8] Schroeder, W. C., Ind. Eng. Chem., Anal. Ed., 5, 403 (1933).

[9] Sheen, R. T., and Kahler, H. L., Ind. Eng. Chem., Anal. Ed., 8, 127 (1936); 10, 206 (1938).

[10] Fritz, J. S., and Freeland, M. Q., Anal. Chem., 26, 1593 (1954).

due to anion coprecipitation are still present, but the method appears to offer considerable promise as a control procedure.

12-8. Titration of Zinc with Ferrocyanide

If an acidic solution of zinc ions is titrated with potassium ferrocyanide, a precipitate of potassium zinc ferrocyanide is formed according to the equation

$$3Zn^{++} + 2K^+ + 2Fe(CN)_6^{4-} \rightarrow K_2Zn_3\{Fe(CN)_6\}_2 \qquad (12\text{-}14)$$

The stoichiometry has been studied in detail, particularly by Kolthoff and Pearson[1] and by Richardson and Bryson.[2] The solution must be distinctly acidic to prevent the formation of the normal zinc ferrocyanide. Under favorable conditions, e.g., at a sulfuric acid concentration of 1.7 to 2.1 N in the presence of 1.5 g of ammonium sulfate or larger amounts of potassium sulfate per 100 ml, the results are low by about 1 per cent, but are reproducible within ± 0.2 per cent.[3]

To detect the end point, it is convenient to add a small quantity of ferricyanide and to detect the sudden change in potential at the end point either by direct measurement or by the use of a redox indicator. At the end point, the concentration of ferrocyanide increases suddenly, and the potential decreases correspondingly:

$$E = E^{o\prime} + \frac{RT}{F} \ln \frac{[Fe(CN)_6^{3-}]}{[Fe(CN)_6^{4-}]} \qquad (12\text{-}15)$$

Cone and Cady[4] introduced the use of diphenylamine or diphenyl-benzidine as redox indicators for the titration of zinc. Various other indicators, notably p-ethoxychrysoidin[5] and 3,3'-dimethylnaphthidine sulfonic acid[6] have been proposed.

A curious "false end point," in which the indicator prematurely shows its reduced color, is commonly observed in the direct titration of zinc with ferrocyanide.[7,8] If the solution is allowed to stand, the oxidized color gradually returns, and a sharp end point is eventually observed. Richardson and Bryson[3] found a dip in potential coinciding with the false end point, followed by a rise corresponding to the return of the

[1] Kolthoff, I. M., and Pearson, E. A., *Ind. Eng. Chem., Anal. Ed.*, **4**, 147 (1932).
[2] Richardson, M. R., and Bryson, A., *Analyst*, **78**, 291 (1953).
[2] *Ibid.*
[4] Cone, W H., and Cady, L. C., *J. Am. Chem. Soc.*, **49**, 356 (1927).
[5] Tyler, W. P., *Ind. Eng. Chem., Anal. Ed.*, **14**, 114 (1942).
[6] Belcher, R., Nutten, A. J., and Stephen, W. I., *J. Chem. Soc.*, **1952**, 1269.
[7] Kolthoff and Pearson, *op. cit.*
[8] Richardson and Bryson, *op. cit.*

indicator color. The false end point was ascribed to adsorption of zinc ions by the precipitate before the end point. As the isoelectric point is passed, the precipitate coagulates, releasing zinc ions which use up the temporary excess of ferrocyanide.

Kolthoff and Pearson[1] recommended adding an excess of ferrocyanide and back-titrating, to avoid the false end point. They also used direct and back-titrations at 60°C to permit more rapid titrations. Richardson and Bryson found that, if the acidity was increased from 1 N to 2 N in sulfuric acid, a direct titration gave the most favorable results.

PROBLEMS

12-1. Show that, for the precipitation of a salt MA, the relative precision is given approximately by $\sqrt{K_{sp}}/C$.

12-2. Derive Eq. (12-2). *Hint:* Set the second derivative of pM with respect to X equal to zero.

12-3. Calculate several points on curve C, Fig. 12-3, assuming that a solution initially 0.01 M in bromide and chloride is titrated without dilution with silver ion. Take $K_{sp,AgCl} = 2 \times 10^{-10}$, $K_{sp,AgBr} = 5 \times 10^{-13}$, $D = 0.0025$, and assume homogeneous solid solution formation.

12-4. Neglecting coprecipitation, calculate the ratio of chloride to bromide concentration at which the positive and negative errors in the bromide titration would just cancel if all three halides were present. *Ans.* 0.125.

12-5. In the Mohr titration of bromide, what concentration of chromate would be theoretically required in order that the precipitation of silver chromate should just begin at the equivalence point? If a concentration of 0.002 M is actually used, what is the relative error, when titrating 0.01 M bromide? *Ans.* 5 M; 3.2 per cent.

12-6. In Swift's modification of the Volhard method for the direct titration of chloride, confirm the estimated error of 0.1 per cent when using $Fe^{3+} = 0.2$ at a final concentration of 0.025 per cent. What would be the error if a ferric iron concentration of 0.1 M were used? *Ans.* −0.2 per cent.

12-7. One liter of a solution containing 0.1 mole of bromide and 0.01 mole of chloride is treated with 0.1 mole of silver ion. Assuming that a homogeneous solid solution is formed, calculate the percentage of the chloride that is precipitated. *Ans.* 85.5 per cent.

12-8. If 0.01 M chloride is adjusted to pH 11.3 and titrated to the first appearance of silver oxide, what is the theoretical titration error?[2] Take $K_{sp,Ag_2O} = [Ag^+] \cdot [OH^-] = 5 \times 10^{-8}$, and $K_{sp,AgCl} = 2 \times 10^{-10}$, and neglect dilution. *Ans.* 0.17 per cent.

---

[1] Kolthoff and Pearson, *op. cit.*

[2] See Loscalzo, A. G., and Benedetti-Pichler, A. A., *Anal. Chem.*, **30**, 2018 (1958).

13. Complex Formation Titrations

Until relatively recently, complex formation titrations were of minor significance in analytical chemistry. In 1945 Schwarzenbach[1] published the first of a series of fundamental studies of aminopolycarboxylic acids as analytical reagents. Of these reagents, ethylenediaminetetraacetic acid, sometimes called (ethylenedinitrilo)-tetraacetic acid, and usually abbreviated EDTA, has become one of the most important of all the reagents used in titrimetry. Another important contribution made by Schwarzenbach and his coworkers was the use of metal ion indicators, or substances that respond to changes in metal ion activity in a manner analogous to the response of acid-base indicators to changes in hydrogen ion activity. The first of these indicators to be described was murexide,[2] as an indicator for calcium and other metal ions. So rapidly has this subject developed that by 1957 some 950 references had been listed by Welcher,[3] who presented an exhaustive review of analytical applications. The fundamental equilibria are considered in the important monograph of Schwarzenbach, which was later translated by Irving.[4]

13-1. Requirements for Titration Reactions Involving Complex Formation

Like other types of titrimetric reactions, complex formation reactions must be rapid, stoichiometric, and quantitative. Most reactions involving the formation of inorganic complexes fail to fulfill one or more of these requirements, which will be considered in turn.

[1] Schwarzenbach, G., *Schweiz. Chemiker-Ztg. u. Tech. Ind.*, **28**, 377 (1945).

[2] Schwarzenbach, G., and Gysling, H., *Helv. Chim. Acta*, **32**, 1314 (1949).

[3] Welcher, F. J., "The Analytical Uses of Ethylenediaminetetraacetic Acid," D. Van Nostrand Company, Inc., Princeton, N.J., 1958.

[4] Schwarzenbach, "Complexometric Titrations," translated by H. Irving, Methuen & Co., Ltd., London; Interscience Publishers, Inc., New York, 1957.

Taube[1] has classified a large number of complexes on the basis of the rates of complex formation and substitution reactions (Table 13-1). "Labile" complexes undergo relatively rapid exchange or substitution of ligands in comparison with the "inert" complexes. Another classification, based upon electronic structure, distinguishes between "inner orbital" or "outer orbital" configurations, depending upon whether electrons from a "lower shell" (principal quantum number) are involved in the coordination reaction. The "inert" complexes are mainly of inner orbital configuration (Table 13-1), and these are characterized by a structure in which *all the inner d orbitals are occupied by at least one electron*. The relatively few inert complexes of the outer orbital structure

TABLE 13-1. TAUBE'S CLASSIFICATION OF COMPLEXES

	Inner orbital	Outer orbital
Labile complexes	La(III), Ce(IV), Ti(III), Ti(IV), V(III), V(IV), Nb(V), Ta(V), Mo(V), Mo(VI), W(V), W(VI)	Al(III), Mn(II), Fe(II), Fe(III), Co(II), Ni(II), Zn(II), Cd(II), Hg(II)
Inert complexes	V(II), Cr(III), Mo(III), Mn(III), Mn(IV), Fe(II), Fe(III), Co(III), Pt(IV)	SiF_6^-, PF_6^-, $SbCl_6^-$

[Taube, H., *Chem. Revs.*, **50**, 69 (1952).]

are characterized by *a central ion of high charge*. Most outer orbital structures are labile. Some ions can form complexes of either the inner or outer orbital structure. For example the complexes of Fe(II) or Fe(III) with cyanide or 1,10-phenanthroline are inner orbital and inert, whereas practically all other complexes of these ions are outer orbital and labile. It is evident from Table 13-1 that many complex formation reactions must be ruled out on the basis of reaction rate as far as titrimetry is concerned. Many of the most stable complexes, such as those of Co(III) and Cr(III), fall into the classification inert and are formed slowly and incompletely unless a great excess of complexing agent is present. The EDTA complex of Cr(III) is quite stable (formation constant $= 10^{23}$),* but it is formed very slowly, even upon warming.[2] The Co(III) complex CoY^- is formed slowly by replacement of the ligands of other Co(III)

[1] Taube, H., *Chem. Revs.*, **50**, 69 (1952).
* Schwarzenbach, "Complexometric Titrations."
[2] Hamm, R. E., *J. Am. Chem. Soc.*, **75**, 5670 (1953).

complexes or, better, by oxidation of the Co(II) complex $CoY^=$,* which is formed rapidly from the aquated ion.

Turning now to stoichiometry, we find that the *monodentate ligands*, or coordinating agents that occupy a single coordination position, like NH_3 or CN^-, are invariably added in a succession of steps.[1] Unless one particular step happens to be extraordinarily stable, there will be no extended range of concentration of complexing agent over which a single species of complex is formed (except for the last, or highest, complex). The most important examples of titrations based on monodentate ligands are those involving halide complexes of Hg(II) and the cyanide complex of silver, which will be discussed below. The importance of EDTA as a titrimetric reagent lies largely in the fact that, being a polydentate ligand, it forms very stable 1:1 complexes with many metal ions. The problem of a succession of overlapping complexes, therefore, does not occur.

The third factor of quantitativeness, or completeness, is governed by the stability of the complex, which in turn is favored by the formation of a polydentate complex. Schwarzenbach[2] has used the term "chelate effect" to describe the enhanced stability of a complex that involves the formation of a ring or chelate structure, compared with a similar complex involving no ring formation. The following factors contribute to the unusual stability of complexes of metal ions with the EDTA anion $(^-OOCCH_2)_2NCH_2CH_2N(CH_2COO^-)_2$:

1. The chelate effect becomes more pronounced as the number of chelate rings per ligand molecule increases. The EDTA anion has six possible positions of attachment and, indeed, is known*,[3] to act as a hexadentate ligand in the ion CoY^-. In other cases, EDTA may occupy only four or five coordination positions.[4]

2. The chelate effect is most pronounced for five-membered rings.[5] The EDTA anion forms five-membered rings (including the metal ion) both when the carboxylate group and the nitrogen atoms are involved and when the two nitrogen atoms act as electron-pair donors.

Schwarzenbach[2] found that, if the number of —CH_2— groups between the two central nitrogen atoms is increased from 2 to 3 or more, the stability of the metal ion complexes is decreased.

* Schwarzenbach, *Helv. Chim. Acta*, **32**, 839 (1949).

[1] Bjerrum, J., "Metal Ammine Formation in Aqueous Solution," P. Haase and Son, Copenhagen, 1941; reprinted 1957.

[2] Schwarzenbach, *Helv. Chim. Acta*, **35**, 2344 (1952).

[3] Busch, D. H., and Bailar, J. C., Jr., *J. Am. Chem. Soc.*, **75**, 4574 (1953).

[4] Schwarzenbach, *Helv. Chim. Acta*, **32**, 839 (1949).

[5] Irving, H., Williams, R. J. P., Ferrett, D. J., and Williams, A. E., *J. Chem. Soc.*, **1954**, 3494.

13-2. Titration of Halides with Mercury(II)

If chloride ion is titrated with Hg(II), for example, as mercury(II) nitrate, the reaction

$$2Cl^- + Hg^{++} \rightleftharpoons HgCl_2 \tag{13-1}$$

is essentially stoichiometric, as shown by the successive stepwise formation constants[1] of the ion $HgCl_4^-$: $k_1 = 5.5 \times 10^6$, $k_2 = 3.0 \times 10^6$, $k_3 = 7$, $k_4 = 10$. Sodium nitroprusside, $Na_2Fe(CN)_5NO$, was introduced as an indicator by Votoček.[2] The end point is relatively sensitive, being observed as a white turbidity in a clear solution, and the method has the advantage of being applicable in acidic solution. However, owing to the interaction of excess Hg(II) with the $HgCl_2$ formed during the titration

$$Hg^{++} + HgCl_2 \rightleftharpoons 2HgCl^+ \qquad K_{eq} = \frac{k_1}{k_2} = 1.8 \tag{13-2}$$

an excess of Hg(II) must be added before a sufficient concentration exists to respond to the indicator. Kolthoff and Stenger[3] list correction values, which depend on the concentration of mercuric chloride and, hence, on the total volume and concentration of the sample. The corrections also depend on the acidity of the solution and on the method of viewing the mixture and must, therefore, be determined by each worker for his own experimental conditions.

Dubský and Trtílek[4] used diphenyl carbazide and diphenyl carbazone as indicators. These compounds form blue-violet complexes that are sensitive indicators for Hg(II). The diphenyl carbazone reaction, which may be written

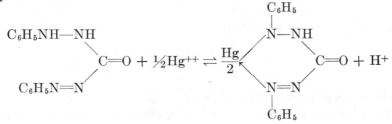

is evidently influenced by pH. In practice, Roberts[5] found good results

[1] Johnson, A., Quarfort, I., and Sillén, L. G., *Acta Chem. Scand.*, **1**, 461, 473 (1947).

[2] Votoček, E., *Chemiker-Ztg.*, **42**, 257, 271, 371 (1918).

[3] Kolthoff, I. M., and Stenger, V. A., "Volumetric Analysis," 2d ed., Interscience Publishers, Inc., New York, 1947.

[4] Dubský, J. V., and Trtílek, J., *Mikrochemie*, **12**, 315 (1933); **15**, 95 (1934).

[5] Roberts, I., *Ind. Eng. Chem., Anal. Ed.*, **8**, 365 (1936).

with diphenyl carbazide only at pH 1.5 to 2.0, and Clarke[1] found the best results with diphenyl carbazone at a pH of 3.0 to 3.5. The sharpness of the end-point color change was improved by using the greenish-yellow acid color of bromphenol blue as a background color, and bromphenol blue was used conveniently also in the adjustment of pH.

The mercurimetric method is suitable for titration of chlorides in very dilute solution, even in the 0 to 10 or 0 to 100 ppm range in natural waters. Bromide, thiocyanate, and cyanide may be determined by similar methods, with suitable adjustment of conditions,[2] but there is no particular advantage over the usual silver methods.

The titration of iodide differs from that of chloride because of the relative insolubility of mercury(II) iodide and the relatively great tendency to form complexes. The successive values of log k for the formation of $HgI_4^=$ at an ionic strength of 0.5 are as follows:[3] log $k_1 = 12.9$, log $k_2 = 10.9$, log $k_3 = 3.8$, log $k_4 = 2.2$. The solubility of HgI_2 is 7.4×10^{-5} M.

The titration of iodide with Hg(II) will result at first in the formation of the tetraiodo complex

$$4I^- + Hg^{++} \rightleftharpoons HgI_4^= \qquad \log K_4 = 29.8 \qquad (13\text{-}3)$$

followed by the precipitation of mercury(II) iodide

$$HgI_4^= + Hg^{++} \rightleftharpoons 2HgI_2 \qquad K_{eq} = \frac{k_1 k_2}{k_3 k_4 (S°)^2} \qquad (13\text{-}4)$$

where $S° =$ intrinsic solubility of HgI_2.

The appearance of the red precipitate was used as long ago as 1832 by Marozeau[4] to mark the end point of this reaction. It has long been recognized that the end point comes too soon, because of the dissociation

$$HgI_4^= \rightleftharpoons HgI_2(\text{soln}) + 2I^- \qquad K = \frac{1}{k_3 k_4} = 10^{-6} \qquad (13\text{-}5)$$

which occurs just before the end point.

The iodide ion concentration at the appearance of the precipitate is given by setting the concentration of HgI_2 equal to the solubility value, or

$$\frac{[I^-]^2[HgI_2]}{[HgI_4^=]} = \frac{[I^-]^2 \times 7.4 \times 10^{-5}}{[HgI_4^=]} = 10^{-6}$$

[1] Clarke, F. E., Anal. Chem., **22**, 553 (1950).
[2] Kolthoff and Stenger, op. cit.
[3] Sillén, Acta Chem. Scand., **3**, 539 (1949).
[4] Marozeau, J., Pharm. Chim., **18**, 302 (1832).

For a titration of 0.1 M iodide with 0.1 M mercuric ion, the end-point concentration of tetraiodomercurate(II) ion is 0.02 M, and the corresponding iodide concentration is 1.6×10^{-2} M. Thus the end point occurs considerably too early. The experimental correction values are so large[1] (of the order of 1 ml) as to make the titration of little practical value. However, in a recent paper,[2] it is stated that, in 96 per cent ethanol with diphenyl carbazone as indicator, iodide can be successfully titrated with mercuric nitrate because the alcohol prevents the appearance of a premature turbidity.

13-3. Titration of Cyanide with Silver(I)

If a solution of cyanide is titrated with silver nitrate, the complex $Ag(CN)_2^-$ is quantitatively formed:

$$2CN^- + Ag^+ \rightleftharpoons Ag(CN)_2^- \qquad K_{eq} = K_2 = 7 \times 10^{19} \qquad (13\text{-}6)$$

with the addition of more silver ion, silver cyanide is precipitated:

$$Ag(CN)_2^- + Ag^+ \rightleftharpoons 2AgCN(\text{solid})$$

The solubility equilibrium of silver cyanide can be written either as

$$AgCN(\text{solid}) \rightleftharpoons Ag^+ + CN^- \qquad \qquad K_{sp} = [Ag^+][CN^-]$$
$$= 1.2 \times 10^{-16} \qquad (13\text{-}7)$$

or as

$$Ag\{Ag(CN)_2\}(\text{solid}) \rightleftharpoons Ag^+ + Ag(CN)_2^- \qquad K'_{sp} = [Ag^+][Ag(CN)_2]$$
$$= K_2 K_{sp}^2 = 10^{-12} \qquad (13\text{-}8)$$

If $S°$ is the intrinsic solubility of AgCN, $K_{sp} = S°/k_1$, where k_1 is the formation constant of the complex AgCN in solution. Therefore, $K'_{sp} = S°^2 K_2/k_1^2 = S°^2 k_2/k_1$. The original method of Liebig[3] was based on the appearance of a turbidity of silver cyanide to mark the end point of the complexation reaction. The precipitation occurs slightly before the equivalence point, as shown by the following approximate calculation.

Example 13-1. Estimate the titration error for the Liebig titration of 0.2 M cyanide with 0.1 M silver ion.

Answer. The end point concentration of $Ag(CN)_2^-$ is 0.05 M. Ignoring hydrolysis of the cyanide ion and the formation of AgCN, and recalling that at the equivalence point $[Ag^+] = [CN^-]/2$, we can calculate $[Ag^+] = 5.6 \times 10^{-8}$ M at the equivalence point. The end point, taken as the point of precipitation of silver cyanide, occurs when $[Ag^+] = K'_{sp}/[Ag(CN)_2^-] = 10^{-12}/0.05 = 2 \times 10^{-11}$. The corresponding titration error may be estimated by letting X be the fraction of the stoichiometric amount of silver added at the end point. Then we find that the cyanide concentration is $0.1(1 - X)$, remembering that a twofold dilution has occurred. Solving the forma-

[1] Kolthoff and Stenger, *op. cit.*
[2] Zamanov, R. Kh., *Zhur. Anal. Khim.*, **11**, 329 (1956).
[3] Liebig, J., *Ann. Chem. Liebigs*, **77**, 102 (1851).

tion-constant equation (13-6), we obtain

$$\frac{0.05}{(0.1)^2(1 - X)^2 \, 2 \times 10^{-11}} = 7 \times 10^{19}$$

whence $1 - X = 6 \times 10^{-5}$, corresponding to an error of 0.006 per cent.

The error, calculated more rigorously and taking into consideration the hydrolysis of cyanide,[1] turns out to be 0.018 per cent. Actually, this titration would be theoretically satisfactory, but in practice silver cyanide precipitated locally before the end point is very slow to redissolve and the titration is quite time-consuming.

In the Denigès[2] modification of the Liebig method, potassium iodide ($\sim$0.01 M) is used as the indicator, and ammonia ($\sim$0.2 M) is introduced to solubilize silver cyanide. The end point is marked by the appearance of a turbidity due to silver iodide and occurs theoretically when $[Ag^+] = K_{sp,AgI}/[I^-] = 8.5 \times 10^{-17}/0.01 = 8.5 \times 10^{-15}$. To estimate the titration error, consider the equilibrium

$$Ag(CN)_2^- + 2NH_3 \rightleftharpoons Ag(NH_3)_2^+ + 2CN^- \qquad K = \frac{K_{2,Ag(NH_3)_2^+}}{K_{2,Ag(CN)_2^-}}$$

Then $$K = \frac{1.6 \times 10^7}{7 \times 10^{19}} = 2.3 \times 10^{-13}$$

Example 13-2. Estimate the titration error for the Liebig-Denigès titration of 0.2 M cyanide with 0.1 M silver ion, taking the end point concentrations of iodide and ammonia to be 0.01 M and 0.2 M, respectively.

Answer. At the equivalence point, let $y = [Ag(NH_3)_2^+] = [CN^-]/2$. The concentration $[Ag(CN^-)_2]$ at the end point is 0.05 M.

Then $$\frac{y(2y)^2}{0.05 \times (0.2)^2} = 2.3 \times 10^{-13} \qquad \text{and} \qquad y = 5 \times 10^{-6}$$
$$[CN^-] = 2y = 10^{-5}$$
$$[Ag^+] = \frac{0.05}{7 \times 10^{19} \times (10^{-5})^2} = 7 \times 10^{-12}$$

Consequently, the end point occurs before the equivalence point.

Let X be the fraction of the stoichiometric quantity of silver added at the end point. The cyanide concentration is $0.1(1 - X)$; so

$$\frac{0.05}{(0.1)^2(1 - X)^2 \times 8.5 \times 10^{-15}} = 7 \times 10^{19}$$

whence $1 - X = 2.9 \times 10^{-3}$, corresponding to an error of 0.29 per cent.

In the above example, the hydrolysis of cyanide is largely repressed by the hydroxyl ion furnished by the ammonia. If the initial concentration of cyanide is 0.02 M and if the titration is carried out with 0.01 M silver ion, the final concentration of $Ag(CN)_2^-$ is 0.005 M, and the theoretical error is 0.9 per cent.

[1] Ricci, J. E., *Anal. Chem.*, **25**, 1650 (1953).
[2] Denigès, G., *Compt. rend.*, **117**, 1078 (1893).

In actual practice, the visual end point has been proved to be accurate within 0.2 per cent and probably within 0.1 per cent, by reference to pure potassium cyanide[1] and to the potentiometric end point.[1,2] An end point is visible down to a concentration of 2×10^{-4} M, and results accurate to within 1 per cent can be obtained at a concentration of 2×10^{-3} M cyanide.[3]

13-4. Determination of Metals by Cyanide Titration

The reaction between silver and cyanide ions can be utilized indirectly for the determination of several metals, notably nickel, cobalt, copper, and zinc, which form stable, stoichiometric complexes with cyanide. For example, if a Ni(II) salt, in ammoniacal solution, is treated with an excess of cyanide, the ion $Ni(CN)_4^=$ is quantitatively formed. Since it is more stable than $Ag(CN)_2^-$, the excess cyanide can be determined by the Liebig-Denigès method.[4,5]

It is, however, possible to avoid a back titration by adding to the ammoniacal solution of Ni(II), potassium iodide and a few drops of standard silver nitrate to produce an opalescence due to silver iodide and then titrating with standard potassium cyanide solution[6] to the disappearance of the turbidity. It is advantageous to titrate the bulk of the nickel, as shown by the fading of the color of the tetrammine nickel(II) ion, before adding the silver nitrate. In accurate work, correction is made for the cyanide required to react with the silver iodide.

Cobalt may be determined[7] by a method involving the addition of a controlled excess of cyanide in a mildly alkaline solution followed by air oxidation of the cobalt under carefully specified conditions to produce a cobalt(III)-cyanide complex of ratio 1:5. After the addition of ammonia, the solution that contains iodide is treated with silver nitrate until a permanent turbidity of silver iodide is observed, then is back-titrated to a clear solution with cyanide. By this method the sum of cobalt and nickel is determined. To determine nickel in the presence of cobalt, Evans[8] has devised a procedure involving oxidation of Co(II) with hydrogen peroxide in the presence of ammonia and cyanide to form the very stable hexacyanocobaltate(III). After decomposition of the excess

[1] Thompson, M. R., *J. Research Natl. Bur. Standards*, **6**, 1051 (1931).

[2] Wick, R. M., *J. Research Natl. Bur. Standards*, **7**, 913 (1931).

[3] Laitinen, H. A., Jennings, W. P., and Parks, T. D., *Ind. Eng. Chem., Anal. Ed.*, **18**, 574 (1946).

[4] Moore, I., *Chem. News*, **72**, 92 (1895).

[5] Bayer, W. J., *Ind. Eng. Chem., Anal. Ed.*, **10**, 175 (1938).

[6] Kolthoff, I. M., and Griffith, F. S., *J. Phys. Chem.*, **42**, 542 (1938).

[7] Evans, B. S., *Analyst*, **62**, 363 (1937).

[8] *Ibid.*

peroxide and cyanide, the nickel is determined by the cyanide-silver method.

13-5. Ethylenediaminetetraacetic Acid (EDTA)

Schwarzenbach and Ackermann[1] determined the successive acid pK values of ethylenediaminetetraacetic acid, H_4Y, to be as follows: $pK_1 = 2.0$, $pK_2 = 2.67$, $pK_3 = 6.16$, $pK_4 = 10.26$ at 20°C and an ionic strength of 0.1. From the infrared spectra of the acid and its di- and tetrasodium salts, Chapman[2] concluded that the first and second protons

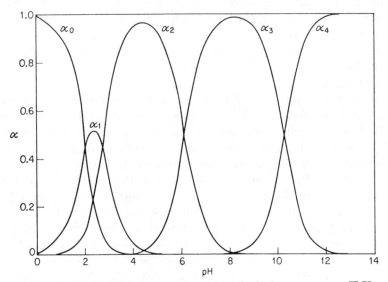

Fig. 13-1. Fraction of EDTA present in various ionic forms. α_0, as H_4Y: α_1, as H_3Y^-; α_2, as $H_2Y^=$; α_3, as HY^{3-}; α_4, as Y^{4-}.

are removed from opposite ends of the molecule. The divalent anion $H_2Y^=$ has a hydrogen-bonded structure in which the remaining two acidic protons are coordinated between the carboxyl group and carboxylate ion at each end of the molecule. This structure accounts for the much weaker third ionization step. The remaining acidic proton on the ion HY^{3-} migrates to a neighboring nitrogen atom; the large pK_4 value then corresponds to the removal of a proton from a nitrogen atom.

Ionization of EDTA. The fraction of EDTA in each of its ionic forms can be calculated at any pH value by the method described in Chap. 3, Sec. 3-5. The results of such a calculation are shown graphically in Fig. 13-1. The fraction α_4 present as the tetravalent anion is of particular

[1] Schwarzenbach, G., and Ackermann, H., *Helv. Chim. Acta.*, **31**, 1029 (1948).

[2] Chapman, D., *J. Chem. Soc.*, **1955**, 1766.

importance for equilibrium calculations. Its magnitude at various pH values is given in Table 13-2.

TABLE 13-2. VARIATION OF α_4 WITH pH

pH	$- \log \alpha_4$	pH	$- \log \alpha_4$
2.0	13.44	7.0	3.33
2.5	11.86	8.0	2.29
3.0	10.60	9.0	1.29
4.0	8.48	10.0	0.46
5.0	6.45	11.0	0.07
6.0	4.66	12.0	0.00

Formation of metal-EDTA complexes. The formation of metal- EDTA complexes may be represented by the equations:

$$M^{n+} + H_2Y^= \rightleftharpoons MY^{(n-4)+} + 2H^+ \qquad \text{pH 4 to 5} \qquad (13\text{-}9)$$
$$M^{n+} + HY^{3-} \rightleftharpoons MY^{(n-4)+} + H^+ \qquad \text{pH 7 to 9} \qquad (13\text{-}10)$$

in which metal ions of charge $n+$ displace the remaining protons from Y^{4-} ions to form the complex $MY^{(n-4)+}$.

The formation constants of the EDTA complexes of various metals, which are equilibrium constants of reactions of the type

$$M^{n+} + Y^{4-} \rightleftharpoons MY^{(n-4)+} \qquad K_{MY} = \frac{[MY^{(n-4)+}]}{[M^{n+}][Y^{4-}]} \qquad (13\text{-}11)$$

are listed in Table 13-3.

TABLE 13-3. FORMATION CONSTANTS OF EDTA COMPLEXES
20°C, ionic strength 0.1

Metal ion	$\log K_{MY}$	Metal ion	$\log K_{MY}$
Fe^{3+}	25.1	Al^{3+}	16.13
Th^{4+}	23.2	La^{3+}	15.50
Hg^{++}	21.80	Fe^{++}	14.33
Cu^{++}	18.80	Mn^{++}	13.79
Ni^{++}	18.62	Ca^{++}	10.70
Pb^{++}	18.04	Mg^{++}	8.69
Zn^{++}	16.50	Sr^{++}	8.63
Cd^{++}	16.46	Ba^{++}	7.76
Co^{++}	16.31	Ag^+	7.3

[With permission from Schwarzenbach, G., "Complexometric Titrations," translated by H. Irving, p. 8, Methuen & Co., Ltd., London, 1957.]

In practice, an auxiliary complexing agent is usually added during EDTA titrations to prevent the precipitation of heavy metals as hydroxides or basic salts. The concentration of auxiliary complexing agents is generally high compared with the metal ion concentration, and the solution is sufficiently well buffered so that the hydrogen ions produced in reaction (13-9) or (13-10) do not cause an appreciable change in pH.

It is, therefore, convenient to define a *conditional* formation constant K'_{MY},* which is a function of the pH and the concentration of auxiliary complexing agent.

By definition,

$$K'_{MY} = \frac{[MY^{(n-4)+}]}{C_M C_Y} \tag{13-12}$$

where C_M = total concentration of metal not complexed with EDTA
$\quad\quad = [M^{n+}]/\beta$, where β is the fraction of metal ion not complexed with EDTA that is present as the aquated ion
$\quad C_Y$ = total concentration of EDTA not complexed with metal
$\quad\quad = [Y^{4-}]/\alpha_4$, where α_4 is the fraction of free EDTA present as the tetravalent anion.

From Eqs. (13-11) and (13-12), we have

$$K'_{MY} = K_{MY}\alpha_4\beta$$

or $\quad\quad\quad \log K'_{MY} = \log K_{MY} + \log \alpha_4 + \log \beta \tag{13-13}$

where α_4 is a function of pH (Table 13-2) and where β is a function of the nature and concentration of auxiliary complexing agent.

Many EDTA titrations are carried out in ammonia–ammonium chloride buffers, which serve also to provide ammonia as an auxiliary

TABLE 13-4. SUCCESSIVE FORMATION CONSTANTS OF AMMINE COMPLEXES
20°C, ionic strength 0.1

Cation	$\log k_1$	$\log k_2$	$\log k_3$	$\log k_4$	$\log k_5$	$\log k_6$
Ag^+	3.20	3.83	–	–	–	–
Cu^{++}	4.13	3.48	2.87	2.11	–	–
Zn^{++}	2.27	2.34	2.40	2.05	–	–
Cd^{++}	2.60	2.05	1.39	0.88	−0.3	−1.7
Co^{++}	2.05	1.57	0.99	0.70	0.12	−0.68
Ni^{++}	2.75	2.20	1.69	1.15	0.71	−0.01

[With permission from Bjerrum, J., "Metal Ammine Formation in Aqueous Solution," P. Haase and Son, Copenhagen, 1941; reprinted 1957.]

complexing agent. The successive formation constants of several metal-ammonia complexes are listed in Table 13-4. From these constants β

* Ringbom, A., *J. Chem. Educ.*, **35**, 282 (1958).

can readily be calculated, using the equation

$$\frac{1}{\beta} = \sum_{i=0}^{i=n} K_i [NH_3]^i \tag{13-14}$$

where K_i = successive over-all formation constants
$\quad\quad K_0 = 1$, by definition
[Compare Eq. (6-24), Sec. 6-5.]

The use of apparent, or conditional, formation constants has been discussed by Schwarzenbach,[1] by Ringbom,[2] by Ringbom and Vänninen,[3] and by Wehber.[4] Přibil, in a recent review,[5] emphasized the advantages of using "Ringbom's curve,"[2] in which the pH at which the quantity $K_{MY}\alpha_4$ becomes 10^8 is plotted against log K_{MY} for various metals. From Eq. (13-13), the quantity $K_{MY}\alpha_4$ is the conditional formation constant for $\beta = 1$ (absence of auxiliary complexing agents). From Eq. (13-12), the value $K'_{MY} = 10^8$ corresponds to a 99.9 per cent conversion of metal ion to EDTA complex, $[MY^{(n-4)+}]/C_M = 1,000$, at a concentration C_Y of reagent equal to 10^{-5} M, which corresponds to 0.1 per cent relative excess of reagent in the titration of 0.01 M metal ion. Such a curve, taken from a paper by Reilley and Schmid[6] is shown in Fig. 13-2; it represents the *minimum* pH for effective titration of various metal ions in the absence of competing complexing agents.

Example 13-3. Calculate the conditional formation constant of NiY$^-$ in a buffer containing 0.05 M NH$_3$, 0.10 M NH$_4$Cl.

Answer. From Eq. (13-14) and Table 13-4, $1/\beta = 1 + 28 + 223 + 545 + 385 + 99 + 5 = 1,286$; $\beta = 7.8 \times 10^{-4}$. Taking $K_{a.NH_4^+} = 5 \times 10^{-10}$, we calculate $[H^+] = 1.0 \times 10^{-9}$ and $\alpha_4 = 5.1 \times 10^{-2}$. From Table 13-3 and Eq. (13-13), $K'_{MY} = 10^{18.62} \times 5.1 \times 10^{-2} \times 7.8 \times 10^{-4} = 1.7 \times 10^{14}$.

Titration Curves. It is convenient to plot pM $= -\log [M]$ against the fraction titrated, in analogy to a pH titration curve.[7] Under the usual titration conditions, in which the concentration of metal ions is small compared with the buffer and auxiliary-complexing-agent concentrations, α_4 and β are essentially constant during the titration, so that the conditional formation constant also remains constant. It is then a simple matter to calculate the titration curve.

[1] Schwarzenbach, "Complexometric Titrations."
[2] Ringbom, *op. cit.*
[3] Ringbom, A., and Vänninen, E., *Anal. Chim. Acta*, **11**, 153 (1954).
[4] Wehber, P., *Z. anal. Chem.*, **153**, 249 (1956).
[5] Přibil, R., *Analyst*, **83**, 188 (1958).
[6] Reilley, C. N., and Schmid, R. W., *Anal. Chem.*, **30**, 947 (1958).
[7] Schwarzenbach, *op. cit.*

Example 13-4. Calculate the value of pNi at the following percentages of the stoichiometric amount of EDTA added under the conditions of Example 13-3, taking the initial concentration of nickel to be 10^{-3} M and neglecting dilution: 0, 50, 90, 99, 99.9, 100, 100.1, 101, 110 per cent.

Answer. Before the end point, $C_M = C_M^o(1 - X)$, where C_M^o is the initial concentration of metal, and X is the fraction of the stoichiometric quantity added. At the equivalence point, $C_M = C_Y = \sqrt{C_M^o/K_{MY}'}$. Beyond the equivalence point,

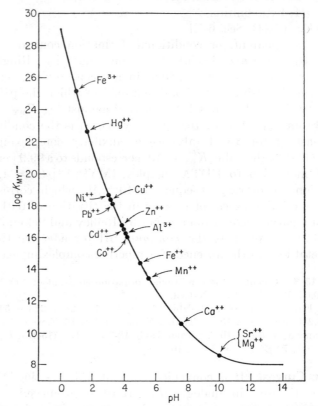

FIG. 13-2. Minimum pH for EDTA titration of various metal ions. [*With permission from Reilley, C. N., and Schmid, R. W., Anal. Chem.,* **30,** 947 (1958).]

$C_Y = C_M^o(X - 1)$, and, from Eq. (13-12), $C_M = 1/(X - 1)K_{MY}'$, or $[M^{n+}] = 1/(X - 1)\alpha_4 K_{MY}$. At all points pNi $= - \log [Ni^{++}] = - \log \beta C_M = 3.11 - \log C_M$. The results are as follows: pNi $= 6.11, 6.41, 7.11, 8.11, 9.11, 11.73, 14.34, 15.34, 16.34$.

The calculated titration curves of 10^{-3} M Ni(II) at various pH values in buffers of ammonia-ammonium ion at a total buffer concentration of 0.1 M are shown plotted in Fig. 13-3. The following features are of interest:

1. *Before the end point,* the curves at low pH values (4 to 6) coincide, because no appreciable complexation between Ni(II) and ammonia

occurs.   At higher pH values the amount of lifting of the curves is determined by the stabilities of the various Ni^{++}-NH_3 complexes. Beyond pH 11, essentially all the buffer is present as ammonia; so no further pH effect exists.

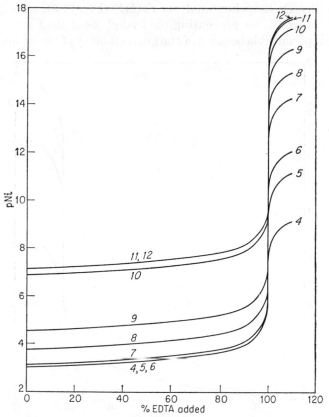

FIG. 13-3. Titration curves of Ni(II) with EDTA. $[NH_3] + [NH_4^+] = 0.1$; $C_{Ni}^o = 10^{-3}$.   The numbers refer to pH values.

2. *After the end point, the placement of the curves does not depend upon β but only upon K_{MY} and α_4.*   Therefore, the titration curves beyond the end point for a given metal depend only on the pH and not on the nature of the auxiliary complexing agent.

Schwarzenbach[1] has published similar titration curves for various metal ions.   The curves for calcium ions (Fig. 13-4) and magnesium ions differ from those for nickel in two ways.   (1) Before the end point, the curves are essentially independent of pH because no auxiliary complexing

[1] *Ibid.*

agent is present. (2) After the end point, the jump in pM is smaller than it is for nickel because of the smaller value of the formation constant K_{MY}.

At low pH values α_4 is so small that no pM break occurs; at high pH, α_4 approaches unity, so it is advantageous to perform the titrations at pH 10 to 12. On the other hand, for Fe(III) (Fig. 13-5), a low pH range (3 to 4) is favorable for preventing the hydrolysis of the ferric ion; a low pH value is permissible because of the great stability of the complex FeY^-.

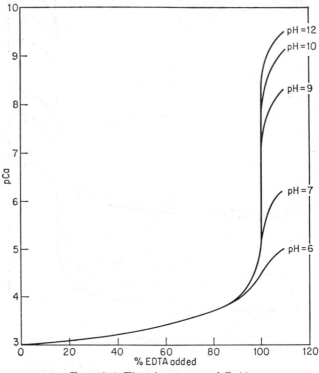

Fig. 13-4. Titration curves of Ca^{++}.

Metal Ion Indicators. An important factor in the development of the EDTA titration methods has been the discovery of suitable metal ion indicators, which permit visual titrations to be carried out at great dilution.

A metal ion indicator, in general, is a dyestuff that can form a colored metal ion complex at some characteristic range of values of pM, exactly as an acid-base indicator forms a "hydrogen ion complex" at a characteristic range of pH values. Since the metal ion indicators are in general also hydrogen ion indicators, it is necessary to consider the acid-base equilibria as well as the metal ion equilibria for each indicator.

For the sake of brevity, we shall consider in detail only one such indicator, because the principles involved are similar for all of them. Various other indicators are described in the books of Schwarzenbach,[1] Přibil,[2] and Welcher,[3] and in the original literature.[4] Examples of the applications of a few of the most widely useful indicators are given in Table 13-5.

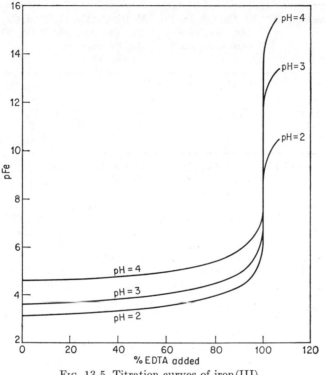

FIG. 13-5. Titration curves of iron(III).

The indicator EBT, eriochrome black T (color index 203), is one of the most widely used metal indicators. Its complexing properties were studied by Schwarzenbach and Biedermann.[5] The indicator anion, which we shall designate H_2In^-, has the formula

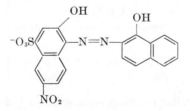

[1] *Ibid.*
[2] Přibil, "Komplexometrie," Chemapol, Prague, 1954.
[3] Welcher, *op. cit.*
[4] Přibil, *Analyst*, **83**, 188 (1958).
[5] Schwarzenbach, G., and Biedermann, W., *Helv. Chim. Acta*, **31**, 678 (1948).

TABLE 13-5. APPLICATIONS OF IMPORTANT METAL ION INDICATORS

Indicator	Direct titration	Back titration	Replacement titration
Eriochrome black T*	Ba, Ca, Cd, In, Pb, Mg, Mn, rare earths, Sr, Zn	Al, Bi, Ca, Co, Ga, Fe, Pb, Mn, Hg, Ni, Pd, rare earths, Tl	Au, Ca, Cu, Pb, Hg, Pd, Tl
Murexide†	Ca, Co, Cu, Ni	Ca, Ga	Au, Pd, Ag
1-(2-Pyridylazo)-2-naphthol (PAN)‡	Cd, Cu, In, Sc, Zn	Bi, Co, Cu, Ga, Fe, Pb, Ni, Sc, Zn	Al, Ca, Co, Ga, In, Fe, Pb, Mg, Mn, Hg, Ni, V, Zn
Pyrocatechol violet§	Al, Cd, Co, Cu, Ga, Fe, Pb, Mg, Mn, Ni, Th, Ti	Al, Ga, In, Fe, Ni, Pd, Th, Ti, Zn	–

* Schwarzenbach, G., and Biedermann, W., *Helv. Chim. Acta*, **31**, 678 (1948).

† Schwarzenbach, G., Biedermann, W., and Bangerter, F., *Helv. Chim. Acta*, **29**, 811 (1946); Schwarzenbach, G., and Gysling, H., *ibid.*, **32**, 1108, 1314, 1484 (1949).

‡ Cheng, K. L., and Bray, R. H., *Anal. Chem.*, **27**, 782 (1955).

§ Malat, M., Suk, V., and Ryba, O., *Collection Czechoslov. Chem. Communs.*, **19**, 258, 679 (1954); Suk, V., and Malat, M., *Chemist Analyst*, **45**, 30 (1956).

and exhibits the following acid-base behavior:

$$H_2In^- \underset{Red}{\overset{pK\ 6.3}{\rightleftharpoons}} HIn^= \underset{Blue}{\overset{pK\ 11.5}{\rightleftharpoons}} In^{3-}_{Yellow\text{-}orange} \tag{13-15}$$

In the pH range 7 to 11, in which the dye itself exhibits a blue color, many metal ions form red complexes. These include Mg, Ca, Zn, Cd, Hg, Al, Ga, In, Pb, Ti, Fe, Co, Ni, Cu, as well as the rare earths and platinum metals. The colors are extremely sensitive, as illustrated, for example, by the fact that 10^{-6} to 10^{-7} M solutions of magnesium ion give a distinct red color with EBT.

With calcium and magnesium ions the color-change reaction is represented by

$$\underset{Blue}{HIn^=} + M^{++} \rightleftharpoons \underset{Red}{MIn^-} + H^+ \tag{13-16}$$

With zinc ions, a similar reaction occurs, but a 1:2 complex $ZnIn_2^{4-}$ is also formed. This complication is of only minor importance under usual titration conditions[1] and will be neglected here.

[1] Schwarzenbach, *op. cit.*

According to Eq. (13-16), the indicator color change is affected by the hydrogen ion concentration. From the practical viewpoint it is convenient to define the *conditional indicator constant* K'_{In}, which varies with pH:

$$K'_{In} = \frac{[MIn^-]}{[M^{n+}]C_{In}} \quad (13\text{-}17)$$

where [MIn⁻] = concentration of metal-indicator complex
     [Mⁿ⁺] = concentration of aquated metal ion
           = βC_M
    C_{In} = analytical concentration of indicator not complexed with metal ion
           = $[H_2In^-] + [HIn^=] + [In^{3-}]$

From Eq. (13-17),

$$\log K'_{In} = pM + \log \frac{[MIn^-]}{C_{In}} \quad (13\text{-}18)$$

and $\log K'_{In}$ gives the value of pM when half the total indicator is present as the metal ion complex. Some numerical values are given in Table 13-6. From these values it is easy to estimate the titration error under a given set of conditions.

TABLE 13-6. APPARENT INDICATOR CONSTANTS OF EBT

pH	$\log K'_{In}$ at $\mu = 0.1$ for:		
	CaIn⁻	MgIn⁻	ZnIn⁻
7	0.85	2.45	8.4
8	1.85	3.45	9.4
9	2.85	4.45	10.4
10	3.84	5.44	11.4
11	4.74	6.34	12.3
12	5.27	6.87	–

[From Schwarzenbach, G., *Helv. Chim. Acta*, **32**, 32 (1949).]

Example 13-5. Estimate the theoretical titration error for the titration of 10^{-3} M magnesium ion at pH 10, using EBT as the indicator. Assume that the end point is taken (a) at 9 per cent and (b) at 91 per cent conversion of the indicator from MgIn⁻ to HIn⁻. Neglect dilution and hydrolysis of magnesium ion.

Answer. From Tables 13-2, 13-3, 13-6 we have $\log K'_{MgY} = 8.69 - 0.46 = 8.23$; $\log K'_{In} = 5.44$. At the equivalence point, $[Mg^{++}] = \sqrt{C^\circ/K'_{MgY}}$; whence, pMg $= 5.62$.

a. At 9 per cent indicator conversion, from Eq. (13-18), pMg $= 4.44$; so the end point occurs before the equivalence point. Setting $C_{Mg}C_Y = C^\circ/K'_{MgY}$, $C_{Mg} = C^\circ(1 - X) + C_Y$, and we have $1 - X = C_{Mg}/C^\circ - 1/C_{Mg}K'_{MgY} = 0.036$. Titration error $= -3.6$ per cent.

b. At 91 per cent indicator conversion, pMg = 6.44; so the end point occurs after the equivalence point. Setting $C_Y = C^\circ(X - 1) + C_{Mg}$ and $C_{Mg}C_Y = C^\circ/K'_{MgY}$, we have $X - 1 = 1/C_{Mg}K'_{MgY} - C_{Mg}/C^\circ = 0.0163$. Titration error = +1.6 per cent.

Flaschka and Khalafallah[1,2] have derived equations that take into account the indicator blank for various concentrations of metal ion and indicator and for various values of the apparent formation constants of the metal-EDTA complex, K'_{MY}, and the metal indicator complex, K'_{In}. Factors favorable to a small titration error, with practical limits that are useful as a guide, are:

1. Large conditional indicator constant: $K'_{In} > 10^4$
2. Large ratio of K'_{MY} to K'_{In}: $K'_{MY}/K'_{In} > 10^4$
3. Small ratio of indicator concentration to metal ion concentration: $C^\circ_{In}/C^\circ_M < 0.01$

A detailed discussion of end point detection by metal ion indicators has been presented by Reilley and Schmid.[3]

Other End-point Detection Methods. At first thought, it would seem that the direct measurement of electrode potential would, in analogy to pH measurements, afford a simple means for the determination of pM during the course of EDTA titrations. Unfortunately, many metal electrodes do not behave reversibly, particularly at the extremely low metal-ion concentrations that are involved. Not only are the exchange current densities often prohibitively small (for the transition metals, reversible behavior cannot be observed even at relatively high metal-ion concentrations), but often electrode side reactions would lead to "mixed potential" phenomena (see Sec. 15-10). This would be particularly true of the more active metals in solutions containing very low concentrations of their ions, which would have strongly reducing potentials and would, therefore, be subject to many interferences. In particular, hydrogen evolution would often intervene.

The mercury-mercury(II) EDTA complex electrode is almost uniquely suitable as an indicator electrode, because

1. The mercury-mercury(I) electrode has an exceptionally high exchange current density.[4,5]

2. The equilibrium between metallic mercury and mercury(II) to give mercury(I) is very rapid.

3. Mercury is relatively noble, so that, in spite of the stable EDTA complex of mercury(II) (log $K_{HgY} = 22.1$), the equilibrium potential is not excessively negative.

[1] Flaschka, H., and Khalafallah, S., *Z. anal. Chem.*, **156**, 401 (1957).
[2] Flaschka, *Talanta*, **1**, 60 (1958).
[3] Reilley and Schmid, *Anal. Chem.*, **31**, 887 (1959).
[4] Gerischer, H., and Staubach, K., *Z. physik. Chem. Leipzig*, **6**, 118 (1956).
[5] Oldham, K. B., *Trans. Faraday Soc.*, **53**, 80 (1957).

4. The high hydrogen overpotential of mercury prevents mixed potential behavior due to hydrogen evolution.

Reilley and Schmid[1] made the important observation that the mercury–mercury(II) EDTA electrode can be used indirectly as an indicator electrode for various metal ions. If a metal ion–EDTA complex $MY^{(n-4)+}$ is present in equilibrium with mercury and the mercury(II) complex $HgY^=$, we have the half-cell

$$M^{n+}, \ MY^{(n-4)+}, \ HgY^=, \ Hg^{++} \ | \ Hg \qquad (13\text{-}19)$$

It can readily be shown that the potential at equilibrium is given by

$$E = E^{o\prime}_{Hg^{++},Hg} + \frac{RT}{2F} \ln \frac{[HgY^=]}{[MY^{(n-4)+}]} \frac{K_{MY}}{K_{HgY}} + \frac{RT}{2F} \ln [M^{n+}] \quad (13\text{-}20)$$

The first two terms on the right-hand side of Eq. (13-20) are essentially constant during a titration, especially in the region of the end point; so the measured potential of the mercury electrode becomes a linear function of pM.

Example 13-6. Calculate the relationship between the potential and pNi of an electrode of the type (13-19), to be used as an indicator electrode for Ni(II) during an EDTA titration.

Answer. Taking $E^{o\prime}_{Hg^{++},Hg} = E^o = 0.858$, $[HgY^=] = [NiY^=] = 10^{-3}$, and, from Table 13-3, log $K_{NiY}/K_{HgY} = 18.62 - 21.80 = -3.18$ we calculate from Eq. (13-20), $E = 0.762 - 0.0296$ pNi.

Reilley, Schmid, and Lamson[2] have applied the mercury indicator electrode to the determination of 29 individual metal ions, either by direct or back-titration procedures.

The type of potential-pH diagram shown in Fig. 13-6, left, is helpful in portraying the course of the titration curve (Fig. 13-6, right). On the potential-pH diagram, curve II represents the potential corresponding to the half-reaction

$$HgO + H_2O + 2e^- \rightleftharpoons Hg + 2OH^- \qquad (13\text{-}21)$$

which is the potential-determining reaction in the absence of EDTA. Curve I represents the potential corresponding to the half-reaction

$$HgY^= + 2e^- + mH^+ \rightleftharpoons Hg + H_mY^{(m-4)+} \qquad (13\text{-}22)$$

for equimolar concentrations of $HgY^=$ and reagent $H_mY^{(m-4)+}$ and, therefore, corresponds to a point 50 per cent beyond the end point for the

[1] Reilley and Schmid, *Anal. Chem.*, **30**, 947 (1958).

[2] Reilley, C. N., Schmid, R. W., and Lamson, D. W., *Anal. Chem.*, **30**, 953 (1958).

titration of a solution of metal ion to which half of its molar concentration of HgY^- has been added. Over the pH range $pK_2 <$ pH $< pK_3$, or approximately from pH 2 to 6, $m = 2$ and the species H_2Y^- is formed. At higher pH values, $m = 1$, corresponding to the formation of HY^{3-}.

The lines connecting curves I and II correspond to the half-cell (13-19), at equimolar concentrations of $MY^{(n-4)+}$ and M^{n+} and, therefore, represent points halfway along the titration curve. Curve ABC represents the titration of Mn(II) at pH 5. At pH $= 7.3$, the initial potential

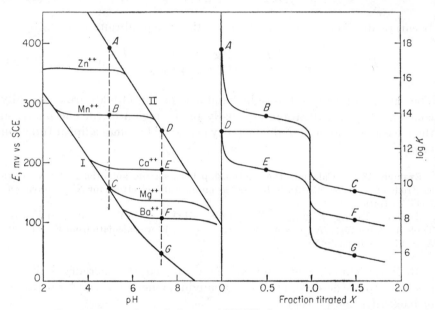

FIG. 13-6. Use of mercury electrode for metal-EDTA titrations. Right: potentiometric titration curves. Left: potential-pH diagrams; I, $HgY^- + 2e^- + mH^+ \rightleftharpoons Hg + H_mY^{(m-4)-}$ [Eq. (13-22)]; II, $HgO + H_2O + 2e^- \rightleftharpoons Hg + 2OH^-$ [Eq. (13-21)]. [With permission from Reilley, C. N., and Schmid, R. W., Anal. Chem., **30**, 947 (1958).]

corresponding to point D is maintained until the vicinity of the end point, at which a sudden break to point G occurs. If Mn(II) and Ba(II) were present in equimolar concentrations, the titration curve after the end point would reach point F instead of G, with a correspondingly smaller break. The titration of calcium ion at pH 7.3 would follow the curve DEG in the absence of barium and DEF in the presence of an equimolar concentration of barium.

Another type of potentiometric indication, which is of less general interest, is based on an electrode reaction involving two different oxidation states of the same metal. Such an electrode reaction has been used to follow the titration of Fe(III) with EDTA, measuring the potential of the Fe(III)-Fe(II) couple.[1]   At pH 3, Fe(II) remains uncomplexed with EDTA during the titration, and a large potential change accompanies the abrupt change of Fe(III) concentration in the end-point region.   Redox indicators, e.g., variamine blue B[2] and Bindschedlers' green,[3] can also be used as visual indicators to detect the change in potential.

It is beyond the scope of the present treatment to consider the details of the various other instrumental methods for the detection of EDTA titration end points.   However, we may mention spectrophotometric end-point detection methods, which are of two types.   The first, based on instrumental observation of the color changes of metal ion indicators, has been considered theoretically by Fortuin, Karsten, and Kies[4] and by Ringbom and Vänninen.[5]   The second, based on the absorption of radiation in the visible or ultraviolet regions of the spectrum by the metal-EDTA complex, was first applied by Sweetser and Bricker.[6]   The complex $MgY^=$, shows for example, appreciable absorbance at a wavelength of 222 mμ, whereas the reagent $H_2Y^=$ is nearly transparent. Therefore, magnesium can be determined directly, and calcium, cadmium, and zinc can be determined indirectly, by titration at this wavelength. With a recording spectrophotometer, the titrations can be performed automatically.[7]

Types of Titration.   *Direct titrations* are commonly carried out using disodium dihydrogenethylenediaminetetraacetate, Na_2H_2Y, which is available in pure form.   Auxiliary complexing agents such as citrate, tartrate, or triethanolamine are added, if necessary, to prevent the precipitation of metal hydroxides or basic salts.   If a pH range of 9 to 10 is suitable, a buffer of ammonia and ammonium chloride is often added in relatively concentrated form, both to adjust the pH and to supply ammonia as a complexing agent for those metal ions which form ammine complexes.   A few metals, notably Fe(III), bismuth, and thorium, are titrated in acid solution.

Reilley and Porterfield[8] devised an electrolytic method of generation of EDTA that can be used in place of the usual titration.   By means of the cathode reaction

$$HgY^= + 2e^- \rightarrow Hg + Y^{4-}$$

[1] Přibil, R., Kondela, Z., and Matyska, B., *Collection Czechoslov. Chem. Communs.*, **16**, 80 (1951).

[2] Flaschka, *Mikrochim. Acta*, **1954**, 361.

[3] Wehber, *Z. anal. Chem.*, **149**, 161 (1956).

[4] Fortuin, J. M. H., Karsten, P., and Kies, H. L., *Anal. Chim. Acta*, **10**, 356 (1954).

[5] Ringbom, and Vänninen, *op. cit.*

[6] Sweetser, P. B., and Bricker, C. E., *Anal. Chem.*, **25**, 253 (1953); **26**, 195 (1954).

[7] Malmstadt, H. V., and Gohrbandt, E. C., *Anal. Chem.*, **26**, 442 (1954).

[8] Reilley, C. N., and Porterfield, W. W., *Anal. Chem.*, **28**, 443 (1956).

the EDTA anion Y^{4-} can be generated at a rate proportional to the current and used for the titration of metal ions such as Ca^{++}, Cu^{++}, Zn^{++} and Pb^{++}.

Back titrations[1] based on the addition of excess EDTA followed by back titration of the excess reagent are useful in certain situations. If a given indicator forms so stable a complex with a metal ion that EDTA cannot compete with the indicator or if the metal ion is to be determined in the presence of a precipitating anion, an excess of EDTA can be added and the excess determined by titration with standard solutions of magnesium or zinc ion. These titrants are chosen because they form EDTA complexes of relatively low stability, thereby avoiding the possible titration of EDTA bound by the sample metal ion. Examples of the indirect method are:

1. The use of EBT for the determination of cobalt, nickel, or aluminum, which form such stable complexes with EBT that the direct titration would fail

2. The determination of metals in precipitates; for example, lead in lead sulfate, magnesium in magnesium ammonium phosphate, or calcium in calcium oxalate

3. Determination of thallium, which forms a stable EDTA complex but which does not respond to the usual metal ion indicators

Replacement titrations[2] can be based on a reaction of the type

$$M^{n+} + MgY^= \rightarrow MY^{(n-4)+} + Mg^{++}$$

in which the metal ion M^{n+} displaces magnesium ion from its relatively weak EDTA complex. The magnesium-EDTA solution can be added in excess and the resulting magnesium ion titrated with EDTA, using EBT as the indicator. Of course, in principle ions other than magnesium could equally well be used if they form a weaker EDTA complex than the metal ion being determined. Examples of replacement titrations include:

1. Determination of calcium by displacement of magnesium, which uses to advantage the superior magnesium-EBT color reaction

2. Determination of barium by displacement of zinc ions in a strongly ammoniacal medium

A special case of replacement titration is the displacement of hydrogen ions from $H_2Y^=$, followed by the titration of the liberated hydrogen ion. Although this method is historically interesting,[3] it is no longer of practical value now that many suitable metal ion indicators are available. The obvious disadvantage is that the solution must first be adjusted to the pH value to be reached at the end point of the back titration. This procedure

---

[1] Biedermann and Schwarzenbach, *Chimia Switz.*, **2**, 1 (1948).

[2] *Ibid.*

[3] Schwarzenbach and Biedermann, *Helv. Chim. Acta*, **31**, 456 (1948).

often leads to difficulties because of hydrolysis of metal ions and the necessity of avoiding substances that buffer the solution. Nevertheless, it is sometimes advantageous to use an alkalimetric method as a preliminary step when a back titration of excess EDTA is to be carried out, thereby avoiding the addition of an unnecessarily large excess of EDTA.

Redox titrations can be carried out in the presence of excess EDTA. Here EDTA acts to change the oxidation potential by forming a more stable complex with one oxidation state than the other. If $M_{ox}Y$ and $M_{red}Y$ represent the EDTA complexes of the oxidized and reduced forms of the metal and if $K_{M_{ox}Y}$ and $K_{M_{red}Y}$ are the formation constants, we have the following equation for the electrode potential [see Eq. (15-63), Sec. 15-8]:

$$E = E^{\circ\prime}_{M_{ox}, M_{red}} - \frac{RT}{nF} \ln \frac{K_{M_{ox}Y}}{K_{M_{red}Y}} + \frac{RT}{nF} \ln \frac{[M_{ox}Y]}{[M_{red}Y]}$$

Generally the oxidized form of the metal forms a more stable complex than the reduced form; so $K_{M_{ox}Y} > K_{M_{red}Y}$, and the couple becomes a stronger reducing agent in the presence of excess EDTA. For example, the Co(III)-Co(II) potential is shifted about 1.2 volts,[1] so that Co(II) can be titrated with Ce(IV).* Alternatively, Co(III) can be titrated to Co(II), with Cr(II) as a reducing agent.[2,3]

Manganese(II) can be titrated directly to Mn(III) using ferricyanide as the oxidant.[4] Alternatively, Mn(III), prepared by oxidation of the Mn(II)-EDTA complex with lead dioxide, can be determined by titration with standard iron(II) sulfate.[5] It should be noted here that Fe(II) becomes a much stronger reducing agent in the presence of EDTA. The formal potential of the Fe(III)-Fe(II) couple is 0.117 volt (vs. standard hydrogen electrode) at pH values of 4 to 6, where both Fe(III) and Fe(II) form stable EDTA complexes.[6] Ferrous iron becomes such a strong reductant that air must be carefully excluded. It has been used as a reducing reagent for iodine,[7] Ag(I),† Cu(II),‡ and Fe(III).§ For the latter titration, the Fe(II)-EDTA complex was generated electrolytically by reduction of the Fe(III)-EDTA complex.

[1] Přibil, *Collection Czechoslov. Chem. Communs.*, **14**, 320 (1949).
* Harris, W. F., and Sweet, T. R., *Anal. Chem.*, **26**, 1649 (1954).
[2] Přibil, *op. cit.*
[3] Přibil, R., and Švestka, L., *Collection Czechoslov. Chem. Communs.*, **15**, 31 (1950).
[4] Přibil, *Collection Czechoslov. Chem. Communs.*, **14**, 454 (1949).
[5] Přibil, R., and Horacek, J., *Collection Czechoslov. Chem. Communs.*, **14**, 626 (1949).
[6] Schwarzenbach, G., and Heller, J., *Helv. Chim. Acta*, **34**, 576 (1951).
[7] Přibil, R., Simon, V., and Doležal, J., *Collection Czechoslov. Chem. Communs.*, **16**, 573 (1951).
† Přibil, Doležal, and Simon, *Chem. listy*, **47**, 1017 (1953).
‡ Cheng, K. L., *Anal. Chem.*, **27**, 1165 (1955).
§ Schmid and Reilley, *Anal. Chem.*, **28**, 520 (1956).

Indirect determinations of several types have been carried out. Sulfate has been determined by adding an excess of standard barium ion solution and back-titrating the excess.[1] By titrating the cations in moderately soluble precipitates, other ions can be determined indirectly. Thus sodium has been determined by titration of zinc in sodium zinc uranyl acetate,[2] and phosphate by titration of magnesium in magnesium ammonium phosphate.[3] The quantitative formation of tetracyano-nickelate(II) has been used for the indirect determination of cyanide.[4] Palladium(II) and silver(I) displace Ni(II) from its cyanide complex; the titration of the liberated nickel constitutes an indirect method for these metals.[5]

13-6. Other Chelating Reagents

Of the many chelating reagents that have been studied only a few offer appreciable advantages over EDTA as analytical reagents.

For instance, 1,2-diaminocyclohexanetetraacetic acid has been recommended by Přibil and coworkers[6] because its complexes with most metal ions are more stable than those of EDTA. Schwarzenbach[7] pointed out, however, that this advantage is more apparent than real, because the *conditional* formation constants in moderately acid solution are more strongly affected by pH than those of EDTA, owing to the more weakly acidic character of the reagent ($pK_1 = 2.4$, $pK_2 = 3.52$, $pK_3 = 6.12$, $pK_4 = 11.70$.)

On occasion, there may be reasons to take advantage of the greater selectivity accompanying weaker complex formation and weaker acidity of a chelating reagent. For example, triethylenetetramine ("trien") was used by Flaschka and Soliman[8] with a photometric end point and by Reilley and Sheldon with metal ion indicators[9] and with a mercury indicator electrode.[10] With trien, the first two acid-dissociation steps are considerably weaker than with EDTA ($pK_1 = 3.32$, $pK_2 = 6.67$, $pK_3 = 9.20$, $pK_4 = 9.92$), and the metal ion complexes are also weaker,

[1] Anderegg, G., Flaschka, H., Sallman, R., and Schwarzenbach, G., *Helv. Chim. Acta*, **37**, 113 (1953).

[2] Flaschka, *Mikrochemie ver. Mikrochim. Acta*, **39**, 391 (1952).

[3] Flaschka, H., and Holasek, A., *Mikrochemie ver. Mikrochim. Acta*, **39**, 101 (1952).

[4] Huditz, F., and Flaschka, H., *Z. anal. Chem.*, **136**, 185 (1952).

[5] Flaschka, *Mikrochemie ver. Mikrochim. Acta*, **40**, 21 (1952); *Mikrochim. Acta*, **1953**, 226.

[6] Přibil, R., Roubal, Z., and Svátek, E., *Collection Czechoslov. Chem. Communs.*, **18**, 43 (1953).

[7] Schwarzenbach, "Complexometric Titrations," p. 104, Interscience, 1957.

[8] Flaschka, H., and Soliman, A., *Z. anal. Chem.*, **158**, 254 (1957).

[9] Reilley, C. N., and Sheldon, M. V., *Chemist Analyst*, **46**, 59 (1957).

[10] Reilley and Sheldon, *Talanta*, **1**, 127 (1958).

so that in acid solution only Cu(II) and Hg(II) form complexes with trien that are of sufficient stability to permit a direct titration.

Finally, a particular reagent may have the advantage of being particularly selective for a given pair of metal ions. An outstanding example of this type of selectivity was pointed out by Schwarzenbach[1] in the case of ethyleneglycol-bis(-β-aminoethyl ether)-N,N'-tetraacetic acid. This reagent forms a calcium ion complex of unusual stability (log $K = 10.7$) in comparison with its magnesium ion complex (log $K = 5.4$), which is so weak that the usual metal ion indicators would not give sharp end points. Schmid and Reilley,[2] who called this reagent EGTA, showed that it can be used for the selective titration of calcium in the presence of magnesium with the aid of the mercury indicator electrode. This method appears to be distinctly superior to the EDTA method, which usually involves a selective precipitation of magnesium hydroxide at a controlled pH.[*]

Another example of a selective titrant is tetraethylenepentamine ("tetren") which was demonstrated to be superior to trien as a selective reagent.[3] Mercury, copper, nickel, zinc, and cadmium, alone and in various mixtures, were titrated using a potentiometric end point with a mercury indicator electrode. Using EDTA and tetren in combination, a large number of metal ions can be determined in multicomponent mixtures.

PROBLEMS

13-1. If 0.1 mole AgNO₃, 0.01 mole KI, 0.2 mole KCN, and 0.2 mole NH₃ are made up to 1 liter and mixed, (a) Does a precipitate of AgI exist? (b) Calculate the concentrations of Ag^+, $Ag(NH_3)_2^+$, and CN^- at equilibrium. *Ans.* (b) 8.5×10^{-15}, 5.7×10^{-9}, 4×10^{-4} M.

13-2. If, at the end point of a titration of chloride with mercuric ion, there is 100 ml of a 0.01 M HgCl₂ solution, calculate the ml of 0.1 M Hg⁺⁺ reagent required to give a concentration of 10^{-5} M mercuric ion. See Eq. (13-2). *Ans.* 0.21 ml.

13-3. Using the data of Table 13-4, calculate the fraction of Zn⁺⁺ in the uncomplexed form in solutions containing 0.01, 0.1, and 1 M free ammonia, respectively. *Ans.* 0.035, 8.0×10^{-6}, 8.6×10^{-10}.

13-4. For a series of buffers containing ammonia (p$K_b = 4.7$) and ammonium ion at a total concentration of 0.1 M, calculate the fraction of zinc in the uncomplexed form at pH values of 8, 9, 10, and 11. Starting with a total Zn(II) concentration of 10^{-3} M, calculate the titration curves of zinc with EDTA at these pH values. (See Tables 13-2 and 13-3.) It is convenient to use points corresponding to 0, 50, 91, 99, 99.9, 100, 100.1, 100, 110 per cent of the stoichiometric amounts of EDTA.

Ans. At   99.9, pZn = 6.70, 9.11, 10.78, 11.06
At 100.0, pZn = 8.95, 10.66, 11.91, 12.24
At 100.1, pZn = 11.21, 12.21, 13.04, 13.43

[1] Schwarzenbach, "Complexometric Titrations," p. 103.
[2] Schmid and Reilley, *Anal. Chem.*, **29**, 264 (1957).
[*] Kenney, A. D., and Cohn, V. H., *Anal. Chem.*, **30**, 1366 (1958).
[3] Reilley, C. N., and Vavoulis, A., *Anal. Chem.*, **31**, 243 (1959).

13-5. Using the values given in Table 13-6 and the titration curves calculated in Prob. 13-4, estimate the indicator errors using EBT for the zinc titration at the four pH values listed. Assume that the end point is taken when the indicator is half-converted to $ZnIn^-$.

13-6. Derive Eq. (13-20), starting with $E = E^{o'}_{Hg^{++},Hg} + \dfrac{RT}{2F} \ln [Hg^{++}]$. If the measured potential $E = 0.355$ volt (vs. hydrogen) when $[HgY^-] = 10^{-3}$, $[ZnY^-] = 10^{-4}$, what is the corresponding zinc ion concentration? *Ans.* $2 \times 10^{-13}\ M$.

13-7. Estimate the standard potential of the half-reaction $FeY^- + e^- \rightleftharpoons FeY^-$ from the formation constants given in Table 13-3 and the standard potential of the half-reaction $Fe^{3+} + e^- \rightleftharpoons Fe^{++}$. *Ans.* 0.136 volt.

14. Organic Reagents for Precipitation and Extraction of Metals

Organic reagents are becoming increasingly important in analytical chemistry because of the inherent sensitivity and selectivity of their reactions with metal ions. Much of the early work in the field was highly empirical in character, being pointed toward a search for specific, or at least highly selective, reagents for particular metals. In recent years, a more fundamental approach to the study of organic reagents has involved consideration of the structural factors that lead to selectivity. Another important development has been the quantitative consideration of the various equilibria involved. Sufficient selectivity can be achieved for a particular purpose by controlling such variables as the pH and the reagent concentration and by taking advantage of secondary complexing reagents (masking agents) that enhance the differences in behavior among various metals. In extraction separations, the choice of solvents and even the rate of extraction may be important in achieving a given separation.

The number of organic reagents has become so large that it would be futile to attempt to compile even a list of all the reagents for the various metal ions. Our treatment of the subject will be limited to a brief classification of reagents, an outline of the structural factors influencing chelation, a consideration of precipitation and extraction equilibria with suitable examples, and selected examples of the most important reagents.

14-1. Classification of Organic Reagents

The most important organic reagents are those which form *chelate* complexes, which involve the formation of one or more rings including

247

the metal atom. Such chelates are more stable than the corresponding coordination compounds involving no ring formation, and even greater stability is imparted by a structure involving two or more fused chelate rings.[1] Welcher[2] in his comprehensive treatise, classified organic reagents according to the number of hydrogen ions displaced from a neutral molecule in forming one chelate ring. The three classes, with examples, are as follows:

Class I: Displacement of Two Hydrogen Ions. The coordination reaction involves a metal ion and a divalent anion, with the result that the charge of the complex becomes two units more negative than that of the metal ion with each step of coordination.

If the coordination number of the metal ion for the reagent is equal to the charge on the metal ion, the resulting complex is a neutral molecule, generally insoluble in water. An example is α-benzoin oxime, $C_6H_5CHOHC{=}NOH(C_6H_5)$, which has two acidic hydrogen atoms and forms a 1:1 coordination compound with Cu(II).* The substituted arsonic acids, $RAsO(OH)_2$, which form 1:2 complexes with tetravalent metals, are sometimes considered to belong to this class. However, Ti(IV) and Zr(IV) are present largely as hydrolyzed species such as TiO^{++} and ZrO^{++}. Therefore, the bonding is more likely to involve displacement of only a single hydrogen ion of each of two molecules of reagent.[3]

If, as often happens, the coordination number of the metal ion for the reagent exceeds the charge on the metal ion, an anionic complex, usually soluble in water, is formed. Examples are the soluble complexes of metal ions with oxalate, citrate, tartrate, etc. The formation of such complexes is often useful in preventing the precipitation of metal hydroxides in alkaline solutions.

Class II: Displacement of One Hydrogen Ion. The coordination reaction involves a metal ion and a univalent anion, with the result that each step of coordination lowers the charge of the metal ion by 1 unit and uses two coordination positions. If the coordination number of the metal ion for the reagent is twice the charge on the ion, a neutral species, generally insoluble in water, is formed. The product can usually be extracted into an organic solvent. It should be noted that coordination is often completed when the charge has become zero even if the coordina-

---

[1] Bailar, J. C., Jr. (ed.), "Chemistry of the Coordination Compounds," p. 220, Reinhold Publishing Corporation, New York, 1956.

[2] Welcher, F., "Organic Analytical Reagents," vol. 1, D. Van Nostrand, Inc., Princeton, N.J., 1947.

* Feigl, F., *Ber. deut. chem. Ges.*, **856**, 2083 (1923).

[3] Flagg, J. F., "Organic Reagents," p. 108, Interscience Publishers, Inc., New York, 1948.

tion positions are not fully occupied by reagent, because further coordination would require ionization of the reagent and dissolution of the insoluble product. Since most reagents are only very weakly acidic, such ionization is not energetically favorable.

For example, magnesium ion reacts with 8-hydroxyquinoline (oxine), which may be represented by HX, to form a dihydrate

$$Mg(H_2O)_6^{++} + 2HX \rightarrow MgX_2 \cdot 2H_2O + 2H^+ + 4H_2O$$

because the coordination number is 6 and the charge has become zero when two molecules of reagent have reacted with one magnesium ion. On the other hand, aluminum ion forms an anhydrous oxinate because the coordination number is just twice the ion charge.

By far the greatest number of analytically important organic reagents fall into class II. Examples are 1-nitroso-2-naphthol for Co(II), dimethylglyoxime and 1,2-cyclohexanedionedioxime (nioxime) for Ni(II), oxine and diphenylthiocarbazone (dithizone) for various heavy metals.

Class III: Displacement of No Hydrogen Ions. The coordination reaction involves the replacement of water by neutral molecules of reagent. The product is, therefore, a cation of the same charge as the original metal ion. Although the product is usually water-soluble, the unusually bulky cation together with appropriate anions can sometimes be extracted into organic solvents. For example,[1] salts of the Cu(I) and Fe(II) derivatives of substituted 1,10-phenanthrolines can be extracted into such solvents as the higher alcohols.

Reagents that do not fall into the above three classes are those which form more than one chelate ring per molecule of reagent (e.g., ethylenediaminetetraacetic acid) and those which form no chelate rings. As examples may be cited the ionic precipitants such as tetraphenylarsonium ion, which precipitates thallium as $(C_6H_5)_4AsTlCl_4$, and the tetraphenylborate(III) anion, which precipitates potassium as $KB(C_6H_5)_4$.

14-2. Structural Factors that Influence Coordination

A brief outline of the more important structural factors, with respect to the metal ion as well as the ligand, that determine the stability of coordination compounds should be helpful as a guide to qualitative predictions about the applicability of organic reagents for analytical purposes. For further study, the excellent discussions of Martell and

---

[1] Smith, G. F., and McCurdy, W. H., *Anal. Chem.*, **24**, 371 (1952); Wilkins, D. H., and Smith, G. F., *Anal. Chim. Acta*, **9**, 538 (1953); Schilt, A. A., and Smith, G. F., *Anal. Chim. Acta*, **15**, 567 (1956).

Calvin,[1] Irving and Williams,[2] and Parry and Keller[3] are recommended.

At the outset it should be recognized that the stability of a coordination compound, expressed by its formation constant, is only one of several factors that determine the completeness of precipitation or extraction of a metal ion.

In precipitation, the intrinsic solubility[4] of the complex and the acid dissociation constant of the reagent are involved. Freiser observed[5] that the $Cu(II)$-dimethylglyoxime complex is actually more stable than the corresponding $Ni(II)$ complex in 50 per cent dioxane, yet nickel is precipitated preferentially. The intrinsic solubility of the nickel complex is abnormally low, owing to metal-metal bonding between adjacent molecules in the solid planar structure.[6] It is interesting that, although copper dimethylglyoxime also has a planar structure with nearly the same lattice parameters, the arrangement of molecules in the lattice is such as to preclude a metal-metal interaction.[7]

In extraction, the partition coefficients P_r and P_c of the reagent and complex, respectively, and the acid dissociation constant K_a of the reagent are involved in addition to the formation constant K_c of the complex. Also, the rate of extraction may be so low that equilibrium is not actually attained for one component of a mixture. Examples will be given later.

Effect of the Nature of the Metal Ion on Stability of Complexes. For metal ions that form complexes of predominantly ionic character, the stability increases with increasing charge and decreasing size of the (unhydrated) metal ion. This holds for metal ions possessing the electronic structure of the inert gases and for the rare earth ions. In the alkali metal and alkaline earth families the stabilities are generally in the order: $Li^+ > Na^+ > K^+ > Rb^+ > Cs^+$ and $Mg^{++} > Ca^{++} > Sr^{++} > Ba^{++} > Ra^{++}$. In the lanthanide family the ionic size decreases and the stability of complexes increases with increasing atomic number.

For metal ions that form complexes of predominantly covalent character, valid generalizations can be made only within closely related groups. For the divalent ions of the first transition metal series, Irving and

[1] Martell, A. E., and Calvin, M., "Chemistry of the Metal Chelate Compounds," Prentice-Hall, Inc., Englewood Cliffs, N.J., 1952.

[2] Irving, H., and Williams, R. J. P., *Analyst*, **77**, 813 (1952); *J. Chem. Soc.*, **1953**, 3192.

[3] Parry, R. W., and Keller, R. N., in Bailar, J. C., Jr. (ed.), "Chemistry of the Coordination Compounds," chaps. 3–5, Reinhold Publishing Corporation, New York, 1956.

[4] Irving and Williams, *op. cit.*

[5] Freiser, H., *Analyst*, **77**, 830 (1952).

[6] Sharpe, A. G., and Wakefield, D. B., *J. Chem. Soc.*, **1957**, 281.

[7] Godyki, L. E., and Rundle, R. E., *Acta Cryst.*, **6**, 487 (1953).

Williams[1] found the order of stability to be $Mn^{++} < Fe^{++} < Co^{++} <$ $Ni^{++} < Cu^{++} < Zn^{++}$ for many ligands. A correlation exists between the stabilities of chelates and the second ionization potentials (a measure of the expected strength of covalent bonds) for many heavy metals.[2]

A *steric factor*, reflecting the fact that for each metal ion there is a particular preferred orientation of coordinated groups, is occasionally to be considered. This factor seems to be of secondary importance. For example, a square planar configuration is preferred over the tetrahedral configuration for tetracovalent complexes of Cu(II). Nevertheless, a reagent such as trimethylenetetramine, which could not form a planar complex, for steric reasons forces the tetrahedral configuration upon Cu(II) with only a small loss of expected stability.[3]

Reference has already been made (Chap. 13) to Taube's classification of complexes according to electronic structure. This classification has to do more with *rate* than with *stability* of complex formation.

Effect of the Nature of the Ligand on Stability of Complexes. The basic dissociation constant K_b is a measure of the tendency of a ligand to coordinate with the hydrogen ion. It is, therefore, to be expected that, if *a series of ligands of sufficient structural similarity* is compared, a linear relationship should exist between $\log K$, where K is the formation constant, and pK_b or pK_a for the ligand.[4] Examples are the Ag(I) complexes of primary amines and the Cu(II) complexes of β-diketones.

Steric factors, however, are more apt to influence coordination with metal ions than with hydrogen ions. Not only are metal ions larger, but usually they have larger coordination numbers than hydrogen ions, which at most can be bonded to two groups. Striking examples of steric effects are encountered, for example, in the use of high-molecular-weight amines as extraction reagents. Chain branching in the vicinity of the amine nitrogen causes interference with the coordinating tendency of the amine. These effects will be discussed below in further detail.

Irving, Cabell, and Mellor[5] found that 2-methyl-1,10-phenanthroline is a stronger base than 1,10-phenanthroline; yet it forms weaker complexes with Fe(II).

The relative instability of the Fe(III) complex with 1,10-phenanthroline compared with the Fe(II) complex also seems to be due, at least in part, to steric hindrance. Steric hindrance plays an important role in the reagent 2-methyl-8-hydroxyquinoline, which precipitates zinc and magnesium but not aluminum.[6]

---

[1] Irving and Williams, *op. cit.*
[2] Martell and Calvin, *op. cit.*
[3] Schwarzenbach, G., *Helv. Chem. Acta*, **35**, 2344 (1952).
[4] Parry and Keller, *op. cit.*
[5] Irving, H., Cabell, M. J., and Mellor, D. H., *J. Chem. Soc.*, **1953**, 3417.
[6] Merritt, L. L., and Walker, J. K., *Ind. Eng. Chem., Anal. Ed.*, **16**, 387 (1944).

Some special factors of particular interest in the formation of chelates as opposed to monodentate complexes have already been mentioned in Chap. 13 (page 222). These include the "chelation effect," or entropy effect, which increases stability as greater numbers of chelate rings are formed, the special stability of five- and six-membered rings, and the special stability of fused-ring systems. Also to be mentioned is a resonance effect, which includes the central metal ion with its coordinated ligands[1] and which increases stability.

14-3. Precipitation Equilibria

The most important type of precipitation equilibrium involves a reagent of class II, which forms an uncharged chelate or "inner complex" that is insoluble. In general, it is necessary to consider stepwise equilibria:[2]

$$
\begin{aligned}
\mathrm{M}^{n+} + \mathrm{X}^- &\rightleftharpoons \mathrm{MX}^{(n-1)+} & K_{eq} &= k_1 \\
\mathrm{MX}^{(n-1)+} + \mathrm{X}^- &\rightleftharpoons \mathrm{MX}^{(n-2)+} & K_{eq} &= k_2 \\
&\cdots\cdots\cdots\cdots\cdots \\
\mathrm{MX}^+_{n-1} + \mathrm{X}^- &\rightleftharpoons \mathrm{MX}_n(\text{soln}) & K_{eq} &= k_n
\end{aligned}
\tag{14-1}
$$

where $k_1, k_2, \ldots, k_n$ are the successive stepwise formation constants of the complexes.

At first, however, we shall neglect the lower complexes and consider that the uncharged species MX_n is formed in one step:

$$
\mathrm{M}^{n+} + n\mathrm{X}^- \rightleftharpoons \mathrm{MX}_n(\text{soln}) \qquad K_{eq} = K_n = k_1 k_2 \cdots k_n \tag{14-2}
$$

where K_n is the over-all formation constant.

Precipitation occurs when the solubility $S°$ of the species MX_n has been exceeded.

$S°$ was called the "intrinsic solubility" by Irving and Williams,[3] who stressed its importance in the behavior of organic precipitating reagents. Following Freiser,[4] we write the solubility equilibrium

$$
\mathrm{MX}_n(\text{solid}) \rightleftharpoons \mathrm{MX}_n(\text{soln}) \qquad K_{eq} = S° \tag{14-3}
$$

and the solubility product expression

$$
K_{sp} = [\mathrm{M}^{n+}][\mathrm{X}^-]^n = \frac{S°}{K_n} \tag{14-4}
$$

Example 14-1. Christopherson and Sandell[5] estimated that the solubility of nickel dimethylglyoxime, NiX_2, in water at an ionic strength of 0.5 was 9.7×10^{-7} M and

---

[1] Martell and Calvin, *op. cit.*
[2] Irving and Williams, *op. cit.*
[3] *Ibid.*
[4] Freiser, *op. cit.*
[5] Christopherson, H., and Sandell, E. B., *Anal. Chim. Acta*, **10**, 1 (1954).

that the solubility product was 4.3×10^{-24}. The formation constant of NiX_2 is, therefore, $9.7 \times 10^{-7}/4.3 \times 10^{-24} = 2.3 \times 10^{17}$.

The order of precipitation of two metals M_1 and M_2 of the same charge is, from Eq. (14-4), given by the ratio $[M_1^{n+}]/[M_2^{n+}]$ and, therefore, by the ratio $S_1^\circ K_{n,2}/S_2^\circ K_{n,1}$ rather than by the ratio of stability constants.

In view of the fact that HX is a weak acid, the anion concentration is expressed conveniently in terms of the fraction that is ionized [cf. Eq. (3-61), Sec. 3-5].

$$[X^-] = \alpha_1 C_{HX} = \frac{K_a C_{HX}}{[H^+] + K_a} \tag{14-5}$$

where C_{HX} is the total reagent[1] concentration $[HA] + [A^-]$.

For the special, simple case in which the reagent is applied in an acidic solution so that $K_a \ll [H^+]$ and in which the lower complexes are unimportant, we have $[X^-] \cong C_{HX} K_a/[H^+]$ and

$$K_{sp} = [M^{n+}][X^-]^n = \frac{[M^{n+}]K_a^n C_{HX}^n}{[H^+]^n} \tag{14-6}$$

If γ represents the fraction precipitated, C_M° is the initial concentration of metal, and C_{HX}° is the initial concentration of reagent, then $[M^{n+}] = C_M^\circ(1 - \gamma)$; $C_{HX} = C_{HX}^\circ - n\gamma C_M^\circ$; and Eq. (14-6) becomes

$$[H^+] = \frac{\{C_M^\circ(1 - \gamma)\}^{1/n} K_a (C_{HX}^\circ - n\gamma C_M^\circ)}{K_{sp}^{1/n}} \tag{14-7}$$

Equation (14-7) was derived by Flagg[2] and shown to be adequate to describe the precipitation of copper, zinc, and cadmium with excess quinaldic acid (Fig. 14-1).

It is important to note that the pH of incipient precipitation, corresponding to $\gamma = 0$, for a given reagent depends first of all on the value of K_{sp} but also upon the initial concentrations of metal ion and reagent. Therefore it is necessary to specify these quantities before quantitative meaning can be attached to the pH at which precipitation begins. The pH of "complete" precipitation can be calculated by taking γ equal to, say, 0.999. The steepness of the precipitation curve, or the change in pH to go from $\gamma = 0$ to $\gamma = 0.999$, depends on the value of n, the charge on the metal ion.

In principle, it is possible to calculate from Eq. (14-7) the theoretical degree of separation of two metals at a given pH value. However, as

---

[1] If the reagent HX is amphoteric, the cation H_2X^+ may be regarded as a divalent acid with ionization constants $K_1 = K_w/K_b$ and $K_2 = K_a$, where K_b and K_a are the classical base and acid dissociation constants. Then the anion concentration becomes $[X^-] = \alpha_2 C_{HX} = K_1 K_2 C_{HX}/([H^+]^2 + K_1[H^+] + K_1 K_2)$. Cf. Eq. (3-64c).

[2] Flagg, *op. cit.*, p. 53.

will be seen below, the theoretical separation may not actually be achieved, owing to coprecipitation phenomena.

Turning now to a more complete treatment of the problem, we shall consider the effect of lower complexes. The total metal concentration C_M is given by

$$C_M = [M^{n+}] + [MX] + [MX_2] + \cdots + [MX_{n-1}] \qquad (14\text{-}8)$$

where the charges of the complexes have been omitted for the sake of simplicity and where the concentration of MX_n, or the intrinsic solubility, has been neglected.

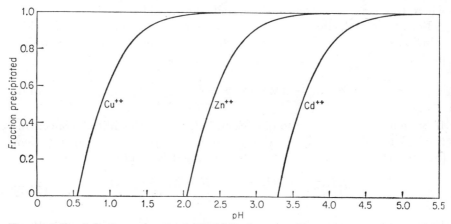

Fig. 14-1. Precipitation curves for 0.001 M divalent metal ions with 0.003 M quinaldic acid. (*With permission from Flagg, J. F., "Organic Reagents," pp. 63, 248, Interscience Publishers, Inc., New York, 1948.*)

If β is the fraction of the metal ion existing as the uncomplexed ion M^{n+}, we have [cf. Eq. (6-24), Sec. 6-5]

$$C_M = \frac{[M^{n+}]}{\beta} = [M^{n+}] \sum_{i=0}^{i=n-1} K_i[X^-]^i$$

$$= [M^{n+}] \sum_{i=0}^{i=n-1} K_i \alpha_1^i C_{HX}^i \qquad (14\text{-}9)$$

where K_0 is unity by definition and where α_1 is given by Eq. (14-5).

From (14-4),

$$K_{sp} = [M^{n+}][X^-]^n = \beta C_M \alpha_1^n C_{HX}^n \qquad (14\text{-}10)$$

or $$C_M C_{HX}^n = \frac{K_{sp}}{\beta \alpha_1^n} \qquad (14\text{-}11)$$

The quantity $K_{sp}/\beta\alpha_1^n$ may be regarded as a *conditional* solubility product,[1] which is a function of the pH and of the reagent concentration. Equation (14-11) is also useful if one wishes to take into account the effect of hydrolysis or of secondary complexing agents (masking agents) that may be present. It is necessary only to make the appropriate calculation of β from the hydrolysis constants or from the formation constants of the secondary complexes, as was done for inorganic precipitates in Chap. 6.

14-4. Separation by Precipitation

As a general rule, it appears unsafe to rely on separation procedures that require control of pH over a narrow range, because the pH of incipient precipitation varies with the concentration of metal ion and of reagent.

Thus, it has been reported[2] that a quantitative separation of copper from cadmium can be made using quinaldic acid, with negligible coprecipitation of cadmium. However, Flagg[3] prefers to make this separation with salicylaldoxime, because the cadmium salt of this reagent is very soluble in acid solution and the conditions, therefore, need not be so carefully controlled.

Coprecipitation can, of course, occur even though the pH of incipient precipitation of the second metal has not been reached. For example, Mayer and Remington[4] found that serious coprecipitation of magnesium occurred with zinc 8-hydroxyquinolate unless the pH was kept at least 2 pH units below the value at which magnesium alone begins to be precipitated.

Biefeld and Howe[5] found, however, that copper could be separated from nickel using salicylaldoxime with very little coprecipitation, if the pH was kept even 0.2 pH unit below the value at which nickel alone precipitated. In contrast, iron was seriously coprecipitated over a wide pH range.

14-5. Selected Examples of Precipitation Reagents

Oxine, or 8-hydroxyquinoline, is a precipitant for many metals. For the separation of heavy metals, extraction is generally a more attractive method than precipitation. Coprecipitation difficulties can thus be avoided, and advantage can be taken of complexation with auxiliary reagents to render the separations more selective. However, oxine has

[1] See footnote to Eq. (6-8), Sec. 6-2.
[2] Majumdar, A. K., *Analyst*, **68**, 242 (1943); *J. Indian Chem. Soc.*, **21**, 24 (1944).
[3] Flagg, *op. cit.*, p. 251.
[4] Mayer, H. V., and Remington, W. J., *Ind. Eng. Chem., Anal. Ed.*, **10**, 210 (1938).
[5] Biefeld, L. P., and Howe, D. E., *Ind. Eng. Chem., Anal. Ed.*, **11**, 251 (1939).

long been used[1,2] to separate aluminum from the alkali metals and alkaline earths, including magnesium and beryllium. An acetic acid–ammonium acetate buffer is used. Other separations are described by Flagg.[3] Magnesium may be separated from the alkali and alkaline earths by precipitation from ammoniacal buffers.[4] It has already been mentioned that 2-methyl-8-hydroxyquinoline (8-hydroxyquinaldine) does not precipitate aluminum.[5] It is, therefore, possible to determine zinc in the presence of aluminum and magnesium by precipitation with 8-hydroxyquinaldine from an acetate buffer. At a higher pH, above 9.3, magnesium forms a precipitate.

Dimethylglyoxime has long been used as a precipitant for nickel and palladium. Nickel[6] is usually precipitated from an ammoniacal tartrate buffer of pH about 8. Under these conditions, even large amounts of iron and many other metals do not interfere. Palladium[7] is precipitated from hydrochloric or sulfuric acid solution. Nioxime[8] (1,2-cyclohexane-dionedioxime) has the advantage of being more soluble in water than dimethylglyoxime and, therefore, less subject to coprecipitation with the metal chelate.

1-Nitroso-2-naphthol is important as a selective precipitant for cobalt.[9] However, the organic derivative is unsuitable as a weighing form, and so the precipitate is ignited to Co_3O_4. For larger amounts of cobalt, metallic cobalt or $CoSO_4$ are recommended as weighing forms.

Cupferron (ammonium salt of N-nitrosophenylhydroxylamine) is of use principally as a group precipitant and extractant for several higher-charged metal ions from strongly acid solution. Several separations are discussed by Clarke.[10] The precipitates are not sufficiently stable to be dried and weighed as such, but are generally ignited to the metal oxide. It is interesting that the reaction between Zr(IV) and cupferron is essentially stoichiometric, as shown by the fact that a direct amperometric titration can be carried out in 10 per cent sulfuric acid solution.[11]

N-benzoylphenylhydroxylamine, $C_6H_5CO(C_6H_5)NOH$, has been suggested[12] as a reagent similar to cupferron in its reactions but more stable.

[1] Kolthoff, I. M., and Sandell, E. B., *J. Am. Chem. Soc.*, **50**, 1900 (1928).

[2] Knowles, H. B., *J. Research Natl. Bur. Standards*, **15**, 87 (1935).

[3] Flagg, *op. cit.*, p. 163.

[4] Miller, C. C., and McLennan, I. C., *J. Chem. Soc.*, **1940**, 656.

[5] Merritt and Walker, *op. cit.*

[6] Fowler, R. M., *Ind. Eng. Chem., Anal. Ed.*, **4**, 382 (1932).

[7] Beamish, F. E., and Scott, M., *Ind. Eng. Chem., Anal. Ed.*, **9**, 460 (1937).

[8] Voter, R. C., Banks, C. V., and Diehl, H., *Anal. Chem.*, **20**, 456, 652 (1948).

[9] Hillebrand, W. F., Lundell, G. E. F., Bright, H. A., and Hoffman, J. I., "Applied Inorganic Analysis," 2d ed., p. 421, John Wiley & Sons, Inc., New York, 1953.

[10] Clarke, S. G., *Analyst*, **52**, 466, 527 (1927).

[11] Olson, E. C., and Elving, P. J., *Anal. Chem.*, **26**, 1747 (1954); **28**, 251, 338 (1956).

[12] Schome, S. C., *Analyst*, **75**, 27 (1950).

The Cu(II), Fe(III), and aluminum complexes can be weighed as such, but the titanium compound must be ignited to the oxide.

The arsonic acids, notably phenylarsonic acid,[1] $C_6H_5AsO(OH)_2$, p-hydroxyphenylarsonic acid,[2] and n-propylarsonic acid,[3] are selective precipitants for quadrivalent metals in acid solution. The metals are weighed as dioxides.

Tannin can hardly be classified with the usual organic reagents, because it acts, apparently, as a negative colloid that is a flocculant for positively charged hydrous oxide sols, such as those of WO_3, Nb_2O_5, and Ta_2O_5. For example, if a tungstate solution is treated with tannin and acidified, most of the tungsten is precipitated. A small amount remains colloidally dispersed and is flocculated with a tannin precipitant such as the alkaloid cinchonine.[4] In this way, tungsten can be separated from many ions. The separation of tantalum from niobium is also of interest; tantalum is precipitated selectively from a slightly acidic oxalate solution.[5] The precipitation of germanium with tannin after distillation of the tetrachloride has been applied to the analysis of steel.[6] An exceptionally selective precipitant for tungsten is anti-1,5-di(p-methoxyphenyl)-1(hydroxylamine-3-oximino-4-pentene), which forms a 1:1 complex with tungstate in acid solution.[7] The weighing form is WO_3.

Our discussion of precipitants will be concluded with a few examples of ionic reagents.

Tetraphenylarsonium chloride is recommended by Smith[8] as a precipitant for Tl(III) as $(C_6H_5)_4AsTlCl_4$, which is weighed as such. The principal interferences are cations that form insoluble chlorides and various anions other than chloride. A similar reagent is triphenylmethylarsonium iodide, which has been suggested for the determination of cadmium in the presence of zinc.[9] The weighing form is $\{(C_6H_5)_3CH_3As\}_2CdI_4$. Metals that form insoluble iodides or anionic iodide complexes interfere.

Benzidine, $H_2NC_6H_4$—$C_6H_4NH_2$, is used in slightly acid solution as the hydrochloride for the precipitation of sulfate as $C_{12}H_{12}N_2H_2^{++}SO_4^{=}$. The precipitate may be weighed as such, or may be titrated with standard alkali. The main disadvantages are its relatively great solubility in water (98 mg liter^{-1}) and even greater solubility in dilute hydrochloric

[1] Rice, A. C., Fogg, H. C., and James, C., *J. Am. Chem. Soc.*, **48**, 895 (1926).
[2] Simpson, C. T., and Chandlee, G. C., *Ind. Eng. Chem., Anal. Ed.*, **10**, 642 (1938).
[3] Geist, H. H., and Chandlee, G. C., *Ind. Eng. Chem., Anal. Ed.*, **9**, 169 (1937).
[4] Lambie, D. A., *Analyst*, **68**, 74 (1943).
[5] Schoeller, W. R., *Analyst*, **57**, 750 (1932).
[6] Weissler, A., *Ind. Eng. Chem., Anal. Ed.*, **16**, 311 (1944).
[7] Yoe, J. H., and Jones, A. L., *Ind. Eng. Chem., Anal. Ed.*, **16**, 45 (1944).
[8] Smith, W. T., Jr., *Anal. Chem.*, **20**, 937 (1948).
[9] Dwyer, F. P., and Gibson, N. A., *Analyst*, **75**, 201 (1950).

acid.[1] Belcher and coworkers have studied various related precipitants that form more insoluble sulfates. The best appears to be 4-chloro-4'-aminobiphenyl,[2] ClC_6H_4—$C_6H_4NH_2$.

A very important ionic precipitant for potassium ion is sodium tetraphenyl borate, $Na^+B(C_6H_5)_4^-$. The solubility product[3] of the potassium salt is 2.25×10^{-8}. Introduced by Raff and Brotz[4] in 1951, this reagent has found application for many analytical purposes. A review of various applications was given by Cluley,[5] who also described procedures for the determination of potassium in silicates. In acid solution at pH 2 or at pH 6.5 in the presence of EDTA, the method is almost specific for potassium. Mercury(II), which interferes in acid solution, does not interfere at high pH in the presence of EDTA. The most important interferences are rubidium and cesium. Ammonium ion, which forms a slightly soluble salt, can be removed by ignition. Alternatively, this interference can be prevented by the addition of formaldehyde if the precipitation is carried out in alkaline solution.[6] Unfortunately, the precipitate formed under alkaline conditions is poorly filterable. Although filter aids are helpful,[7] an acid solution should be used when possible. Excessive acidity (pH < 2) or elevated temperatures tend to promote decomposition of the reagent[8] and to give high results.

The precipitation of potassium tetraphenylborate is readily made the basis of volumetric methods.[9] The simplest procedure is based on the fact that potassium tetraphenylborate is soluble in acetone-water mixtures whereas the silver salt is insoluble.[10] A titration with potassium chromate as the indicator can be used for as little as 0.5 mg of potassium.[11]

14-6. Extraction Equilibria

Organic reagents are often important in converting metal ions into forms that can readily be extracted from water into virtually immiscible organic solvents such as carbon tetrachloride, chloroform, ether, or benzene. Usually, but not always, the organic reagent is also preferentially extracted by the organic phase. Extraction has the advantage over precipitation of avoiding coprecipitation and also of being applicable to

[1] Meldrum, W. B., and Newlin, I. G., Ind. Eng. Chem., Anal. Ed., 1, 231 (1929).
[2] Belcher, R., Nutten, A. J., and Stephen, W. I., J. Chem. Soc., 1953, 1334.
[3] Geilmann, W., and Gebauhr, W., Z. anal. Chem., 139, 161 (1953).
[4] Raff, P., and Brotz, W., Z. anal. Chem., 133, 241 (1951).
[5] Cluley, H. J., Analyst, 80, 354 (1955).
[6] Berkhout, H. W., Chem. Weekblad, 48, 909 (1952).
[7] Berkhout, H. W., and Iongen, G. H., Chemist Analyst, 45, 6 (1956).
[8] Berkhout, op. cit.
[9] Flaschka, H., Chemist Analyst, 44, 60 (1955).
[10] Rüdorff, W., and Zannier, H., Z. anal. Chem., 137, 1 (1952).
[11] Berkhout and Iongen, op. cit.

much smaller quantities of metal. The selectivity of a given reagent may also be improved by the fact that another equilibrium step is added in the separation.

For a nonionic solute that exists in the same molecular form in the two phases (i.e., if no polymerization, ionization, or other secondary reactions need be considered), the equilibrium constant for the extraction equilibrium is approximately equal to the ratio between the solubilities of the solute in the two phases. This is evident from the following considerations.

The distribution equilibrium of a solute A between water, indicated by subscript w, and an organic phase, indicated by subscript o, is described by

$$A_w \rightleftharpoons A_o \qquad P = \frac{a_{A_o}}{a_{A_w}} \qquad (14\text{-}12)$$

where P is the *partition coefficient*. For a nonionic solute the activity ratio a_{A_o}/a_{A_w} may be replaced by the concentration ratio, to give the approximate equation

$$P = \frac{[A]_o}{[A]_w} \qquad (14\text{-}12a)$$

which is the Nernst partition law.[1] Now, if a solid phase is also present, *both* liquid phases are saturated and at equilibrium with each other. If the respective solubilities are S_o and S_w, then the partition coefficient is

$$P = \frac{S_o}{S_w} \qquad (14\text{-}12b)$$

Equation (14-12b), however, is valid only if the saturated solutions in both liquid phases can be regarded as ideal and if the same molecular species is present in the two phases.

For some extractions, especially those involving ion pairs rather than neutral molecules, the approximation (14-12a) may lead to serious errors, as shown by a salt effect on the partition coefficient. For example, Scott[2] took advantage of the "salting out" effect of ferric nitrate and nitric acid in improving the extraction of uranyl nitrate from water into ether. The salting out effects have been interpreted on the basis of changes in the activity coefficient of the uranyl nitrate.[3] This complication, however, is beyond the scope of the present treatment.

[1] Nernst, W., Z. physik. Chem. Leipzig, **8**, 110 (1891).
[2] Scott, T. R., Analyst, **72**, 486 (1949).
[3] Jenkins, I. L., and McKay, H. A. C., Trans. Faraday Soc., **50**, 107 (1954).

If the solute exists in different states of aggregation or association in the two solvents, the equilibrium may be represented by

$$n(A_m)_w \rightleftharpoons m(A_n)_o \qquad P = \frac{a_{A_o}^m}{a_{A_w}^n}$$

and the apparent partition coefficient given by Eq. (14-12) or (14-12a) will vary with the concentration of A. This complication is more often encountered in extraction of inorganic halides than in extraction of chelate complexes. For example, Fe(III) is extracted from aqueous hydrochloric acid by diisopropyl ether as solvated $(H^+FeCl_4^-)_n$, where n varies from 2 to 4 depending on the iron concentration.[1] A comprehensive theoretical treatment of metal halide extractions, considering various cationic, anionic, and polymeric species, has been presented by Diamond,[2] who was particularly interested in Mo(VI) halides.

Irving, Rossotti, and Williams[3] have considered the extraction of inorganic compounds in a generalized way. They considered such effects as ion aggregation, solvation, stepwise complex formation between metal ion and inorganic anions or chelating reagent, and polymerization in the two phases. The general treatment is useful as a guide in planning experiments to determine the nature of the species present in both phases. For example, by determining the partition coefficient and function of the metal concentration it is possible to determine the difference in degree of association of the metal in the two phases.

However, from the analytical viewpoint, the most important type of extraction is that of uncharged molecules of chelate MX_n, which undergo no polymerization in the organic phase. In addition to the equilibria in the aqueous phase, the partition equilibria:

$$(MX_n)_w \rightleftharpoons (MX_n)_o \qquad P_c = \frac{[MX_n]_o}{[MX_n]_w} \qquad (14\text{-}13)$$

and
$$(HX)_w \rightleftharpoons (HX)_o \qquad P_r = \frac{[HX]_o}{[HX]_w} \qquad (14\text{-}14)$$

must be considered, because both the uncharged reagent and chelate are extracted to a greater or lesser extent into the organic phase. The subscripts c and r refer to the chelate and the reagent, respectively.

Extraction of a Single Chelate Complex. A quantity of analytical importance is the distribution ratio D,* which is defined as the ratio of

[1] Myers, R. J., Metzler, D. E., and Swift, E. H., *J. Am. Chem. Soc.*, **72**, 3767 (1950); Myers and Metzler, *ibid.*, p. 3772.

[2] Diamond, R. M., *J. Phys. Chem.*, **61**, 69, 75 (1957).

[3] Irving, H., Rossotti, F. J. C., and Williams, R. J. P., *J. Chem. Soc.*, **1955**, 1906.

* Sometimes called the "extraction coefficient."

total metal concentration in the organic phase to that in the water phase, or

$$D = \frac{C_{M_o}}{C_{M_w}}$$

If we assume that the only form of the metal in the organic phase is the chelate MX_n and if we neglect the formation of lower complexes in the aqueous phase, we have

$$D = \frac{[MX_n]_o}{[MX_n]_w + [M^{n+}]_w} = \frac{P_c}{1 + [M^{n+}]_w/[MX_n]_w} \tag{14-15}$$

Introducing the over-all formation constant K_c of the complex MX_n in the aqueous phase

$$K_c = \frac{[MX_n]_w}{[M^{n+}]_w[X^-]_w^n}$$

and the acid dissociation constant K_a of the reagent in the aqueous phase

$$K_a = \frac{[H^+]_w[X^-]_w}{[HX]_w}$$

we have $\quad \dfrac{[M^{n+}]_w}{[MX_n]_w} = \dfrac{[H^+]_w^n}{K_c K_a^n [HX]_w^n} = \dfrac{[H^+]_w^n P_r^n}{K_c K_a^n [HX]_o^n}$

Substituting in Eq. (14-15),

$$D = \frac{P_c}{1 + [H^+]_w^n P_r^n / K_c K_a^n [HX]_o^n} \tag{14-16}$$

Equation (14-16) expresses the change in the distribution ratio of the metal in terms of the constants P_c, P_r, K_c, and K_a, which represent properties of the solvent and metal chelate system, and of the variables $[H^+]_w$ and $[HX]_o$, which are subject to experimental variation for a given system. It can readily be shown that Eq. (14-16) is equivalent to

$$\frac{1}{D} = \frac{1}{D'} + \frac{1}{P_c} \tag{14-17}$$

where $\quad D' = \left(\dfrac{K_a[HX]_o}{P_r[H^+]_w}\right)^n P_c K_c \tag{14-18}$

Equation (14-18) corresponds to the approximate value of D that obtains under the condition that the second term of the denominator of Eq. (14-16) is very large compared with unity. From Eq. (14-15) it is evident that this condition is equivalent to $[M^{n+}]_w \gg [MX_n]_w$, or that only a small fraction of the metal in the aqueous phase is present as the chelate. From Eq. (14-17) it appears that Eq. (14-18) is generally a good approximation when $P_c \gg 1$, or when the chelate is preferentially extracted into the organic phase—unless $D \gg 1$, corresponding to a very large percentage of extraction.

At the other extreme, if the metal in the aqueous phase is practically all present as the chelate, $[M^{n+}]/[MX_n]_w \ll 1$, and, from Eq. (14-15) or (14-17), $D \cong P_c$. This situation was encountered by Steinbach and Freiser[1] for acetylacetone extractions of metals. See also Example 14-3, page 264.

An equation of the form of (14-18) was first derived and verified experimentally by Kolthoff and Sandell[2] for the dithizone extraction of zinc. Equation (14-18) may be derived by writing the equilibrium constant K_{ext} of the reaction

$$M_w^{n+} + n(HX)_o \rightleftharpoons (MX_n)_o + nH_w^+ \qquad K_{ext} = \frac{[MX_n]_o[H^+]_w^n}{[M^{n+}]_w[HX]_o^n}$$

which can readily be shown to yield

$$K_{ext} = \left(\frac{K_a}{P_r}\right)^n P_c K_c$$

and
$$D' = K_{ext}\frac{[HX]_o^n}{[H^+]_w^n} = \left(\frac{K_a[HX_o]}{P_r[H^+]_w}\right)^n P_c K_c$$

which is identical with Eq. (14-18).

Irving and Williams[3] defined the quantity $pH_{1/2}$ as the pH corresponding to $D = 1$, or to equal concentrations of metal in the two phases. If the volumes of the two phases are equal, $pH_{1/2}$ corresponds to the pH at which half the metal is extracted into the organic phase. In general, if E is the percentage of metal extracted into the organic phase and if V_o and V_w are the volumes of the organic and water phases, respectively, then

$$D = \frac{E}{100 - E}\frac{V_w}{V_o}$$

Expressing Eq. (14-18) in logarithmic form,

$$\log D' = n \log \frac{K_a}{P_r} + \log P_c K_c + n(pH + \log [HX]_o)$$

Setting $pH = pH_{1/2}$ for $\log D' = 0$, and subtracting,

$$n(pH_{1/2} - pH) = -\log D' = \log \frac{100 - E}{E}\frac{V_o}{V_w} \qquad (14\text{-}19)$$

and
$$pH_{1/2} = \log \frac{P_r}{K_a} - \frac{1}{n}\log P_c K_c - \log [HX]_o \qquad (14\text{-}20)$$

[1] Steinbach, J. F., and Freiser, H., *Anal. Chem.*, **26**, 375 (1954).
[2] Kolthoff and Sandell, *J. Am. Chem. Soc.*, **63**, 1906 (1941).
[3] Irving and Williams, *J. Chem. Soc.*, **1949**, 1841.

In Fig. 14-2 are plotted several theoretical curves of percentage extraction vs. pH calculated from Eq. (14-19) for $V_o = V_w$. It is evident that the curves become steeper with increasing values of n, the charge of the metal ion. The value of $pH_{1/2}$ for a given system depends upon the stability constant of its chelate and the concentration of excess reagent, but not on the concentration of metal ion [see Eq. (14-20)]. For various metal ions but for the same reagent and solvent system, the variation in $pH_{1/2}$ is determined primarily by K_c, the formation constant of the chelate, because P_r and K_a are properties of the reagent alone and because P_c would not be very different for the chelates of the different metals.

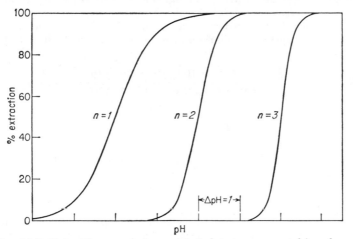

FIG. 14-2. Extraction curves for metal chelates. n = metal ion charge.

Irving and Williams[1] have warned against the uncritical acceptance of experimental extraction curves of the type given in Fig. 14-2, because (1) the concentration of excess reagent is often not specified or is not maintained constant as the percentage extraction is varied, and (2) equilibrium may not have been attained.

Particularly when the chelating reagent is present largely in the organic phase, its concentration in the aqueous phase may be so low that the chelation equilibrium may be attained only slowly. Irving and Williams,[1] for example, found that the extraction of zinc dithizonate into carbon tetrachloride was faster than into chloroform, in approximately the same ratio as the partition coefficients of dithizone between water and these two solvents. Thus the extraction rate appeared to be determined primarily by chelation rate, which in turn was proportional to the concentration of dithizone in the aqueous phase. Irving, Andrew, and Risdon[2] found

[1] *Ibid.*
[2] Irving, H., Andrew, G., and Risdon, E. J., *J. Chem. Soc.,* **1949,** 541.

that a similar situation prevailed for the extraction of copper dithizonate, whereas mercury(II) dithizonate was extracted rapidly by both solvents at pH = 1. By using chloroform to slow down the extraction of copper and by restricting the extraction time to 1 min, they were able to improve the separation of Hg(II) from copper beyond what could be achieved at equilibrium.

Examples of calculations based on Eqs. (14-15) to (14-20) are given here to illustrate situations that may be encountered.

Example 14-2. Given that a metal M^{++} is 33 per cent extracted as MX_2 from 100 ml of 10^{-5} M solution at pH = 5 using 20 ml of 10^{-3} M solution of a chelating reagent HX in an organic solvent. Calculate the percentage extraction expected for the same metal ion solution at pH = 6 using 50 ml of 5×10^{-4} M reagent.

Answer. The extraction equilibrium constant [see Eqs. (14-18) and (14-20)] is

$$K_{ext} = D \frac{[H^+]_w^2}{[HX]_o^2} = \frac{E}{100 - E} \frac{V_w [H^+]_w^2}{V_o [HX]_o^2} = \frac{33}{67} \frac{100}{20} \left(\frac{10^{-5}}{10^{-3}} \right)^2 = 2.5 \times 10^{-4}$$

from which we calculate for the new conditions

$$\frac{E}{100 - E} = K_{ext} \frac{[HX]_o^2}{[H^+]_w^2} \frac{V_o}{V_w} = 2.5 \times 10^{-4} \frac{(5 \times 10^{-4})^2}{(10^{-6})^2} \frac{50}{100} = 31.2$$

and $E = 96.9$ per cent.

Example 14-3. Geiger and Sandell[1] reported for the extraction of Cu^{++} with dithizone from water into CCl_4 the following values: $K_a = 3 \times 10^{-5}, P_r = 1.1 \times 10^4$, $P_c = 7 \times 10^4, K_c = 5 \times 10^{22}, n = 2$.

If 100 ml of an aqueous solution containing 10^{-7} M Cu^{++} in (a) 1 M HCl, and (b) 0.1 M HCl is extracted with 10 ml of 0.01 per cent dithizone in CCl_4 (4×10^{-4} M HX), calculate $pH_{1/2}$ and the percentage of the Cu^{++} remaining unextracted in each case.

Answer. (a) At pH = 0, from Eq. (14-20), $pH_{1/2} = -5.21 - \log [HX]_o$; and, from Eq. (14-19), $2(pH_{1/2} - pH) = \log \{(100 - E)V_o/EV_w\}$. We find $pH_{1/2} = -5.21 - \log (4 \times 10^{-4}) = -1.81$ and, since $V_o/V_w = 0.1$, $\log (100 - E)/E = -2.62$ at pH = 0, $(100 - E)/E = 2.4 \times 10^{-3}$, and $(100 - E) = 0.24$ per cent unextracted. To find whether the approximate expression Eq. (14-18) is applicable, we calculate the second term in the denominator of Eq. (14-16), which turns out to be 16.8 and, therefore, considerably greater than unity. From Eq. (14-17), a better value of $D = P_c/17.8 = 3.9 \times 10^3 = EV_w/(100 - E)V_o$; and $100 - E = 0.256$ per cent unextracted.

(b) At pH = 1, the second term in the denominator becomes 0.168, and $D = P_c/1.168 = 6 \times 10^4$, from which $100 - E = 0.017$ per cent instead of 0.0024 per cent which would be calculated from Eq. (14-18). At higher pH values D approaches a limiting value of $D = P_c = 7 \times 10^4$, corresponding to $100 - E = 0.014$ per cent unextracted.

[1] Geiger, R. W., and Sandell, E. B., *Anal. Chim. Acta.*, **8**, 197 (1953).

Effect of Competing Complexing Reactions. An important limitation on the use of Eqs. (14-15) to (14-20) is that competing complex-formation reactions, including hydrolysis of the metal ion, have been neglected.

The effect of hydrolysis was considered first by Kolthoff and Sandell[1] and later in more detail by Connick and McVey.[2] The combined effects of hydrolysis, complex formation with competing reagents, and formation of lower complexes with the chelating reagent have been considered in the generalized treatment of Irving, Rossotti, and Williams,[3] and in a simplified way by Morrison and Freiser.[4]

Neglecting in the organic phase any species other than the fully coordinated chelate MX_n, the distribution ratio is

$$D = \frac{[MX_n]_o}{[M^{n+}] + \sum_i [MX_i] + \sum_j [M(OH)_j] + \sum_p [MY_p]} \qquad (14\text{-}21)$$

where $\sum_i [MX_i]$ = sum of concentrations of the complexes of the metal with the chelating reagent

$\sum_j [M(OH)_j]$ = sum of concentrations of all hydroxyl complexes, including hydrolyzed species and anionic complexes of amphoteric metals

$\sum_p [MY_p]$ = sum of concentrations of the complexes of the metal with a foreign complexing agent (masking reagent)

In Eq. (14-21), the polymeric species in both phases have been neglected. As mentioned above, such species are of importance in certain metal halide extraction systems, but are usually absent in chelate extractions.

In most cases, the denominator of Eq. (14-21) can be greatly simplified because of the virtual absence of many of the possible species.

Case 1. Lower Chelates in Aqueous Phase. Particularly with multi-valent metals, an appreciable fraction of the metal ion in the aqueous phase may exist as lower complexes. Thus, Rydberg[5] found that, in studying the extraction of thorium acetylacetonate from water into benzene, it was necessary to consider all the lower complexes ThX^{3+}, ThX_2^{++}, and ThX_3^+ but that there was no need to consider the hydroxyl complexes, even though aquated thorium ion undergoes extensive hydrolysis in the absence of complexing agents. For such a case the

[1] Kolthoff and Sandell, *op. cit.*

[2] Connick, R. E., and McVey, W. H., *J. Am. Chem. Soc.*, **71**, 3182 (1949).

[3] Irving, Rossotti, and Williams, *op. cit.*

[4] Morrison, G. H., and Freiser, H., "Solvent Extraction in Analytical Chemistry," p. 50, John Wiley & Sons, Inc., New York, 1957.

[5] Rydberg, J., *Acta Chem. Scand.*, **4**, 1503 (1950).

distribution ratio is given by

$$D = \frac{[MX_n]_o}{[MX_n]_w + \sum\limits_{i=0}^{i=n-1} [MX_i]_w} = \frac{[MX_n]_o}{[MX_n]_w + [M^{n+}]_w/\beta} \qquad (14\text{-}22)$$

where $\dfrac{1}{\beta} = \sum\limits_{i=0}^{i=n-1} K_i[X^-]_w^i$, and where $K_0 = 1$.

The summation is carried out over the lower complexes, from MX to MX_{n-1}.

Equation (14-22) can be applied readily only if the concentration of chelating anion X^- is known, e.g., in alkaline solutions when a relatively large excess of chelating agent is present.

At lower pH values, the reagent is present partly or largely as HX, which is extracted into the organic layer according to its partition coefficient. Thus

$$[X^-]_w = \frac{K_a[HX]_w}{[H^+]_w} = \frac{K_a[HX]_o}{P_r[H^+]_w}$$

and

$$\frac{1}{\beta} = \sum\limits_{i=0}^{i=n-1} K_i\left(\frac{K_a[HX]_o}{P_r[H^+]_w}\right)^i \qquad (14\text{-}23)$$

Comparing Eq. (14-22) with (14-15), we may write a modified equation analogous to Eq. (14-16):

$$D = \frac{P_c}{1 + [H^+]_w^n P_r^n/\beta K_c K_a^n[HX]_o^n} \qquad (14\text{-}24)$$

and the approximate expression analogous to Eq. (14-18) will hold when the second term of the denominator is large compared with unity:

$$D' = \left(\frac{K_a[HX]_o}{P_r[H^+]_w}\right)^n \beta P_c K_c \qquad (14\text{-}25)$$

Equation (14-25), however, is not so convenient to use as Eq. (14-18), because β varies with the hydrogen ion concentration. Therefore, the extraction curves will be distorted from the symmetrical shapes shown in Fig. 14-2, depending upon the magnitudes of the formation constants of the lower chelates.

Example 14-4. According to Rydberg,[1] the following data describe the extraction of thorium acetylacetonate, ThX_4, from water into benzene: $K_a = 1.17 \times 10^{-9}$, $P_c = 315$, $P_r = 5.95$. The successive over-all formation constants for the acetylacetone complexes of Th(IV) are $K_1 = 7 \times 10^7$, $K_2 = 3.8 \times 10^{15}$, $K_3 = 7.2 \times 10^{21}$, $K_4 = 7.2 \times 10^{26}$.

[1] *Ibid.*

Calculate the percentage extraction of thorium at a pH of 6, using a final equilibrium concentration of 10^{-3} M acetylacetone in the organic phase, and a volume ratio $V_o/V_w = \frac{1}{5}$.

Answer. From (14-23) we calculate $K_a[HX]_o/P_r[H^+]_w = 2 \times 10^{-7}$ and $1/\beta = 1 + 7 \times 10^7 \times 2 \times 10^{-7} + 3.8 \times 10^{15} \times 4 \times 10^{-14} + 7.2 \times 10^{21} \times 8 \times 10^{-21} = 225$. The second term in the denominator of (14-24) is calculated to be 210, from which

$$D = \frac{E}{100 - E} \frac{V_w}{V_o} = \frac{315}{1 + 210} = 1.49 \qquad \text{and} \qquad E = 23 \text{ per cent}$$

Case 2. Competing Foreign Complexing Agents. We shall consider only the case of a reagent Y (written without regard to its charge), which forms a series of complexes MY, MY_2, . . . , MY_p. It will be assumed that hydrolysis may be neglected and that the lower chelates with the extracting reagent may be neglected. Otherwise the more general equation (14-21) would have to be used.

The distribution ratio is given by

$$D = \frac{[MX_n]_o}{[MX_n]_w + \sum\limits_{i=0}^{i=p} [MY_i]} = \frac{[MX_n]_o}{[MX_n]_w + [M^{n+}]/\beta} \qquad (14\text{-}26)$$

where $\dfrac{1}{\beta} = \sum\limits_{i=0}^{i=p} K_i[Y]_w^i$, and where $K_0 = 1$.

Comparing (14-22) and (14-26), we may write expressions identical with Eqs. (14-24) and (14-25), the only change being the different definition of β.

As shown by the following example, Cu(II) should be extracted with dithizone even in the presence of EDTA in acid solution.

Example 14-5. Using the data in Example 14-3, calculate the distribution ratio for the extraction of copper(II) dithizonate using 10^{-4} M dithizone in carbon tetrachloride, (a) at pH 4 and (b) at pH 2, in the presence of 0.01 M EDTA.

Answer. From Table 13-1, (Sec. 13-1), log K_{CuY} is 18.8.

a. From Table 13-2 (Sec. 13-5), $-\log \alpha_4$ for EDTA is 8.48 at pH = 4. The conditional formation constant K'_{MY} of the Cu(II)-EDTA complex is, therefore, $10^{10.3}$; whence, $1/\beta = 1 + 10^{10.3} \times 0.01 = 2 \times 10^8$. Equation (14-24) becomes $D = 7 \times 10^4/(1 + 538) = 130$.

b. At pH 2, $- \log \alpha_4 = 13.44$, and $1/\beta = 2.3 \times 10^3$; so $D = 7 \times 10^4/(1 + 62) = 1.1 \times 10^3$.

When Friedeberg,[1] however, carried out an extraction of silver using dithizone in carbon tetrachloride at pH 2, he found that copper was left in solution. Evidently, this separation is based on a slow equilibrium of the copper extraction in the presence of EDTA, for it is stated that, at

[1] Friedeberg, H., *Anal. Chem.*, **27**, 305 (1955).

higher concentrations, the copper is extracted very slowly. Friedeberg found that EDTA prevents the extraction by dithizone of lead, zinc, bismuth, cadmium, nickel, cobalt, and thallium at any pH value.

Recently Schweitzer and Honaker[1] have studied the effect of competing complex formation on the extraction of zinc with dithizone, using a number of extraction solvents.

The special case of hydroxyl ion as a competing complexing agent is encountered when hydrolysis or amphoteric behavior is to be considered. If hydrolysis can be represented by the successive formation of the monomeric complexes $M(OH)^{(n-1)+}$, $M(OH)^{(n-2)+}$, etc., evidently Eq. (14-27) can be applied. However, hydrolysis is often complicated by the presence of species containing more than one metal atom per ion (see Sec. 6-4), particularly when higher-charged metal ions are involved. Each metal ion–reagent–solvent system then represents a particular case that must be studied in detail to determine whether lower chelates or hydrolyzed species must be considered.

However, when a relatively large excess of hydroxyl ion is present and the metal is amphoteric, relatively simple anionic species (hydroxyl complexes) are usually formed. If the solution is sufficiently alkaline ($pH > pK_a + \log P_r$), the reagent is present largely in the aqueous phase as the anion X^-. If chelates lower than MX_n can be neglected and $M(OH)_j^{(n-i)+}$ is the highest hydroxy complex formed, we may write

$$D = \frac{[MX_n]_o}{[MX_n]_w + \sum\limits_{i=0}^{i=j} [M(OH)_i^{(n-i)+}]} = \frac{P_c}{1 + [M^{n+}]_w/\beta[MX_n]_w}$$

where

$$\frac{1}{\beta} = \sum\limits_{i=0}^{i=j} K_i[OH^-]_w^i$$

But

$$\frac{[M^{n+}]_w}{[MX_n]_w} = \frac{1}{K_c[X^-]_w^n}$$

So

$$D = \frac{P_c}{1 + 1/K_c\beta[X^-]_w^n} \tag{14-27}$$

Since most of the metal in the aqueous phase is present as hydroxy complexes, the second term of the denominator is large compared with unity, and

$$D' = P_cK_c\beta[X^-]_w^n$$

Consider the case of an amphoteric metal that forms a single hydroxy complex $M(OH)_j^{(n-j)+}$ of formation constant K_j. Then

[1] Schweitzer, G. K., and Honaker, C. B., Anal. Chim. Acta, 19, 224 (1958).

$$\frac{1}{\beta} = 1 + K_j[OH^-]_w^j \cong K_j[OH^-]_w^j$$

and
$$D' = \frac{P_c K_c}{K_j} \frac{[X^-]_w^n}{[OH^-]_w^j} = \frac{P_c K_c [X^-]_w^n [H^+]_w^j}{K_j K_w^j}$$

whence
$$j(pH - pH_{1/2}) = -\log D' = \log \frac{V_o(100 - E)}{V_w E} \qquad (14\text{-}28)$$

where
$$pH_{1/2} = \frac{1}{j} \log \frac{P_c K_c}{K_j K_w^j} + \frac{n}{j} \log [X^-]_w \qquad (14\text{-}29)$$

Equation (14-28) indicates that the value of E decreases with increasing pH; that is, that the metal is extracted from the organic phase into the aqueous phase at sufficiently high pH values. The value of $pH_{1/2}$ is determined primarily by K_c/K_j or the relative stabilities of the chelate and hydroxyl complexes, and varies with the chelating ion concentration.

Examples of "back extraction" of amphoteric metals into an alkaline aqueous phase are extractions of aluminum, lead, and zinc with either oxine or dithizone as reagent.

14-7. Selected Examples of Extraction Reagents

8-Hydroxyquinoline (oxine) has been used extensively as a chelating and extraction reagent, taking advantage of the solubility of many oxinates in chloroform. The distribution of the reagent itself between water and chloroform was studied in detail by Lacroix.[1] Since the reagent is amphoteric, it may be regarded as a cationic acid; $pK_1 - 5.09$, and $pK_2 = 9.82$. Only the neutral molecule is extracted appreciably into chloroform. Therefore, the distribution ratio of the reagent is given by

$$D_r = \frac{[HX]_o}{C_{HX_w}} = \frac{[HX]_o}{[HX]_w/\alpha_0} = P_r \alpha_0$$

where $\alpha_0 = K_1[H^+]_w/([H^+]_w^2 + K_1[H^+]_w + K_1 K_2)$, the fraction of the reagent in the aqueous phase present as the neutral molecule. The value of P_r found by Lacroix was 720.

Morrison and Freiser[2] have listed conditions for the extraction of some 20 metals. In most cases, the detailed extraction equilibria have not been studied. Lacroix,[3] however, has considered the precipitation and extraction equilibria for aluminum, indium, and gallium. Dyrssen[4] stressed the importance of the lower oxinates of thorium. His extraction data could not be explained by assuming that only Th^{4+} and ThX_4

[1] Lacroix, S., *Anal. Chim. Acta.*, **1**, 260 (1947).
[2] Morrison and Freiser, *op. cit.*, p. 164.
[3] Lacroix, *op. cit.*
[4] Dyrssen, D., *Svensk Kem. Tidskr.*, **65**, 43 (1953).

existed in the aqueous phase. The results were not sufficiently accurate to allow a quantitative evaluation of the formation constants of the lower oxinates, but they could be explained satisfactorily according to the "two-parameter" method of Dyrssen and Sillén,[1] in which it is assumed that the ratio K_{n+1}/K_n of successive formation constants is a constant.

Dyrssen[2] also studied the extraction of strontium into chloroform, using oxine. He evaluated the equilibrium constants:

$$Sr^{++} + X^- \rightleftharpoons SrX^+ \qquad \log k_1 = 2.39$$
$$SrX^+ + X^- \rightleftharpoons SrX_2 \qquad \log k_2 = 0.84$$
$$SrX_2 \cdot 2H_2O(\text{solid}) \rightleftharpoons SrX_2 + 2H_2O \qquad \log S_w = -5.42$$

Strontium oxinate is extracted into chloroform as $SrX_2 \cdot 2HX$, as shown by the fact that the solubility in the organic phase was found to be proportional to the square of the concentration of oxine in the organic phase, or

$$\log S_o = 2 \log [HX]_o - 3.41$$

Thus, a high concentration of organic reagent favors the extraction of strontium into the organic layer. As the following sample calculation shows, strontium is effectively extracted at pH 11 and $[HX]_o = 1$ M.

Example 14-6. Calculate the distribution ratio of strontium between water and chloroform, using $[HX]_o = 1$ M, at pH 11.

Answer. From Dyrssen's data, $\log S_o = -3.41$; $\log P_c = \log S_o - \log S_w = 2.01$, or $P_c = 102$. From the data of Lacroix, $D_r = 720\alpha_0 = 44.5$. Therefore $(C_{HX})_w = [HX]_o/D_r = 0.0225$. $[X^-]_w = K_2(C_{HX})_w/([H^+] + K_2) = 0.021$. $1/\beta = 1 + K_1[X^-]_w = 6.15$. $D = P_c(1 + 1/K_c\beta[X^-]^2)^{-1} = 9.7$.

If the pH is raised further, the reagent is extracted largely into the aqueous layer, thus lowering the partition coefficient of the complex. On the other hand, if the pH is lowered, the strontium complex in the aqueous phase is weakened by competition of hydrogen ions (see Prob. 14-4 below). The conditions for quantitative extraction are, therefore, unusually critical.

Diphenylthiocarbazone (dithizone) extractions have been mentioned above as examples of equilibrium calculations. Sandell[3] has discussed many separations that take advantage of competing complexing reagents (masking agents) to increase the selectivity of the method. Dithizone is widely recognized as a sensitive qualitative reagent as well as an

[1] Dyrssen, D., and Sillén, L. G., *Acta Chem. Scand.*, **7**, 663 (1953).

[2] Dyrssen, *Svensk Kem. Tidskr.*, **67**, 311 (1955).

[3] Sandell, "Colorimetric Determination of Traces of Metals," 2d ed., Interscience Publishers, Inc., New York, 1950.

important reagent for quantitative determinations. Colorimetric determinations are based on the intense green color of the reagent and the contrasting (usually orange or red) colors of the metal dithizonates in chloroform or carbon tetrachloride.

Acetylacetone is exceptional in that it is useful both as a solution, in various organic solvents (carbon tetrachloride, chloroform, benzene, etc.), and as the pure liquid.[1-3] Rydberg[4] has evaluated pK_a (= 8.82 in 0.1 M sodium perchlorate) as well as the partition coefficient of acetylacetone between chloroform ($P_r = 23.5$) or methylisobutyl ketone ($P_r = 5.9$) and aqueous 0.1 M sodium perchlorate. The acetylacetonates of most metals are much more soluble in organic solvents than other chelates used in analytical applications. Thus, relatively large amounts of metals can be handled. Yet, very small amounts can also be extracted, as illustrated by the isolation of the carrier-free radio isotope Fe^{59} from the cobalt from which it was prepared, using a xylene solution of acetylacetone.[5] The selectivity can be increased by using EDTA as a masking agent.[6]

Thenoyltrifluoroacetone (TTA) is a fluorinated β-diketone[7] which is much more acidic in character than acetylacetone and which, therefore, permits extractions at lower pH values, in spite of the fact that its complexes are less stable than those of acetylacetone. Bolomey and Wish,[3] in developing a method for isolating carrier-free radioberyllium, studied the extraction of various metals using a dilute (0.01 M) solution of acetylacetone in benzene. In certain cases, especially for beryllium and Fe(III), equilibrium was attained very slowly, particularly at low pH values. The extraction rate can, however, be increased by increasing the reagent concentration or raising the pH. The differences in extraction behavior among the lanthanides and actinides are especially noteworthy.[9] A summary discussion of the extraction of various metals with TTA has been given by Moore.[10]

N-Nitrosophenylhydroxylamine is used as its ammonium salt (cupferron) for many extractive separations. The equilibria involved in chloroform extractions have been considered by Furman, Mason, and Pekola,[11] who give a detailed summary of the properties of metallic cup-

[1] Steinbach, J. F., and Freiser, H., *Anal. Chem.*, **25**, 881 (1953); **26**, 375 (1954).

[2] Krishen, A., and Freiser, H., *Anal. Chem.*, **29**, 288 (1957).

[3] McKaveney, J. P., and Freiser, H., *Anal. Chem.*, **29**, 290 (1957); **30**, 1965 (1958).

[4] Rydberg, *Svensk Kem. Tidskr.*, **65**, 37 (1953).

[5] Kenny, A. W., Maton, W. R. E., and Spragg, W. T., *Nature*, **165**, 483 (1950).

[6] McKaveney and Freiser, *op. cit.*

[7] Reid, J. C., and Calvin, M., *J. Am. Chem. Soc.*, **72**, 2948 (1950).

[8] Bolomey, R. A., and Wish, L., *J. Am. Chem. Soc.*, **72**, 4483 (1950).

[9] Magnusson, L. B., and Anderson, M. L., *J. Am. Chem. Soc.*, **76**, 6207 (1954).

[10] Moore, F. L., *Am. Soc. Testing Materials Spec. Tech. Publ. No. 238*, 13 (1958).

[11] Furman, N. H., Mason, W. B., and Pekola, J. S., *Anal. Chem.*, **21**, 1325 (1949).

ferrates.   A list of conditions for the extraction of various metals is given by Morrison and Freiser.[1]

Sodium diethyldithiocarbamate, $(C_2H_5)_2NCSS^-Na^+$, is effective for the extraction of some 20 metals,[2,3] into various organic solvents such as ethyl acetate, carbon tetrachloride, etc.   The stabilities of the diethyldithiocarbamates are in general parallel with the insolubilities of the sulfides.   Bode[4] has carried out systematic studies of various metals, and has used various masking agents for selective extractions.

Long-chain amines and amine salts, which had been studied in a preliminary way by Smith and Page,[5] have been investigated extensively at the Oak Ridge National Laboratory, both from the preparative and from the analytical viewpoints.[6]   High-molecular-weight amines, dissolved in solvents such as kerosene, benzene, or chloroform, are preferable to low-molecular-weight amines primarily because of the low solubility of the amines and amine salts in the aqueous phase as compared with the non-aqueous phase.

The extraction reactions are of the following types:

1. The amine can extract an aqueous acid to form the amine salt in the organic phase:

$$(R_3N)_o + H_w^+ + A_w^- \rightleftharpoons (R_3NH^+A^-)_o$$

In alkaline solution, the extraction is reversed.   For the common mineral acid anions the extraction typically decreases in the order: sulfate $>$ bisulfate $>$ chloride $>$ nitrate.   Examples of such extractions are: $Cr(VI)$ as dichromate, $Mo(VI)$ as polymolybdate, and $V(V)$ as vanadate or polyvanadate.   The extraction coefficient, of course, increases with total metal concentration if the degree of polymerization is greater in the organic phase than in the aqueous phase.

2. An amine salt in the organic phase can undergo anion exchange with an ion in the aqueous phase:

$$(R_3NH^+A^-)_o + B_w^- \rightleftharpoons (R_3NH^+B^-)_o + A_w^-$$

It is interesting that, in general, the same order of anion extraction is observed as that found with anion exchange resins, so that previous

[1] *Op. cit.* p. 170.

[2] Chernikov, Y. A., and Dobkina, *Zavodskaya Lab.*, **15**, 1143 (1949); *Chem. Abstr.*, **44**, 1358 (1950).

[3] Bode, H., *Z. anal. Chem.*, **144**, 165 (1955).

[4] *Ibid.*

[5] Smith, E. L., and Page, J. E., *J. Soc. Chem. Ind. London*, **67**, 48 (1948).

[6] Moore, *Anal. Chem.*, **29**, 1660 (1957); Coleman, C. F., Brown, K. B., Moore, J. G., and Allen, K. A., paper UN-510, presented at 1958 Geneva Atomic Energy Conference.

studies with resins can serve as a useful guide for extractions. An example of considerable practical importance is the extraction of U(VI) as the sulfate complex $UO_2(SO_4)_2^=$.

The structure of the amine and the nature of the organic diluent exert profound influences upon the extraction coefficients. Although the amine class (primary, secondary, or tertiary) exerts an effect, these effects are strongly modified by the extent of branching of the alkyl groups and by the nature of the diluent. Highly branched chains generally interfere with efficient extraction, presumably owing to steric effects, but the branched-chain amines may be at the same time more compatible with the diluent, and so the net effect of chain branching on extraction coefficient depends upon the nature of the diluent. In general, a branched-chain secondary amine behaves more like a straight-chain tertiary than like a straight-chain secondary amine. Examples of analytical separations carried out by amine extraction methods are the separation of niobium and tantalum,[1] cobalt and zinc,[2] and protoactinium and niobium.[3] The stabilities of uranyl sulfate complexes have been evaluated from extraction studies with tri-*n*-octylamine.[4]

Other compounds that have been investigated extensively at the Oak Ridge National Laboratory are the organo-phosphorus compounds. Tri-*n*-butylphosphate having long been used as an extractive reagent, it is interesting that the distribution ratio increases regularly in the sequence: trialkylphosphate, $(RO)_3PO$ < dialkylalkylphosphonate, $(RO)_2RPO$ < alkyldialkylphosphinate, ROR_2PO < trialkylphosphine oxide, R_3PO. This trend is evidently associated with the increasing polarity of the P—O bond as the number of such bonds decreases.[5]

Of the various types of compounds, tri-*n*-octylphosphine oxide (TOPO) has received the most intensive study as an analytical reagent.[6] Its remarkable properties as an extractant are illustrated by the fact that the distribution ratio of U(VI) is of the order of 10^5 times greater for TOPO than for tributylphosphate. It is often possible to carry out direct colorimetric determinations in the organic phase to achieve a rapid, sensitive, and selective determination. A few illustrative examples will be given here.

Cr(VI), extracted in microgram quantities from chloride or sulfate

[1] Ellenburg, J. Y., Leddicotte, G. W., and Moore, F. L., *Anal. Chem.*, **26**, 1045 (1954).

[2] Mahlman, H. A., Leddicotte, G. W., and Moore, F. L., *Anal. Chem.*, **26**, 1939 (1954).

[3] Moore, *Anal. Chem.*, **27**, 70 (1955).

[4] Allen, *J. Am. Chem. Soc.*, **80**, 4133 (1958).

[5] Blake, C. A., Jr., Baes, C. F., Jr., Brown, K. B., Coleman, C. F., and White, J. C., paper UN-511, presented at 1958 Geneva Atomic Energy Conference.

[6] White, *Am. Soc. Testing Materials Spec. Tech. Publ. No. 238*, 27 (1958).

solutions into benzene as $H_2Cr_2O_7 \cdot 2TOPO$, is determined by adding an alcoholic solution of diphenylcarbazide and reading the color intensity.[1]

U(VI) is extracted from nitric acid solution as $UO_2(NO_3)_2 \cdot 2TOPO$, using TOPO in cyclohexane. A yellow color is developed by the addition of dibenzoylmethane and pyridine in ethyl alcohol.[2]

Zr(IV) is extracted from chloride solutions into cyclohexane as $ZrCl_4 \cdot 2TOPO$ and determined by measuring the color intensity of the zirconium-pyrocatechol violet complex. By using a nitrate rather than a chloride medium, a different set of interferences is observed. By proper choice of conditions, all interferences except hafnium can be avoided.[3]

Ti(IV) is extracted as a thiocyanate complex from sulfuric or hydrochloric acid solutions by means of a cyclohexane solution of TOPO. The method is free of interference from other quadrivalent metal ions or from anions such as fluoride, phosphate, or oxalate.[4]

Other reagents of lesser importance for extractive separations are morin,[5] dimethylglyoxime, salicylaldoxime, α-benzoinoxime, 1-nitroso-2-naphthol, 1-(2-pyridylazo)-2-naphthol,[6] and thiosalicylidenethylenediimine.[7]

For the details of the various extraction procedures, the reader is referred to the original papers. It is apparent that organic extraction reagents represent a fruitful and active research field in which noteworthy developments can be expected to come at a rapid pace.

PROBLEMS

14-1. Pilipenko[8] reported the values for the equilibrium constant

$$K = \frac{[M^{n+}][HX]_o^n K_a^n}{[MX_n]_o[H^+]_w P_r^n}$$

for the extraction of several metals into carbon tetrachloride using dithizone. His values of K were as follows: Hg(II), 7×10^{-45}; Bi(III), 1.1×10^{-37}; Cu(II), 1.1×10^{-27}; Ag(I), 2.3×10^{-18}; Co(II), 5×10^{-18}; Ni(II), 1.7×10^{-17}; and Sn(II), 4.5×10^{-16}.

a. Show that the above equilibrium constant is related to the constants in the present treatment as follows:

$$K = \frac{1}{K_{ext}}\left(\frac{K_a}{P_r}\right)^n = \frac{1}{P_c K_c}$$

[1] Mann, C. K., and White, J. C., *Anal. Chem.*, **30**, 989 (1958).

[2] Horton, C. A., and White, J. C., *Anal. Chem.*, **30**, 1779 (1958).

[3] Young, J. P., and White, J. C., *Talanta*, **1**, 263 (1958).

[4] Young and White, *Anal. Chem.*, **31**, 393 (1959).

[5] Sandell, "Colorimetric Determination of Traces of Metals," Interscience, 1950.

[6] Cheng, K. L., and Bray, R. H., *Anal. Chem.*, **27**, 782 (1955).

[7] Beck, G., *Mikrochemie ver. Mikrochim. Acta*, **33**, 188 (1947).

[8] Pilipenko, A. T., *Zhur. Anal. Khim.*, **8**, 286 (1953).

b. Compare the value of K for Cu(II) with that calculated from the results of Geiger and Sandell (see Example 14-3, Sec. 14-6).

c. Derive the relationship between pK and $pH_{1/2}$. Calculate $pH_{1/2}$ for the above metals, taking $[HX]_o = 10^{-4}$.

d. Taking the logarithms of the successive stepwise formation constants of $HgBr_4^-$ to be $\log k_1 = 9.0$, $\log k_2 = 8.3$, $\log k_3 = 2.4$, $\log k_4 = 1.3$, calculate the value of $pH_{1/2}$ for the extraction of Hg(II) using $10^{-4} M$ reagent, (i) from $1 M$ bromide solution and (ii) from $0.1 M$ bromide solution. *Ans.* $-1.7, 0.2$.

e. A mixture of $10^{-5} M$ Ag^+ and $10^{-4} M$ Cu^{++} is treated to give a solution $0.01 M$ in EDTA and buffered at a pH of 6. If 100 ml of the mixture is shaken with 10 ml of 10^{-3} dithizone in CCl_4, what percentages of the silver and copper will remain in the aqueous layer? Assume that P_c for silver dithizonate is 10^4. *Ans.* 0.10 per cent of Ag, 98.1 per cent of Cu, using Geiger and Sandell's values, or 99.5 per cent of Cu, using Pilipenko's value for P_cK_c.

14-2. Using Rydberg's data for the extraction of thorium acetylacetonate (Example 14-4), calculate the complete extraction curve of E vs. pH, for $[HX]_o = 10^{-3}$, $V_o = V_w$.

14-3. Christopherson and Sandell[1] have reported the following data for the extraction of nickel dimethylglyoxime, NiX_2, from water into chloroform at an ionic strength of 0.05: $P_c = 410$, $K_c = 2.3 \times 10^{17}$, $K_a = 2.6 \times 10^{-11}$. The reagent HX is more soluble in water ($S_w = 5.4 \times 10^{-3}$) than in chloroform ($S_o = 4.5 \times 10^{-4}$). Therefore, they wrote the equilibrium in terms of a water solution of reagent:

$$Ni_w^{++} + 2(HX)_w \rightleftharpoons (NiX_2)_o + 2H_w^+$$

a. Express the equilibrium constant of this reaction in terms of the above constants, and find its value. *Ans.* 0.064.

b. Derive an expression for $D' = [NiX_2]_o/[Ni^{++}]_w$ and for $D = [NiX_2]_o/([Ni^{++}]_w + [NiX_2]_w)$. Show that $1/D = 1/D' + 1/P_c$.

c. Calculate D' and D for the extraction of Ni^{++} using a solvent system saturated with dimethylglyoxime (i) at a pH of 5 and (ii) at a pH of 3. *Ans.* (i) 1.9×10^4, 410; (ii) 1.87, 1.86.

14-4. Calculate the distribution ratio of strontium between water and chloroform, using oxine at a concentration of $0.1 M$ in the chloroform layer, at pH 10. *Ans.* 1.8×10^{-4}.

14-5. Derive an expression for the percentage extraction of a metal M^{n+}, using V_o ml of *pure* acetylacetone as the extractant for V_w ml of aqueous solution as a function of pH, (*a*) considering that only the chelate MX_n is formed, (*b*) considering that lower chelates $MX, \ldots, MX_{n-1}$ are formed in aqueous solution but are not extracted.

[1] Christopherson and Sandell, *Anal. Chim. Acta*, **10**, 1 (1954).

15. Electrode Potentials

At the 17th Conference of the International Union of Pure and Applied Chemistry (IUPAC) in Stockholm in 1953, the Commission on Electrochemistry and the Commission on Physico-chemical Symbols and Terminology reached agreement on a "Convention concerning the Signs of Electromotive Forces and Electrode Potentials." As will be pointed out below, the recommended sign convention is not inconsistent either with the practice of American physical chemists or with that of European scientists. In the hope of encouraging universal adoption of a single system, the recommendations of the IUPAC commissions will be followed here.

Licht and de Béthune[1] have presented a brief history of electrochemical sign conventions and have also made readily available the text of the IUPAC report. All the essential features will be presented here. A more comprehensive historical account is given by de Béthune.[2] The significant feature of the so-called "European" convention (which can be traced back to J. Willard Gibbs's immortal "Equilibrium of Heterogeneous Substances," written between 1875 and 1878) is that *the sign of the potential is invariant and corresponds to the electrostatic charge of the metal.* This system was adopted by Ostwald[3] and, after falling into temporary disuse, was revived in 1911 by Abegg, Auerbach, and Luther.[4] Since that time it has been used throughout Europe and extensively in America by physicists, practical electrochemists, engineers, and many analytical chemists and biochemists.

The so-called "American" convention, on the other hand, has as its

[1] Licht, T. S., and de Béthune, A. J., *J. Chem. Educ.*, **34**, 433 (1957).

[2] De Béthune, *J. Electrochem. Soc.*, **102**, 288C (1955).

[3] Ostwald, W., *Z. physik. Chem. Leipzig*, **1**, 583 (1887).

[4] Abegg, R., Auerbach, F., and Luther, R., "Messungen elektromotorischer Krafte galvanischer Ketten," *Abhandl. deut. Bunsengesellschaft*, no. 5, Halle, 1911.

essential feature that *the sign of the potential depends on the direction of writing the half-reaction.* Although de Béthune[1] traces the "ambivalent" sign back to Nernst (a European!), the consistent usage in its present form was first set forth clearly by Lewis and Randall.[2] It has been followed by Latimer[3] in his important reference book. In essence, the IUPAC agreement consists in using the word "potential" only to describe the quantity associated in the Lewis and Randall convention with the *half-reaction written as a reduction process and with a sign that corresponds to the electrostatic charge of the metal.* De Béthune[1] proposed the symbol *V* and the name "Gibbs-Stockholm" electrode potential for the IUPAC system. The symbol *E*, however, has received such widespread use in the electroanalytical literature that we shall retain it here. This system has the advantage of conforming to European usage when a potential is given without a corresponding half-reaction and yet of being consistent with the Lewis and Randall convention. The quantity of sign opposite to the electrostatic potential of the metal was not given a name in the IUPAC report. It has recently been proposed by Ramsey[4] that this quantity be denoted by the term "electron chemical potential" and be given the symbol ε. Lingane[5] uses the term "electrode potential" in exactly the sense recommended in the IUPAC report, but he uses the term "potential of a half-reaction" to represent the Lewis-Randall ambivalent sign notation. This usage differs from the Stockholm convention only in permitting the name "potential" to be applied to a quantity opposite in sign from the electrostatic charge of the metal phase.

15-1. Electrical Potential

The difference in electrical potential between two points is defined as the amount of electrical work (per unit of charge) required to move an infinitesimal positive charge from one point to the other. If the charge is measured in coulombs and the electrical work in joules, the potential difference is measured in volts. If an arbitrary point (say, at infinity) is assigned a potential of zero, the sign of the electrical potential of a point represents the work done in transporting a positive charge from the arbitrary point of zero potential to the point in question. Thus a region

[1] De Béthune, *op. cit.*

[2] Lewis, G. N., and Randall, M., "Thermodynamics and the Free Energy of Chemical Substances," McGraw-Hill Book Company, Inc., New York, 1923.

[3] Latimer, W. M., "Oxidation Potentials," 2d ed., Prentice-Hall, Inc., Englewood Cliffs, N.J., 1952.

[4] Ramsey, J. B., *J. Electrochem. Soc.*, **104**, 255 (1957).

[5] Lingane, J. J., "Electroanalytical Chemistry," 2d ed., Interscience Publishers, Inc., New York, 1958.

of higher potential is a region of higher density of positive charge, or deficiency of electrons.

15-2. The Electromotive Force of a Cell

1. The cell should be represented by a diagram,[1] e.g.,

$$Zn \mid Zn^{++} \parallel Cu^{++} \mid Cu \tag{15-1}$$

The electromotive force is equal in sign and in magnitude to the electrical potential of the *right*-hand electrode (metallic phase) when the potential of the left-hand electrode is taken as zero.

2. The cell reaction corresponding to the diagram is written in the direction corresponding to the passage of positive electricity from left to right within the cell.

In the example chosen, the cell reaction is

$$Zn + Cu^{++} \rightarrow Zn^{++} + Cu \tag{15-2}$$

3. If this is the direction of the current when the cell is short-circuited, the cell emf will be positive.

Thus, for any reasonable concentrations of Zn^{++} and Cu^{++}, the cell reaction above is spontaneous, and the emf is positive.

If the cell had been written

$$Cu \mid Cu^{++} \parallel Zn^{++} \mid Zn \tag{15-3}$$

the corresponding cell reaction would have been

$$Cu + Zn^{++} \rightarrow Cu^{++} + Zn \tag{15-4}$$

and the emf would have been *negative*, corresponding to a negative potential for zinc (the right-hand electrode) compared with copper.

The cell emf conforms to the rule that the sign of the emf is positive if the right-hand electrode is the positive terminal of the cell (the + right rule). This rule is in agreement with the conventions pursued for many years by American physical chemists (Lewis and Randall convention).

15-3. The Electrode Potential

When we speak of the electromotive force of a half-cell $Zn^{++} \mid Zn$, we mean the electromotive force of the cell

$$Pt, H_2 \mid \underset{a\,=\,1}{H^+} \parallel \underset{a\,=\,1}{Zn^{++}} \mid Zn \tag{15-5}$$

---

[1] In the diagram, a single vertical line represents a phase boundary at which a potential difference is taken into account. A double vertical line represents a liquid junction at which the potential difference is ignored or is considered to be eliminated by a salt bridge.

implying the reaction

$$H_2 + Zn^{++} \rightarrow 2H^+ + Zn \tag{15-6}$$

where the electrode on the *left* is the standard hydrogen electrode. According to IUPAC convention, such a cell emf may properly be called *the electrode potential*. Thus the half-reaction

$$Zn^{++} + 2e^- \rightleftharpoons Zn \tag{15-7}$$

may be written to correspond to the value (-0.76 volt) for the above cell emf, which may be called the *standard electrode potential* of the zinc electrode, if both zinc and zinc ions are at unit activity.

If we speak of the half-cell Zn | Zn^{++}, we imply the cell

$$\underset{a\,=\,1 \quad a\,=\,1}{Zn \mid Zn^{++} \parallel H^+ \mid H_2, Pt} \tag{15-8}$$

and the corresponding reaction

$$Zn + 2H^+ \rightarrow H_2 + Zn^{++} \tag{15-9}$$

This cell emf, which is $+0.76$ volt, should *not* (by IUPAC convention) be called the electrode potential of zinc.

This convention for electrode potentials requires that the *electrostatic sign* of the electrical potential (with respect to hydrogen) be preserved in the designation of electrode potentials. Thus, metals more active than hydrogen acquire a negative charge (compared with a hydrogen electrode) and are given negative values of electrode potential.

The convention is *not* in disagreement with American practice, but it usually requires a change in the direction of writing the half-reaction and a corresponding change in sign. Thus Latimer[1] writes

$$Zn \rightleftharpoons Zn^{++} + 2e^- \qquad E^\circ = 0.76 \text{ volt} \tag{15-10}$$

which is perfectly proper according to IUPAC convention, but E° should not be denoted by the word *potential*.

Accordingly, we shall adopt the practice of writing all half-reactions as reductions, e.g.,

$$Zn^{++} + 2e^- \rightleftharpoons Zn \qquad E^\circ = -0.76 \text{ volt} \tag{15-11}$$

In general, we have

$$Ox + ne^- \rightleftharpoons Red \tag{15-12}$$

and a positive electrode potential means an oxidant Ox stronger than the hydrogen ion, whereas a negative potential implies a reductant Red stronger than hydrogen. A selected list of standard electrode potentials is given in Table 15-1.

[1] Latimer, *op. cit.*

TABLE 15-1. SELECTED LIST OF STANDARD ELECTRODE POTENTIALS

Half-reaction	$E°$, volts
$Na^+ + e^- \rightleftharpoons Na$	-2.714
$H_2AlO_3^- + H_2O + 3e^- \rightleftharpoons Al + 4OH^-$	-2.35
$Al^{3+} + 3e^- \rightleftharpoons Al$	-1.66
$Sn(OH)_6^= + 2e^- \rightleftharpoons HSnO_2^- + H_2O + 3OH^-$	-0.90
$Zn^{++} + 2e^- \rightleftharpoons Zn$	-0.763
$AsO_4^{3-} + 3H_2O + 2e^- \rightleftharpoons H_2AsO_3^- + 4OH^-$	-0.67
$U^{4+} + e^- \rightleftharpoons U^{3+}$	-0.61
$Fe^{++} + 2e^- \rightleftharpoons Fe$	-0.440
$Cr^{3+} + e^- \rightleftharpoons Cr^{++}$	-0.41
$Cd^{++} + 2e^- \rightleftharpoons Cd$	-0.403
$V^{3+} + e^- \rightleftharpoons V^{++}$	-0.255
$Sn^{++} + 2e^- \rightleftharpoons Sn$	-0.136
$Pb^{++} + 2e^- \rightleftharpoons Pb$	-0.126
$2H^+ + 2e^- \rightleftharpoons H_2$	0.00
$TiO^{++} + 2H^+ + e^- \rightleftharpoons Ti^{3+} + H_2O$	0.1
$S_4O_6^= + 2e^- \rightleftharpoons 2S_2O_3^=$	0.08
$S + 2H^+ + 2e^- \rightleftharpoons H_2S$	0.141
$Sn^{4+} + 2e^- \rightleftharpoons Sn^{++}$	0.15
$SO_4^= + 4H^+ + 2e^- \rightleftharpoons H_2SO_3 + H_2O$	0.17
$AgCl + e^- \rightleftharpoons Ag + Cl^-$	0.222
$BiO^+ + 2H^+ + 3e^- \rightleftharpoons Bi + H_2O$	0.32
$UO_2^{++} + 4H^+ + 2e^- \rightleftharpoons U^{4+} + 2H_2O$	0.334
$Cu^{++} + 2e^- \rightleftharpoons Cu$	0.337
$VO^{++} + 2H^+ + e^- \rightleftharpoons V^{3+} + H_2O$	0.361
$O_2 + 2H_2O + 4e^- \rightleftharpoons 4OH^-$	0.401
$H_2SO_3 + 4H^+ + 4e^- \rightleftharpoons S + 3H_2O$	0.45
$Cu^+ + e^- \rightleftharpoons Cu$	0.521
$I_2 + 2e^- \rightleftharpoons 2I^-$	0.5355
$I_3^- + 2e^- \rightleftharpoons 3I^-$	0.536
$H_3AsO_4 + 2H^+ + 2e^- \rightleftharpoons H_3AsO_3 + H_2O$	0.559
$MnO_4^- + e^- \rightleftharpoons MnO_4^=$	0.564
$MnO_4^- + 2H_2O + 2e^- \rightleftharpoons MnO_2 + 4OH^-$	0.60
$O_2 + 2H^+ + 2e^- \rightleftharpoons H_2O_2$	0.682
$OBr^- + H_2O + 2e^- \rightleftharpoons Br^- + 2OH^-$	0.76
$Fe^{3+} + e^- \rightleftharpoons Fe^{++}$	0.771
$Hg_2^{++} + 2e^- \rightleftharpoons 2Hg$	0.789
$Ag^+ + e^- \rightleftharpoons Ag$	0.7991
$OCl^- + H_2O + 2e^- \rightleftharpoons Cl^- + 2OH^-$	0.89
$2Hg^{++} + 2e^- \rightleftharpoons Hg_2^{++}$	0.920
$V(OH)_4^+ + 2H^+ + e^- \rightleftharpoons VO^{++} + 3H_2O$	1.00
$ICl_2^- + e^- \rightleftharpoons \frac{1}{2}I_2 + 2Cl^-$	1.06
$Br_2(e) + 2e^- \rightleftharpoons 2Br^-$	1.0652
$IO_3^- + 6H^+ + 5e^- \rightleftharpoons \frac{1}{2}I_2 + 3H_2O$	1.195
$MnO_2 + 4H^+ + 2e^- \rightleftharpoons Mn^{++} + 2H_2O$	1.23
$O_2 + 4H^+ + 4e^- \rightleftharpoons 2H_2O$	1.229
$Cr_2O_7^= + 14H^+ + 6e^- \rightleftharpoons 2Cr^{3+} + 7H_2O$	1.33

TABLE 15-1. SELECTED LIST OF STANDARD ELECTRODE POTENTIALS (*Continued*)

Half-reaction	$E°$, volts
$Cl_2 + 2e^- \rightleftharpoons 2Cl^-$	1.3595
$HOI + H^+ + e^- \rightleftharpoons \frac{1}{2}I_2 + H_2O$	1.45
$PbO_2 + 4H^+ + 2e^- \rightleftharpoons Pb^{++} + 2H_2O$	1.455
$Mn^{3+} + e^- \rightleftharpoons Mn^{++}$	1.51
$MnO_4^- + 8H^+ + 5e^- \rightleftharpoons Mn^{++} + 4H_2O$	1.51
$HOBr + H^+ + e^- \rightleftharpoons \frac{1}{2}Br_2 + H_2O$	1.59
$Bi_2O_4 + 4H^+ + 2e^- \rightleftharpoons 2BiO^+ + 2H_2O$	1.59
$H_5IO_6 + H^+ + 2e^- \rightleftharpoons IO_3^- + 3H_2O$	1.6
$Ce^{4+} + e^- \rightleftharpoons Ce^{3+}$	1.61
$HOCl + H^+ + e^- \rightleftharpoons \frac{1}{2}Cl_2 + H_2O$	1.63
$MnO_4^- + 4H^+ + 3e^- \rightleftharpoons MnO_2 + 2H_2O$	1.695
$H_2O_2 + 2H^+ + 2e^- \rightleftharpoons 2H_2O$	1.77
$Ag^{++} + e^- \rightleftharpoons Ag^+$	1.98
$S_2O_8^- + 2e^- \rightleftharpoons 2SO_4^-$	2.01
$O_3 + 2H^+ + 2e^- \rightleftharpoons O_2 + H_2O$	2.07
$F_2 + 2e^- \rightleftharpoons 2F^-$	2.65

[With permission from Latimer, W. M., "Oxidation Potentials," 2d ed., Prentice-Hall, Inc., Englewood Cliffs, N.J., 1952.]

15-4. The Nernst Equation

The electrode potential of a redox couple varies with the activities of the reduced and oxidized forms of the couple in the sense that an increasing activity of oxidant increases the value of the potential. Quantitatively, for the reversible half-reaction

$$Ox + ne^- \rightleftharpoons Red \qquad (15\text{-}12)$$

we have the Nernst equation

$$E = E° + \frac{RT}{nF} \ln \frac{a_{ox}}{a_{red}} \qquad (15\text{-}13)$$

where $E°$ corresponds to the value of the potential E at *unit activities* of oxidant and reductant[1] and is called the *standard potential* of the electrode. When numerical values of RT and F are inserted in Eq. (15-13) and logarithms of base 10 are used, we have at 25°C

$$E = E° + \frac{2.3RT}{nF} \log \frac{a_{ox}}{a_{red}} = E°_{25} + \frac{0.059}{n} \log \frac{a_{ox}}{a_{red}} \qquad (15\text{-}14)$$

or

$$E = E°_{30} + \frac{0.060}{n} \log \frac{a_{ox}}{a_{red}} \qquad \text{at 30°C} \qquad (15\text{-}15)$$

[1] If both activities are variable, e.g., Fe^{3+} and Fe^{++}, $E°$ corresponds to an activity *quotient* of unity.

We may substitute in Eq. (15-13) for each activity the product of activity coefficient and concentration.   Thus

$$E = E° + \frac{RT}{nF} \ln \frac{f_{ox}}{f_{red}} + \frac{RT}{nF} \ln \frac{[Ox]}{[Red]} \tag{15-16}$$

and, combining the first two terms,

$$E = E°' + \frac{RT}{nF} \ln \frac{[Ox]}{[Red]} \tag{15-17}$$

where $E°'$ corresponds to the value of E at *unit concentrations* of oxidant and reductant and is called the *formal potential* of the electrode.   Obviously, the formal potential varies with the activity coefficients and, therefore, with the ionic strength of the solution.   Therefore, for a given half-reaction, a compilation of formal potentials is necessary corresponding to each electrolyte composition.[1]   Thus, to describe the half-reaction

$$Fe^{3+} + e^- \rightleftharpoons Fe^{++} \tag{15-18}$$

a series of values for different concentrations of H_2SO_4, HCl, etc. are necessary.   A list of formal potentials of the Fe(III)-Fe(II) and $Cr_2O_7^=$-Cr^{3+} couples, evaluated from titration curves, is given by Smith and Richter and presented here in Table 15-2.   The actual measurements involved a saturated calomel reference electrode.   Many formal potentials are listed by Charlot.[2,3]

In contrast to formal potentials, a single value of the standard potential characterizes each half-reaction.   Formal potentials are often of greater practical value to the analytical chemist than standard potentials, because they represent quantities subject to direct experimental measurement.   For example, during the course of a titration of Fe(II) with Ce(IV) in 1 N perchloric acid, the ionic strength and the activity coefficients of the reactants remain essentially constant, although the concentration ratio $[Fe^{3+}]/[Fe^{++}]$ changes enormously and in a known way in the vicinity of the end point.   Equation (15-17) is of greater practical value in calculating the course of the titration curve than an equation written in terms of activities.

For more complicated electrode reactions, the Nernst equation includes terms involving all species of variable activity.   Such species may

---

[1] The formal potential also includes implicitly a liquid junction potential between the reference electrode used in the measurement and the half-cell in question.

[2] Charlot, G., "Qualitative Inorganic Analysis," John Wiley & Sons, Inc., New York, 1954.

[3] Charlot, "Selected Constants: Oxidation-Reduction Potentials," Pergamon Press, New York, 1958.

TABLE 15-2. FORMAL POTENTIALS OF IRON AND DICHROMATE SYSTEMS

Acid present	$E^{\circ\prime}_{Fe^{3+},Fe^{++}}$, volts	$E^{\circ\prime}_{Cr_2O_7^-,Cr^{3+}}$, volts
0.1 M HCl	0.73	0.03
0.5 M HCl	0.72	0.07
1 M HCl	0.70	1.00
2 M HCl	0.69	1.05
3 M HCl	0.68	1.08
0.1 M H$_2$SO$_4$	0.68	0.92
0.5 M H$_2$SO$_4$	0.68	1.08
4 M H$_2$SO$_4$	0.68	1.15
0.1 M HClO$_4$	0.735	0.84
1 M HClO$_4$	0.735	1.025

[With permission from Smith, G. F., *Anal. Chem.*, **23**, 925 (1951). Compare Smith, G. F., and Richter, F. P., "Phenanthroline and Substituted Phenanthroline Indicators," p. 37, G. Frederick Smith Chemical Co., Columbus, Ohio, 1944.]

include hydrogen or hydroxyl ion, complexing molecules or ions and the like. Reactants at invariant unit activity, for example, the solvent, pure metals, pure solids, etc., are omitted. As examples we have

$$TiO^{++} + 2H^+ + e^- \rightleftharpoons Ti^{3+} \tag{15-19}$$

$$E = E^\circ + \frac{RT}{F} \ln \frac{a_{TiO^{++}} a^2_{H^+}}{a_{Ti^{3+}}} \tag{15-20}$$

$$AgCl(solid) + e^- \rightleftharpoons Ag + Cl^- \tag{15-21}$$

$$E = E^\circ + \frac{RT}{F} \ln \frac{1}{a_{Cl^-}} = E^\circ - \frac{RT}{F} \ln a_{Cl^-} \tag{15-22}$$

15-5. Combination of Half-reactions to Form Cell Reaction

An oxidation-reduction reaction is composed of (at least) two half-reactions. Any two half-reactions may be combined *by subtraction in such a way as to cancel the electrons* to yield a whole reaction that corresponds to the cell reaction. The cell emf is the algebraic difference between the electrode potentials.

For example, consider

$$
\begin{array}{lll}
Fe(III) + e^- \rightleftharpoons Fe(II) & E^\circ = 0.77 \text{ volt} & (15\text{-}23) \\
Sn(IV) + 2e^- \rightleftharpoons Sn(II) & E^\circ = 0.14 \text{ volt} & (15\text{-}24)
\end{array}
$$

First multiplying the iron half-reaction by 2 to cancel the electrons, then subtracting Eq. (15-24) from (15-23), we have

$$2Fe(III) + Sn(II) \rightarrow 2Fe(II) + Sn(IV)$$
$$E^\circ_{cell} = 0.77 - 0.14 = 0.63 \text{ volt} \tag{15-25}$$

Note that, when the iron half-reaction is doubled, its electrode potential is unaffected, since a Nernst equation written for a doubled reaction is identical with that written for the single reaction.

It is seen that, if the subtraction is carried out in such a direction as to produce a *positive* cell emf, the resulting cell reaction is a *spontaneous* one. This simply follows from the fact that the stronger oxidant [in the above case, Fe(III)] has the higher potential, and the subtraction is performed in the direction corresponding to the reduction of the stronger oxidant.

To calculate the cell emf from the electrode potentials given in a cell diagram, one subtracts the potentials in the following way:

$$E_{cell} = E_{right} - E_{left} \tag{15-26}$$

following the "+ right" rule.

A spontaneous cell reaction, by thermodynamic convention, has a negative free energy change numerically equal to the electrical work (in volt-coulombs or joules) per unit of reaction as written. The total free energy change, in general, is

$$-\Delta F = nFE_{cell} \tag{15-27}$$

and, if all reactants are in their standard states (unit activities),

$$-\Delta F^\circ = nFE_{cell}^\circ \tag{15-28}$$

where n is the number of electrons canceled in subtracting the half-reactions. In numerical units,

$$-\Delta F(\text{joules}) = n \times 96{,}500 \times E_{cell}(\text{volts}) \tag{15-29}$$

or $\quad -\Delta F(\text{calories}) = n \times 23{,}060 \times E_{cell}(\text{volts}) \tag{15-30}$

It is sometimes possible to arrive at a particular cell reaction by different combinations of half-reactions involving different values of n in Eq. (15-28). The free energy change is independent of the method of arriving at the cell reaction, but the value of the cell emf varies correspondingly.

To illustrate, we can arrive at the reaction

$$2MnO_4^- + 3Mn^{++} + 2H_2O \rightleftharpoons 5MnO_2 + 4H^+ \tag{15-31}$$

either by combining the following half-reactions:

$$MnO_4^- + 8H^+ + 5e^- \rightleftharpoons Mn^{++} + 4H_2O \qquad E^\circ = 1.51 \text{ volts} \tag{15-32}$$
$$MnO_2 + 4H^+ + 2e^- \rightleftharpoons Mn^{++} + 2H_2O \qquad E^\circ = 1.23 \text{ volts} \tag{15-33}$$

or by combining

$$MnO_4^- + 4H^+ + 3e^- \rightleftharpoons MnO_2 + 2H_2O \qquad E^\circ = 1.695 \text{ volts} \tag{15-34}$$
$$MnO_2 + 4H^+ + 2e^- \rightleftharpoons Mn^{++} + 2H_2O \qquad E^\circ = 1.23 \text{ volts} \tag{15-35}$$

In the first instance, $n = 10$, $E^\circ_{cell} = 0.28$, and $\Delta F^\circ = -64,000$ cal. In the second, $n = 6$, $E^\circ_{cell} = 0.465$, and ΔF° has the same value. Still another way would be to cancel 15 electrons by combining the 5-electron and the 3-electron reductions of MnO_4^-. Each subtraction of half-reactions corresponds to a particular cell, which does not necessarily represent a physically measurable entity. In the above example, none of the three postulated cells could be measured directly, because of the instability of MnO_4^- (cf. Sec. 19-2). Nevertheless, the value of ΔF° for reaction (15-31) is valid.

15-6. Equilibrium Constant of Cell Reaction

The equilibrium constant of a reaction can be calculated from the standard free energy change by use of the equation

$$-\Delta F^\circ = RT \ln K = nFE^\circ_{cell} \qquad (15\text{-}36)$$

We note that, for a spontaneous reaction, ΔF° is negative and that, correspondingly, the equilibrium constant is greater than unity.

Introducing numerical values of RT and F at 25°C,

$$\log K = \frac{nE^\circ_{cell}}{0.0591} = \frac{n(E^\circ_{right} - E^\circ_{left})}{0.0591} \qquad (15\text{-}37)$$

To illustrate, consider the cell,

$$\underset{a=1}{Zn \mid Zn^{++}} \; \underset{a=1}{\| \; H^+} \; \mid H_2, Pt \qquad (15\text{-}38)$$

with the cell reaction

$$Zn + 2H^+ \rightleftharpoons H_2 + Zn^{++} \qquad (15\text{-}39)$$

The equilibrium constant is given by

$$\log K = \frac{2\{0 - (-0.76)\}}{0.0591} = 25.8 \qquad (15\text{-}40)$$

15-7. Combination of Half-reactions to Form New Half-reactions

It is sometimes desirable to be able to calculate the electrode potential of a half-reaction that may be derived by a combination of two or more half-reactions.

To do this, we recall that the electrode potential is actually the emf of a cell involving the desired half-reaction on the right and the standard hydrogen electrode on the left. Since the potential of the standard hydrogen electrode is arbitrarily taken as zero, we may for convenience consider that the $nFE^\circ_{electrode}$ that is numerically equal to the nFE°_{cell} is associated with the half-reaction of the electrode in question. Thus, the free energy change of the cell reaction involving the standard hydrogen electrode on the left is assigned to the half-reaction of the right-hand electrode.

We may combine two half-reactions by addition if we regard the free energy change, or its negative, $nFE°$, as being additive. However, since the faraday is common to all such additions, the summation is simplified by regarding the quantity $nE°$ or the volt-electrons as additive.

To illustrate, we combine

$$Fe^{3+} + e^- \rightleftharpoons Fe^{++} \qquad E° = 0.77 \qquad nE° = 0.77 \qquad (15\text{-}41)$$
$$Fe^{++} + 2e^- \rightleftharpoons Fe \qquad E° = -0.44 \qquad nE° = -0.88 \qquad (15\text{-}42)$$

to form

$$Fe^{3+} + 3e^- \rightleftharpoons Fe \qquad\qquad\qquad nE° = -0.11 \qquad (15\text{-}43)$$

and then $\qquad\qquad\qquad E° = -0.04$

In passing, it may be noted that the final half-reaction is not subject to direct measurement (see page 295). Its potential, however, can be used in making free-energy calculations.

Example 15-1. As another example, combine the following two half-reactions by the subtraction $(a) - (b) = (c)$:

(a)	$Cu^{++} + 2e^- \rightleftharpoons Cu$	$E° = 0.337$	$nE° = 0.674$	(15-44)
(b)	$Cu^+ + e^- \rightleftharpoons Cu$	$E° = 0.521$	$nE° = 0.521$	(15-45)
(c)	$Cu^{++} + e^- \rightleftharpoons Cu^+$		$nE° = 0.153$	(15-46)
		$E° = 0.153$		

By inspection of the values of $E°$, we can see that Cu^+ is a stronger oxidant against Cu than Cu^{++} is against Cu^+. Therefore, if Cu^{++} is reduced, the product must be Cu, since Cu^+ is even more readily reduced. We also infer that Cu^+ should disproportionate according to the equation

$$2Cu^+ \rightleftharpoons Cu + Cu^{++} \qquad\qquad (15\text{-}47)$$

which is obtained by any of the following operations: $2(b) - (a)$; $(a) - 2(c)$; or $(b) - (c)$. The first two give $E°_{cell} = 0.184$; the third gives $E°_{cell} = 0.368$. All three give $\Delta F° = -0.368 \times 23,060 = -8,490$ cal. By forming a stable complex or insoluble compound, Cu^+ can be stabilized. The effect is to lower the $E°$ of half-reaction (a) and to raise that of (c) until their order is reversed. As an exercise, calculate the potentials in 0.01 N Cl^-, which precipitates CuCl $(K_{sp} = 3.2 \times 10^{-7})$.

15-8. Effect of Complex Formation on Electrode Potentials

Consider first the half-reaction

$$M^{n+} + ne^- \rightleftharpoons M \qquad\qquad (15\text{-}48)$$

and suppose that the aquated ion M^{n+} forms a series of complexes MX, $MX_2, \ldots, MX_q$, with a complexing agent X, which may be either charged or uncharged. For the sake of simplicity, we will omit the charge on the complex species.

Referring to Chap. 6, we recall [Eqs. (6-35) to (6-41)] that β, the fraction of metal ion in the aquated form, is given by

$$\frac{1}{\beta} = \frac{C_{M^{n+}}}{[M^{n+}]} = \sum_{i=0}^{i=q} K_i[X]^i \qquad \text{where } K_0 = 1 \qquad (15\text{-}49)$$

Writing the Nernst equation for (15-48) in terms of concentrations,

$$E = E^{o\prime}_{M^{n+},M} + \frac{RT}{nF} \ln [M^{n+}] \qquad (15\text{-}50a)$$

$$E = E^{o\prime}_{M^{n+},M} + \frac{RT}{nF} \ln C_{M^{n+}} + \frac{RT}{nF} \ln \beta \qquad (15\text{-}50b)$$

If the successive formation constants of MX_q are known, the value of β can be calculated from (15-49), and the electrode potential can be calculated from (15-50). Conversely, from measurements of the electrode potential at various concentrations of complexing agent X, the value of β can be determined for each value of [X]. If sufficient data are available, the values of the formation constants K_n can be evaluated. Obviously, if there are q such values, we need q equations, which are available from q determinations of E.

The situation is simpler if only a single species MX_q is formed over a range of concentrations of X. Then the electrode reaction can be written

$$MX_q + ne^- \rightleftharpoons M + qX \qquad (15\text{-}51)$$

The formation constant is

$$K_q = \frac{[MX_q]}{[M^{n+}][X]^q} \qquad \text{and} \qquad \frac{1}{\beta} = 1 + K_q[X]^q \cong K_q[X]^q \qquad (15\text{-}52)$$

Accordingly, by substitution into Eq. (15-50a),

$$E = E^{o\prime}_{M^{n+},M} - \frac{RT}{nF} \ln K_q - q \frac{RT}{nF} \ln [X] + \frac{RT}{nF} \ln [MX_q] \qquad (15\text{-}53)$$

The first three terms on the right-hand side of Eq. (15-53) can be combined to give the formal potential of the half-reaction (15-51), or

$$E = E^{o\prime}_{MX_q,M} + \frac{RT}{nF} \ln [MX_q] \qquad (15\text{-}54)$$

where $\qquad E^{o\prime}_{MX_q,M} = E^{o\prime}_{M^{n+},M} - \frac{RT}{nF} \ln K_q - q \frac{RT}{nF} \ln [X] \qquad (15\text{-}55)$

Equation (15-55) indicates that, if the formal potential of the complex is plotted against log [X], a straight line of slope $-2.3q\dfrac{RT}{nF}$ is obtained. From the slope, the value of q and, hence, the formula of the complex can be determined. From the intercept, which is $E^{\circ\prime}_{M^{n+},M} - \dfrac{RT}{nF}\ln K_q$, the value of the formation constant can be calculated if the formal potential $E^{\circ\prime}_{M^{n+},M}$ is known.

If a series of complexes is formed, the plot of log [X] against E for a given total metal ion concentration [Eq. (15-50)] is a curve, because $1/\beta$ is a polynomial in [X].

It is evident from (15-50), since $\beta < 1$, and from (15-55), since $K_q > 1$, that the potential E corresponding to a given total concentration of metal ions $C_{M^{n+}}$ or $[MX_q]$ is shifted in a negative direction by complex formation. Thus the metal becomes a stronger reducing agent, or the complex becomes more difficult to reduce, than the aquated ion.

To evaluate the true thermodynamic formation constants in terms of activities, rather than the apparent formation constants in terms of concentrations, it is necessary to extrapolate the apparent values to zero ionic strength.

To do this, it is first necessary to measure the electrode potential as a function of [X] at several ionic-strength levels. If X is an uncharged species, varying [X] does not change the ionic strength; moreover, the various complexes MX, MX_2, etc., have the same charge as the aquated ion M^{n+}, and so the activity coefficients of all these species are approximately the same. Under these circumstances, it is relatively straightforward to evaluate the formation constants at various ionic-strength levels and, thus, to evaluate the true formation constants.

If X is a charged species, however, it is necessary, in order to maintain a constant ionic strength, to compensate for the addition of X by removal of a noncomplexing electrolyte. This may require the presence of a relatively high ionic strength throughout the series. Moreover, the various species MX, MX_2, etc., each have a different charge and, therefore, a different activity coefficient. Finally, the assumption that the activity coefficient is constant for constant ionic strength but varying composition becomes progressively less valid as the ionic strength increases. For these reasons, it is seldom possible to evaluate the true thermodynamic formation constants if the complexing agent is an ion. Nevertheless, many useful formal constants have been evaluated at relatively high ionic strengths.[1]

[1] Bjerrum, J., Schwarzenbach, G., and Sillén, L. G., "Stability Constants of Metal Ion Complexes with Solubility Products of Inorganic Substances," *Chem. Soc. London Spec. Publ. Nos.* 6 (1957), 7 (1958).

Turning now to a half-reaction involving two oxidation states of a metal in solution,

$$M_{ox} + ne^- \rightleftharpoons M_{red} \tag{15-56}$$

an equation analogous to (15-50) can be written in terms of the fractions β_{ox} and β_{red} of M_{ox} and M_{red} in the aquated form. Thus

$$\frac{1}{\beta_{ox}} = \frac{C_{Mox}}{[M_{ox}]} = \sum_{n=0}^{n=p} (K_{ox})_n[X]^n \qquad \text{where } (K_{ox})_0 = 1 \tag{15-57}$$

and

$$\frac{1}{\beta_{red}} = \frac{C_{Mred}}{[M_{red}]} = \sum_{n=0}^{n=q} (K_{red})_n[X]^n \qquad \text{where } (K_{red})_0 = 1 \tag{15-58}$$

and

$$E = E^{o\prime}_{M_{ox},M_{red}} + \frac{RT}{nF} \ln \frac{\beta_{ox}}{\beta_{red}} + \frac{RT}{nF} \ln \frac{C_{Mox}}{C_{Mred}} \tag{15-59}$$

In the same way, an equation analogous to (15-55) can be written if the oxidized and reduced forms form the single complex species MX_p and MX_q, respectively. The electrode reaction now becomes

$$MX_p + ne^- \rightleftharpoons MX_q + (p - q)X \tag{15-60}$$

and we introduce the formation constants

$$(K_p)_{ox} = \frac{[MX_p]}{[M_{ox}][X]^p} \qquad \text{and} \qquad (K_q)_{red} = \frac{[MX_q]}{[M_{red}][X]^q} \tag{15-61}$$

But, from Eqs. (15-57) and (15-58), since $C_{Mox} \cong [MX_p]$ and $C_{Mred} \cong [MX_q]$, and

$$\frac{1}{\beta_{ox}} \cong (K_p)_{ox}[X]^p \qquad \text{and} \qquad \frac{1}{\beta_{red}} \cong (K_q)_{red}[X]^q \tag{15-62}$$

which, by substitution into Eq. (15-59), yield[1]

$$E = E^{o\prime}_{M_{ox},M_{red}} - \frac{RT}{nF} \ln \frac{(K_p)_{ox}}{(K_q)_{red}} - (p - q) \frac{RT}{nF} \ln [X] + \frac{RT}{nF} \ln \frac{[MX_p]}{[MX_q]} \tag{15-63}$$

The first three terms on the right-hand side are combined to give the formal potential of the complex system (15-60), or

$$E = E^{o\prime}_{MX_p,MX_q} + \frac{RT}{nF} \ln \frac{[MX_p]}{[MX_q]} \tag{15-64}$$

where
$$E^{o\prime}_{MX_p,MX_q} = E^{o\prime}_{M_{ox},M_{red}} - \frac{RT}{nF} \ln \frac{(K_p)_{ox}}{(K_q)_{red}} - (p - q) \frac{RT}{nF} \ln [X] \tag{15-65}$$

[1] Eq. (15-63) can also be obtained directly by substituting Eq. (15-61) into Eq. (15-17).

By plotting the value of the formal potential $E^{\circ\prime}_{MX_p, MX_q}$ against log [X], the slope gives $-2.3(p - q)\dfrac{RT}{nF}$, from which $p - q$ is evaluated. If both oxidized and reduced forms have the same coordination number and if each forms its ultimate complex, then $p = q$, and the oxidation potential does not vary with concentration of complexing agent. The relationship between the oxidation potentials of the complex and aquated systems depends on the *relative* stabilities of the two complexes, or upon the ratio $(K_p)_{ox}/(K_q)_{red}$. If the oxidant forms the more stable complex, as is usual, the potential is lowered by complexation, or shifted in the negative direction, corresponding to a weaker oxidant, as we would expect intuitively.

To illustrate, the potential of the half-reaction

$$Fe(CN)_6^{3-} + e^- \rightleftharpoons Fe(CN)_6^{4-} \qquad E^\circ = 0.356 \text{ volt} \qquad (15\text{-}66)$$

is lower than that of the ferric-ferrous iron couple, because ferricyanide is more stable as a complex than ferrocyanide.[1] Moreover, since $p = q = 6$, no shift of potential with cyanide concentration is anticipated. However, the acid $H_4Fe(CN)_6$ is a weak acid in its third and fourth steps of ionization[2,3] ($pK_3 = 3$; $pK_4 = 4.3$), whereas $H_3Fe(CN)_6$ is a strong acid, and so the electrode reaction is best represented

$$Fe(CN)_6^{3-} + H^+ + e^- \rightleftharpoons HFe(CN)_6^{3-} \qquad pH = 4$$

or $\qquad Fe(CN)_6^{3-} + 2H^+ + e^- \rightleftharpoons H_2Fe(CN)_6^= \qquad 2 > pH > 0 \qquad (15\text{-}67)$

and the formal potential of (15-66) increases with decreasing pH below a pH of about 5. The effect of hydrogen ion could be considered by means of an equation analogous to Eq. (15-59) where the ions $HFe(CN)_6^{3-}$ and $H_2Fe(CN)_6^=$ are considered to be hydrogen ion complexes whose formation constants are the reciprocals of the third and fourth ionization constants of the acid $H_4Fe(CN)_6$.

Owing to the high charge of the anions, the salt effect is also large ($E^{\circ\prime} = 0.46$ volt for 0.1 M solutions of both potassium ferro- and ferricyanides) and opposite in direction to that of the aquo iron(III)-iron(II) couple, because the higher-charged species is the reductant rather than the oxidant.

For the 1,10-phenanthroline complexes of iron, we have

$$Fe(ophen)_3^{3+} + e^- \rightleftharpoons Fe(ophen)_3^{++} \qquad E^{\circ\prime} = 1.06 \text{ volts}*$$
$$\text{in } 1 \ M \ H_2SO_4 \quad (15\text{-}68)$$

---

[1] It must not be inferred that the reduction of ferricyanide actually proceeds by dissociation followed by reduction of ferric iron and reassociation, for the reversible potential is independent of the reaction path.

[2] Kolthoff, I. M., and Tomsicek, W. J., *J. Phys. Chem.*, **39**, 945 (1935).

[3] Nekrasov, V. V., and Zotov, G. V., *J. Appl. Chem. USSR*, **14**, 264 (1941).

* Hume, D. N., and Kolthoff, I. M., *J. Am. Chem. Soc.*, **65**, 1895 (1943).

The fact that this value of $E^{\circ\prime}$ is higher than that of the ferric-ferrous ion couple implies a greater stability of the Fe(II) complex, which is confirmed by experiment.[1] Again, the potential is independent of complexing agent concentration, as long as there is sufficient complexing agent is present to react with both species of iron.

15-9. Dependence of Potential on pH

Whenever hydrogen or hydroxyl ions appear in the half-reaction, the electrode potential varies with pH. Consider the reaction

$$Ox + mH^+ + ne^- \rightleftharpoons Red \qquad (15\text{-}69)$$

The Nernst equation will be of the form

$$E = E^\circ + \frac{RT}{nF} \ln \frac{a_{ox}}{a_{red}} \, a_{H^+}^m \qquad (15\text{-}70)$$

or

$$E = E^\circ + \frac{RT}{nF} \ln \frac{a_{ox}}{a_{red}} + \frac{m}{n} \frac{RT}{F} \ln a_{H^+} \qquad (15\text{-}71)$$

If we convert the last term to Briggsian logarithms and use the definition pH $= -\log a_{H^+}$, we have

$$E = E^\circ + \frac{RT}{nF} \ln \frac{a_{ox}}{a_{red}} - \frac{m}{n} \times 0.0591 \text{ pH} \qquad \text{at } 25^\circ C \quad (15\text{-}72)$$

The pH-dependence of potential is often depicted graphically in the form of the *potential*-pH *diagram*.[2]

To illustrate the potential-pH diagram, the system Fe,Fe(II),Fe(III) will be used. For a more extensive description, see Delahay *et al.*[2] The lines in Fig. 15-1 represent the potentials corresponding to *unit activity* of Fe(II) or Fe(III) at the pH in question.

Line 1: $Fe^{++} + 2e^- \rightleftharpoons Fe$; $E^\circ = -0.44$ volt (independent of pH)
Line 2: $Fe^{3+} + e^- \rightleftharpoons Fe^{++}$; $E^\circ = 0.77$ volt (independent of pH)
Line 3: $Fe(OH)_2 \rightleftharpoons Fe^{++} + 2OH^-$; $\log K_{sp} = -14.8$; at $a_{Fe^{++}} = 1$,
       pOH $= 7.4$; pH $= 6.6$ (independent of E)
Line 4: $Fe(OH)_3 \rightleftharpoons Fe^{3+} + 3OH^-$; $\log K_{sp} = -37.4$; at $a_{Fe^{3+}} = 1$,
       pOH $= 12.5$; pH $= 1.5$ (independent of E)
Line 5: $Fe(OH)_3 + 3H^+ + e^- \rightleftharpoons Fe^{++} + 3H_2O$; at $a_{Fe^{++}} = 1$, from $1.5 <$
       pH < 6.6, $E = 0.77 - 3 \times 0.0591(\text{pH} - 1.5)$
Line 6: $Fe(OH)_2 + 2H^+ + 2e^- \rightleftharpoons Fe + 2H_2O$; at pH > 6.6,
       $E = -0.44 - 0.0591(\text{pH} - 6.6)$
Line 7: $Fe(OH)_3 + H^+ + e^- \rightleftharpoons Fe(OH)_2 + H_2O$; at pH > 6.6,
       $E = -0.134 - 0.0591(\text{pH} - 6.6)$

[1] Lee, T. S., Kolthoff, I. M., and Leussing, D. L., *J. Am. Chem. Soc.*, **70**, 2348 (1948).

[2] For a discussion, see Delahay, P., Pourbaix, M., and van Rysselberghe, P., *J. Chem. Educ.*, **27**, 683 (1950). For numerous examples, see Charlot, "Qualitative Inorganic Analysis" *op. cit.*

A potential-pH diagram is a useful graphic device for depicting the oxidation-reduction and acid-base behavior of an element in concise fashion.   Naturally, it contains only the information used in its construction and, consequently, it may present an over-simplified or inexact picture.   In the above example, no account was taken of hydrolysis of ferric ion or of ferrous ion, which would give lines 1 and 2 a downward

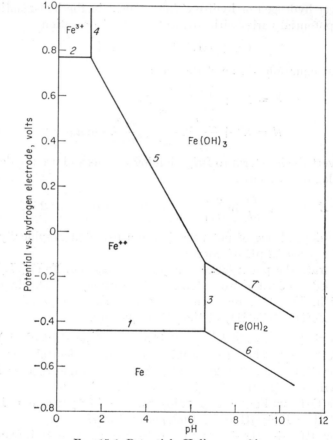

Fig. 15-1. Potential-pH diagram of iron.

slope.   In a complete diagram, the existence of species such as magnetite, Fe_3O_4, and ferrate(VI), $FeO_4^=$, would have to be considered.

Potential-pH diagrams are often convenient as an aid in predicting the direction and course of redox reactions.   If two such diagrams are superimposed, the system of higher potential at any given pH will act as an oxidant.   If the lines of the two systems intersect, the direction of reaction may be reversed by a change in pH.   As an example, the iodine-iodide and arsenate-arsenite systems will be compared (page 402) to show that iodine acts as an oxidant at higher pH values and that arsenate acts as the oxidant to produce iodine at low pH values.

15-10. Irreversible Electrode Reactions

A thermodynamically reversible half-reaction can be defined as one that can be made to proceed in either of two opposing directions by an infinitesimal shift of the potential from its equilibrium value. This definition, however, cannot necessarily be used as the basis for an experimental test, for two reasons: (1) a finite potential shift must be made to produce a finite net current, and (2) the point of zero current is not necessarily the equilibrium potential.

Regarding the first point, it will be seen below that, if the current drawn in the measurement is kept very small compared with the exchange current that passes in both directions at equilibrium, the shift of potential (polarization) can be made small enough to be considered negligible. With modern instrumentation the current drain can be made so low that this condition need not be the limiting factor. However, when the exchange current is very small, the rate of attainment of the equilibrium potential may be very low.

Consider the half-reaction

$$Ox + ne^- \rightleftharpoons Red$$

which is at equilibrium. The two opposing processes proceed at the same rate, which can be expressed conveniently in terms of the *exchange current density* I_0, in amperes per square centimeter. If the potential is shifted a *small* amount η, the net current density I is proportional to the potential change [cf. Eq. (16-18)].

$$\eta = -\frac{RT}{nF}\frac{I}{I_0} \tag{15-73}$$

where η is the overpotential, in volts, and where RT/nF is expressed in volt-coulombs (joules) per n faradays, having the value $0.0257/n$ at 25°C. The minus sign comes from the convention that a negative overpotential corresponds to a cathodic current, which is arbitrarily given a positive sign. The quantity RT/nFI_0 has the dimensions ohm-cm^2 and is the "polarization resistance" for an electrode 1 cm^2 in area. From Eq. (15-73) it is evident that, if $I = 0.01I_0$, $\eta = 0.257/n$ millivolts. Thus the polarization is negligible if the current drain is very small compared with the exchange current.

Now, for the electrode to change its potential, the electrical double layer must be charged (or discharged) by the passage of current, which must flow through an effective resistance equal to the polarization resistance. The time constant for the charging process is the product of resistance and capacitance, or

$$\tau = \frac{RT}{nFI_0} C_{dl} \qquad (15\text{-}74)$$

where τ = time constant, sec
C_{dl} = differential capacity of the double layer, farads cm^{-2}
The decay of overpotential is then given by

$$\eta_t = \eta_0 e^{-t/\tau} \qquad (15\text{-}75)$$

where η_t and η_0 are the overpotentials at times $t = t$ and $t = 0$, respectively. For $t = \tau$, η is $1/e$, or 0.36 of its original value. For $t = 2.3\tau$, η is 0.10 of its original value. Thus, if the required accuracy is 0.1 mv, the time required for the overpotential to decay from 1 to 0.1 mv is 2.3τ, and the same interval is needed for a drift from 10 to 1 mv. For larger values of the overpotential the shift of potential is more rapid, because the overpotential no longer varies linearly with the current but varies instead with the logarithm of the current [Tafel equation, Eq. (16-21)]; so the effective resistance is lower.

Example 15-2. According to Bockris and Huq,[1] the exchange current density for the oxygen electrode in acid solution is of the order of 10^{-10} amp cm^{-2} on a platinum surface. The polarization resistance is $RT/4FI_o = 6 \times 10^7$ ohm-cm^2. The double-layer capacity C_{dl} is of the order of 40 μf cm^{-2}, considering the true area, or perhaps 100 μf cm^{-2}, based on the geometric or projected area, on which the current density was based. Thus $\tau = 6 \times 10^7 \times 100 \times 10^{-6} = 6 \times 10^3$ sec, and the time for overpotential decay from 10 to 1 mv is estimated to be $2.3\tau \cong 4$ hr. It would, therefore, be very difficult to make measurements accurate to within 1 mv, but an accuracy of ± 10 mv can be reasonably expected. The actual behavior of an oxygen electrode is complicated by the oxidation of the platinum surface. Even traces of impurities cause currents of the order of magnitude of the exchange current to flow, and ordinarily the oxygen electrode is regarded as irreversible, although in ultrapure solutions it behaves reversibly.

Example 15-3. As an example of a reaction normally considered reversible, consider the reaction

$$Zn^{++} + Hg + 2e^- \rightleftharpoons Zn(Hg)$$

for which Gerischer[2] found an exchange current density of 5.4×10^{-3} amp cm^{-2} for 0.02 M Zn^{++} against 1 mole per cent zinc amalgam. The polarization resistance is $RT/2FI_0 = 2.4$ ohm-cm^2. Taking $C_{dl} = 20$ μf cm^{-2} for the liquid surface, $\tau = 2.4 \times 20 \times 10^{-6} = 5 \times 10^{-5}$ sec. The overpotential would decay from 10 to 0.1 mv in $4.6 \times 5 \times 10^{-5} = 2.3 \times 10^{-4}$ sec. To avoid polarization exceeding 0.1 mv, a current density $I \leqq \eta I_0 nF/RT = 4.2 \times 10^{-5}$ amp cm^{-2} can be used in the measurement.

[1] Bockris, J. O'M., and Huq, A. K. M. S., *Proc. Roy. Soc. London*, **237A**, 277 (1956).
[2] Gerischer, H., *Z. Elektrochem.*, **59**, 604 (1955).

We now turn to the second problem, which concerns the relationship between the point of zero current and the equilibrium potential. Clearly, for the net current to be zero it is necessary only that the total cathodic current be equal to the total anodic current. If the cathodic half-reaction is not just the reverse of the anodic one, a net chemical reaction is proceeding at the electrode, and the potential is not characteristic of either half-reaction.

To take a simple example, consider a solution of ferric iron containing an electrode of metallic iron. The reactions

$$2Fe^{3+} + 2e^- \rightarrow 2Fe^{++}$$
and
$$Fe \rightarrow Fe^{++} + 2e^-$$

are proceeding *at equal rates;* hence the current is zero. The potential, however, is not characteristic of the Fe^{3+}-Fe system, but lies somewhere between 0.77 volt (the Fe^{3+}-Fe^{++} potential) and -0.44 volt [the Fe^{++}-Fe(0) potential]. Such a potential is called a mixed potential,[1,2] and bears no simple relationship (such as that given by the Nernst equation) to the concentrations or activities of the reacting species. The rates of electron-transfer reactions as well as the rates of transport of the reactants to and from the electrode surface are involved (cf. Chap. 16).

Another example of a mixed potential is encountered in the hypothetical case of a perfectly pure solution of one form of a redox couple. Consider, for instance, a platinum electrode in a solution of ferrous iron containing absolutely no ferric iron. According to the Nernst equation, the potential would have a negative value of infinity. Actually, the potential would be limited by the fact that a cathodic reaction would occur at some finite potential. In an oxygen-free solution, reduction of hydrogen ions to hydrogen would occur, and the potential would shift to a value such that the rate of reduction would just equal the rate of oxidation of ferrous iron to ferric iron. Ferric ions are, of course, produced in the reaction. Eventually an equilibrium would be reached in which both half-reactions would be at the same potential.

A practical criterion of reversibility is that the Nernst equation be obeyed. From what has been said above, this cannot ever be true when two reactants that will interact with each other appear in the half-reaction. Thus, a half-reaction such as

$$MnO_4^- + 8H^+ + 5e^- \rightleftharpoons Mn^{++} + 4H_2O \qquad E^\circ = 1.52 \text{ volts}$$

cannot follow the Nernst equation, because MnO_4^- and Mn^{++} tend to interact to form MnO_2, and the potential must be a mixed one. Suppose,

[1] Wagner, C., and Traud, W., *Z. Elektrochem.*, **44**, 391 (1938).
[2] Kolthoff, I. M., and Miller, C. S., *J. Am. Chem. Soc.*, **62**, 2171 (1940).

however, that this interaction is so slow as to be negligible. Even then, the Nernst equation cannot be followed unless the reaction can be made to go as written in both directions. In this example, the reduction half-reaction can presumably be carried out, but the oxidation of Mn^{++} would at best yield Mn^{3+}. Note that the standard potentials of both the Mn(VII)-Mn(VI) and Mn(III)-Mn(II) couples lie above the theoretical decomposition potential of water. The permanganate potential is probably a mixed potential in which the cathodic current due to permanganate reduction is compensated for by an anodic current due to oxidation of water. The potential becomes more positive with increasing permanganate concentration because the cathodic current is increased. The only effect of manganous ion, in the absence of complexing agents that stabilize Mn(III), is to render the permanganate ion less stable.

Another fundamental consideration is that a reversible couple can act as an "electron-transfer catalyst" for an irreversible one. Consider, for example, the half-reaction

$$Cr_2O_7^= + 14H^+ + 6e^- \rightleftharpoons 2Cr^{2+} + 7H_2O$$

which has been described as behaving irreversibly.[1,2] The potential of a platinum electrode in a solution of dichromate is poorly reproducible and tends to drift slowly. Moreover, the potential is insensitive to changes of Cr(III) and does not vary in the expected linear fashion with pH. On the other hand, as will be discussed further in Chap. 17, the shapes of certain titration curves of Fe(II) with dichromate are remarkably similar in shape to those expected for a reversible Cr(VI)-(III) couple. It appears likely that the Fe(III)-(II) couple, which reaches chemical equilibrium with the Cr(VI)-(III) couple and, therefore, has the same potential, is the active potential-determining couple.

In conclusion, it should be noted that many of the potentials listed in tables of standard electrode potentials are values calculated from thermodynamic data rather than values obtained directly from cell-emf data. As such, they are valuable for calculating equilibrium constants of reactions, but caution should be exercised in using them to predict the behavior of electrodes.

PROBLEMS

15-1. From the standard potentials of the S-H_2S and H_2SO_3-S couples, calculate (a) the standard potential for the half-reaction

$$H_2SO_3 + 6H^+ + 6e^- \rightarrow H_2S + 3H_2O$$

[1] Luther, R., Z. phys. Chem. Leipzig, **30**, 630 (1899).
[2] Kolthoff, Chem. Weekblad, **16**, 450 (1919).

and (b) the standard free energy change for the reaction

$$H_2SO_3 + 2H_2S \rightarrow 3S + 3H_2O$$

Ans. (a) 0.35 volt; (b) −28.5 kcal.

15-2. Derive an equation for the effect of complex formation on the potential of the half-reaction $M_{ox} + ne^- \rightleftharpoons M_{red}$ for the case in which M_{ox} forms a series of complexes MX, MX_2, etc., but M_{red} forms no complex with X.

15-3. From the standard potentials of the Pb^{++}-Pb and PbO_2-Pb^{++} couples, calculate (a) the standard potential of the half-reaction

$$PbO_2 + 4H^+ + 4e^- \rightleftharpoons Pb + 2H_2O$$

and (b) the standard free energy change of the reaction

$$PbO_2 + Pb + 4H^+ \rightleftharpoons 2Pb^{++} + 2H_2O$$

(c) Sketch a potential-pH diagram, showing regions of stability of Pb, Pb^{++}, $Pb(OH)_2$, PbO_2, and $HPbO_2^-$, given that K_{sp} of $Pb(OH)_2$ is $10^{-15.6}$, and that, for $Pb(OH)_2$ (solid) $\rightleftharpoons HPbO_2^- + H^+$, $K_a = 10^{-15}$. *Ans.* (a) 0.665 volt; (b) −72.9 kcal.

15-4. From appropriate data in Table 15-1, calculate (a) the standard potential for the half-reaction

$$VO^{++} + 2H^+ + 2e^- \rightleftharpoons V^{++} + H_2O$$

and (b) the standard free energy change of the reaction

$$VO^{++} + V^{++} + 2H^+ \rightleftharpoons 2V^{+3} + H_2O$$

Ans. (a) 0.053 volt; (b) −14.2 kcal.

15-5. From the following standard potential:

$$BrO_3^- + 6H^+ + 5e^- \rightleftharpoons \tfrac{1}{2}Br_2 + 3H_2O \qquad E^0 = 1.52 \text{ volt}$$

and the standard potential of the HOBr-Br_2 couple (Table 15-1), estimate the equilibrium constant of the reaction

$$5HBrO \rightleftharpoons BrO_3^- + H^+ + 2Br_2 + 2H_2O$$

Ans. 8.5×10^5.

15-6. The logarithms of the successive formation constants of the ammonia complexes of silver are $\log k_1 = 3.2$, $\log k_2 = 3.8$. Calculate the equilibrium potential of a silver electrode in a solution $10^{-2} M$ in total silver, in a NH_3-NH_4NO_3 buffer of total concentration 0.1 M and pH = 10. Take pK_a of $NH_4^+ = 9.3$, and neglect activity coefficients. *Ans.* 0.394 volt.

16. Electrolytic Separations and Electroanalysis

Although electrodeposition has long been used for the quantitative separation and determination of metals, much of the work has been highly empirical in nature. Various factors such as current density, concentration, acidity, temperature, stirring rate, and presence of complexing agents and organic additives must be controlled within certain limits to assure satisfactory results. It is our purpose here to examine the fundamental basis of electrolytic separations, as a guide to the understanding of practical procedures.

16-1. Definitions

The *cathode* is defined as the electrode at which reduction occurs. In an electrolytic cell, the cathode is the electrode attached to the negative terminal of the source, since electrons leave the source and enter the electrolysis cell at that terminal. On the other hand, the cathode is the positive terminal of a galvanic cell, because such a cell accepts electrons at its positive terminal.

Conversely, the *anode* is defined as the electrode at which oxidation occurs. It is the positive terminal of an electrolysis cell or the negative terminal of a galvanic cell.

In certain cells, a third electrode serving as a nonworking reference is often added. The polarity of a particular working electrode (say, the cathode) may be either positive or negative with respect to the reference electrode, depending upon the potential of the latter.

An electrode is *polarized* if its potential deviates from the reversible or equilibrium value. The amount of polarization is the overvoltage, or, better, the *overpotential*[1] of the electrode. An electrode is said to be

[1] Kortüm, G., and Bockris, J. O'M., "Textbook of Electrochemistry," p. 395, Elsevier Press, Inc., Houston, Tex., 1951.

depolarized by a substance if that substance lowers the amount of polarization. An ideally depolarized electrode is one that allows the passage of a finite current without any appreciable change of potential from its equilibrium value. It will be seen below that even a small current must cause a finite polarization and that, therefore, an ideally depolarized electrode is nonexistent. However, for practical purposes, an electrode may pass, say, 10 μa of current with a polarization of less than 1 mv, which may be negligible for a particular purpose.

The term *polarization* is also used to represent the deviation of a cell emf from its reversible value. The terms emf and *voltage* will be used to refer to a cell, whereas the term *potential* will refer to a single electrode. Thus "overvoltage" represents the additional voltage above the reversible cell emf required to permit the passage of a finite current, and "overpotential" will refer to the deviation of the potential of a single electrode from its reversible value. Customarily in both cases, the ohmic voltage drop iR is first subtracted, as will be seen below.

16-2. Basic Principles

The usual and simplest electrolytic separation is carried out by inserting a pair of electrodes, ordinarily of platinum, into a solution and applying an external source of emf.

If a net chemical change is to be effected, the anodic reaction cannot be simply the reverse of the cathodic reaction. Therefore, owing to the formation of electrolytic products at the electrodes, a galvanic cell is set up when current is caused to flow. The polarity of the galvanic cell is always in opposition to the applied emf, giving rise to the so-called "back emf." The amount of current that flows is given by Ohm's law,

$$E_{appl} - E_{back} = iR \qquad (16-1)$$

where R is the total resistance of the circuit, mainly the electrolytic resistance of the cell. It should be emphasized, however, that Ohm's law can be applied only after subtraction of the back emf and *that the back emf in general increases with increasing current.*

The back emf can be regarded as being made up of three components: (1) a reversible back emf, (2) a concentration polarization emf or concentration overvoltage, and (3) an activation overvoltage.

1. The *reversible back emf* is the reversible emf of the galvanic cell set up by the passage of the electrolytic current, based on concentrations of solutes in the bulk of the solution. For example, if an acidic solution of copper sulfate is electrolyzed between platinum electrodes, the electrode reactions are

$$Cu^{++} + 2e^- \rightarrow Cu \qquad \text{at the cathode}$$
and
$$2H_2O \rightarrow O_2 + 4H^+ + 4e^- \qquad \text{at the anode}$$

The reversible back emf is the difference in potential between the copper electrode and the oxygen electrode and is calculated from the Nernst equation applied to the prevailing concentrations of copper ion, hydrogen ion, and oxygen in solution. Note that this emf is indeterminate if no oxygen is initially present in solution, but, as oxygen reaches saturation, a finite reversible back emf is attained. Thus, for $[Cu^{++}] = [H^+] = 1\ M$, $p_{O_2} = 1$ atm,

$$E_{back,rev} = E^{\circ\prime}_{O_2, H^+} - E^{\circ\prime}_{Cu^{++}, Cu} \cong 1.23 - 0.34 = 0.89 \text{ volt}$$

2. The term "concentration polarization" is commonly used in electrochemistry to denote the effect of changes in concentration at an electrode surface with reference to the concentration of the bulk of the solution. It is something of a misnomer, because "polarization" implies a deviation of the potential of an electrode from its reversible value, and in this case the electrode is presumed to be acting reversibly with respect to the actual solute concentrations at its surface. Referring once more to the example given above, concentration changes occur both at the cathode and at the anode. At the cathode, a depletion of copper ions occurs near the surface, causing the reversible potential of the copper electrode to shift in the negative direction. At the anode, an accumulation of hydrogen ions and perhaps of oxygen if the solution is not already saturated with it, causes the reversible potential of the oxygen electrode to shift in the positive direction. Both effects tend to increase the back emf. Stirring acts to decrease the effect of concentration overvoltage, and increased current density increases its magnitude.

3. The *activation overpotential* is a departure of the potential of an electrode from its reversible value owing to the passage of the electrolytic current. The magnitude of the polarization is, as will be seen below, determined primarily by the ratio of the electrolytic current to the exchange current, which is the current passing equally in each direction at the equilibrium potential. The direction of the polarization is to shift the cathode potential in the negative direction, the anode potential in the positive direction, thus once more increasing the back emf. For small currents (compared with the exchange current), the potential of an electrode shifts nearly linearly with increasing current. For large currents, the overpotential is linear with the logarithm of the current.

16-3. Concentration Overpotential

As pointed out above, concentration changes occur in the vicinity of both anode and cathode upon passage of electrolytic current. To study these effects more fully, it is convenient to consider the two electrodes separately. This is done experimentally by introduction of a third, *reference* electrode by means of a salt bridge. The reference electrode (e.g., silver–silver chloride or calomel electrode) passes practically no current and, therefore, may be regarded as a point of constant potential against which the anode and cathode potentials may be measured. The experimental values of cathode and anode potentials each include a portion of the ohmic, or iR, drop between the two working electrodes. This may often be made negligibly small by the use of a capillary salt bridge (Luggin capillary) inserted with its opening very close to the surface of the electrode under study or in a region of low current density.

A schematic cathodic polarization curve is shown in Fig. 16-1 for a platinum cathode in an acidic air-free solution of metal ion, e.g., Cu(II).*

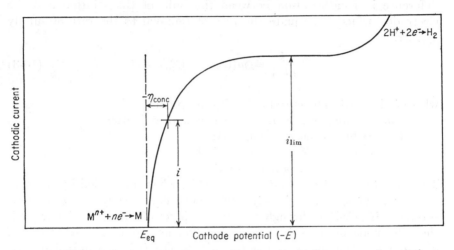

FIG. 16-1. Schematic representation of cathodic polarization curve of a platinum electrode in acidic solution of metal ion M^{n+}.

No appreciable current flows until the equilibrium potential of the metal–metal ion electrode has been reached. As the cathode potential is made increasingly negative the copper ion concentration at the electrode surface adjusts itself to correspond to the applied potential. We consider here that the Nernst equation can be applied (we neglect activation polarization) and that the potential has been corrected for iR drop. Then, if $C^{\circ}_{M^{n+}}$ is the surface concentration of metal ion,

$$E_{appl} = E^{\circ\prime}_{M^{n+},M} + \frac{RT}{nF} \ln C^{\circ}_{M^{n+}} \qquad (16\text{-}2)$$

For each $0.059/n$ volt ($= 2.3RT/nF$) of increasingly negative potential, the surface concentration is diminished tenfold. Thus, if the cathode

* Laitinen, H. A., and Kolthoff, I. M., *J. Phys. Chem.*, **45**, 1061, 1079 (1941).

potential is maintained at a value $3 \times 0.059/n$ volt more negative than the equilibrium potential, the surface concentration is only 0.1 per cent of the bulk concentration. Further increase in (negative) cathode potential can cause no appreciable further increase in $C_{M^{n+}} - C^{\circ}_{M^{n+}}$, the difference between the bulk concentration and the surface concentration.

Opposing the tendency toward removal of metal ions at the electrode is the transfer of these ions from the bulk of the solution to the surface. At any applied potential, a steady state is reached when the rate of removal by deposition is equal to the rate of *mass transfer* by diffusion or convection or both.[1] If the rate of mass transfer is proportional to the difference in concentration between the bulk of the solution and the electrode surface, we equate the rate of removal to the rate of supply and write

$$\frac{i}{nFA} = m(C_{M^{n+}} - C^{\circ}_{M^{n+}}) \tag{16-3}$$

where i/A = cathodic current density, amp cm^{-2}

nF = number of coulombs per mole of reduction

$C_{M^{n+}}$ = bulk concentration of M^{n+}

$C^{\circ}_{M^{n+}}$ = surface concentration of M^{n+}

m = mass transport constant

The mass transport constant m (cm sec^{-1}), when multiplied by the concentration (moles cm^{-3}) gives the flux (moles cm^{-2} sec^{-1}) at the electrode surface. If diffusion through a boundary layer of effective thickness δ is the sole mode of mass transport, the flux according to Fick's law of diffusion is given by $D(C_{M^{n+}} - C^{\circ}_{M^{n+}})/\delta$, where D is the diffusion coefficient (cm^2 sec^{-1}). The mass transport constant is, therefore, given by $m = D/\delta$. If convection is the sole mode of transport, m becomes the convection coefficient[2] (cubic centimeters of solution per square centimeter brought by convection to the surface per second) measured in centimeters per second. In practice, both convection and diffusion usually play a role, and the diffusion coefficient enters into m with a fractional exponent, instead of the exponent unity for pure diffusion or zero for pure convection.

Now when the surface concentration $C^{\circ}_{M^{n+}}$ reaches a negligible value compared with the bulk concentration, the current reaches its limiting value, denoted by i_{lim}.

$$\frac{i_{\text{lim}}}{nFA} = mC_{M^{n+}} \tag{16-4}$$

[1] Jordan, J., *Anal. Chem.*, **27**, 1708 (1955).

[2] Kolthoff and Jordan, *J. Am. Chem. Soc.*, **76**, 3843 (1954); Kolthoff, I. M., Jordan, J., and Prager, S., *J. Am. Chem. Soc.*, **76**, 5221 (1954).

Substituting from Eq. (16-4) into (16-3), the surface concentration is given by

$$C^{\circ}_{M^{n+}} = C_{M^{n+}} \left(1 - \frac{i}{i_{\text{lim}}} \right) \qquad (16\text{-}5)$$

From the Nernst equation, the concentration overpotential η_{conc} is calculated to be

$$\eta_{\text{conc}} = \Delta E = \frac{RT}{nF} \ln \frac{C^{\circ}_{M^{n+}}}{C_{M^{n+}}} = \frac{RT}{nF} \ln \left(1 - \frac{i}{i_{\text{lim}}} \right) \qquad (16\text{-}6)$$

According to Eq. (16-6), the concentration overpotential is zero when the current is zero. For $0 < i < i_{\text{lim}}$, the value of η_{conc} is negative, corresponding to cathodic polarization, and increases without limit as i approaches i_{lim}.

The limiting current i_{lim} is determined by the rate of mass transfer to a region of vanishingly small concentration at the surface. Since stirring generally increases the mass transfer rate, the value of i_{lim} increases; therefore, i/i_{lim} decreases with increased rate of stirring. Correspondingly, the concentration overpotential decreases with increased stirring rate.

The current increases beyond i_{lim} when the back emf for another cathodic process has been reached. In the present case, hydrogen discharge is the next cathodic process. The back emf for this process is initially indeterminate, because of the absence of hydrogen gas, but soon reaches a finite value when saturation is reached. The gradual nature of the increase in current due to hydrogen discharge is due largely to the change in activation overpotential of hydrogen at the cathode. This will be considered in a later section.

Concentration overpotential is also observed when the surface concentration is *increased* over the bulk concentration. An example is encountered in the anodic dissolution of a metal. Suppose that, after part of the metal ion has been plated out from the solution in the above example, the applied emf is decreased to a value below the reversible back emf. The cell will now operate as a galvanic cell, the metal-plated electrode acting as the anode. The metal ion concentration at the anode surface becomes greater than the bulk concentration of metal ion. However, as anodic polarization is increased, there is no particular limit to the surface concentration of metal ion except that imposed by the solubility of a salt. Since the surface concentration would have to be 10 times the bulk concentration to produce a concentration overpotential of $59.1/n$ mv, the anodic concentration overpotential for metal dissolution is generally small unless the bulk concentration is very low.

Another example of concentration overpotential is encountered in the generation of hydrogen and oxygen from unbuffered solutions. The cathode region tends to become alkaline and the anode region to become acidic. In unbuffered solutions the changes in pH can be very large. For example, for pH 3 near the anode and pH 11 near the cathode, the corresponding back emf is $8 \times 0.059 = 0.47$ volt due to concentration overvoltage, in addition to the reversible back emf of 1.23 volts due to decomposition of water.

16-4. Activation Overpotential

To cause the passage of a finite current at an electrode, it is necessary to shift the potential from its equilibrium value. This shift of potential,

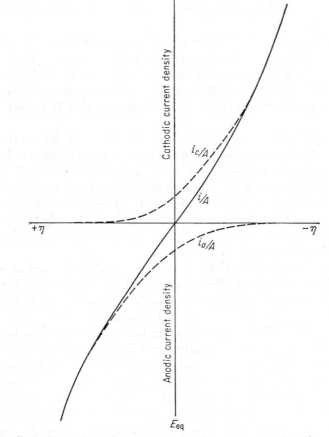

FIG. 16-2. Cathodic and anodic components of current as a function of electrode polarization η.

assuming no changes of concentration in the vicinity of the electrode, is called the "activation overvoltage," or, better, the *activation overpotential*.

Qualitatively, the behavior of a single electrode is shown in Fig. 16-2.

In general, the net current at an electrode is the algebraic sum of two opposing currents. We adopt here the convention, common in the electroanalytical literature, that a cathodic current is given a positive sign and an anodic current is given a negative sign. At the equilibrium potential the anodic and cathodic currents are equal, or,

$$i_c = i_a \quad \text{at equilibrium} \tag{16-7}$$

At any other potential there is a net current i given by the arithmetic difference

$$i = i_c - i_a \tag{16-8}$$

For the sake of simplicity, we shall consider here only a half-reaction that proceeds in a single step, $viz.$,

$$\text{Ox} + ne^- \underset{k_a}{\overset{k_c}{\rightleftharpoons}} \text{Red}$$

where Ox and Red are the oxidized and reduced forms of the couple, and k_c and k_a are rate constants of the cathodic and anodic half-reactions. We neglect such situations as those in which a chemical reaction precedes or follows the electron transfer step, which are considered, for example, by Delahay.[1] The reactants may be in solution or they may exist as separate phases, as, for example, when the metal itself is the reductant.

Consider a half-reaction in which both reactants are in solution at concentrations C_{ox}^{o} and $C_{\text{red}}^{\text{o}}$ *at the electrode surface*. The rates of the forward (cathodic) and backward (anodic) half-reactions are proportional to C_{ox}^{o} and $C_{\text{red}}^{\text{o}}$, the proportionality constants being k_c and k_a, respectively. The rates are also proportional to the electrode area A. If the rate is expressed in mole-cm^2 sec^{-1}, it can be equated to i/nF, where i is the current (cathodic or anodic) and where nF is the number of coulombs per mole of electrode reaction. Thus,

$$i = i_c - i_a = nFA(k_c C_{\text{ox}}^{\text{o}} - k_a C_{\text{red}}^{\text{o}}) \tag{16-9}$$

If the concentrations are expressed in moles cm^{-3}, the heterogeneous rate constants k_c and k_a have the units cm sec^{-1}. Thus $k_c C_{\text{ox}}^{\text{o}}$ or $k_a C_{\text{red}}^{\text{o}}$ have the dimensions moles cm^{-2} sec^{-1}, or reaction rate per unit of surface.

Both k_c and k_a vary exponentially with the electrode potential.[2-4] If we consider the special case of $C_{\text{ox}}^{\text{o}} = C_{\text{red}}^{\text{o}}$, at equilibrium, we have

[1] Delahay, P., "New Instrumental Methods in Electrochemistry," Interscience Publishers, Inc., New York, 1954.

[2] Butler, J. A. V., *Trans. Faraday Soc.*, **19**, 729 (1924).

[3] Eyring, H., Glasstone, S., and Laidler, K. J., *J. Chem. Phys.*, **7**, 1053 (1939).

[4] Kimball, G. E., *J. Chem. Phys.*, **8**, 199 (1940).

$i = 0$, and $k_c = k_a = k°$ (by definition). Thus $k°$ is defined as *the value of k_c or k_a at the formal potential of the couple*.[1] This definition has the advantage of expressing both the cathodic and anodic rates in terms of a single rate constant.

The dependence of k_c and k_a upon the electrode potential may be written[2-4]

$$k_c = k° \exp\left\{ -\frac{\alpha nF}{RT}(E - E^{°\prime}) \right\} \qquad (16\text{-}10)$$

and
$$k_a = k° \exp\left\{ \frac{(1-\alpha)nF}{RT}(E - E^{°\prime}) \right\} \qquad (16\text{-}11)$$

where α is the *transfer coefficient* of the electrode reaction. From Eqs. (16-10) and (16-11) it can be seen that α may be regarded as the fraction of the change ΔE in electrode potential in the cathodic direction that acts to increase the rate of the cathodic reaction. Similarly, the fraction $1 - \alpha$ acts to decrease the rate of the anodic reaction.

The significance of the transfer coefficient may be clarified by considering the potential energy curves in Fig. 16-3. Curve A represents a potential energy curve for the reductant; curve B represents the oxidant plus electron in the metal at the equilibrium potential of the couple.[5] For an electron to transfer from metal to oxidant or from reductant to metal, an energy barrier of height $\Delta F_0^\ddagger$ must be surmounted. $\Delta F_0^\ddagger$ is the free energy of activation, or the free energy necessary to take a mole of reactant to the activated state in the reaction. The rate of passage of electrons in either direction, and, therefore, the exchange current density also, are proportional to $\exp\{-\Delta F_0^\ddagger / RT\}$. Thus *the exchange current density may be regarded as a measure of the height of the energy barrier.*

Now, if the electrode potential is changed by an amount $-\Delta E$, to favor the cathodic reaction, the free energy of the system oxidant plus electron is changed by an amount $-nF \Delta E$, the effect being to lower curve B to the position represented by curve C in Fig. 16-3. The cathodic free energy of activation now becomes $\Delta F_c^\ddagger = \Delta F_0^\ddagger - \alpha nF \Delta E$, and the anodic value becomes $\Delta F_a^\ddagger = \Delta F_0 + (1 - \alpha)nF \Delta E$, where $\alpha = \tan \beta / (\tan \beta + \tan \gamma)$ and $\tan \beta$ and $\tan \gamma$ are the absolute slopes of lines A and C at their intersection. Thus α is the fraction of the total energy $-nF \Delta E$ that acts to *decrease* the height of the *cathodic* energy

[1] More exactly, at the standard potential, if the actitivy coefficients of oxidant and reductant are included in Eq. (16-9). For simplicity, we shall neglect the activity coefficients in this treatment.

[2] Butler, *op. cit.*

[3] Eyring, Glasstone, and Laidler, *op. cit.*

[4] Kimball, *op. cit.*

[5] For a more complete discussion, see Randles, J. E. B., *Trans. Faraday Soc.*, **48**, 828 (1952).

barrier, and $1 - \alpha$ is the fraction that tends to *increase* the height of the *anodic* energy barrier.[1]   The *transfer coefficient may thus be interpreted as a measure of the symmetry of the energy barrier.*   Over a reasonable range of potential, α may be regarded as constant.

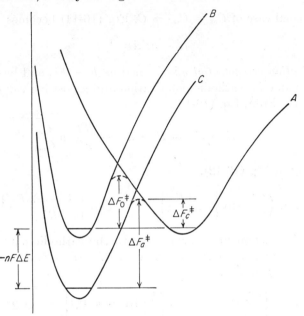

FIG. 16-3. Potential energy curves for an electrode reaction.

From Eqs. (16-9), (16-10), and (16-11), it follows readily that

$$i = nF'Ak^{\circ}\left(C_{\text{ox}}^{\prime\circ}\exp\left\{-\frac{\alpha nF}{RT}(E - E^{\circ\prime})\right\}\right.$$
$$\left. - C_{\text{red}}^{\circ}\exp\left\{\frac{(1 - \alpha)nF}{RT}(E - E^{\circ\prime})\right\}\right) \quad (16\text{-}12)$$

At the equilibrium potential, $E = E_{\text{eq}}$ and $i = 0$.   Since no net current flows, the surface concentrations C_{ox}° and C_{red}° are equal to the bulk concentrations C_{ox} and C_{red}; so

$$\frac{C_{\text{ox}}}{C_{\text{red}}} = \exp\left\{\frac{nF}{RT}(E_{\text{eq}} - E^{\circ\prime})\right\}$$

or
$$E_{\text{eq}} = E^{\circ\prime} + \frac{RT}{nF}\ln\frac{C_{\text{ox}}}{C_{\text{red}}} \quad (16\text{-}13)$$

This shows that the Nernst equation does not involve the transfer coefficient α.

[1] Some authors (e.g., Gerischer) define α in terms of the anodic reaction and $1 - \alpha$ in terms of the cathodic reaction.

The *exchange current* i_0 is given by either i_c or i_a at equilibrium. From either the first or second terms of Eq. (16-12), it follows readily that

$$i_0 = nFAk°C_{ox}^{1-\alpha}C_{red}^{\alpha} \tag{16-14}$$

For the special case of $C_{ox} = C_{red} = C$, Eq. (16-14) becomes

$$i_0 = nFAk°C$$

The *activation overpotential* η is defined as $E - E_{eq}$ and has, therefore, a negative value for cathodic polarization and a positive value for anodic polarization. From Eq. (16-13),

$$\eta = E - E_{eq} = E - E^{°\prime} - \frac{RT}{nF} \ln \frac{C_{ox}}{C_{red}} \tag{16-15}$$

Substituting in Eq. (16-12),

$$i = i_0 \left(\frac{C_{ox}°}{C_{ox}} \exp \left\{ \frac{-\alpha nF}{RT} \eta \right\} - \frac{C_{red}°}{C_{red}} \exp \left\{ \frac{(1-\alpha)nF}{RT} \eta \right\} \right) \tag{16-16}$$

where the first exponential term refers to the cathodic current and the second to the anodic current. Since $2.3RT/F = 59.1$ mv at 25°C, Eq. (16-16) may be written

$$i = i_0 \left\{ \frac{C_{ox}°}{C_{ox}} 10^{-\alpha n\eta/59.1} - \frac{C_{red}°}{C_{red}} 10^{(1-\alpha)n\eta/59.1} \right\} \qquad \text{at 25°C} \tag{16-17}$$

where the overpotential η is given in millivolts.

For very small values of η, the overpotential is proportional to the current, as we see from the following approximation. Under these conditions $C_{ox} \cong C_{ox}°$ and $C_{red} \cong C_{red}°$ (negligible concentration polarization). The exponentials in Eq. (16-16) can be expanded in a power series, $e^x = 1 + x + x^2/2! + \cdots$, which, for $x \ll 1$, yields the approximation $e^x = 1 + x$. Equation (16-16) then becomes

$$i = -\frac{i_0 nF}{RT} \eta \tag{16-18}$$

where the minus sign arises from the convention that i is positive and η is negative for cathodic polarization. It is of interest that α cancels out in the approximation. For Eq. (16-18) to be valid, $\alpha nF\eta/RT$ and $(1 - \alpha)nF\eta/RT$ must be small compared with unity, or, since RT/F has the value 0.0257 volt-coulombs (joules) per faraday at 25°C, η must be small compared with $0.0257/\alpha n$ and $0.0257/(1 - \alpha)n$. Taking $\alpha = 0.5$, η must be small compared with 51 mv for $n = 1$ or small compared with 25.7 mv for $n = 2$.

If the cathodic current i is plotted as ordinate and the cathodic polarization $-\eta$ as abscissa, then the quantity $-i_0 nF/RT$ is the slope $\left(\dfrac{di}{d\eta}\right)_{i=0}$ of the current-potential curve at the point of zero current (the equilibrium potential). Its reciprocal RT/nFi_0, taken without regard to sign, has the dimensions of resistance and is often called, in fact, the "polarization resistance."[1,2]   It is the effective resistance imposed at the electrode surface by the finite rate of the electron transfer process (cf. page 293).

For sufficiently large absolute values of η, the back reaction can be neglected.   Thus, if $\alpha = 0.5$ and $\eta = 118/n$ mv, Eq. (16-17) becomes $i = \pm i_0(10 - 0.1)$.   For this symmetrical case ($\alpha = 0.5$), the back reaction is only 1 per cent of the forward reaction if the current is 10 times the exchange current.   For cathodic polarization greater than $-59.1/n\alpha$ mv, Eq. (16-16) becomes

$$i_c = i_0 \exp\left(-\frac{\alpha nF}{RT}\eta_c\right) \tag{16-19}$$

or, in logarithmic form,

$$\eta_c = \frac{2.3RT}{\alpha nF}\log i_0 - \frac{2.3RT}{\alpha nF}\log i_c \tag{16-20}$$

An analogous equation can be written for anodic polarization.

If I_0 and I_c represent the current densities i_0/A and i_c/A, respectively, it is apparent that Eq. (16-20) can equally well be expressed in the form

$$\eta_c = a + b \log I_c \tag{16-21}$$

which is the well-known Tafel[3] equation expressing overpotential as a linear function of the logarithm of current density.   An equation of this form has long been used to describe hydrogen and oxygen evolution at various electrodes.

As will be seen below, the mechanism of hydrogen discharge cannot be represented by the simple one-step reaction considered above.   However, even a complex reaction can be resolved into a kinetically equivalent reaction pair,[4] which can be represented as a single half-reaction.   Whenever the net cathodic or anodic current becomes large compared with the exchange current, a linear "Tafel plot" is to be expected.   On the other hand, if the net current is small compared with the exchange current, the current-voltage relationship is approximately linear.

[1] Glasstone, "Introduction to Electrochemistry," p. 461, D. Van Nostrand Company, Inc., Princeton, N.J., 1942.

[2] Vetter, K. J., Z. physik. Chem. Leipzig, **194**, 199, 284 (1950).

[3] Tafel, J., Z. physik. Chem. Leipzig, **A50**, 641 (1905).

[4] Oldham, K. B., J. Am. Chem. Soc., **77**, 4697 (1955).

If the linear logarithmic plot, Eq. (16-21), is extrapolated back to zero overpotential, the cathodic component I_c approaches the exchange current density I_0. Thus $\log I_0 = -a/b$.

For hydrogen evolution at various metals, the Tafel slope b is typically about 0.12 volt, whereas I_0 varies greatly from one metal to another, being of the order of 10^{-3} amp cm^{-2} for platinum and 10^{-13} amp cm^{-2} for mercury[1] in acid solutions.

The mechanism of hydrogen discharge has been a subject of controversy for many years. Bockris *et al.*[2,3] have stressed the importance of stringent purification of electrodes, solutions, and gases in achieving reproducible and significant data. It is beyond the scope of this discussion to present the evidence in detail, but the final conclusions presented by Conway and Bockris[4] will be summarized very briefly.

The hydrogen discharge process consists of two steps, the first being the formation of adsorbed hydrogen atoms (designated MH).

$$(a_1) \qquad \mathrm{H^+ + e^- \xrightarrow{M} MH} \qquad \text{(acid soln)}$$

$$\text{or} \quad (a_2) \qquad \mathrm{H_2O + e^- \xrightarrow{M} MH + OH^-} \qquad \text{(alkaline soln)}$$

The second step is either the combination of adsorbed atoms

$$(b) \qquad \mathrm{2MH \rightarrow 2M + H_2}$$

or the so-called "electrochemical reaction"

$$(c) \qquad \mathrm{H^+ + MH + e^- \rightarrow H_2} \qquad \text{(adsorbed)}$$

Reaction (c) is, of course, no more "electrochemical" than (a_1) or (a_2); Gerischer and Mehl,[5] therefore, propose that it be called the "Horiuti reaction." It was first proposed by Heyrovsky[6] and later considered in detail by Horiuti and Okamoto.[7]

In alkaline solution on nickel or copper, (a_2) is the rate-determining step and is followed by (b). In acid solution, at low current densities on platinum or palladium, the sequence is (a_1) followed by (b), which is rate-determining. At high current densities on platinum, reaction (a_1) is followed by (c), which is rate-determining. The same mechanism holds

---

[1] Bockris, *J. Electrochem. Soc.*, **99**, 366C (1952).

[2] Bockris, *Chem. Revs.*, **43**, 525 (1948); *Ann. Rev. Phys. Chem.*, **5**, 477 (1954).

[3] Pentland, N., Bockris, J. O'M., and Sheldon, E., *J. Electrochem. Soc.*, **104**, 182 (1957).

[4] Conway, B. E., and Bockris, J. O'M., *J. Chem. Phys.*, **26**, 532 (1957).

[5] Gerischer, H., and Mehl, W., *Z. Elektrochem.*, **59**, 1049 (1955).

[6] Heyrovsky, J., *Rec. Trav. Chim.*, **44**, 499 (1925).

[7] Horiuti, J., and Okamoto, G., *Sci. Papers Inst. Phys. Chem. Research Tokyo*, **28**, 231 (1956).

for various other metals in acid solution, including copper, nickel, tungsten, iron, and palladium. On the other hand, (a_1) is rate-determining, followed by (c), for mercury, thallium, and lead. Gerischer and Mehl[1] found that the latter mechanism also held for silver.

The Tafel equation also describes the evolution of oxygen at a platinum anode. Bockris and Huq[2] found that with solutions carefully purified by preelectrolysis, the oxygen electrode exhibits reversible behavior ($E = 1.24$ volts, compared with the theoretical 1.23 volts). The exchange current density, however, is only of the order of 10^{-9} to 10^{-10} amp cm^{-2} in dilute sulfuric acid; so polarization occurs readily, and relatively large overpotentials are observed at moderate current densities. In solutions of the usual chemical purity, the Nernst relation fails for the oxygen electrode because of mixed potential behavior.

For metal–metal ion half-reactions, it is especially difficult to make quantitative observations because of the difficulty of preparing clean and reproducible surfaces. The exchange current density is relatively high for metals that readily give reversible potentials against their ions (Cu, Ag, Zn, Cd, Hg), and so the activation overpotential is small at the current densities used in electroanalysis. On the other hand, the transition metals (e.g., Fe, Cr, Ni, Co, etc.) have extremely low exchange currents.[3] These metals do not follow Nernst behavior against their ions because other potential-determining systems exert their influence, thus giving rise to mixed potential behavior due to two or more redox couples. For electron exchange half-reactions involving oxidants and reductants in solution, it is also difficult to make quantitative kinetic studies, particularly at solid electrodes. There is considerable evidence,[4,5] for example, that oxide films form at platinum surfaces in the presence of strong oxidants or at high positive potentials. The films are removed by electroreduction or chemical reduction. Such oxide films, as well as adsorbed layers of traces of organic impurities,[6] usually have the effect of decreasing the exchange current and, therefore, of increasing the polarization at a given current density.

16-5. Effects of Complexation and Addition Agents

It is often found to be beneficial to carry out electrodeposition from solutions that contain metal ions in the form of a complex rather than as aquated ion. A striking example is silver, which forms large, loose

[1] Gerischer and Mehl, *op. cit.*

[2] Bockris, J. O'M., and Huq, A. K. M. S., *Proc. Roy. Soc.*, **A237**, 277 (1956).

[3] Piontelli, R., *J. chim. phys.*, **46**, 288 (1949); *Z. Elektrochem.*, **55**, 128 (1951).

[4] Anson, F. C., and Lingane, J. J., *J. Am. Chem. Soc.*, **79**, 4901 (1957).

[5] Enke, C. G., Ph.D. thesis, University of Illinois, Urbana, 1959.

[6] Randles, J. E. B., and Somerton, K. W., *Trans. Faraday Soc.*, **48**, 937, 951 (1952).

crystals when deposited from silver nitrate, but a smooth, adherent, white layer when deposited from a cyanide bath. Nickel cannot be deposited at all from strongly acidic solution, whereas quantitative deposition can be achieved from ammoniacal solutions.

Complexation has two types of effect on electrodeposition: (1) a thermodynamic effect, or shift of the equilibrium potential, and (2) a kinetic effect, or alteration of the exchange current. The thermodynamic effect is always in the direction of negative potential; i.e., it makes deposition more difficult [cf. Eq. (15-50b)]. The kinetic effect may be in either direction, because the rate of electron exchange between the electrode and the complex species may be greater or less than the rate of exchange with the aquated ion. In fact, if the discharge of the aquated ion is accompanied by a large overpotential due to very small exchange current, the formation of a complex may increase the exchange current so much that the decrease in overpotential more than compensates for the shift in the equilibrium potential. In this case, deposition occurs more readily from the complex than from the aquated ion. An excellent example is the aquated nickel ion, which is discharged at a dropping mercury electrode[1] with an overpotential of more than 0.5 volt. In the presence of any of several complexing agents, e.g., thiocyanate ion, pyridine, or high concentrations of chloride, the nickel ion is more readily reduced.

Relatively few quantitative studies of complex formation on electrode kinetics have been made. The work of Gerischer[2] on zinc and cadmium amalgam electrodes is illustrative of the effects that may be encountered. If excess cyanide is added to a cadmium ion solution, the exchange current is greatly decreased, but not nearly so much as the concentration of aquated cadmium ion is diminished. Thus, electron exchange between complex species and electrode must occur. From measurements of the rate of change of exchange current with cyanide ion concentration, Gerischer concluded that the main species undergoing reduction were $Cd(CN)_2$ at low concentrations of cyanide and $Cd(CN)_3^-$ at high cyanide concentrations, even though the major species present in all solutions was $Cd(CN)_4^=$. Similarly, for zinc, the neutral species $Zn(OH)_2$ accounted for most of the exchange current in solutions containing $Zn(CN)_4^=$ or $Zn(OH)_4^=$ as the main equilibrium species. Electron exchange appears to be discouraged, although certainly not prevented, by the negative charge of the complex. If the *rate* of dissociation or replacement of coordinated groups is sufficiently high, a relatively scarce species can play a predominant role in the electrodeposition process.

[1] Kolthoff and Lingane, "Polarography," 2d ed., p. 486, Interscience Publishers, Inc., New York, 1952.

[2] Gerischer, *Z. physik. Chem. Leipzig,* **202,** 292 (1953); *Z. Elektrochem,* **57,** 604 (1953).

Lyons[1] has stressed the importance of the structure of the complex. Usually, deposition occurs readily if the complex is labile, or of outer orbital configuration,[2] but only as a "flash deposit" or not at all if the complex is inert, a property associated with a particular type of inner orbital configuration (see page 221). The distinction lies in the rate of exchange of coordinated groups (ligands) between solution and metal ion or in the rate of aquation (replacement of coordinated ligands by water molecules). Lyons has postulated that the plating act involves the removal of one or more ligands from the species in solution, which may be the aquated ion or the complex. The electron orbital thus released interacts with the metallic or conducting orbital of the cathode, permitting the ready access of electrons to the metal ion. The remaining coordinated groups are then released or remain adsorbed on the metal. For aquated zinc ion, the "active intermediate" is pictured as $Zn(H_2O)_3^{++}$, which interacts with an adsorbed water molecule to form $Zn(H_2O)_4^{++}$(adsorbed), which in turn loses a water molecule to form the electron pair bond with the metal. This picture is at least a good working hypothesis that accounts for a great many observations. Groups such as cyanide ion, ammonia, or halide ions can act as "bridging" groups if they have a tendency to be bound in labile fashion both to the metal ion and to the electrode.

It appears that the physical character of plated deposits must be governed, at least in part, by the magnitude of the exchange current. Large metallic crystals and dendritic growths are characteristic of deposition carried out near the reversible potential. We have observed, for example, in molten LiCl-KCl eutectic at 450°C that even the transition metals (Cr, Mn, Fe, Co, Ni) behave reversibly[3] and that all are plated in the form of dendritic growths. If the current density is extremely low compared with the exchange current density, a marked recrystallization quite analogous to the aging of crystalline precipitates causes the formation of relatively large crystals. On the other hand, at high current densities, the deposition is favored on certain crystal faces so that dendritic growths appear. At high overpotentials, the slight energy differences favoring one face over another are washed out by the large activation energy, and so nucleation of new crystals can readily occur and a microcrystalline deposit is formed.

The striking effects of traces of surface-active compounds can be attributed to the addition of a large energy barrier for deposition, with the result that the exchange current is greatly diminished. This, of

---

[1] Lyons, E. H., Jr., *J. Electrochem. Soc.*, **101**, 363, 376 (1954); Lyons, E. H., Jr., Bailar, J. C., Jr., and Laitinen, H. A., *ibid.*, **101**, 410 (1954).

[2] Taube, H., *Chem. Revs.*, **50**, 69 (1952).

[3] Laitinen, H. A., and Liu, C. H., *J. Am. Chem. Soc.*, **80**, 1051 (1958).

course, does not change the equilibrium potential. A "reversible" electrode reaction then takes on the character of an irreversible one if an appreciable current density is caused to flow. Thus the addition of a trace of gelatin causes silver to deposit as a smooth coating rather than as a dendritic growth.[1] For electrogravimetric analysis, it is advisable to minimize the concentrations of organic addition agents or to omit them entirely if possible, because of the danger of inclusions of organic matter.

In the past, the use of complexing and addition agents has been very largely empirical. As our knowledge of electrode reaction mechanisms grows, we can hope to develop electrodeposition procedures on a more scientific basis. In the meantime, we should be cautious about making arbitrary changes in procedures that have been shown to give satisfactory results.

16-6. Electrolytic Separation at Constant Current

The classical method for carrying out gravimetric electroanalytical determinations is to adjust the voltage of the source to give the desired

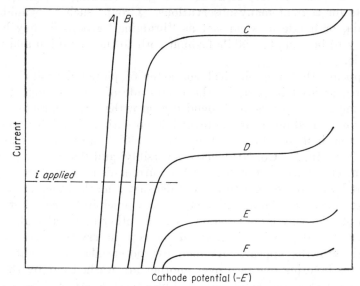

Fig. 16-4. Current–cathode potential curves. Curves A to F represent decreasing concentrations of metal ion.

electrolytic current, which is maintained at a relatively constant value during the electrolysis.

Suppose that it is desired to make a quantitative deposition of copper from a solution containing copper sulfate and sulfuric acid. The cathode behavior is readily understood by reference to Fig. 16-4. As electrolysis

[1] Laitinen and Kolthoff, *J. Phys. Chem.*, **45**, 1079 (1941).

proceeds, copper ions removed from solution at the cathode are replaced by hydrogen ions produced at the anode, so the electrolytic resistance undergoes relatively little change. The curves A to F represent the behavior of the cathode potential plotted against current during the gradual removal of copper ions. A and B differ only in a displacement of the reversible potential of the copper electrode as the concentration of Cu^{++} is decreased. C to F show limiting current regions in which the current is controlled by the mass transfer rate. Now, if i_{appl} represents the constant current applied from the source, it is evident that the cathode potential changes very slowly until the limiting current approaches i_{appl}. At this point a sudden change in cathode potential occurs,[1] and both copper and hydrogen ions are discharged. The deposition of copper continues as fast as the mass transfer rate permits, but the current efficiency for copper discharge gradually approaches zero.

The hydrogen evolution reaction unfortunately causes the copper deposit to be rough, spongy, and poorly adherent. Therefore nitric acid is generally added as a *cathodic depolarizer*. Nitrate ion is reduced to ammonium ion at a copper cathode

$$NO_3^- + 8e^- + 10H^+ \rightarrow NH_4^+ + 3H_2O$$

at a lower (i.e., less negative) cathode potential than hydrogen ion and, therefore, acts to decrease hydrogen evolution.

A cathodic depolarizer has the effect of controlling the cathode potential by restricting its value to that corresponding to the working potential (i.e., reversible potential plus overpotential) at the particular current density that is used. If this working potential lies between the deposition potentials of two metals, a selective deposition of the more readily reduced metal can be achieved. Thus, nitric acid permits the deposition of copper but prevents that of lead. Lead can, therefore, be deposited quantitatively as lead dioxide at the anode. To be of practical value, a cathodic depolarizer must be reduced without the formation of gaseous products, and it must not be occluded appreciably within the metallic deposit.

Similarly, *anodic depolarizers* act to control the anode potential. For example, if it is desired to deposit metallic lead at the cathode, the anodic deposition of lead dioxide can be prevented by using hydroxylamine as an *anodic depolarizer* in dilute hydrochloric acid. Lingane and Jones[2] have studied in detail the behavior of hydroxylamine and hydrazine as anodic depolarizers. Hydrazine was found to be superior both in keeping the anode potential at a lower value and also in forming simpler

---

[1] Lingane, *Anal. chim. Acta,* **2,** 584 (1948).

[2] Lingane, J. J., and Jones, S., *Anal. Chem.,* **23,** 1804 (1951).

oxidation products (nitrogen instead of mixtures of nitrous oxide, nitrate, and nitrite).

16-7. Examples of Electrolytic Determinations at Constant Current

The following examples are presented to illustrate some of the sources of error and some of the precautions that are necessary if accurate results are to be obtained.

Copper is determined from a solution free of noble metals such as the platinum metals, silver, mercury, bismuth, etc., and containing both sulfuric and nitric acids. To remove any nitrous acid, which can oxidize the copper deposit, urea or sulfamic acid is sometimes added. Low temperature and low current density are favored, since they also tend to prevent oxidized deposit. Chloride is avoided for two reasons: (1) platinum tends to dissolve anodically and to plate out at the cathode, unless a suitable anodic depolarizer such as hydrazine or hydroxylamine is present; and (2) $Cu(I)$ is stabilized as a chloro complex and remains in solution to be reoxidized at the anode unless a controlled-cathode-potential method[1] is used. Copper can be separated from zinc, cadmium, cobalt, nickel, manganese, and aluminum by the classical procedure. Small amounts of $Fe(II)$ do not interfere, but large amounts must be avoided because of anodic oxidation to $Fe(III)$, which is reduced back to $Fe(II)$ at the cathode. If oxidation of the $Fe(II)$ is avoided by addition of anodic depolarizers, complete deposition of copper is attained, but the results are high.[2]

Nickel is deposited quantitatively from ammoniacal solutions, incompletely from weakly acidic solutions, and not at all from strongly acidic ones. (To effect a quantitative separation of copper from nickel, it is therefore necessary to keep the acid concentration sufficiently high.) Among the important interferences in the determination of nickel are silver, copper, arsenic, and zinc, which can be removed by precipitation with hydrogen sulfide. Ferrous iron and chromates are objectionable[3] but can be removed by precipitation of the hydrous oxides. If cobalt is present, both elements are deposited, but sulfite must be added to ensure the quantitative deposition of cobalt by preventing the formation of cobalt(III) ammines. The presence of sulfite causes contamination of the deposited metals with sulfur. By dissolving the plated metal, determining nickel by the dimethylglyoxime method and sulfur by precipitation as barium sulfate, cobalt can be determined by difference. In

---

[1] Diehl, H., and Brouns, R., *Iowa State Coll. J. Sci.*, **20**, 155 (1945).

[2] Hillebrand, W. F., Lundell, G. E. F., Bright, H. A., and Hoffman, J. I., "Applied Inorganic Analysis," 2d ed., p. 247, John Wiley & Sons, Inc., New York, 1953.

[3] Lundell and Hoffmann, *Ind. Eng. Chem.*, **13**, 541 (1921).

accurate work, the residual nickel and cobalt that is undeposited (usually less than 1 mg, mainly cobalt) must be recovered.

Lead is determined by deposition as the dioxide. The standard potential of the reaction

$$PbO_2 + 4H^+ + 2e^- \rightleftharpoons Pb^{++} + 2H_2O \qquad E^\circ = 1.456 \text{ volts}$$

is so high that anodic depolarizers must be avoided, and advantage must be taken of the high oxygen overpotentials of platinum and of lead dioxide. Chloride must be absent, because it is oxidized without appreciable overpotential at a lower potential ($E^\circ = 1.36$ volts). A relatively high concentration of nitric acid is useful in preventing cathodic deposition of lead. The use of a copper-plated cathode or the presence of copper in solution is favorable, because the reduction of nitrate proceeds smoothly to ammonia rather than partly to nitrous acid, which would prevent the formation of lead dioxide by being oxidized back to nitrate at the anode.

The above represent by far the most important of the classical electro-analytical procedures. It is possible to deposit various other elements, e.g., silver, cadmium, zinc, tin, and iron, quantitatively on platinum. This is impractical for most applications, however, because, owing to lack of selectivity in deposition, a cumbersome procedure of prior separations is usually necessary. Moreover, the more active metals are subject to air oxidation and loss during washing. The controlled-potential method has the advantage of being much more selective; also, in favorable cases the weighing operation can be avoided entirely, and the determination can be based on measurement of the amount of electricity required for quantitative deposition.

Mercury cathode separations at constant current, although not suitable for electrogravimetric determinations, are often useful as adjuncts to other analytical methods. Casto[1] has summarized various procedures for the electrolytic removal of metallic impurities from uranium. An especially interesting procedure, devised by Furman and Bricker, consists of quantitative deposition of various metals into a small mercury cathode. The mercury is removed by distillation, and the residue is analyzed polarographically or colorimetrically. A similar procedure could be used for isolation of trace impurities from other metals, e.g., aluminum, magnesium, alkali metals, and alkaline earths, which behave like uranium in that they do not form amalgams by electrolysis in acid solutions. Parks, Johnson, Lykken[2] used a procedure involving several small

[1] Casto, C. C., in Rodden, Clement J. (Ed.), "Analytical Chemistry of the Manhattan Project: Uranium and Thorium," chap. 23, National Nuclear Energy Series, div. VIII, vol. 1, McGraw-Hill Book Company, Inc., New York, 1950.

[2] Parks, T. D., Johnson, H. O., and Lykken, L., *Anal. Chem.*, **20**, 148 (1948).

batches of mercury for the removal of large quantities of heavy metals such as copper, chromium, iron, cobalt, nickel, cadmium, zinc, mercury, tin, and lead, leaving quantitatively in solution even small quantities of aluminum, magnesium, and alkali and alkaline earths for determination by appropriate methods.

16-8. Electrolytic Separations at Controlled Potential

If electrolysis is carried out under conditions such that the cathode potential corresponds to a point on the limiting-current plateau, the current is limited by the rate of mass transfer. For a given set of conditions (cell, electrode geometry, and stirring) the limiting current represents the maximum current that can be passed at 100 per cent current efficiency at the cathode. Therefore, by using an apparatus that maintains a constant cathode potential regardless of changes in current or in anode potential, it is possible in principle to achieve *the most rapid deposition rate possible* under the given conditions and yet avoid secondary cathode reactions. Since the deposition of hydrogen is avoided, the metal is plated in a smooth and compact form that is especially suitable for electrogravimetric determination.

In favorable cases, in which the metal is plated from a definite oxidation state at 100 per cent current efficiency and in which no secondary oxidation or reduction reactions occur in solution, the determination can be made coulometrically, i.e., by application of Faraday's law. A comprehensive discussion of controlled-potential electrolysis and coulometric analysis is given by Lingane.[1]

Since the rate of decrease in concentration is proportional to the current (Faraday's law) and since the current is proportional to the concentration, the concentration decreases with time in accordance with a first-order law, analogous to the radioactive-decay law,

$$- \frac{dC}{dt} = \lambda C \qquad (16\text{-}22)$$

which can also be written in terms of the current

$$- \frac{di}{dt} = \lambda i \qquad (16\text{-}23)$$

The proportionality constant λ, which represents the fraction of the solute removed per unit of time at any instant of the electrolysis, can readily be shown to be given by $\lambda = Am/V$, where A = electrode area, V = volume, and m = mass transfer constant [see Eq. (16-3)]. The value of λ depends upon the particular cell geometry (A/V) and the

---

[1] Lingane, "Electroanalytical Chemistry," 2d ed., Interscience Publishers, Inc., New York, 1958.

stirring rate (m). If the initial current is i^0 and if the proportionality holds throughout the electrolysis, we have, after integration,

$$\ln \frac{i^0}{i} = 2.3 \log \frac{i^0}{i} = \lambda t \tag{16-24}$$

Lingane[1] has found that Eq. (16-24) is obeyed in the deposition of copper onto a platinum cathode from a tartrate solution and in the deposition of lead and reduction of picric acid at a mercury cathode.[2] Lingane and Small[3] found the same type of relationship in the anodic formation of silver chloride.

MacNevin and Baker[4] have pointed out that, if Eq. (16-24) is obeyed, the total quantity of electricity required for quantitative deposition can be determined by integration of the current-time equation. Thus,

$$Q = \int_0^t i \, dt = \int_0^t i^0 e^{-\lambda t} \, dt = \frac{i^0}{\lambda} (1 - e^{-\lambda t}) \tag{16-25}$$

The limiting value of Q as t becomes large is i^0/λ. From the linear plot of $\log i$ versus t, the constants i^0 and λ can be evaluated in principle, since $\log i^0$ is the intercept for $t = 0$ and $-\lambda/2.303$ is the slope. The amount of substance is then calculated from Q, by Faraday's law. Since two points define a straight line, two readings of current and time are needed. It should be borne in mind, however, that the quantity λ is only as accurate as the mass transfer constant m, which depends on the stirring rate. Also, it is necessary that Eq. (16-24) be obeyed throughout the electrolysis. It is possible that the initial current will not be determined by mass transfer rate, as will be seen below. The analytical utility of this procedure, therefore, appears to be limited.

In analogy with the half-life in radioactive decay, the "half-time" of electrolysis is a convenient concept. If $t = t_{1/2}$ when $i/i^0 = \frac{1}{2}$, we find from Eq. (16-24) that $t_{1/2} = 2.3 \log 2/\lambda = 0.69/\lambda$ and that $\log i/i^0 = -0.30 t/t_{1/2}$. The time required for the removal of a particular fraction of the metal in solution may be estimated from Table 16-1.

From Table 16-1 it can be seen that deposition may be regarded as quantitative after a period 10 times as long as the period required for the deposition of half the metal.

The completeness of deposition can be judged from the magnitude of the electrolysis current. When the current has decreased to 0.1 per cent of the initial current, the deposition may be regarded as quantitative.

[1] Lingane, *Anal. Chim. Acta*, **2**, 584 (1948).
[2] Lingane, *J. Am. Chem. Soc.*, **67**, 1916 (1945).
[3] Lingane, J. J., and Small, L. A., *Anal. Chem.*, **21**, 1119 (1949).
[4] MacNevin, W. M., and Baker, B. B., *Anal. Chem.*, **24**, 986 (1952).

TABLE 16-1. RATE OF DEPOSITION AT CONTROLLED POTENTIAL

Fraction deposited $1 - \dfrac{i}{i^0}$	$\log \dfrac{i}{i^0}$	Number of "half-times" $\dfrac{t}{t_{1/2}}$
0.50	−0.30	1
0.90	−1.0	3.3
0.99	−2.0	6.7
0.999	−3.0	10.0
0.9999	−4.0	13.3

In some practical cases the current ceases to decrease after a certain low level has been reached. This residual current is due to traces of extraneous depolarizers such as oxygen or to a slow discharge of hydrogen. In such cases, electrolysis is carried out until the current has ceased to diminish for several minutes.

In some cases, Eq. (16-24) does not hold at the beginning of the electrolysis, because the initial concentration may be so high that the proportionality between current and concentration does not hold. Thus if the source is unable to supply the total voltage $(E_{back} + iR)$ at the level of current that can be sustained by the mass transfer rate, the current is determined initially by the back emf and the electrolytic resistance [Eq. (16-1)]. This amounts to saying that the cathode potential corresponds to a rising portion of the cathodic current-voltage curve rather than to a point on the plateau.

A fundamental advantage of controlled-potential electrolysis over constant-current electrolysis is that the theoretical limit of separation efficiency that is imposed by the electrode potentials can be much more closely approached. The situation is illustrated by the following example.

Example 16-1. Suppose that silver and copper are to be separated when both are present in 0.1 M solution. We take the formal potentials to be approximately equal to the standard potentials 0.80 and 0.34 volt, respectively. Suppose that the mass transfer constant m is 10^{-2} cm sec^{-1}. For diffusion control, this corresponds to an effective diffusion-layer thickness $\delta = D/m$ of the order of 10^{-3} cm, since D is usually of the order of 10^{-5} cm^2 sec^{-1}. For unstirred solutions, δ is of the order of 0.04 cm; it decreases rapidly with increasing stirring rate until convection control sets in; then it is of the order of 10^{-5} cm.* The constant $\lambda = Am/V = 20 \times 10^{-2}/100 = 2 \times 10^{-3}$ sec^{-1}, for a cell volume of 100 cm^3 and a cathode area of 20 cm^2. This corresponds to a half-time of $0.69/\lambda = 345$ sec. Quantitative deposition, within 0.1 per cent, is reached in 10 half-times, or 3,450 sec. The initial current is $i^0 = nFAmC = 2$ amp; the final current is 2 ma, corresponding to a final silver ion concentration of 10^{-4} M. The equilibrium potential of the silver-plated electrode begins at $0.80 - 0.059 =$

* Kolthoff and Jordan, *J. Am. Chem. Soc.*, **76**, 3843 (1954).

0.74 volt; the final equilibrium potential is $0.80 - 4 \times 0.059 = 0.56$ volt. The control potential should be $2 \times 0.059 = 0.118$ volt more negative than the final equilibrium potential (neglecting any overpotential), to correspond to a surface silver-ion concentration of 10^{-6} M (1 per cent of the final solution concentration) to assure mass transfer control. The limits of control potential are, therefore, $0.44 > E_c > 0.31$. The lower limit corresponds to the equilibrium potential of copper.

Now suppose that we are to carry out the same separation at constant current. Using the same apparatus, the current cannot exceed 2 ma, the limit imposed by the mass transfer rate of 10^{-4} M Ag^+. This separation would require 5×10^5 sec, or 5.8 days! By starting with a higher initial current, say, 1 amp, which would make it possible to plate out half the silver in 500 sec, the time could be shortened, but at the risk of plating out copper accidentally as the mass transfer rate of silver gradually decreases. Only by interposing a cathodic depolarizer to consume the excess current could the rate be increased. Such a depolarizer should be reducible at the proper current density in just the potential range calculated above. Indeed, the use of a depolarizer constitutes an internal form of controlled-potential electrolysis. An ideal depolarizer would permit the same performance as that calculated above for controlled-potential electrolysis.

In principle, if the potential is controlled so as to be just positive to the equilibrium potential of copper (0.31 volt), a separation of all but 10^{-8} M Ag^+ (calculated from the Nernst equation) is possible. This would require 23.3 half-times, or 8,000 sec.

16-9. Examples of Analysis by Controlled-potential Electrolysis

Controlled-potential electrolysis is carried out to advantage for the following purposes: (1) electrogravimetric determinations, (2) coulometric determinations, and (3) selective removal of constituents for separation purposes. For convenience in weighing, platinum electrodes must be used for procedure of the first type. Mercury electrodes are often advantageous for applications in which weighing is not involved. For a general discussion of principles, apparatus, and procedures, the monograph by Lingane[1] is especially recommended.

As an example of an electrogravimetric determination, consider the determination of copper. Torrance[2] and Diehl[3] recommended using a hydrochloric acid solution with anodic depolarizers and controlling the cathode potential at a value sufficiently negative (-0.40 volt vs. the saturated calomel electrode) to avoid forming soluble copper(I) chloro complexes. Lingane,[4] however, found a tartrate buffer of pH 4 to 6 to be superior to hydrochloric acid solution. Copper can be determined directly in all common alloys, containing, for example, antimony, arsenic, lead, tin, nickel, and zinc, with an accuracy fully equal to that obtained by far more laborious methods.

[1] Lingane, "Electroanalytical Chemistry," Interscience, 1958.

[2] Torrance, S., *Analyst*, **62**, 719 (1937); **63**, 488 (1938).

[3] Diehl, "Electrochemical Analysis with Graded Cathode Potential Control," G. Frederick Smith Chemical Co., Columbus, Ohio, 1948.

[4] Lingane, *Ind. Eng. Chem.*, *Anal. Ed.*, **17**, 640 (1945).

Lingane and Jones[1] devised an electrogravimetric procedure for the successive determinations of copper, bismuth, lead, and tin in the presence of various other metals. After each deposition, the pH and electrode potential are adjusted, and the cathode is replaced in the solution for continued electrodeposition.

Other examples of selective electrodeposition are given in the books of Lingane,[2] Diehl,[3] Schleicher,[4] and Sand.[5] As examples may be cited the separation of silver from copper, bismuth from copper, antimony from tin, cadmium from zinc, and rhodium from iridium.

Coulometric determinations of metals with the mercury cathode have been described by Lingane.[6,7] From a tartrate solution, copper, bismuth, lead, and cadmium were successively removed by applying the appropriate cathode potential, which was selected to correspond to a region of diffusion-controlled current determined from current-voltage curves with the dropping mercury electrode. With a silver anode, iodide, bromide, and chloride can be deposited quantitatively as the silver salt. By controlling the anode potential, Lingane and Small[8] determined iodide in the presence of bromide or chloride. However, the separation of bromide and chloride was not successful because of solid solution formation (cf. page 171). MacNevin, Baker, and McIver[9] performed a successful analysis of bromide-chloride mixtures by devising a "coulogravimetric" analysis in which the total quantity of electricity to deposit both halides and the combined weights of the halides are measured to determine the amounts of each.

Coulometric determinations can be carried out, of course, in which no physical separation occurs but simply a quantitative change in oxidation state. For example, MacNevin and Baker[10] determined iron and arsenic by anodic oxidation of Fe(II) to (III) and As(III) to (V). Various other applications of coulometry at constant potential may be found in the recent literature.

Electrolysis at controlled potential can also serve as an elegant method of removing interfering metals from samples to be analyzed by other

[1] Lingane and Jones, *Anal. Chem.*, **23**, 1798 (1951).

[2] Lingane, "Electroanalytical Chemistry," Interscience, 1958.

[3] Diehl, *op. cit.*

[4] Schleicher, A., "Electroanalytische Schnellmethoden," Ferd. Enke Verlag, Stuttgart, 1947.

[5] Sand, H. J. S., "Electrochemistry and Electrochemical Analysis," Blackie & Son, Ltd., Glasgow, 1949.

[6] Lingane, *op. cit.*

[7] Lingane, *Ind. Eng. Chem., Anal. Ed.*, **16**, 147 (1945).

[8] Lingane and Small, *op. cit.*

[9] MacNevin, W. M., Baker, B. B., and McIver, R. D., *Anal. Chem.*, **25**, 274 (1953).

[10] MacNevin and Baker, *Anal. Chem.*, **24**, 986 (1953).

methods such as spectrophotometry or polarography. The electrogravimetric and coulometric procedures mentioned above, of course, represent such separations. However, the electrolysis can be carried out primarily as a selective separation with the actual determination being carried out in the remaining solution. As an example of this technique, Lingane[1] removed copper, together with any antimony and bismuth, from hydrochloric acid solutions of copper-base alloys by controlled-potential electrolysis with a mercury cathode. Lead and tin were determined polarographically in the remaining solution and then were quantitatively removed by electrolysis at a more negative potential. Finally, nickel and zinc were determined in the residual solution. Other examples of selective deposition with mercury cathodes are described by Lingane.[2]

A final example will be given, of the use of controlled-potential electrolysis for the preparation of carrier-free radioactive silver. Griess and Rogers[3] isolated tracer quantities of radioactive silver, which had been prepared by neutron bombardment of palladium, by selectively depositing the silver onto a platinum surface. A small amount of palladium was codeposited, but a complete separation was achieved by anodic stripping and redeposition.

16-10. Titrations with Coulometrically Generated Reagents

Another method of applying Faraday's law to analysis is to generate a titration reagent by means of a suitable electrode reaction. If a current efficiency of 100 per cent can be maintained, the rate of addition of reagent can be calculated accurately from the current. If the current is maintained accurately at a constant value, it is possible to carry out a titration in which time rather than reagent volume is measured. The end point can be determined by any convenient means, either with a visual indicator or by instrumental methods.

Two methods are used. In the first, or internal-generation method, the reagent is generated directly within the titration solution by oxidation or reduction of some component present at relatively high concentration. This condition is necessary in order to maintain 100 per cent current efficiency and yet permit the passage of a sufficiently high current. For example, Swift and coworkers generated bromine,[4] iodine,[5] and chlorine[6] by the anodic oxidation of the halide ion and carried out the titration of various reducing agents such as As(III), Sb(III), iodide,

[1] Lingane, *Ind. Eng. Chem., Anal. Ed.*, **18**, 429 (1946).
[2] Lingane, "Electroanalytical Chemistry," Interscience, 1958.
[3] Griess, K. C., Jr., and Rogers, L. B., *J. Electrochem. Soc.*, **95**, 129 (1949).
[4] Sease, J. W., Nilmann, C., and Swift, E. H., *Anal. Chem.*, **19**, 197 (1947).
[5] Ramsey, W. J., Farrington, P. S., and Swift, E. H., *Anal. Chem.*, **22**, 332 (1950).
[6] Buck, R. P., Farrington, P. S., and Swift, E. H., *Anal. Chem.*, **24**, 1195 (1952).

thiocyanate, thiodiglycol, etc. Similarly, various titrations have been carried out using electrolytically generated Fe(II)* or Ce(IV).† Numerous other applications have been made. We have recently applied this principle to titrations in molten salts, where the addition of titrating reagents would pose serious problems of technique.[1] Iron(III), which is a strong oxidant in molten lithium chloride–potassium chloride eutectic at 450°C, served as a titrant for Cr(II) and V(II).

Whenever the system being titrated forms a reversible redox couple with its reaction product, it is necessary that the second electrode used in the generation reaction be shielded from the bulk of the sample solution. For example, in the titration of Fe(II) with anodically generated Ce(IV),‡ the cathode is placed in a separate compartment to prevent the reduction of Fe(III). In this example, Fe(II) of course undergoes *direct* anodic oxidation during the bulk of the titration until the bulk concentration of Fe(II) is so low that its mass transfer rate can no longer sustain the applied current. At this point, the intermediate oxidation of Ce(III) permits 100 per cent current efficiency to be maintained to the end point.

The second method of coulometric titration, based upon the use of an *externally* generated reagent was devised by DeFord and coworkers.[2] In this method, the electrolytic generation reaction is carried out in a flowing stream of supporting electrolyte solution, which is added to the sample. Again, a constant generating current is used, and the time required to reach an end point is measured. This system has the advantage that it is possible to select a supporting electrolyte to assure an efficient generating electrode reaction independent of the composition of the sample solution. The reaction product at the second generating electrode can be physically discarded, if desired. Examples of applications include the generation of hydroxyl ion at the cathode or hydrogen ion at the anode for acid-base titrations and the generation of iodine for the titration of As(III). Disadvantages of the external generation method are (1) a finite time lag due to the necessity of a finite volume of solution between the generating electrode and the sample solution, and (2) a comparatively stringent requirement for chemical stability of the coulometric intermediate. The time lag can be compensated for by use of proper indicating electrodes and circuits that anticipate the approach of the end point.

It appears that the external-generation method will prove more widely applicable for automatic control operations than the internal-generation

* Cooke, W. D., and Furman, N. H., *Anal. Chem.*, **22**, 896 (1950).

† Furman, N. H., Cooke, W. D., and Reilley, C. N., *Anal. Chem.*, **23**, 945 (1951).

[1] Laitinen, H. A., and Bhatia, B. B., *Anal. Chem.*, **30**, 1995 (1958).

‡ Furman, Cooke, and Reilley, *op. cit.*

[2] DeFord, D. D., Pitts, J. N., and Johns, C. J., *Anal. Chem.*, **23**, 938, 941 (1951).

method. The latter, however, possesses a wider scope of possible applicability and is particularly valuable for the titration of trace quantities.

PROBLEMS

16-1. Derive Eq. (16-14) by substitution of Eq. (16-13) into (a) the first term and (b) the second term of Eq. (16-12).

16-2. For a metal deposition reaction $M^{n+} + ne^- \rightleftharpoons M$, write expressions for the cathodic and anodic currents as a function of the potential. Note that the concentration factor is missing from the expression for anodic current but that the exponential factor remains. Show that the Nernst equation does not involve the transfer coefficient. Write an expression for the exchange current, and show that Eq. (16-16) is valid.

16-3. Taking the electron transfer rate constant $k°$ to be equal to 10^{-3} cm sec^{-1} for a one-electron reaction $Ox + e^- \rightleftharpoons Red$, and $\alpha = 0.25$, calculate (a) the exchange current density for $C_{ox} = C_{red} = 1$ M; (b) the exchange current density for $C_{ox} = 0.01$ M, $C_{red} = 1$ M; (c) the current density at a cathodic polarization of 118 mv, concentration as in (b); (d) same as (c) except for anodic polarization. *Ans.* (a) 0.096; (b) 0.00305; (c) 0.00955; (d) −0.0955 amp cm^{-2}.

16-4. Prove the relationship $\lambda = Am/V$ given on page 318.

16-5. In a constant-potential electrodeposition, it is found that the current has fallen to 20 per cent of its initial value in 10 min. Estimate the time required for 99.9 per cent deposition. *Ans.* 43 min.

16-6. A 100-ml sample of 0.1 M Cu^{++} is electrolyzed at a constant current of 1.0 amp under conditions such that the mass transfer constant is 10^{-2} cm sec^{-1}, using a cathode area of 10 cm^2. (a) Calculate the concentration of Cu^{++} remaining when the current efficiency has dropped below 100 per cent. (b) How long does it take to reach this point? (c) How much longer does it take to plate out 99.9 per cent of the original copper? (d) What is the over-all cathode-current efficiency? *Ans.* (a) 0.052 M; (b) 928 sec; (c) 6,260 sec; (d) 27 per cent.

16-7. According to Gerischer[1], the exchange current of the Pt | Fe^{3+}, Fe^{++} electrode in 1 M H_2SO_4 is 300 ma cm^{-2} for $[Fe^{3+}] = [Fe^{++}] = 1$ M. The value of α is 0.42. Calculate (a) the polarization resistance of an electrode of 0.1 cm^2 area in a solution in which $[Fe^{3+}] = [Fe^{++}] = 10^{-4}$ M; (b) the value of the electron-transfer-rate constant $k°$; (c) the exchange current density for a solution in which $[Fe^{3+}] = 10^{-2}$, $[Fe^{++}] = 10^{-3}$ M. *Ans.* (a) 8600 ohms; (b) 3.1 × 10^{-3} cm sec^{-1}; (c) 1.14 × 10^{-3} amp cm^{-2}.

[1] Gerischer, *Z. Elektrochem.*, **54**, 366 (1950).

17. Oxidation-Reduction Titration Curves and Redox Indicators

The course of an oxidation-reduction titration is most adequately described by means of a titration curve in which potential is plotted as a function of titration volume.

A titration curve may for convenience be considered to consist of three portions: (1) the region before the equivalence point, (2) the equivalence point, and (3) the region beyond the equivalence point. At all points except at the very beginning before any titrant has been added, we have two redox couples present, corresponding to the sample and the titrant.

After each addition of titrant, the concentrations of reactants are adjusted by reaction until, *at equilibrium, the oxidation potentials of the two systems become equal at every point of the curve.* In the region before the equivalence point, the potential is calculated conveniently from the known concentration ratio of the sample redox couple. After the equivalence point, the concentration ratio of the titrant redox couple is known from the stoichiometry. At the equivalence point, both the sample and titrant redox couple are present in the stoichiometric ratio.

These three regions will now be considered in turn for the reaction

$$n_2\text{Red}_1 + n_1\text{Ox}_2 \rightleftharpoons n_2\text{Ox}_1 + n_1\text{Red}_2 \qquad (17\text{-}1)$$

in which the reductant Red_1 is titrated with the oxidant Ox_2. The stoichiometric reaction is derived from the half-reactions

$$\text{Ox}_1 + n_1\text{e}^- \rightleftharpoons \text{Red}_1 \qquad \text{sample} \qquad (17\text{-}2)$$

and $$\text{Ox}_2 + n_2\text{e}^- \rightleftharpoons \text{Red}_2 \qquad \text{titrant} \qquad (17\text{-}3)$$

by subtracting n_1 times reaction (17-3) from n_2 times reaction (17-2) to cancel n_1n_2 electrons. Both (17-2) and (17-3) are considered to be reversible electrode half-reactions.

17-1. Region before the Equivalence Point

The Nernst equation applied to reaction (17-2), written in terms of the formal potential and concentrations, is

$$E = E_1^{\circ\prime} + \frac{RT}{n_1 F} \ln \frac{[Ox_1]}{[Red_1]} \qquad (17\text{-}4)$$

If the sample is initially in the reduced form and if X is the percentage oxidized, we have, for $0 < X < 100$,

$$E = E_1^{\circ\prime} + \frac{RT}{n_1 F} \ln \frac{X}{100 - X} \qquad (17\text{-}5)$$

as the equation of the titration curve. We see that

$$\text{at } X = 50, \frac{X}{100 - X} = 1 \qquad E = E_1^{\circ\prime}$$

which shows that the formal potential of the system made up of the sample and its oxidation product is reached at the mid-point of the titration curve. At other points, the potential is given by the set of equations (at 25°C)

$$\text{at } X = 91, \frac{X}{100 - X} \cong 10 \qquad E = E_1^{\circ\prime} + \frac{0.059}{n_1} \qquad (17\text{-}6)$$

$$\text{at } X = 99, \frac{X}{100 - X} \cong 100 \qquad E = E_1^{\circ\prime} + 2 \times \frac{0.059}{n_1} \qquad (17\text{-}7)$$

. . . .

17-2. The Equivalence Point

At the exact equivalence point of reaction (17-1), n_1 moles of Ox_2 have been added to n_2 moles of Red_1. Regardless of the state of incompleteness of the reaction, at this point the concentrations of reactants and products will both be in the stoichiometric ratio of n_2 to n_1. Thus,

$$\left(\frac{[Red_1]}{[Ox_2]} \right)_{equiv} = \frac{n_2}{n_1} = \left(\frac{[Ox_1]}{[Red_2]} \right)_{equiv} \qquad (17\text{-}8)$$

$$\left(\frac{[Ox_1]}{[Red_1]} \right)_{equiv} = \left(\frac{[Red_2]}{[Ox_2]} \right)_{equiv} \qquad (17\text{-}9)$$

Applying the Nernst equation to system 1 (the sample),

$$E_{equiv} = E_1^{\circ\prime} + \frac{RT}{n_1 F} \ln \left(\frac{[Ox_1]}{[Red_1]} \right)_{equiv} \qquad (17\text{-}10)$$

and to system 2 (the titrant) at the equivalence point:

$$E_{equiv} = E_2^{\circ\prime} + \frac{RT}{n_2 F} \ln \left(\frac{[Ox_2]}{[Red_2]} \right)_{equiv} \qquad (17\text{-}11)$$

Multiplying Eq. (17-10) by n_1 and Eq. (17-11) by n_2, and adding, we find that the last terms cancel, in view of Eq. (17-9), and that

$$(n_1 + n_2)E_{equiv} = n_1E_1^{\circ\prime} + n_2E_2^{\circ\prime} \tag{17-12}$$

or

$$E_{equiv} = \frac{n_1E_1^{\circ\prime} + n_2E_2^{\circ\prime}}{n_1 + n_2} \tag{17-13}$$

The potential at the equivalence point is a weighted arithmetic mean of the formal potentials of the two redox couples involved in the titration. If $n_1 = n_2$,

$$E_{equiv} = \frac{E_1^{\circ\prime} + E_2^{\circ\prime}}{2} \tag{17-14}$$

and the titration curve is symmetrical in the vicinity of the equivalence point.

17-3. Region beyond the Equivalence Point

The Nernst equation is applied to reaction (17-3) to yield

$$E = E_2^{\circ\prime} + \frac{RT}{n_2F} \ln \frac{[Ox_2]}{[Red_2]} \tag{17-15}$$

At the equivalence point, from the stoichiometry of reaction (17-1), we have, for each 100 initial millimoles of Red_1, $100n_1/n_2$ millimoles of Red_2 formed, corresponding to $X = 100$. For $X > 100$, we have $[Ox_2]/[Red_2] = (X - 100)/100$ and

$$E = E_2^{\circ\prime} + \frac{RT}{n_2F} \ln \frac{X - 100}{100} \tag{17-16}$$

At $X = 200$, we see that $E = E_2^{\circ\prime}$.

17-4. Theoretical Properties of Redox Titration Curves

It can readily be shown[1] by differentiating the titration curve twice, then equating the second derivative to zero, that, for a symmetrical titration curve ($n_1 = n_2$), the point of maximum slope theoretically coincides with the equivalence point. This is the basis for potentiometric end-point detection methods. On the other hand, if $n_1 \neq n_2$, so that the titration curve is asymmetrical in the vicinity of the equivalence point, there is a small theoretical error if the end point is taken as the inflection point. In practice, the error from this source is generally insignificant compared with errors due to inexact stoichiometry, slowness of titration reaction, slowness of attainment of electrode equilibria, etc.

[1] Laitinen, H. A., Potentiometric Analysis, in Berl, W. H. (ed.), "Physical Methods of Chemical Analysis," vol. 1, Academic Press, Inc., New York, 1950.

An important property of the calculated titration curve for reaction (17-1) is that *the theoretical shape is independent of the concentration of reactants*. Thus the sharpness of the titration is theoretically unaffected by dilution.

It should be noted, however, that Eq. (17-1) is not perfectly general, because the simple relationship of n_1 and n_2 for reactants and products is not always valid. Consider, for example, the reaction

$$2Fe^{++} + Br_2 \rightleftharpoons 2Fe^{3+} + 2Br^-$$

for which the equivalence-potential expression is

$$E_{equiv} = \frac{E_1^{\circ\prime} + 2E_2^{\circ\prime}}{3} - \frac{RT}{3F} \ln 2[Br^-]_{equiv}$$

if no bromide other than that produced in the reaction is present. Clearly, the equivalence potential varies with dilution.

The rate of attainment of equilibrium also varies with dilution. We should distinguish between the attainment of equilibrium of the reactants and the attainment of equilibrium of the electrode or visual indicator that is used to detect the end point.

Nightingale[1] has defined a quantity $\rho = dC_R/dE$, which he called the "redox poising capacity index," analogous to buffer capacity in acid-base systems. If dC_R is the change in concentration of reductant necessary to cause a change dE in potential, ρ is a measure of *the stability of the potential of a redox system with respect to addition of oxidant or reductant in solution*. Nightingale derived expressions for ρ as a function of various titration parameters. It is beyond the scope of this treatment to discuss the expressions in detail. However, it is important to recognize that the poising capacity defined by Nightingale bears no simple relationship to the *stability of an electrode potential with respect to passage of a cathodic or anodic current* or to the rate of attainment of electrode equilibrium. The Nightingale treatment is concerned with the situation in solution after the attainment of equilibrium and not with the rate of attainment of the equilibrium either in solution or at the electrodes.

The exchange current density, which governs the attainment of electrode equilibrium, varies enormously from one potential-determining redox couple to another. It varies not only with the initial concentration but also with the ratio of oxidant to reductant [cf. Eq. (16-14)]. Near the end point the equilibrium may be reached very slowly in titrations carried out at great dilution. Therefore, it may be advantageous to select a method of end-point detection that is not dependent upon reaching equilibrium near the end point.

[1] Nightingale, E. R., Jr., *Anal. Chem.*, **30**, 267 (1958).

As an example we may cite the titration of arsenic(III) with bromate.[1] In a hydrochloric acid solution containing excess bromide, the end point can be determined potentiometrically, using the bromine-bromide couple as the potential-determining system. Alternatively, the same titration can be followed amperometrically, measuring the diffusion-controlled current due to excess bromine slightly beyond the end point. At an initial concentration of 10^{-3} N arsenite, the potentiometric titration could barely be carried out, because several minutes were required for electrode equilibrium at each point of the titration. The amperometric method gave a successful end point even at 10^{-6} N arsenite, the whole titration taking only a few minutes.

When visual indicators are used, the rate of attainment of equilibrium depends on the type of color reaction, which may be slow. For simple electron exchange reactions like that of ferroin, the rate of indicator response is usually rapid. However, if the indicator undergoes a more deep-seated structural change, one can anticipate kinetic complications. The oxidation of diphenylamine, for example, is *induced* by the Fe(II)-dichromate reaction.

17-5. Experimental Titration Curves

If both the half-reactions involved in a redox titration can be made to behave reversibly at a suitable electrode, the shapes of the titration curves should conform rather closely to the calculated values, although, as pointed out above, the electrode potential reaches its equilibrium values more and more slowly as the dilution is increased.

The titration of ferrous iron represents a very important practical example, which also serves nicely to illustrate several principles. Since the Fe(III)-Fe(II) couple behaves in a typically reversible fashion, the shape of curve theoretically predicted by Eq. (17-5) is closely achieved, provided that the electrolyte composition is essentially constant during the titration except for the concentration ratio [Fe(III)]/[Fe(II)]. This condition is necessary if the formal potential $E_1^{\circ\prime}$ is to be constant during the titration. The value of the formal potential varies with the nature and concentration of acid present. We can distinguish three effects on the activity ratio $a_{Fe(III)}/a_{Fe(II)}$ as the concentration of any particular acid is increased.

1. The increasing ionic strength tends to decrease the activity coefficient ratio $f_{Fe(III)}/f_{Fe(II)}$ and, therefore, the activity ratio also.

2. The increasing hydrogen ion activity tends to increase the activity ratio by suppressing hydrolysis of the ferric iron.

3. The increasing anion concentration may tend to decrease the activity ratio by forming complexes with Fe(III) in preference to Fe(II).

Effects 1 and 3 cause the value of $E_1^{\circ\prime}$ to decrease, i.e., to become less positive; effect 2 has the opposite effect.

[1] Laitinen, H. A., and Kolthoff, I. M., *J. Phys. Chem.*, **45**, 1079 (1941).

These effects are seen clearly in the experimental curves of Figs. 17-1 and 17-2. Before the end point, the shapes are independent of the nature of the oxidant. With perchloric acid $E_1^{\circ\prime}$ has its highest value, because hydrolysis of Fe(III) is largely suppressed and the perchlorate ion has little tendency to form complexes. With sulfuric acid, the two effects of hydrolysis and complex formation tend to counteract each other.

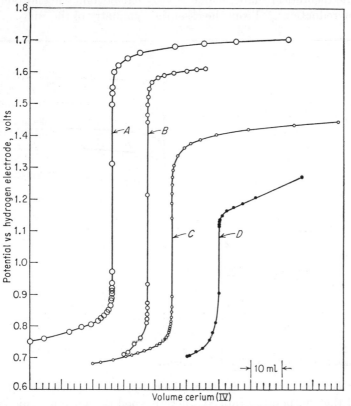

FIG. 17-1. Potentiometric titration curves of Fe(II) with Ce(IV). A, HClO$_4$; B, HNO$_3$; C, H$_2$SO$_4$; D, HCl. (*With permission from Smith, G. F., "Cerate Oxidimetry,"* *Fig.* II, *p.* 23, *G. Frederick Smith Chemical Co., Columbus, Ohio, 1942.*)

In the presence of phosphoric acid, complex formation predominates, and $E_1^{\circ\prime}$ is distinctly lower.

The shape of the curve beyond the end point is determined primarily by the properties of the oxidant. For Ce(IV) in various media, the value of $E_2^{\circ\prime}$ is different, and the magnitude of the potential change varies correspondingly. The reasons for these effects are qualitatively the same as they are for the Fe(III)-Fe(II) couple. For further details, see the discussion of Ce(IV) as a reagent (Chap. 20). However, it is noteworthy that all the experimental curves in Fig. 17-1 closely resemble the expected shapes, with the exception of the curve in hydrochloric acid which is distorted after the end point. This effect is due to the gradual oxidation of chloride by the excess Ce(IV).

In Fig. 17-2 several titration curves of Fe(II) with permanganate are shown. Beyond the end point, the experimental curves differ greatly from the theoretical shape, which is very flat beyond the end point (five-electron reduction). From the essential symmetry of the curves, it seems

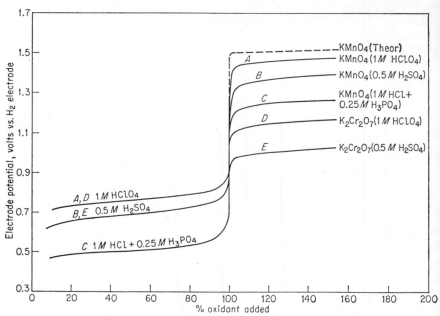

Fig. 17-2. Titration curves for Fe(II). 25 ml, 0.1 N Fe(II) in initial volume of 300 ml of specified acid, titrated with 0.1 N oxidant.

likely that the potential is determined by the Mn(III)-Mn(II) couple beyond the end point. Indeed, there is good evidence for this behavior in solutions containing sulfate, phosphate, etc., which tend to stabilize Mn(III) (cf. page 370). The fact that sulfuric and phosphoric acids have about the same effect before and after the end point (curves A, B, C, Fig. 17-2) is consistent with the fact that the Mn(III)-Mn(II) system and the Fe(III)-Fe(II) system should behave similarly with respect to changes in activity coefficients, as well as with respect to hydrolysis and complex formation.

The behavior of Fe(II)-dichromate titration curves is especially interesting. In hydrochloric acid and sulfuric acid solutions, Smith[1] and

[1] Smith, G. F., *Anal. Chem.*, **23**, 925 (1951).

Richter[1] found that the titration curves had shapes that closely resembled those of the theoretical curves for reversible systems, but with a variety of values for the formal potentials $E_1^{o'}$ and $E_2^{o'}$ depending on the nature and concentration of acid. (See Table 23-1, Sec. 23-1.) Particularly striking is the asymmetrical shape corresponding to $n_1 = 1$, $n_2 = 3$. The asymmetry is clearly visible in curve E, Fig. 17-2, and in curve A, Fig. 17-3.

It might be thought that the asymmetry should correspond to $n_1 = 1$, $n_2 = 6$, because six electrons are required for the reduction of one dichromate ion. However, the equilibrium $2HCrO_4^- \rightleftharpoons Cr_2O_7^= + H_2O$ is shifted far to the left at the small concentrations of Cr(VI) existing just beyond the end point [see Eq. (23-7), Sec. 23-1]; so monomeric Cr(VI) should be regarded as the oxidant.

Winter and Moyer[2] observed a time-dependence of the potential after the end point. If the potential readings were taken soon after each addition, a very unsymmetrical titration curve was observed, but, if a time interval of 10 to 15 min was allowed after each addition, the curve approached the theoretical shape. We have noted that automatically recorded titration curves for the Fe(II)-dichromate titration show a considerably smaller potential jump than manually observed curves, the difference being due to lower potentials after the end point. However, curves plotted with 15 sec of waiting for each point differed only slightly from curves taken with 150 sec of waiting. Ross and Shain[3] also studied the drift of potential of platinum electrodes with time, and noted hysteresis effects in recorded potentiometric titration curves. These effects, which are due to oxidation and reduction of the platinum surface, will be discussed below.

First, however, let us consider the final curves, which closely approximate the theoretical shapes. That they do so is at first thought surprising, since the Cr(VI)-Cr(III) couple does not behave reversibly (cf. page 296). It makes sense, however, if we assume that *the Fe(III)-Fe(II) couple acts as the potential-determining couple immediately after the end point.* After all, at equilibrium both couples have the same potential, and it is only because the exchange current density of the Fe(III)-Fe(II) couple becomes very low beyond the end point that some other couple with a higher exchange current usually takes over as the potential-determining system. From the following calculation, we see that this interpretation is reasonable.

[1] Smith, G. F., and Richter, F. P., "Phenanthroline and Substituted Phenanthroline Indicators," G. Frederick Smith Chemical Co., Columbus, Ohio, 1944.

[2] Winter, P. K., and Moyer, H. V., *J. Am. Chem. Soc.*, **57**, 1402 (1935).

[3] Ross, J. W., and Shain, I., *Anal. Chem.*, **28**, 548 (1956).

At a potential of 1.0 volt (vs. hydrogen electrode) the ratio $[Fe(III)]/[Fe(II)]$ is 3×10^5 in $1\ N$ H_2SO_4, calculated from $E^{o\prime} = 0.68$. For $[Fe(III)] = 0.01$, $[Fe(II)] = 3 \times 10^{-8}$, corresponding to the conditions 20 per cent beyond the end point in curve E, Fig. 17-2, we calculate from the data of Gerischer[1] an exchange current density of 1.5×10^{-5} amp cm^{-2}, which is sufficient to give a stable potential. On the other hand, at a potential of 1.3 volts, corresponding to a point just beyond the permanganate end point (curve B, Fig. 17-2) the ratio $[Fe(III)]/[Fe(II)]$ is about 10^{10}, and the exchange current density is only 1.8×10^{-8} amp cm^{-2}, which is much more easily swamped out by another potential-determining couple, such as Mn(III)–Mn(II).

The above calculation, however, should be regarded only as a rough approximation, because the exchange current depends upon the state of the surface.

A great deal of evidence[2,3] has accumulated to show that surfaces of supposedly "inert" metals readily undergo oxidation. For example, Hickling[4] was able to achieve a cyclic oxidation and reduction of a platinum surface, which could be repeated indefinitely without permanent changes in the metal. He pictured the formation of a monolayer of PtO, which is formed and removed at a potential near the reversible potential of the PtO-Pt couple at the pH value of the solution. Kolthoff and Tanaka[5] showed that the oxidation could be carried out either electrochemically or chemically with such strong oxidants as dichromate, Ce(IV), and permanganate. Similarly, gold and palladium surfaces are attacked by strong oxidants.[6] Anson and Lingane[7] analyzed chemically the oxide formed on a platinum surface and found both PtO and PtO$_2$, in a molar ratio of 6 to 1.*

Kolthoff and Nightingale[8] observed that in a sulfuric acid solution the Fe(III)-Fe(II) couple behaved *more* nearly reversibly (i.e., evidenced a higher exchange current density) if the surface of platinum was in the *oxidized* condition. This rather surprising effect was attributed to the surface oxide acting as a "bridging" atom between the electrode and the

[1] Gerischer, H., *Z. Elektrochem.*, **54**, 366 (1950).

[2] El Wakkad, S. E. S., and Emara, S. H., *J. Chem. Soc.*, **1952**, 461.

[3] El Wakkad, S. E. S., and El Din, A. M. S., *J. Chem. Soc.*, **1954**, 3094, 3098.

[4] Hickling, A., *Trans. Faraday Soc.*, **41**, 333 (1945).

[5] Kolthoff, I. M., and Tanaka, N., *Anal. Chem.*, **26**, 632 (1954).

[6] Lee, J. K., Adams, R. N., and Bricker, C. E., *Anal. Chim. Acta*, **17**, 321 (1957).

[7] Anson, F. C., and Lingane, J. J., *J. Am. Chem. Soc.*, **79**, 4901 (1957).

* Recent evidence (Enke, C. G., Ph.D. Thesis, University of Illinois, 1959), however, indicates that the PtO-Pt couple should not be regarded as the potential-determining system and that intermediate species, such as the radical ·OH, formed in the anodic evolution of oxygen are involved in the oxidation of the surface. The reduction of the surface oxide occurs at a lower potential than its formation, even at very low current densities. Amounts of oxygen in excess of two atoms per surface platinum atom are retained by grain boundary diffusion of oxygen atoms into platinum, a very slow process.

[8] Kolthoff and Nightingale, *Anal. Chim. Acta*, **17**, 329 (1957).

aquated ferric or ferrous ion. On the other hand, in a hydrochloric acid medium, the oxide layer did not form; nevertheless, the Fe(III)-Fe(II) system behaved as though the exchange current density were high. Here it appears likely that chloride, which forms weak complexes with Fe(III) and strong complexes with the ions of platinum, could perform the bridging function.

Surface oxide formation, no doubt, is involved in the Fe(II)-dichromate titration curves, which Smith and Brandt[1] found to be entirely

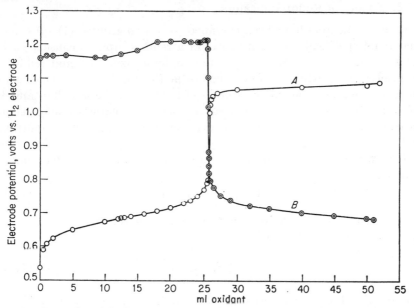

Fig. 17-3. Potentiometric titration curves. *A*, Fe(II) with dichromate; *B*, dichromate with Fe(II). [*With permission from Smith, G. F., and Brandt, W. W., Anal. Chem.*, **21**, 948 (1949).]

different when the direction of titration was reversed. Smith and Brandt's curves for 1 *M* sulfuric acid are shown in Fig. 17-3. Kolthoff and Tanaka[2] found that the rate of oxidation with dichromate was slow, whereas the rate of reduction with Fe(II) was fast. Ross and Shain[3] found the same sort of behavior and noted also that the rates of oxidation and reduction decreased in more dilute solutions. The oxidized surface in a dichromate solution may be largely covered with adsorbed dichromate, as chromium surfaces have been shown to be in some experiments

[1] Smith, G. F., and Brandt, W. W., *Anal. Chem.*, **21**, 948 (1949).
[2] Kolthoff and Tanaka, *op. cit.*
[3] Ross and Shain, *op. cit.*

with radiochromium,[1] so that it is relatively ineffective as an electron-transfer surface for the Fe(III)-Fe(II) system.

It is evident from the above discussion that the exact mechanism of the behavior of "inert" electrodes in redox titrations is still obscure in many cases, especially where "irreversible" half-reactions are involved. Further research is needed on the kinetics and mechanism of oxide formation reactions and on the influence of the surface oxide and of adsorbed substances on the rates of electron transfer reactions.

17-6. Theory of Redox Indicators

Redox indicators have been classified[2] into two groups: (1) substances that react specifically with one form of a redox couple to cause a visible color change, and (2) substances that undergo oxidation and reduction themselves and exhibit different colors in the two forms. The first of these classes, exemplified by starch as an indicator for iodine and by thiocyanate for ferric iron, is limited in scope and not amenable to general treatment. The second type, however, is of great practical importance and can be treated in a general way.

The two forms of the indicator comprise a redox couple undergoing the half-reaction

$$In_{ox} + ne^- \rightleftharpoons In_{red} \tag{17-17}$$

At a potential E, the ratio of concentrations of the two forms is determined by the Nernst equation

$$E = E_{In}^{o\prime} + \frac{RT}{nF} \ln \frac{[In_{ox}]}{[In_{red}]} \tag{17-18}$$

where $E_{In}^{o\prime}$ is the formal potential of the indicator. The value of $E_{In}^{o\prime}$, of course, varies to some extent with the composition of the solution (activity-coefficient effect) and should, therefore, be determined in the actual titration medium.

If the color intensities of the two forms are comparable, a practical estimate of the color-change interval corresponds to the change in the ratio $[In_{ox}]/[In_{red}]$ from $\frac{1}{10}$ to 10. The corresponding interval of potential is

$$E = E_{In}^{o\prime} \pm \frac{0.059}{n} \quad \text{volts} \quad \text{at } 25°C \tag{17-19}$$

If one form is much more intensely colored than the other, the intermediate color is attained at a potential somewhat removed from $E_{In}^{o\prime}$.

[1] Hackerman, N., and Powers, R. A., *J. Phys. Chem.*, **57**, 139 (1953).

[2] Kolthoff, I. M., and Stenger, V. A., "Volumetric Analysis," 2d Ed., vol. 1, p. 105, Interscience Publishers, Inc., New York, 1942.

If an indicator is to change color within 0.1 per cent of the end point, the color change must occur between $X = 99.9$ and 100.1 and, therefore, in the potential region

$$E_1^{o\prime} + \frac{3 \times 0.059}{n_1} < E < E_2^{o\prime} - \frac{3 \times 0.059}{n_2} \qquad (17\text{-}20)$$

as is seen from Eqs. (17-5) and (17-16).

To take an example, in the titration of Fe(II) with Ce(IV) in 1 N H_2SO_4, we have $n_1 = n_2 = 1$, $E_1^{o\prime} = 0.68$, $E_2^{o\prime} = 1.44$; and we calculate the interval

$$0.86 < E < 1.26$$

In the titration of Fe(II) with dichromate in 1 N HCl, we have $n_1 = 1$, $n_2 = 3$, $E_1^{o\prime} = 0.69$, $E_2^{o\prime} = 1.09$; and the useful indicator interval is

$$0.87 < E < 1.03$$

In the titration of Fe(II) with dichromate in 1 M HCl containing 0.25 M H_3PO_4, $E_1^{o\prime} = 0.50$, $E_2^{o\prime} = 1.05$; and the useful interval becomes

$$0.68 < E < 0.99$$

17-7. Examples of Redox Indicators

A great many substances have been studied for use as redox indicators. For detailed discussions, the reader is referred to appropriate monographs[1-4] and review papers.[5-8]

Our discussion here is limited to the two most important classes of redox indicators, namely, diphenylamine and 1,10-phenanthroline iron(II) complex and their derivatives.

Diphenylamine. This compound was introduced by Knop[9] as an indicator for the Fe(II)-dichromate titration. It undergoes oxidation first to the colorless diphenylbenzidine

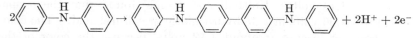

[1] Kolthoff and Stenger, *op. cit.*

[2] Tomiček, E., "Chemical Indicators," Butterworth & Co. (Publishers) Ltd., London, 1951.

[3] Brennecke, E., and Blasius, E., in Jander, G. (ed.), "Neuere massanalytische Methoden," p. 251, Ferd. Enke Verlag, Stuttgart, 1956.

[4] Kolthoff, I. M., and Belcher, R., "Volumetric Analysis," vol. 3, pp. 24, 123, 170, Interscience Publishers, Inc., New York, 1957.

[5] Whitehead, T. H., and Wills, C. C., *Chem. Revs.*, **29**, 69 (1941).

[6] Nutten, A. J., *Metallurgia*, **42**, 271, 407 (1950).

[7] Kolthoff, *Anal. Chem.*, **22**, 65 (1950).

[8] Belcher, *Chim. anal.*, **40**, 35 (1958).

[9] Knop, J., *Z. anal. Chem.*, **63**, 79 (1923); *J. Am. Chem. Soc.*, **46**, 263 (1924).

which undergoes further oxidation to diphenylbenzidine violet

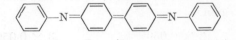

The color formation reaction is reversible ($E^{\circ\prime}$ = 0.76 volt in 0.5 to 1 M sulfuric acid).   Diphenylbenzidine violet undergoes further oxidation if it is allowed to stand with excess dichromate.   The excessive oxidation is irreversible in character, and red or yellow products of unknown composition are produced.

Kolthoff and Sarver[1] introduced diphenylaminesulfonic acid, which has the advantage of being water-soluble in the form of its sodium or barium salt.   The color change occurs through a mechanism similar to that of diphenylamine, but it occurs at a potential of 0.85 volt in 0.5 M sulfuric acid, which is significantly higher than the potential for diphenylamine. From the titration curves (Fig. 17-2) it is evident that in 0.5 M sulfuric acid the color change of diphenylamine occurs too early.   The addition of phosphoric acid is beneficial, for it lowers the formal potential of the Fe(III)-Fe(II) system so that the equivalence potential coincides more nearly with that of the indicator.   The higher potential of diphenyl-amine sulfonate is advantageous.   Most authorities recommend the addition of phosphoric acid, although Stockdale[2] obtained good results, and a better warning of the approach of the end point, by omitting the phosphoric acid and titrating to the fully developed violet color of the indicator.

Ferroin.   With the introduction of Ce(IV) as an oxidant and the evaluation of the formal potential of the Ce(IV)-Ce(III) couple,[3] the need for indicators with higher oxidation potentials became evident.   The indicator ferroin, tris(1,10-phenanthroline) iron(II), was discovered by Walden, Hammett, and Chapman,[4] and its standard potential was evaluated at 1.14 volts.   Kolthoff and Hume[5] found that the formal potential was 1.06 volts in 1 M hydrochloric or sulfuric acid.   The color change, however, occurs at about 1.12 volts, because the color of the reduced form (orange-red) is so much more intense than that of the oxidized form (pale blue).   From Fig. 17-1 it is evident that ferroin should be ideally suited to titrations of ferrous iron and other reductants with Ce(IV), particularly if sulfuric acid is the titration medium.   It has

[1] Kolthoff, I. M., and Sarver, L. A., *J. Am. Chem. Soc.*, **52**, 4179 (1930).

[2] Stockdale, D., *Analyst*, **75**, 150 (1950).

[3] Kunz, A. H., *J. Am. Chem. Soc.*, **53**, 98 (1931).

[4] Walden, G. H., Jr., Hammett, L. P., and Chapman, R. P., *J. Am. Chem. Soc.*, **53**, 3908 (1931); **55**, 2649 (1933).

[5] Kolthoff, I. M., and Hume, D. N., *J. Am. Chem. Soc.*, **65**, 1895 (1943).

the further advantage of undergoing a reversible oxidation-reduction reaction and of being relatively stable even in the presence of excess oxidant.

The formal potential of ferroin can be modified greatly by the introduction of various substituents into the 1,10-phenanthroline nucleus. The first such derivative was nitroferroin,[1] the $Fe(II)$ complex of 5-nitro-1,10-phenanthroline.

Smith and Richter[2] determined the formal potentials of several substituted ferroins in various concentrations of sulfuric acid. Brandt and Smith[3] studied a series of methyl-substituted 1,10-phenanthrolines and found an interesting regularity in the formal potential values. The effect of substitution was found to be additive, in the sense that each methyl group in the 3 or 8 position lowered the formal potential by 0.03 volt; in the 5 or 6 position by 0.04 volt; and in the 4 or 7 position by 0.11 volt. In this way, the formal potential could be varied in 0.01-to-0.03-volt increments from 0.84 to 1.10 volts.

The most important substituted ferroins are 5-nitro-1,10-phenanthroline and 4,7-dimethyl-1,10-phenanthroline.[4] The former ($E^{\circ\prime} = 1.25$ volts) is especially suitable for titrations using $Ce(IV)$ in perchloric or nitric acid solution,[5] where the formal potential of the oxidant is especially high. The 4,7-dimethyl derivative has a formal potential sufficiently low ($E^{\circ\prime} = 0.88$ volt) to make it useful for the titration of $Fe(II)$ with dichromate in 0.5 M sulfuric acid.[6] It should also be satisfactory for $Fe(II)$ titrations in HCl, with either dichromate or $Ce(IV)$.

In the above discussion it has been tacitly assumed that the indicator comes rapidly to equilibrium at each point of the titration curve. That this is an oversimplification is evident from a number of experimental observations. Kolthoff and Sarver[7] found that the oxidation of diphenylamine with dichromate is *induced* by the $Fe(II)$-dichromate reaction. The direct oxidation is so slow that the indicator blank is best determined by comparison of the visual end point with the potentiometric one. With ferroin, Smith and Brandt[8] and Stockdale[9] found that the reverse titration, i.e., dichromate with iron, gave satisfactory results at sufficiently high acidities, whereas the direct titration failed because the

[1] Hammett, L. P., Walden, G. H., Jr., and Edmonds, S. M., *J. Am. Chem. Soc.*, **56**, 1092 (1934).

[2] Smith, and Richter, *Ind. Eng. Chem., Anal. Ed.*, **16**, 580 (1944).

[3] Brandt and Smith, *Anal. Chem.*, **21**, 1313 (1949).

[4] Smith, *Anal. Chem.*, **23**, 925 (1951).

[5] Smith, G. F., and Getz, C. A., *Ind. Eng. Chem., Anal. Ed.*, **10**, 304 (1938).

[6] Smith, *op. cit.*

[7] Kolthoff and Sarver, *J. Am. Chem. Soc.*, **53**, 2902, 2906 (1931).

[8] Smith and Brandt, *Anal. Chem.*, **21**, 948 (1949).

[9] Stockdale, *op. cit.*

indicator could not be oxidized. Here the oxidation seems to be slow and the reduction rapid because of the "irreversible" nature of the oxidant and the "reversible" nature of the reductant.

Using As(III) as a reductant and Ce(IV) as the oxidant in sulfuric acid, the situation is just reversed. The oxidized indicator, ferriin, is reduced hardly at all by excess As(III), even in the presence of osmium tetroxide as the catalyst. However, if a drop of Ce(IV) solution is added the red color of ferroin is rapidly developed, evidently because of an induced reduction. In hydrochloric acid the induced reduction does not occur, ferroin is oxidized by the first drop of Ce(IV), and so the titration fails. A small amount of chloride (for example, 0.1 N HCl in 1 N sulfuric acid) does not interfere. Addition of excess mercuric perchlorate prevents the interference by complexation of the chloride.[1]

PROBLEMS

17-1. A titration of Fe(II) is carried out in a sulfuric acid medium with Ce(IV), the end point being taken at $E = 0.88$ volt. If the formal potentials of the Fe(III)-Fe(II) and Ce(IV)-Ce(III) couples are 0.68 and 1.44 volts, respectively, what is the theoretical titration error? *Ans.* -0.04 per cent.

17-2. Calculate the potentials for the following percentages of the equivalent amount of reagent added in the titration of Sn(II) with Fe(III): 9, 50, 91, 99, 99.9, 100, 100.1, 101, 110, 200 per cent. Take the formal potentials of the Fe(III)-Fe(II) and Sn(IV)-Sn(II) couples to be 0.66 and 0.15 volt, respectively. *Ans.* 0.12, 0.15, 0.18, 0.21, 0.24, 0.32, 0.48, 0.54, 0.60, 0.66 volt.

17-3. Derive an expression for the minimum difference of formal potentials, $E_2^{\circ'} - E_1^{\circ'}$, for which a redox indicator would show an essentially complete change of color within the interval -0.1 to $+0.1$ per cent of the end point. Assume that $E_{ind}^{\circ'} = E_{equiv}$ and that the color-change interval is given by Eq. (17-19). *Ans.* $E_2^{\circ'} - E_1^{\circ'} = (3/n_2 + 2/n_{ind} + 3/n_1)0.059$.

17-4. Derive the expression given on page 329 for the equivalence potential of the Fe(II)-bromine reaction. Given the standard potentials $E_{Br_2,aqBr^-}^{\circ} = 1.087$ volts and $E_{Fe^{3+},Fe^{++}}^{\circ} = 0.771$ volt, calculate the equivalence potential for (a) the titration of 0.01 M Fe^{++} with 0.01 M Br$_2$, neglecting activity coefficients; (b) the same titration at tenfold higher concentrations of sample and reagent; (c) the titration of part (a), except with 0.1 M KBr initially present. *Hint:* New equation necessary. *Ans.* (a) 1.019 volts; (b) 0.999 volt; (c) 0.991 volt.

17-5. Using the standard potentials given in Table 15-1 and neglecting activity coefficients,

  a. Estimate the equivalence potential at pH = 0 and at pH = 1 for the titration reaction

$$V(OH)_4^+ + Cr^{++} + 2H^+ \rightarrow Cr^{3+} + VO^{++} + 3H_2O$$

  b. At pH = 0, calculate the potential at 50, 99, 99.9, 100.1, 101, and 200 per cent of the equivalent amount of Cr^{++} added.

[1] Gleu, K., *Z. anal. Chem.*, **95**, 305 (1933).

c. Sketch the titration curve for the stepwise reduction of V(V) to (IV) to (III) to (II) using Cr(II) as the titrant. *Ans.* (*a*) 0.295; 0.236 volt; (*b*) 1.00, 0.882, 0.823, −0.233, −0.351, −0.410 volt.

17-6. For the titration of 0.01 *M* V(V) with relatively concentrated V(II) at pH = 0, neglecting dilution and neglecting activity coefficients, calculate the potential at the following points:

a. At the point where half the V(V) has been titrated to V(IV).

b. At the V(IV) equivalence point. *Hint:* Calculate the equilibrium constant of the reaction $2VO^{++} + 2H_2O \rightleftarrows V(OH)_4^+ + V^{3+}$.

c. At the point where half the V(IV) has been titrated to V(III).

d. At the V(III) equivalence point.

e. At a point beyond the second equivalence point equal to the volume required to reach the first equivalence point.

Ans. (*a*) 0.990; (*b*) 0.681; (*c*) 0.343; (*d*) 0.053; (*e*) −0.209 volt.

18. Prior Oxidation and Reduction

In many analyses it is necessary to carry out oxidation or reduction steps prior to the actual determination in order to bring the sample constituent quantitatively to a particular oxidation state. The following conditions must be fulfilled:

1. The oxidation or reduction step must be quantitative. This means not only that the equilibrium conditions, as calculated from standard or formal potentials, must be such as to represent a quantitative reaction but also that the rate of reaction must be fast enough for practical application.

2. It must be possible to remove the excess oxidant or reductant in a convenient and complete manner. The removal may be accomplished by a selective reaction in solution, by a physical separation of phases, or occasionally simply by dilution.

3. The oxidation or reduction step must be sufficiently selective to avoid interference from other components of the sample. This is usually accomplished by judicious choice of oxidant or reductant of the proper standard potential. Sometimes selective oxidation or reduction can be accomplished by taking advantage of favorable reaction rates even though the equilibrium condition does not lead to selectivity.

It is convenient to classify oxidants and reductants according to their physical state, i.e., whether they are gaseous, insoluble solids, or in solution. A reagent is classified as gaseous if it is removed by volatilization, even though it may have been added in the form of a solution. The following discussion is not intended to be a complete review, but rather to present a comparison of a number of reagents chosen as representative examples.

18-1. Oxidizing Agents

Gaseous oxidants. *Ozone* is a very strong oxidant, as shown by the potential of the half-reaction

$$O_3 + 2H^+ + 2e^- \rightleftharpoons O_2 + H_2O \qquad E° = 2.07 \text{ volts}$$

Willard and Merritt[1] showed that Mn(II) can be oxidized quantitatively to permanganate in perchloric acid solution using silver ion as a catalyst. Cerium(III) is oxidized to cerium(IV) phosphate, which precipitates from a solution containing sulfuric and phosphoric acids. The precipitate can be dissolved in sulfuric acid. Other oxidations that can be performed quantitatively are V(IV) to (V) in acid solution, hypophosphite and phosphite to phosphate, selenite to selenate, tellurite to tellurate, nitrite to nitrate, and iodide to periodate in alkaline solution.

Chlorine, in the form of chlorine water, is used in the old Winkler[2] method of determining iodide by oxidation to iodate, which is then determined iodometrically. Hypochlorite or bromine water is more convenient and equally effective.

Bromine vapor was used by Sadusk and Ball[3] for the iodide oxidation. Bromine water oxidizes Tl(I) to (III). The excess is readily removed with phenol.[4,5] Many other oxidation reactions may be carried out using bromine or chlorine.

Homogeneous oxidants. *Peroxydisulfate* ion, $S_2O_8^=$, which is often called "persulfate," is a very strong oxidant in acid solution in the presence of silver ion, which acts as a catalyst. The mechanism of the catalysis, according to Dekker, Levy, and Yost,[6] involves the following rate-controlling step, which is a first-order reaction with respect to peroxydisulfate and silver ions:

$$S_2O_8^= + Ag^1 \rightarrow 2SO_4^- + Ag^{3+}$$

The resulting Ag(III) is the active oxidant. More recent evidence, however, indicates that silver(II) and sulfate radical ion $\cdot SO_4^-$ (cf. page 389) are formed in the rate-controlling step

$$S_2O_8^= + Ag^+ \rightarrow SO_4^= + \cdot SO_4^- + Ag^{++}$$

and act as active oxidants.[7,8]

An important application involves the oxidation of Mn(II) to permanganate in nitric or sulfuric acid solution containing orthophosphoric[9] or metaphosphoric acid,[10] which is necessary to prevent the precipitation

[1] Willard, H. H., and Merritt, L. L., *Ind. Eng. Chem., Anal. Ed.*, **14**, 486, 489 (1942).
[2] First published by von Weszelszky, J., *Z. anal. Chem.*, **39**, 81 (1900).
[3] Sadusk, J. F., and Ball, E. G., *Ind. Eng. Chem., Anal. Ed.*, **5**, 386 (1933).
[4] Proszt, J., *Z. anal. Chem.*, **73**, 401 (1928).
[5] Reith, J. F., and Gerritsma, K. W., *Rec. trav. chim.*, **65**, 770 (1946).
[6] Dekker, A. O., Levy, H. A., and Yost, D. M., *J. Am. Chem. Soc.*, **59**, 2129 (1937).
[7] Bawn, C. E. H., and Margerison, D., *Trans. Faraday Soc.*, **51**, 925 (1955).
[8] Fronaeus, S., and Östman, C. O., *Acta Chem. Scand.*, **10**, 320 (1956).
[9] Bright, H. A., and Larrabee, C. P., *J. Research Natl. Bur. Standards*, **3**, 573 (1929).
[10] Lang, R., and Kurtz, F., *Z. anal. Chem.*, **85**, 181 (1931).

of MnO_2. After the excess oxidant is decomposed by boiling, the permanganate is titrated with Fe(II),[1] arsenite,[2] or a mixture of arsenite and nitrite.[3] Arsenite has the advantage over Fe(II) of permitting the selective reduction of permanganate in the presence of Cr(VI) or V(V), but suffers from the disadvantage that the permanganate is reduced only to an effective oxidation state of manganese of 3.3. Using the arsenite-nitrite mixture,[1] permanganate is reduced to Mn(II), and the color change is improved. Hillson[4] retarded the decomposition of the permanganate by carrying out the oxidation in a buffered phosphate solution. After acidification, the permanganate was titrated with arsenite using osmium tetroxide as the catalyst. Under these conditions, a stoichiometric reduction was achieved.

Other important applications of the silver-catalyzed peroxydisulfate reaction are the oxidation of Ce(III) to Ce(IV),[*,†] Cr(III) to dichromate, W(V) to W(VI), and V(IV) to V(V).[‡]

Permanganate is used in the selective oxidation[1] of V(IV) to (V) in the presence of Cr(III). The V(V) is then titrated with Fe(II). Chromium(III) is oxidized slowly in acid solutions,[5] and rapidly in alkaline solutions[6] to form Cr(VI). The excess permanganate can be reduced by adding sodium azide, which is oxidized to nitrogen. The excess hydrazoic acid is destroyed by boiling. Alternatively, the excess permanganate may be removed by adding sodium nitrite; the excess nitrite is then destroyed by adding urea.[7] Older procedures for removing excess permanganate involve boiling with hydrochloric acid or boiling with excess manganous sulfate to form manganese dioxide, which is filtered off.

Periodate is used in the oxidation of Mn(II) to permanganate, according to the equation

$$2Mn^{++} + 5IO_4^- + 3H_2O \rightarrow 2MnO_4^- + 5IO_3^- + 6H^+$$

The mechanism of this reaction has been studied by Strictland and Spicer[8] and by Waterbury, Hayes, and Martin,[9] who found it to be autocatalytic

[1] *Ibid.*

[2] Bright and Larrabee, *op. cit.*

[3] Sandell, E. B., Kolthoff, I. M., and Lingane, J. J., *Ind. Eng. Chem., Anal. Ed.*, **7**, 256 (1935).

[4] Hillson, H. D., *Ind. Eng. Chem., Anal. Ed.*, **16**, 560 (1944).

[*] Furman, N. H., *J. Am. Chem. Soc.*, **50**, 755 (1928).

[†] Willard, H. H., and Young, P., *J. Am. Chem. Soc.*, **50**, 1379 (1928).

[‡] Willard and Young, *Ind. Eng. Chem., Anal. Ed.*, **4**, 187 (1932); **5**, 154, 158 (1933).

[5] Fales, H. A., and Roller, P. S., *J. Am. Chem. Soc.*, **51**, 345 (1929).

[6] Reinitzer, B., and Conrath, P., *Z. anal. Chem.*, **68**, 81 (1926).

[7] Lang and Kurtz, *Z. anal. Chem.*, **86**, 288 (1931).

[8] Strictland, J. D. H., and Spicer, G., *Anal. Chim. Acta*, **3**, 517 (1949).

[9] Waterbury, G. R., Hayes, A. M., and Martin, D. S., Jr., *J. Am. Chem. Soc.*, **74**, 15 (1952).

in character. The rate is proportional to the concentrations of $Mn(II)$ and periodate and also increases with permanganate concentration. In perchloric acid solution, a violet-colored complex of $Mn(III)$ is formed as an intermediate. The proposed mechanism may be written (cf. page 362)

$$Mn(II) + MnO_4^- \rightleftharpoons Mn(III) + MnO_4^=$$
$$Mn(II) + MnO_4^= \rightarrow 2Mn(IV)$$
$$Mn(IV) + Mn(II) \rightarrow 2Mn(III)$$
$$Mn(III) + 2IO_4^- \rightarrow MnO_4^- + 2IO_3^-$$

According to this mechanism, $Mn(IV)$ cannot be oxidized unless it is first reduced by $Mn(II)$, which of course is being removed. Some manganese may, therefore, be trapped as $Mn(IV)$, if its concentration ever exceeds that of $Mn(II)$. This accounts for the fact that, in the colorimetric method of Willard and Greathouse,[1] the use of standard samples is necessary for color comparison.

By precipitating the excess periodate and most of the iodate as the mercuric salts $Hg_5(IO_6)_2$ and $Hg(IO_3)_2$, Willard and Thompson[2] were able to determine the permanganate by filtering the solution into excess standard $Fe(II)$, which was back-titrated. It is perhaps significant that the addition of phosphoric acid is recommended to prevent the formation of manganese dioxide, particularly when larger amounts of manganese are to be oxidized. Phosphoric acid is not necessary for the oxidation, but it undoubtedly plays a role as a complexing agent for $Mn(III)$ and $Mn(IV)$.

Perchloric acid is an effective oxidant, but only when it is hot and concentrated. It has long been used as an oxidant for chromium[3,4] and vanadium[5] in steels. Manganese(II) is not oxidized. Upon cooling and dilution, the acid no longer has oxidizing properties. Smith[6] has stressed the need for rapid cooling to avoid a partial reduction of chromium, which he has attributed to hydrogen peroxide formed from the hot, concentrated acid. After cooling and dilution, the solution should be boiled to remove chlorine, before the determination is carried out.

Smith[7] has discussed in detail the use of perchloric acid in various combinations with nitric and sulfuric acids for the wet oxidation of organic material. Chromium(III) acts as an indicator to show completeness of oxidation and also acts as a catalyst for some oxidations. Vana-

[1] Willard, H. H., and Greathouse, L. H., *J. Am. Chem. Soc.*, **39**, 2366 (1917).
[2] Willard, H. H., and Thompson, J. J., *Ind. Eng. Chem., Anal. Ed.*, **3**, 399 (1931).
[3] Willard, H. H., and Cake, W. E., *Ind. Eng. Chem.*, **11**, 480 (1919).
[4] Willard, H. H., and Gibson, R. C., *Ind. Eng. Chem., Anal. Ed.*, **3**, 88 (1931).
[5] *Ibid.*
[6] Smith, G. F., *Analyst*, **80**, 16 (1955).
[7] Smith, *Anal. Chim. Acta*, **8**, 397 (1953).

dium is a better catalyst, evidently fluctuating between V(IV) and (V) in the catalytic cycle.

If dilute perchloric acid is heated in the absence of reducing agents, it is concentrated gradually to form an azeotrope containing 72.5 per cent perchloric acid. Thus anhydrous perchloric acid, which is so unstable that it explodes spontaneously upon standing except at very low temperatures, cannot be formed by simple boiling. Hot, concentrated perchloric acid, however, can be made to explode violently by certain types of organic matter, notably ethanol, cellulose, or polyhydric alcohols. According to Smith, this occurs because of the formation of ethyl perchlorate under the dehydrating action of the hot, concentrated acid. Therefore, nitric acid is added to the cold solution, which is then gradually heated. Most of the organic matter is destroyed by the nitric acid, which eventually is volatilized from the mixture.

This procedure, with various modifications, is remarkably effective in oxidizing a wide variety of organic matter. The main precaution to be taken is to see that only very small quantities of organic matter remain unoxidized when the last of the nitric acid has been expelled and the perchloric acid begins to become more concentrated with a corresponding rise in boiling point. For details, the original literature should be consulted, and the recommended procedures should be followed carefully.

Potassium chlorate in acid solution oxidizes Mn(II) slowly to manganese dioxide. Although this procedure has long been used as a quantitative method for the separation and determination of manganese, Kolthoff and Sandell[1] found bromate to be superior as an oxidant. The composition of the precipitate was never exactly MnO_2; results that were 1 to 3.4 per cent low were observed, depending upon the procedure. An empirical correction factor was, therefore, necessary.

Chlorate is useful for the quantitative oxidation of Tl(I) to hexachlorothallate(III) in boiling hydrochloric acid.[2]

Hydrogen peroxide is a good oxidizing agent, particularly in alkaline solution. The excess peroxide is usually decomposed by boiling the alkaline solution. The decomposition is hastened by a number of catalysts, including nickel salts, iodide, and platinum black. Schulek and Szakács[3] removed the excess with chlorine water, followed by potassium cyanide to destroy the excess of chlorine.

Examples of oxidation reactions are the oxidation of Cr(III) to chromate in 2 N sodium hydroxide,[4,5] Co(II) to (III) in bicarbonate solution,[6]

[1] Kolthoff and Sandell, *Ind. Eng. Chem., Anal. Ed.*, **1**, 181 (1929).
[2] Spacu, G., and Pop, A., *Z. anal. Chem.*, **120**, 322 (1940).
[3] Schulek, E., and Szakács, M., *Acta Chim. Acad. Sci. Hung.*, **4**, 457 (1954).
[4] *Ibid.*
[5] Feigl, F., Klanfer, K., and Weidenfeld, L., *Z. anal. Chem.*, **80**, 5 (1930).
[6] Laitinen, H. A., and Burdett, L. W., *Anal. Chem.*, **23**, 1268 (1951).

Mn(II) to (IV) in the presence of tellurate,[1] and Fe(II) to (III) followed by titration with ascorbic acid.[2] Sodium peroxide, even more vigorous as an oxidant, is applied in alkaline fusions. Hardwick[3] and Bryant and Hardwick[4] made a critical study of the fusion of chromite ore to form chromate,

$$2Fe(CrO_2)_2 + 7O_2^= \rightarrow 4CrO_4^= + Fe_2O_3 + 3O^=$$

especially with regard to methods of decomposing the excess peroxide. Good results were obtained by treatment with ammonium peroxydisulfate in acid solution in the presence of silver ion as a catalyst. Equally good results were obtained by destroying the excess peroxide, after acidification, with permanganate. The latter procedure would usually be more convenient, because any manganese in the sample would undergo oxidation to manganate during the fusion. Upon acidification, manganate disproportionates to form permanganate and manganese dioxide. The latter would largely escape oxidation with peroxydisulfate, so that it would be necessary to remove it in any case. Boiling with hydrochloric acid proved successful in removing excess permanganate and manganese dioxide.

Potassium dichromate, although not commonly considered a very strong oxidant, has been used for some interesting oxidation reactions that are induced by the dichromate-arsenite reaction. The mechanism is discussed in Chap. 24. Examples are the oxidation of Mn(II) to (III) in the presence of fluoride[5] or metaphosphate,[6] and V(IV) to (V) and Ce(III) to (IV) in the presence of metaphosphate.[7] Since an excess of arsenite is used, there is no excess dichromate to be disposed of. This method is of particular importance when the interference of chromium is to be avoided.

Solid Oxidants. *Sodium bismuthate* is such a strong oxidant that it will oxidize Mn(II) to permanganate[8,9] at room temperature. Cerium(III) is oxidized quantitatively to Ce(IV) in sulfuric acid solution.[10] The excess is removed by filtration. The bismuthate method has been largely

[1] Issa, I. M., and Hewaidy, I. F., *Chemist Analyst*, **44**, 70 (1955).

[2] Erdey, L., and Bodor, E., *Anal. Chem.*, **24**, 418 (1952).

[3] Hardwick, P. J., *Analyst*, **75**, 9 (1950).

[4] Bryant, F. J., and Hardwick, P. J., *Analyst*, **75**, 12 (1950).

[5] Lang and Kurtz, *Z. anorg. u. allgem. Chem.*, **181**, 111 (1929); Lang, *Z. anal. Chem.*, **170**, 387 (1928); Lang, R., and Zweřina, J., *Z. anal. Chem.*, **170**, 389 (1928).

[6] Lang, *Z. anal. Chem.*, **102**, 8 (1935).

[7] Lang, R., and Faude, E., *Z. anal. Chem.*, **108**, 181 (1937).

[8] Blum, W., *J. Am. Chem. Soc.*, **34**, 1395 (1912).

[9] Lundell, G. E. F., *J. Am. Chem. Soc.*, **45**, 2600 (1923).

[10] Metzger, F. J., *J. Am. Chem. Soc.*, **31**, 523 (1909).

supplanted by the silver-catalyzed peroxydisulfate oxidation because of the inconvenience of the filtration step.

Lead dioxide is a moderately strong oxidant ($E° = 1.45$ in acid solution) which can be used for oxidations such as that of Mn(II) to Mn(III) in the presence of pyrophosphate.[1] Under the same conditions, Cr(III), V(IV) and Ce(III) undergo oxidation. The excess is readily removed by filtration.

Silver(II) oxide has been recommended by Lingane and Davis[2] as an oxidant for Mn(II) to permanganate, Cr(III) to dichromate, and Ce(III) to Ce(IV) in acid solutions. The oxide dissolves in nitric, perchloric, or sulfuric acids, forming Ag^{++}, which is such a powerful oxidant[3] ($E°'_{Ag^{++},Ag^+} = 1.929$ volts in 4 M nitric acid; 2.000 volts in 4 M perchloric acid) that the above oxidation reactions occur rapidly at room temperature. The excess oxidant is easily removed by warming for a few minutes

$$4Ag^{++} + 2H_2O \rightarrow 4Ag^+ + O_2 + 4H^+$$

Alternatively, the solution can be titrated potentiometrically with ferrous iron; two inflections are observed, the first due to reduction of excess Ag^{++} and the second to the reduction of permanganate, dichromate, or Ce(IV).

18-2. Reducing Agents

Gaseous Reductants. *Hydrogen sulfide* was formerly a popular reductant for Fe(III) because of its selectivity. The standard potential of the half-reaction

$$S + 2H^+ + 2e^- \rightleftharpoons H_2S \qquad E° = 0.14 \text{ volt}$$

indicates that Cr(III) and Ti(IV) are not reduced and that V(V) is reduced only to V(IV), which is not reoxidized by dichromate. The removal of the excess requires somewhat lengthy boiling.[4]

Sulfur dioxide is a mild reducing agent:

$$SO_4^= + 4H^+ + 2e^- \rightleftharpoons H_2SO_3 + H_2O \qquad E° = 0.17 \text{ volt}$$

The mechanism of the reduction of Fe(III) is somewhat complicated[5] and involves the intermediate formation of a red material which appears to be a sulfite complex of Fe(III). The reaction rate is slow in the presence of

[1] Kolthoff, I. M., and Watters, J. I., *Ind. Eng. Chem., Anal. Ed.*, **15**, 8 (1943).

[2] Lingane, J. J., and Davis, D. G., *Anal. Chim. Acta*, **15**, 201 (1956).

[3] Noyes, A. A., de Vault, D., Coryell, C. D., and Deahl, T. J., *J. Am. Chem. Soc.*, **59**, 1326 (1937).

[4] British Standard 1121, Part 33, 1955.

[5] Burriel-Marti, F., and Conde, F. L., *Anal. Chim. Acta*, **3**, 547 (1949).

excess sulfuric acid. It is greatly accelerated by the presence of thio-cyanate, which apparently replaces a part of the coordinated sulfite in the intermediate. The reduction then proceeds quantitatively even in 2 N sulfuric acid when the cold solution is treated with sulfur dioxide and slowly heated to boiling. The excess reductant is removed with a stream of carbon dioxide.

Sulfur dioxide has also been used for the reduction of arsenate to arsenite,[1] Sb(V) to Sb(III), Se(IV) and Te(IV) to the elements, Cu(II) to Cu(I) in the presence of thiocyanate, and V(V) to V(IV).

Homogeneous Reductants. *Stannous chloride* rapidly reduces Fe(III) to Fe(II) in hot hydrochloric acid solution. The rate of the reaction was found by Duke and Pinkerton[2] to be proportional to the concentrations of Fe(III) and of Sn(II) and to increase very rapidly with chloride ion concentration. A reevaluation of the kinetic data by Duke and Peterson[3] led to the expression

$$k_2 = 8.7 \times 10^4 C^4 + 26 \times 10^4 C^5$$

where k_2 is the second-order rate constant, in liters mole^{-1} min^{-1}, and C is the concentration of chloride ion not present as complexes of iron or tin. Except at the highest chloride concentrations, the rate was propor-tional to the fourth power of chloride concentration. This may be taken to mean that the rate-determining step involves a total of four chloride ions coordinated to Fe(III) and Sn(II), i.e., a reaction between Fe^{3+} and SnCl$_4^-$ or FeCl^{++} and SnCl$_3^-$. At higher chloride concentrations five chloride ions may be involved. From the analytical viewpoint, it is important to keep the Fe(III) and hydrochloric acid concentrations high if a quantitative reduction is to be achieved with a very small excess of stannous tin.

The excess Sn(II) is destroyed by adding quickly an excess of mercuric chloride

$$\text{Sn(II)} + 2\text{HgCl}_2(\text{excess}) \rightarrow \text{Sn(IV)} + \text{Hg}_2\text{Cl}_2 + 2\text{Cl}^-$$

Excessive stannous chloride must be avoided, because a local excess would cause the formation of metallic mercury

$$\text{Sn(II)}(\text{excess}) + \text{HgCl}_2 \rightarrow \text{Sn(IV)} + \text{Hg} + 2\text{Cl}^-$$

which reacts with the oxidant. A large amount of mercurous chloride, resulting from a large excess of stannous chloride, is also harmful, because

[1] Kurtenacker, A. and Fürstenau, I., *Z. anorg. u. allgem. Chem.*, **212**, 289 (1933).
[2] Duke, F. R., and Pinkerton, R. C., *J. Am. Chem. Soc.*, **73**, 3045 (1951).
[3] Duke, F. R., and Peterson, N. C., *Iowa State Coll. J. Sci.*, **32**, 89 (1957).

it reacts to some extent with the oxidant. In any case, the titration should be completed without undue delay, because Fe(III) slowly oxidizes mercurous chloride.

Wehber[1] used cacotheline as an indicator to detect the excess of stannous tin. Dichromate was then added, first to oxidize the excess Sn(II) shown by the change in the color of cacotheline and then, as usual, to titrate the Fe(II) using diphenylaminesulfonate. Hume and Kolthoff[2] suggested the same indicator, but used Ce(IV) as the titrant. Permanganate is often used as the oxidant, with the addition of Zimmermann-Reinhardt solution (pages 369 to 372).

Stannous chloride has also been used to reduce Mo(VI) to (V)* and arsenate to arsenite.[3] Main[4] used stannous chloride for the reduction of U(VI) to (IV), with ferric chloride as a catalyst, and destroyed the excess as usual with mercuric chloride. An excess of ferric chloride was added, and the resulting Fe(II) was titrated with dichromate.

Chromous chloride, a very strong reducing agent ($E^\circ_{Cr^{3+},Cr^{++}} = -0.41$ volt), was used by Cooke, Hazel, and McNabb[5] to reduce U(VI) to (IV). The excess was removed by air oxidation, using phenosafranine as an indicator. This dye is reduced to a colorless compound by Cr(II). Upon air oxidation, the indicator turns pink. Shatko[6] used Cr(II) to reduce arsenic(III) to the element.

Hydrazine, which is conveniently added as the hydrochloride, the sulfate, or the hydrate, is an interesting reductant because its oxidation product, nitrogen, is innocuous. Sloviter, McNabb, and Wagner[7] reduced HgI_4^- in alkaline solution with hydrazine sulfate, collected the mercury, and determined it bromometrically. Schulek and von Villecz[8] determined arsenic in organic compounds by destroying the organic matter and reducing the arsenic acid to arsenious acid with hydrazine sulfate, the excess being destroyed by heating with concentrated sulfuric acid. The As(III) was titrated with bromate. Arsenic and antimony can be reduced with hydrazine sulfate to the trivalent state and separated by distilling the arsenic as the trichloride.[9] Both distillate and residue are titrated with bromate.

[1] Wehber, P., *Angew. Chem.,* **66,** 271 (1954).

[2] Hume, D. N., Kolthoff, I. M., *Anal. Chim. Acta,* **16,** 415 (1957).

* Lang, R., and Gottlieb, S., *Z. anal. Chem.,* **104,** 1 (1936).

[3] Tribalat, S., *Anal. Chim. Acta.,* **1,** 149 (1947).

[4] Main, A. R., *Anal. Chem.,* **26,** 1507 (1954).

[5] Cooke, W. D., Hazel, F., and McNabb, W. M., *Anal. Chim. Acta,* **3,** 656 (1949).

[6] Shatko, P. P., *Zhur. Anal. Khim.,* **7,** 242 (1952).

[7] Sloviter, H. A., McNabb, W. M., and Wagner, E. C., *Ind. Eng. Chem., Anal. Ed.,* **13,** 890 (1941).

[8] Schulek, E., and von Villecz, P., *Z. anal. Chem.,* **76,** 81 (1929).

[9] Luke, C. L., *Ind. Eng. Chem., Anal. Ed.,* **15,** 626 (1943).

Hydriodic acid, containing hypophosphorous acid, can be used to reduce sulfates quantitatively to hydrogen sulfide, which can be distilled and determined by the iodine method.[1]

Hypophosphorous acid and hypophosphites are strong reducing agents. Arsenate and arsenite are reduced to elemental arsenic,[2,3] Fe(III) to Fe(II),[*] Sn(IV) to Sn(II),[†] Ge(IV) to Ge(II),[‡] and Se(IV) and Te(IV) to the elements.[4]

Metallic Reductants. Metals are used as reducing agents in several forms, including sheet, wire, powder, and shot; as reductor columns and as liquid amalgams. Important considerations for the choice of reductant are the selectivity of the reducing action, which is determined largely by the electrode potential of the metal–metal ion couple, and the method of removal of excess reducing agent, which is determined largely by the physical form of the metal. Occasionally, as with powdered aluminum,[5] the excess is simply dissolved in acid. More often it is physically separated by filtration or by the use of reductor columns or liquid amalgams.

Reductor Columns. The *zinc reductor,* commonly known as the *Jones*[6] *reductor,* is generally prepared from amalgamated zinc. The addition of mercury does not affect the standard potential of the Zn^{++}-Zn couple[7] (-0.76 volt) as long as solid zinc is present. However, the rate of reduction depends on the concentration of zinc at the surface of the amalgam.[8] With relatively strong oxidants, e.g., Fe(III) and Ce(IV), which are reduced by mercury, a mercury content of 1 or even 5 per cent may be used at high acid concentrations to control the rate of hydrogen evolution. With weaker oxidants, the mercury content should be minimized to avoid retarding the reduction reaction.

Zinc is relatively nonselective as a reducing agent because of its negative potential. Examination of a table of standard potentials reveals that the following reductions are to be expected for some of the common metals: Fe(III) → Fe(II); Cr(III) → Cr(II); Ti(IV) → Ti(III); V(V) → V(II). The reduction of U(VI) to U(III) is only partially complete, as would be expected from the highly reducing character of the

[1] Luke, *Ind. Eng. Chem., Anal. Ed.,* **15,** 602 (1943).

[2] Kolthoff, I. M., and Amdur, E., *Ind. Eng. Chem., Anal. Ed.,* **12,** 177 (1940).

[3] Haslam, J., and Wilkinson, N. T., *Analyst,* **78,** 390 (1953).

[*] Sastri, M. N., and Radhakrishnamurti, C., *Z. anal. Chem.,* **147,** 16 (1955).

[†] Evans, B. S., *Analyst,* **56,** 171 (1931); Evans, B. S., and Higgs, D. G., *ibid.,* **69,** 201 (1944).

[‡] Ivanov-Emin, B. N., *Zavodskaya Lab.,* **13,** 161 (1947); *Chem. Abstr.,* **42,** 480 (1948).

[4] Evans, *Analyst,* **63,** 874 (1938).

[5] Riegel, E. R., and Schwartz, R. O., *Anal. Chem.,* **24,** 1803 (1952); **26,** 410 (1954).

[6] Jones, C., *Trans. Inst. Mining Engrs. London,* **17,** 411 (1888–1889).

[7] Clayton, W. J., and Vosburgh, W. C., *J. Am. Chem. Soc.,* **58,** 2093 (1936).

[8] Stone, H. W., and Hume, D. N., *Ind. Eng. Chem., Anal. Ed.,* **11,** 598 (1939).

U(IV)-U(III) couple ($E° = -0.61$ volt). Commonly, air oxidation to U(IV) is carried out before the titration to U(VI). It might be expected from the standard potentials ($E° = -0.44$, -0.28, and -0.25 volt, respectively) that Fe(II), Co(II), and Ni(II) would be displaced as the metals. However, these reduction processes are highly irreversible (cf. Chap. 16) and do not proceed at appreciable rates. The more noble metals (Cu, Ag, Hg, Sb, Bi) are displaced from solution.

There have been reports of the formation of hydrogen peroxide by the reduction of atmospheric oxygen. Burdick[1] found peroxide only when water, and not acid, was used as the solvent in the zinc reductor. Lundell and Knowles[2] showed, in fact, that hydrogen peroxide is completely destroyed by zinc reduction in acid solution. On the other hand, Sill and Peterson[3] found hydrogen peroxide especially when the zinc was heavily amalgamated and air bubbles were passed rapidly through the column. With a lead reductor, much greater amounts of peroxide were found. Traces of hydrogen peroxide have also been found when a silver reductor was used in the presence of air. Particularly when small amounts of iron are being determined, the dissolved air should be removed with hydrogen[4] or carbon dioxide.[5]

The *silver reductor*, often called the *Walden reductor*,[6] is much more selective than zinc as a reducing agent. A hydrochloric acid solution is always used. The reduction potential varies with the concentration of chloride; therefore, the acid concentration is more critical than it is with the zinc reductor. From the standard potential

$$\text{AgCl} + \text{e}^- \rightleftharpoons \text{Ag} + \text{Cl}^- \qquad E° = 0.222 \text{ volt}$$

it can be inferred that, in 1 M hydrochloric acid ($a_{Cl^-} \cong 1$), the reductions Fe(III) $\rightarrow$ Fe(II) and U(VI) $\rightarrow$ U(IV) should be quantitative, whereas Cr(III) and Ti(IV) should not be reduced. These expectations are fully realized. From the standard potential of the V(IV)-V(III) couple (0.36 volt), considerable reduction of vanadium to the trivalent state would be expected. However, Lingane and Meites[7] found that very little V(III) is formed because the reaction is slow. For some reductions, the product depends on the acid concentration. In 2 M hydrochloric acid, Mo(VI) is reduced to Mo(V); in 4 M hydrochloric acid, it is reduced to

[1] Burdick, W. L., *J. Am. Chem. Soc.*, **48**, 1179 (1926).

[2] Lundell, G. E. F., and Knowles, H. B., *Ind. Eng. Chem.*, **16**, 723 (1924).

[3] Sill, C. W., and Peterson, H. E., *Anal, Chem.*, **24**, 1175 (1952).

[4] Fryling, C. F., and Tooley, F. V., *J. Am. Chem. Soc.*, **58**, 826 (1936).

[5] Miller, C. C., and Chalmers, R. A., *Analyst*, **77**, 2 (1952).

[6] Walden, G. H., Jr., Hammett, L. P., and Edmonds, S. M., *J. Am. Chem. Soc.*, **56**, 57 (1934).

[7] Lingane, J. J., and Meites, L., Jr., *J. Am. Chem. Soc.*, **69**, 277 (1947).

Mo(III).* For copper, a high acid concentration favors the formation of the soluble Cu(I) complex rather than insoluble CuCl,

$$CuCl + Cl^- \rightleftharpoons CuCl_2^- \qquad K = 6.5 \times 10^{-2}$$

The potential of the Cu(II)-Cu(I) couple

$$Cu^{++} + e^- + 2Cl^- \rightleftharpoons CuCl_2^- \qquad E^\circ = 0.464 \text{ volt}$$

is increased by increasing the chloride concentration, as is evident from the Nernst equation. Birnbaum and Edmonds[1] recommended reducing in 2 M HCl and passing the reduced solution directly into a solution of Fe(III) to avoid air oxidation. For the reduction of U(VI) to U(IV), the acid concentration was 4 N and the temperature was raised to 60 to 90°C.

The *lead reductor* ($E^\circ = -0.13$ volt) was proposed by Treadwell,[2] but did not gain popularity, mainly because the use of sulfuric acid solutions caused the formation of a film of lead sulfate. However, Cooke, Hazel, and McNabb,[3] showed that, if hydrochloric acid in concentrations greater than 2.5 N is used, no lead sulfate film forms even if high concentrations of sulfuric acid are present. The most important application of the lead reductor is in the reduction of U(VI) to U(IV).[†‡] Its advantages over the zinc reductor lie mainly in reduction of uranium to a definite oxidation state and in avoiding certain interferences. As compared with the silver reductor, the lead reductor has the advantage of achieving quantitative reduction of uranium at room temperature and over a wide range of acid concentrations.

The *cadmium reductor* has been used by Treadwell[4] as a substitute for zinc. An interesting application was the reduction of chlorate to chloride. Perchlorate was reduced to chloride only in the presence of a small amount of titanium ion as the catalyst. After carefully oxidizing the Ti(III) with permanganate, Treadwell determined the chloride by the Volhard method.

Various other reductor columns, including bismuth, antimony, nickel, copper, tin, and iron have been suggested, but have not received wide acceptance.

Liquid Amalgams. The use of liquid amalgams as quantitative reducing agents has been developed largely by several Japanese investigators. The early work has been reviewed in detail by Stephen.[5]

* Birnbaum, N., and Walden, G. H., Jr., *J. Am. Chem. Soc.*, **60**, 64 (1938).
[1] Birnbaum and Edmonds, *Ind. Eng. Chem., Anal. Ed.*, **12**, 155 (1940).
[2] Treadwell, W. D., *Helv. Chim. Acta*, **5**, 732 (1922).
[3] Cooke, W. D., Hazel, F., and McNabb, W. M., *Anal. Chem.*, **22**, 654 (1950).
† *Ibid.*
‡ Sill and Peterson, *op. cit.*
[4] Treadwell, *Helv. Chim. Acta*, **4**, 551 (1921); **5**, 732, 806 (1922).
[5] Stephen, W. I., *Ind. Chemist*, **29**, 31, 79, 128, 169 (1953).

For metals such as zinc, cadmium, lead, and bismuth, the potentials of the liquid amalgams do not differ widely from those of the solid metals, as is clear from the following considerations.[1,2] If solid metal is added to mercury, a solid phase eventually is formed, and at equilibrium both phases of the saturated, two-phase amalgam must of course have the same reduction potential. The emf of the cell

$$M(\text{solid}) \mid M^{n+} \mid M(\text{Hg}), \text{ 2-phase}$$

depends on the free energy of interaction between the metal M and mercury, and is small for most heavy metals; e.g., 0.003 volt for thallium, 0.006 volt for lead, 0.051 volt for cadmium and 0.000 volt for zinc. For the alkali metals, the emf is much greater, *viz.*, 0.780 volt for sodium and 1.001 volt for potassium,[3] indicating that the amalgams are much weaker reducing agents than the pure metals. Of course, the potential varies as the liquid amalgam is diluted, in accordance with the Nernst equation for a concentration cell. However, the potential change upon dilution is only $0.0591/n$ volts for a tenfold change in concentration (neglecting activity coefficients), which is negligible from the analytical viewpoint.

Interesting new applications of liquid amalgams have been suggested by Scribner and Reilley[4] in conjunction with EDTA titrations of metal ions. A liquid amalgam can be used essentially as a controlled-potential reductor. The amount of metal ion entering solution from the amalgam is determined by EDTA titration, which in effect substitutes for a coulometer in integrating the total amount of reduction that has occurred. The principle can be applied both to inorganic and to organic systems. For example, p-nitrophenol was reduced to p-aminophenol by shaking a deoxygenated solution in an acetate buffer for 5 min with a liquid zinc amalgam. The amount of zinc ions produced, as shown by titration with EDTA, corresponded to 5.96 electrons per molecule of p-nitrophenol, as compared with the theoretical value of 6.

In the early Japanese work, amalgams were prepared by heating appropriate amounts of the reducing metal with mercury, filtering off any solid phase, and using this to replenish the amalgam as needed. Most amalgams can be prepared conveniently by electrolysis, a method which would be particularly advantageous when the reducing metal is not available in a form of high purity. A special form of separatory funnel, allowing the amalgam to be drawn off from the reduced solution and permitting the addition of titrant without access of air, was generally

[1] Lingane, *J. Am. Chem. Soc.*, **61**, 2099 (1939).
[2] Von Stackelberg, M., *Z. Elektrochem.*, **45**, 466 (1939).
[3] Lingane, *op. cit.*
[4] Scribner, W. G., and Reilley, C. N., *Anal. Chem.*, **30**, 1452 (1958).

used in the early work.[1] More recently, Smith and Kurtz[2] devised a titration flask with a raised bottom and a gas-entry tube. By addition of carbon tetrachloride or chloroform the reduced solution was separated from the liquid amalgam, and the titration could be carried out without draining off the amalgam. An inert atmosphere could be introduced through the gas-entry tube.

The most important liquid amalgams are those of lead and bismuth, although several other metals, e.g., zinc, cadmium, and tin may be used.

Lead amalgam ($E = -0.13$ volt) is best used in relatively high concentrations of hydrochloric acid to prevent undue separation of lead chloride. Among the reductions that have been described[3] are $Fe(III) \rightarrow Fe(II)$; $U(VI) \rightarrow U(IV)$; $V(V) \rightarrow V(II)$; $Ti(IV) \rightarrow Ti(III)$; $Mo(VI) \rightarrow Mo(III)$; $W(VI) \rightarrow W(III)$.

Bismuth amalgam is a weaker reducing agent ($E = 0.32$ volt) and reduces $V(V)$ only to $V(IV)$. Molybdenum(VI) is reduced to $Mo(V)$ or (III) depending upon the acidity. Tungsten(VI) is reduced to $W(V)$. The other reductions are the same as for lead amalgam.

Sodium amalgam is a very strong reducing agent ($E \cong -1.9$ volt), of interest mainly because it accomplishes rapid reduction at room temperature and does not introduce heavy metal cations into solution.

Other Metals. *Mercury* can be used as a reducing agent of about the same potential as silver in the presence of chloride ions. Furman and Murray[4] showed that hydrogen peroxide is formed by reduction of oxygen in the presence of chloride and, therefore, recommended the rigorous exclusion of air. In 2 to 3.5 N hydrochloric acid, the reductions $Mo(VI) \rightarrow Mo(V)$, $Fe(III) \rightarrow Fe(II)$, $V(V) \rightarrow V(IV)$, and $Sb(V) \rightarrow Sb(III)$ were performed. In 7 to 10 N hydrochloric acid, Caley and Rogers[5] reduced $U(VI)$ to $U(IV)$, but the reduction was not quite complete (the results were 0.4 to 0.7 per cent low).

The idea of using a *low-melting alloy*, which can be removed from solution after solidification, has been studied by several workers. Popov[6] used Wood's metal to reduce chlorate, bromate, and iodate to the corresponding halide, which was determined by the Volhard method. Kaneko and Nemoto[7] had used the same principle in applying a low-melting, 15 per cent cadmium amalgam reductor. For the reduction of

[1] Someya, K., *Sci. Repts. Tôhoku Imp. Univ.*, **14**, 47, 235 (1926); **15**, 399, 417, 421, 515 (1926); **16**, 521 (1927).

[2] Smith and Kurtz, *Ind. Eng. Chem., Anal. Ed.*, **14**, 854 (1942).

[3] Someya, *op. cit.*

[4] Furman, N. H., and Murray, W. M., Jr., *J. Am. Chem. Soc.*, **58**, 429, 1689, 1843 (1936).

[5] Caley, E. R., and Rogers, L. B., *J. Am. Chem. Soc.*, **68**, 2202 (1946).

[6] Popov, P. G., *Ukrain. Khem. Zhur.*, **10**, 428 (1935).

[7] Kaneko, S., and Nemoto, C., *J. Soc. Chem. Ind. Japan*, **35**, 185 (1932).

metals, this procedure is not experimentally attractive, because of the difficulty of working in the absence of air.[1]

Finely divided *copper*[2] has been used as a reducing agent for Fe(III). Activated copper,[3] prepared by reducing CuO with hydrogen, was used to displace cadmium but not zinc from a cyanide solution. It should be noted that copper is a strong reducing agent ($E^{o\prime} = -1.09$ volts) in cyanide solution. Its formal potential lies between those of zinc (-1.26 volts) and cadmium (-0.90 volt). Various heavy metals are likewise displaced (Pb, Bi, Sn, Ag, Hg).

Nickel shot has been used to reduce Fe(III) selectively in the presence of Sn(IV).* After the Fe(II) is titrated, the nickel is returned to the vessel, and Sn(IV) is reduced upon heating. After filtration, the resulting Sn(II) is titrated with iodine.

18-3. Redox Resins

The use of electron exchange resins, or *redox resins*, was originated by Cassidy,[4] who prepared a polymerized vinyl hydroquinone that could be oxidized and reduced. The first product was not entirely satisfactory because it suffered a loss of activity when it was reduced and reoxidized. The material was later[5] shown to be a low-molecular-weight polymer, largely the dimer and trimer, which was nonuniform in behavior. By preparing high-molecular-weight polymers and copolymers of vinyl hydroquinone, resins were prepared that could be oxidized by iodine. The oxidized resins released iodine from iodide solutions.

Manecke[6] described the preparation and properties of several resins prepared by the condensation of hydroquinone, pyrogallol, resorcinol, or pyrocatechol with phenol and formaldehyde. The resins could be oxidized by ferric chloride, dichromate, or cerium(IV) sulfate, and reduced with titanium(III) chloride or hydrazine. The important properties that characterize a redox resin are (1) its total capacity as an oxidant or reductant, typically of the order of 7 milliequivalents per gram for a resin prepared from hydroquinone, phenol, and formaldehyde; (2) the break-through capacity, which is the amount of oxidation (or reduction) performed per unit weight of resin before the appearance of appreciable reduced (or oxidized) form in the solution emerging from the column; (3) the formal oxidation potential of the resin.

[1] Smith, G. F., and Wilcox, C. S., *Ind. Eng. Chem., Anal. Ed.*, **9,** 419 (1937).

[2] Kürschner, K., and Scharrer, K., *Z. anal. Chem.*, **68,** 1 (1926).

[3] Bryson, A., and Lenzer-Lowy, S., *Analyst*, **78,** 299 (1953); **79,** 636 (1954).

* Simon, A. C., Miller, P. S., Edwards, J. C. and Clardy, F. B., *Anal. Chem.* **18,** 496 (1946).

[4] Cassidy, H. G., *J. Am. Chem. Soc.*, **71,** 402 (1949).

[5] Egrin, M., and Cassidy, H. G., *Ann. N.Y. Acad. Sci.*, **57,** 79 (1954).

[6] Manecke, G., *Z. Elektrochem.*, **57,** 189 (1953); **58,** 363, 369 (1954).

The break-through capacity was found to vary with a number of experimental variables, including the concentration of solution, the grain size of the resin, the temperature, and the rate of flow. In general, the oxidation and reduction reactions appear to be relatively slow; in fact, this slowness constitutes an important limitation on the use of the resins that have been prepared up to this time.

The oxidation potential of a resin was expressed by Manecke in the form of a Nernst equation

$$E = E^{\circ\prime} + \frac{RT}{nF} \ln \frac{X}{a - X} \tag{18-1}$$

where $E^{\circ\prime}$ = formal oxidation potential, corresponding to resin half oxidized and half reduced

a = total redox capacity of resin

X = amount of resin in oxidized form

Manecke measured the potential E by measuring the potential of a redox couple in solution which was in equilibrium with the resin and which, therefore, had the same oxidation potential. Equilibrium was found to be slowly attained, and the potential varied to some extent with the nature of the potential-determining couple in solution. Equation (18-1) cannot be applied strictly, because in effect $E^{\circ\prime}$ varies with $X/(a - X)$, the ratio of the amounts of resin in the oxidized and reduced forms. This is equivalent to saying that not every site is equally strongly oxidizing or reducing.

Although redox resins are interesting in principle, few applications appear promising, at least at the present state of their development. Manecke[1] studied the removal of oxygen from solution and found that the principal limitations are the slow reaction rate and the limited range of potentials available. The hydroquinone-phenol-formaldehyde condensation product, for example, has a formal potential $E^{\circ\prime}$ of 0.65 volt in 1 N sulfuric acid, which is comparable to the standard potential E° = 0.699 for hydroquinone at pH = 0. The potential varies with the state of oxidation; therefore, a redox resin cannot be regarded as a particularly selective oxidant or reductant.

Probably the most promising type of application is the quantitative oxidation or reduction of trace constituents without the introduction of oxidation or reduction products of the reagent. An interesting type of possible future development would be redox resins of a wider range of potentials based upon inorganic coordination complexes as the resin phase.

[1] Manecke, *Angew. Chem.*, **67**, 613 (1955).

PROBLEMS

18-1. A sample containing Fe(III) and V(V) is made up to 250 ml. A 25-ml aliquot is passed through a zinc reductor into Fe(III) solution and titrated with standard dichromate, requiring 43.21 ml of 0.1000 N solution. Another 25-ml portion is titrated after passage through a silver reductor, requiring 23.45 ml of 0.1000 N Ce(IV). Calculate the vanadium and iron content in the sample. *Ans.* 1.007 g V, 0.206 g Fe.

18-2. Prepare a chart showing the reduced forms of Fe, Ti, V, and Cr using amalgams of zinc, bismuth, lead, and mercury as reducing agents in HCl solutions of appropriate concentrations. Show in principle how the four reductants could be used to perform an analysis of a sample containing the four constituents.

18-3. Enlarge the chart prepared in Prob. 18-2 by adding the reduced forms of U, Mo, W, Cu; and cadmium amalgam and silver as reducing agents.

18-4. Describe how to perform each of the following operations, giving the appropriate equations:

  a. Reduce permanganate without reducing dichromate or V(V).

  b. Reduce V(V) to V(IV) without reducing V(IV), Ti(IV), or Cr(III).

  c. Oxidize V(IV) without oxidizing Mn(II) or Cr(III).

  d. Oxidize Fe(II) without oxidizing Cr(III) or V(IV).

  e. Oxidize Mn(II) to Mn(III), using dichromate.

19. Permanganate as an Oxidant

Permanganate ranks as one of the earliest titrimetric reagents, having been introduced by Margueritte[1] in 1846 for the titration of ferrous iron produced by reduction with metallic zinc.

19-1. Half-reactions

In acid solution, the permanganate ion is a strong oxidant, as shown by the potential

$$MnO_4^- + 8H^+ + 5e^- \rightarrow Mn^{++} + 4H_2O \qquad E° = 1.51 \text{ volts} \qquad (19\text{-}1)$$

Reaction (19-1) is not a reversible half reaction, and its potential is not subject to direct measurement, because permanganate and Mn(II) react slowly in acid solution [see Eq. (19-10)].

By taking proper precautions (especially by using properly prepared, pure manganese dioxide) it is possible to measure the potential corresponding to the following half-reaction in acid solution:[2,3]

$$MnO_2 + 4H^+ + 2e^- \rightleftharpoons Mn^{++} + 2H_2O \qquad E° = 1.23 \text{ volts} \qquad (19\text{-}2)$$

In alkaline solution, the reversible potential[4] of the half-reaction

$$MnO_4^- + 2H_2O + 3e^- \rightleftharpoons MnO_2 + 4OH^- \qquad E° = 0.588 \text{ volt} \qquad (19\text{-}3)$$

can be directly measured. The standard potential in acid solution

$$MnO_4^- + 4H^+ + 3e^- \rightleftharpoons MnO_2 + 2H_2O \qquad E° = 1.695 \text{ volts} \qquad (19\text{-}4)$$

can be calculated from the pH-dependence of (19-3) but cannot be measured directly, because manganese dioxide catalyzes the decomposi-

---

[1] Margueritte, F., *Ann. chim. et phys.*, [3] **18**, 244 (1846).
[2] Hutchison, A. W., *J. Am. Chem. Soc.*, **69**, 3051 (1947).
[3] Wadsley, A. D., and Walkley, A., *Trans. Electrochem. Soc.*, **95**, 11 (1949).
[4] Andrews, L. V., and Brown, D. J., *J. Am. Chem. Soc.*, **57**, 254 (1935).

tion of permanganate. The standard potential of (19-1) can be calculated readily by combining (19-2) and (19-4).

In neutral, slightly acidic, or moderately alkaline solution permanganate is reduced quantitatively to manganese dioxide [Eqs. (19-3) and (19-4)]. Permanganate is a much weaker oxidant in alkaline than in acid solution, but many reducing agents likewise become stronger in alkaline solution, and so permanganate is an effective and versatile oxidant.

In strongly alkaline solution, permanganate is reduced to manganate

$$MnO_4^- + e^- \rightleftharpoons MnO_4^= \qquad E^\circ = 0.564 \text{ volt} \qquad (19\text{-}5)$$

The electron exchange between manganate and permanganate is measurable but fairly rapid.[1] No direct information seems to be available on the exchange current at electrode surfaces. Stamm[2] took advantage of the insolubility of barium manganate to stabilize the manganate ion and to increase the oxidation potential.

Manganese(III) in the absence of a complexing agent is a very strong oxidant. Latimer estimates[3]

$$Mn^{3+} + e^- \rightleftharpoons Mn^{++} \qquad E^\circ \cong 1.5 \text{ volts} \qquad (19\text{-}6)$$

Taube[4] estimated the value $E^\circ = 1.6$ volts and Vetter and Manecke[5] determined $E^{\circ\prime} = 1.488$ volts in 15 N sulfuric acid, in which weak complexes of Mn(III) are no doubt formed.

In the absence of complexing agents, Mn(III) is unstable with respect to Mn(II) and manganese dioxide:

$$2Mn^{3+} + 2H_2O \rightarrow MnO_2 + Mn^{++} + 4H^+ \qquad \Delta F^\circ = -26 \text{ kcal} \qquad (19\text{-}7)$$

In the presence of pyrophosphate in acid solution, Mn(III) is greatly stabilized, as shown by the half-reaction[6]

$$Mn(H_2P_2O_7)_3^{3-} + 2H^+ + e^- \rightleftharpoons Mn(H_2P_2O_7)_2^=$$
$$+ H_4P_2O_7 \qquad E^\circ \cong 1.15 \text{ volts} \qquad (19\text{-}8)$$

Fluoride ion also exerts a strong stabilizing action on Mn(III).

[1] Sheppard, J. C., and Wahl, A. C., *J. Am. Chem. Soc.*, **79**, 1020 (1957).

[2] Stamm, H., "Die Reduktion von Permanganat zu Manganat abs Grundlage eines neuen Titrationsverfahrens," Akademische Verlag, Halle, 1927.

[3] Latimer, W. H., "Oxidation Potentials," 2d ed., p. 237, Prentice-Hall, Inc. Englewood Cliffs, N.J., 1952.

[4] Taube, H., *J. Am. Chem. Soc.*, **70**, 3928 (1948).

[5] Vetter, K. J., and Manecke, G., *Z. physik. Chem. Leipzig*, **195**, 270 (1950).

[6] Watters, J. I., and Kolthoff, I. M., *J. Am. Chem. Soc.*, **70**, 2455 (1948).

In 15 N sulfuric acid, the formal potential of the couple Mn(IV)-Mn(III) was evaluated[1] as 1.052 volts; the low value indicates that relatively strong Mn(IV) complexes must be present.

19-2. Stability of Aqueous Solutions

Pure solutions of permanganate are surprisingly stable. Solutions have been stored without great deterioration for 1 to 3 years.[2-4] Tenth-normal or stronger solutions under careful storage in diffuse daylight with protection from dust change less than 1 part in 2,000 in several months.[5] Solutions 0.01 N or weaker should be prepared freshly by dilution and standardized each day.

Permanganate is inherently unstable in the presence of Mn(II), because of the "Guyard reaction,"

$$2MnO_4^- + 3Mn^{++} + 2H_2O \rightarrow 5MnO_2 + 4H^+ \tag{19-9}$$

which is slow in acid solution.[6,7] The rate of reaction (19-9) increases with decreasing acidity until, in a neutral solution, it is essentially instantaneous. In fact, the classical Volhard method for manganese,[8] in which Mn(II) is titrated with permanganate in the presence of zinc oxide, is based on the Guyard reaction. On the basis of radioactive exchange measurements, Adamson[9] postulated that the mechanism involves a rapid "preequilibrium" between permanganate and Mn(II) involving two intermediate species

$$3Mn^{++} + MnO_4^- + 6H^+ \rightleftharpoons 3Mn^{3+} + MnO^{++} + 3H_2O \tag{19-10}$$

In the absence of solid manganese dioxide, the hydrolysis rate of the ion MnO^{++} is very slow and rate-determining:

$$MnO^{++} + H_2O \rightarrow MnO_2(solid) + 2H^+ \tag{19-11}$$

the Mn(III) produced in (19-10) disproportionates to give Mn(II) and (IV). Once solid manganese dioxide is formed, the rate of (19-11) increases enormously, and the reaction becomes a more complex heterogeneous reaction.

[1] Vetter and Manecke, Z. physik. Chem. Leipzig, **195**, 337 (1950).

[2] Bruhus, G., Chemiker Ztg., **47**, 613 (1923).

[3] Halverson, J. O., and Bergeim, O., Ind. Eng. Chem. **10**, 119 (1918).

[4] Kato, T., J. Chem. Soc. Japan, **48**, 17 (1927).

[5] Hillebrand, W. F., Lundell, G. E. F., Bright, H. A., and Hoffman, J. I., "Applied Inorganic Analysis," 2d ed., John Wiley & Sons, Inc., New York, 1953.

[6] Polissar, M. J., J. Phys. Chem., **39**, 1057 (1935); J. Am. Chem. Soc., **58**, 1372 (1936).

[7] Tompkins, F. C., Trans. Faraday Soc., **38**, 131 (1942).

[8] Volhard, J., Ann. Chem. Liebigs, **198**, 318 (1879).

[9] Adamson, A. W., J. Phys. Colloid Chem., **55**, 293 (1951).

Waterbury, Hayes, and Martin,[1] on the other hand, postulate that manganate is the product of the initial equilibrium

$$Mn(II) + MnO_4^- \rightleftharpoons Mn(III) + MnO_4^= \qquad (19\text{-}12)$$

and that manganese dioxide is formed from the manganate ion

$$Mn(II) + MnO_4^= \rightarrow 2Mn(IV) \qquad (19\text{-}13)$$

Even in the absence of Mn(II), the decomposition

$$4MnO_4^- + 2H_2O \rightarrow 4MnO_2 + 3O_2 + 4OH^- \qquad (19\text{-}14)$$

is catalyzed by solid manganese dioxide, as has been known for a long time.[2] Presumably the oxygen is formed by a mechanism similar to that postulated for the decomposition of strongly alkaline permanganate, under conditions such that manganate is formed.[3]

$$4MnO_4^- + 4OH^- \rightarrow 4MnO_4^= + 2H_2O + O_2 \qquad (19\text{-}15)$$

From heavy-oxygen isotope experiments, it is known that the oxygen comes exclusively from the solvent. A mechanism involving the free radicals and ions $\cdot OH$, $\cdot O^-$, HO_2^-, and $\cdot O_2^-$ accounts for the evolution of oxygen in one-electron steps such that the permanganate ion is involved only in accepting an electron. These intermediates are, no doubt, involved in many alkaline permanganate oxidations.[4]

19-3. Preparation of Standard Permanganate

In view of the catalytic action of solid manganese dioxide toward decomposition of permanganate, it is essential to eliminate all possible sources of this contaminant.

According to Blum,[5] a standard permanganate solution can be prepared determinately by dissolving weighed portions of recrystallized pure potassium permanganate in water that has been specially purified by distillation from alkaline permanganate. Reagent-grade potassium permanganate usually contains a trace of manganese dioxide, and any organic matter present in the water or on the surface of the storage vessel would reduce permanganate to produce it. For these reasons, it is common practice[6] to heat a freshly prepared solution to boiling and

[1] Waterbury, G. R., Hayes, A. M., and Martin, D. S., Jr., *J. Am. Chem. Soc.*, **74**, 15 (1952).

[2] Morse, H. N., Hopkins, A. J., and Walker, M. S., *Am. Chem. J.*, **18**, 401 (1896).

[3] Symons, M. C. R., *J. Chem. Soc.*, **1953**, 3956; **1954**, 3676.

[4] *Ibid.*

[5] Blum, W., *J. Am. Chem. Soc.*, **34**, 1379 (1912).

[6] Kato, T., *J. Chem. Soc. Japan*, **48**, 408 (1927).

digest it near the boiling point for an hour or so before filtering the solution through a nonreducing filtering medium such as fritted glass. Alternatively, the solution may be allowed to stand for several days at room temperature before filtration. The storage vessel should be a glass-stoppered bottle carefully freed from grease and prior deposits of manganese dioxide. Solutions should be protected from unnecessary exposure to light. Diffuse daylight causes no appreciable decomposition, but direct sunlight decomposes even pure solutions readily.[1] Acidic and alkaline solutions are less stable than neutral ones.

Permanganate is often used without an indicator, since a 10^{-5} N solution has a barely visible pink color. However, the common redox indicators are considerably more sensitive than this, and it is advantageous to use an indicator, particularly if 0.01 N or more dilute permanganate is used. Sometimes it is preferable to add the indicator just before the end point to avoid its oxidation.

19-4. Standardization against Sodium Oxalate

Pure sodium oxalate, suitable for use as a primary standard, is available from the Bureau of Standards. Although neutral solutions of the salt are not very stable, it has been reported[2,3] that solutions prepared in 0.1 M perchloric acid are stable upon storage.

If permanganate solution is added drop by drop to an acidic oxalate solution, the first drop is decolorized very slowly. During the course of the titration, the reaction rate becomes progressively more rapid, owing to the catalytic effect of the Mn(II) produced in the reaction.

Many kinetic studies have been made to elucidate the mechanism, which is discussed in detail by Adler and Noyes.[4] If manganous ion is present initially, the mechanism involves the rapid oxidation of Mn(II) in the presence of oxalate to form oxalate complexes of Mn(III) according to the equation

$$MnO_4^- + 4Mn^{++} + 5nC_2O_4^= + 8H^+ \rightarrow 5Mn(C_2O_4)_n^{(3-2n)+} + 4H_2O$$

$$(19\text{-}16)$$

which takes place in several steps. The first step is the transfer of one electron to a monooxalate complex of Mn(II):

$$MnO_4^- + MnC_2O_4 \rightarrow MnO_4^= + MnC_2O_4^+ \qquad (19\text{-}17)$$

[1] Morse, Hopkins, and Walker, op. cit.
[2] Smith, G. F., and Duke, F. R., Ind. Eng. Chem., Anal. Ed., **13**, 558 (1941).
[3] Kochakian, C. D., and Fox, R. P., Ind. Eng. Chem., Anal. Ed., **16**, 762 (1944).
[4] Adler, J., and Noyes, R. M., J. Am. Chem. Soc., **77**, 2036 (1955).

The manganate ion, $MnO_4^=$, which would disproportionate in acid solution in the absence of reducing agent, is rapidly reduced to Mn(III):

$$Mn(VI) + Mn(II) \rightarrow 2Mn(IV)$$
$$Mn(IV) + Mn(II) \rightarrow 2Mn(III)$$

No significant concentrations of Mn(IV), (V), or (VI) could be detected in solutions containing both permanganate and Mn(III).

Manganese(III) forms oxalate complexes $Mn(C_2O_4)_n^{(3-2n)+}$ in which n may be 1, 2, or 3. They decompose slowly[1] to give Mn(II) and carbon dioxide:

$$2Mn(C_2O_4)_n^{(3-2n)+} \rightarrow 2Mn^{++} + (2n - 1)C_2O_4^= + 2CO_2 \quad (19\text{-}18)$$

The three complexes corresponding to $n = 1$, 2, and 3 are all involved in the decomposition, giving rise to complicated kinetic behavior. This reaction is actually composed of two steps:

$$Mn(C_2O_4)_n^{(3-2n)+} \rightarrow Mn^{++} + (n - 1)C_2O_4^= + CO_2 + CO_2^- \quad (19\text{-}19)$$
$$Mn(C_2O_4)_n^{(3-2n)+} + CO_2^- \rightarrow Mn^{++} + nC_2O_4^= + CO_2 \quad (19\text{-}20)$$

where $n = 1$, 2, or 3, and the first of these two steps is the rate-determining one.

If the concentration of Mn(II) is very low, as it is during the very early part of the titration, maganate can be reduced by oxalate to Mn(IV)

$$Mn(VI) + C_2O_4^= \rightarrow Mn(IV) + 2CO_2 \quad (19\text{-}21)$$

which is then reduced further to Mn(III)

$$2Mn(IV) + C_2O_4^= \rightarrow 2Mn(III) + 2CO_2 \quad (19\text{-}22)$$

The Mn(III) then decomposes slowly according to (19-19) and (19-20).

The mechanism is complicated further if oxygen of the air is present. Kolthoff[2] ascribed the appearance of hydrogen peroxide during the permanganate-oxalate titration to the reaction

$$O_2 + C_2O_4^= + 2H^+ \rightarrow H_2O_2 + 2CO_2 \quad (19\text{-}23)$$

in which 2 equivalents of hydrogen peroxide appear for 2 equivalents of oxalate. Thus, if no decomposition of hydrogen peroxide occurs, there is no noticeable result in the stoichiometry. To account for the effect of oxygen, Launer[3] suggested that oxygen reacts with the ion CO_2^- formed

[1] Taube, *J. Am. Chem. Soc.*, **70**, 1216 (1948).

[2] Kolthoff, *Z. anal. Chem.*, **64**, 185 (1924).

[3] Launer, H. F., *J. Am. Chem. Soc.*, **55**, 865 (1933).

in Eq. (19-19)

$$CO_2^- + O_2 \rightarrow O_2CO_2^- \tag{19-24}$$
$$O_2CO_2^- + Mn(II) + 2H^+ \rightarrow Mn(III) + CO_2 + H_2O_2 \tag{19-25}$$

Now if Eq. (19-19) is written

$$Mn(III) + C_2O_4^- \rightarrow Mn(II) + CO_2 + CO_2^- \tag{19-26}$$

The sum of Eqs. (19-24), (19-25), and (19-26) is, in effect, Eq. (19-23).

Kolthoff[1] has suggested an alternative mechanism, involving the free radical ions $C_2O_4^-$ and O_2^- in a sequence not involving manganese, which adds up to give Eq. (19-23). It should be mentioned that Eq. (19-19) or (19-26) could equally well be written to show the formation of $C_2O_4^-$ rather than $CO_2 + CO_2^-$. Taube[2] pointed out, however, that hydrogen peroxide is formed *even in the absence of oxygen*. This is best accounted for by the dimerization of the species HCO_2 ($= H^+ + CO_2^-$) or HC_2O_4 ($= H^+ + CO_2 + CO_2^-$) to form peroxydiformic acid or peroxydioxalic acid. Either of these acids can hydrolyze to form hydrogen peroxide.

Detailed studies of the effect of experimental conditions on the stoichiometry of the oxalate-permanganate reaction have been made by several investigators, notably Baxter and Zanetti,[3] McBride[4] and Kolthoff.[5] A serious source of error is loss of oxygen owing to decomposition of permanganate in local excess. Thus, depending upon temperature, rate of addition, rate of stirring, concentration of reagents, and acidity, there occurs a greater or lesser decomposition of permanganate. Tending to cancel this error are the errors due to decomposition of oxalic acid

$$H_2C_2O_4 \rightarrow CO + CO_2 + H_2O$$

which is promoted by the presence of manganous salts,[6] and the loss of oxygen due to decomposition of hydrogen peroxide, which becomes increasingly important at temperatures above 90°C. Hydrochloric acid in moderate concentration does not interfere at temperatures above 70°C, but at lower temperature too much permanganate is used.[7] Baxter and Frevert[8] presented evidence that this loss is due to hypochlorous acid rather than to chlorine and found that, at higher hydro-

[1] Kolthoff, I. M., and Belcher, R. (eds.), "Volumetric Analysis," vol. 3, p. 50, Interscience Publishers, Inc., New York, 1957.

[2] Taube, *loc. cit.*

[3] Baxter, G. P., and Zanetti, J. E., *Am. Chem. J.*, **33**, 500 (1905).

[4] McBride, R. S., *J. Am. Chem. Soc.*, **34**, 393 (1912).

[5] Kolthoff, *op. cit.*

[6] *Ibid.*

[7] Baxter and Zanetti, *op. cit.*

[8] Baxter, G. P., and Frevert, J. L., *Am. Chem. J.*, **34**, 109 (1905).

chloric acid concentrations, 0.3 per cent too much permanganate was consumed at 80 to 90°C. The error could be prevented by manganese(II) chloride or, better, by manganese(II) sulfate. The mechanism of this correction will be discussed in connection with the Fe(II) titration. Brasted[1] found that the concentration of sulfuric acid could be varied over wide limits (0.04 to 4 M) without causing appreciable error.

For many years, the procedure recommended for the standardization using oxalate has been to heat to 75 to 85°C* or 80 to 90°C,† to add the permanganate very slowly at first, swirling vigorously, and to add permanganate slowly enough so that the solution remains colorless throughout the titration. The rate of addition can be moderately rapid until the end point is approached. The solution temperature should be above 60°C at the end point.

Fowler and Bright,[2] after an accurate study of reaction variables, concluded that the most reproducible and accurate results could be obtained by a procedure involving the addition of about 90 per cent of the required amount of permanganate at room temperature at a specified and fairly rapid rate with moderate stirring. After a wait for the permanganate to be decolorized, the titration is finished by heating to a temperature of 55 to 60°C and titrating slowly until a faint permanent pink of permanganate is observed.

This procedure has been accurately compared with those using potassium iodide,[3] arsenious oxide,[4−7] and dichromate;[8] all authors agree that the results compare with other primary standards to within 1 part in 3,000. The older procedure of titrating a hot solution slowly leads to the consumption of 0.2 to 0.4 per cent too little permanganate.

It should be noted that the excellent results are the result of cancellation of positive and negative errors, both of which are, however, minimized by careful control of reaction conditions. If the permanganate is to be used for the determination of any reducing agent other than oxalate and if sodium oxalate is to be used as the primary standard, the Fowler and Bright method is clearly the method of choice.

[1] Brasted, R. C., *Anal. Chem.*, **25**, 673 (1953).

* Kolthoff, *op. cit.*

† McBride, *op. cit.*

[2] Fowler, R. M., and Bright, H. A., *J. Research Natl. Bur. Standards*, **15**, 493 (1935).

[3] Kolthoff, I. M., Laitinen, H. A., and Lingane, J. J., *J. Am. Chem. Soc.*, **59**, 429 (1937)

[4] *Ibid.*

[5] Bright, *Ind. Eng. Chem., Anal. Ed.*, **9**, 577 (1937).

[6] Metzler, D. E., Myers, R. J., and Swift, E. H., *Ind. Eng. Chem. Anal. Ed.*, **16**, 625 (1944).

[7] Duggan, R. E., *J. Assoc. Offic. Agr. Chemists*, **31**, 568 (1948).

[8] Kato, *op. cit.*

Arsenious oxide, however, is available in a higher state of purity than sodium oxalate (99.99 per cent as compared with 99.95 per cent, for Bureau of Standards samples), and the reaction appears to be inherently less subject to sources of error.

On the other hand, if oxalate is to be determined, it is often not convenient to use the room-temperature procedure for unknown amounts of oxalate. If this is the case, it is advisable to standardize against sodium oxalate at 70 to 80°C, using the same procedure in the standardization as in the analysis.

19-5. Standardization against Arsenic(III) Oxide

The direct titration of arsenious acid in acid solution does not proceed readily without a catalyst, probably because of the stabilization of Mn(III) by complex formation with arsenate. Lang[1] found that traces of iodine compounds catalyze the reaction and permit the use of pure arsenious oxide as a primary standard for permanganate.

Kolthoff, Laitinen, and Lingane,[2] using potassium iodate (1 drop of 0.0025 M solution), found that the potentiometric end point coincided with the visual end point, using ferroin, to within 0.01 per cent and that the accuracy, tested against pure potassium iodide, was within 0.02 per cent.

Bright[3] made an accurate comparison of the same titration with the Fowler and Bright[4] method using sodium oxalate, and concluded that the precision and accuracy were within 1 part in 3,000. Metzler, Myers, and Swift[5] found that iodine monochloride has the advantages of being more efficient as a catalyst than iodate and of avoiding any blank or uncertainty about final oxidation state that might be encountered in using other iodine compounds. It was shown that relatively large amounts of ICl could be added without error and that the accuracy, tested against the Fowler and Bright procedure, was within 1 part in 3,000.

The mechanism of the iodine monochloride catalysis has been explained by Swift[6] as being due to a rapid oxidation of arsenious acid by iodine monochloride

$$2ICl + H_3AsO_3 + H_2O \rightarrow I_2 + H_3AsO_4 + 2H^+ + 2Cl^-$$

[1] Lang, R., Z. anal. Chem., **45**, 649 (1906); **85**, 176 (1931); Z. anorg. u. allgem. Chem., **152**, 197 (1926).

[2] Kolthoff, Laitinen, and Lingane, op. cit.

[3] Bright, op. cit.

[4] Fowler and Bright, op. cit.

[5] Metzler, Myers, and Swift, op. cit.

[6] Swift, "Introductory Quantitative Analysis," p. 132, Prentice-Hall, Inc., Englewood Cliffs, N.J., 1950.

followed by a rapid reoxidation iodine to iodine monochloride by permanganate:

$$5I_2 + 2MnO_4^- + 10Cl^- + 16H^+ \rightarrow 10ICl + 2Mn^{++} + 8H_2O$$

19-6. Other Primary Standards

Pure electrolytic *iron* can be used as a primary standard[1,2] simply by dissolution in sulfuric acid to yield ferrous sulfate. However, special pains must be taken to avoid impurities (especially carbon, sulfur, and phosphorus), which may consume different amounts of permanganate depending upon the procedure used in dissolving the iron. Precautions must also be taken to avoid air oxidation of the ferrous sulfate.

Ferrous ammonium sulfate (Mohr's salt), $FeSO_4 \cdot (NH_4)_2SO_4 \cdot 6H_2O$, cannot be regarded as a reliable primary standard, because of the common presence of manganese, zinc, nickel, lead, and magnesium which cannot be removed by recrystallization.[3] It can, however, serve as a convenient secondary standard, if it is stored properly to avoid efflorescence. Ferrous ethylenediamine sulfate,[4] $Fe\{C_2H_4(NH_3)_2\}(SO_4)_2$ and ferrous propylenediamine sulfate,[5] $Fe\{C_3H_6(NH_3)_2\}(SO_4)_2$ appear to be fundamentally superior to Mohr's salt.

Potassium ferrocyanide, $K_4\{Fe(CN)_6\} \cdot 3H_2O$, is obtained readily in a pure state. It has the disadvantage of requiring a potentiometric end point or the use of an indicator, because of the pronounced color of ferricyanide at the end point.[6]

Potassium iodide, if specially prepared, is capable of high accuracy as a primary standard.[7] For most practical purposes, the analytical-reagent-quality product is sufficiently pure.[8] The potentiometric method must be used unless a reagent is added to take up the iodine. The methods of Andrews (ICl end point, Sec. 22-1), Lang (ICN end point), and Berg (acetone method) all yield results within 0.1 per cent with 0.1 N reagent.

19-7. Determination of Iron

One of the most important titrations by permanganate is that of Fe(II) in acid solution

$$5Fe^{++} + MnO_4^- + 8H^+ \rightarrow 5Fe^{3+} + Mn^{++} + 4H_2O \qquad (19\text{-}27)$$

[1] Fowler and Bright, *op. cit.*
[2] Moser, L., and Schöninger, W., *Z. anal. Chem.*, **70**, 235 (1927).
[3] Kolthoff, *Z. anal. Chem.*, **64**, 255 (1924).
[4] Caraway, K. P., and Oesper, R. E., *J. Chem. Educ.* **24**, 235 (1947).
[5] Nutten, A. J., *Anal. Chim. Acta*, **3**, 433 (1949).
[6] De Beer, E. J., and Hjort, A. M., *Ind. Eng. Chem., Anal. Ed.*, **7**, 120 (1935).
[7] Kolthoff, Laitinen, and Lingane, *op. cit.*
[8] Kolthoff and Laitinen, *J. Am. Chem. Soc.*, **61**, 1690 (1939).

In sulfuric acid solution, reaction (19-27) is rapid and quantitative.[1] Phosphoric acid is usually added to decolorize the ferric iron, which is pronounced in color, by formation of a colorless complex. The complex $Fe(HPO_4)^+$, of dissociation constant 4.4×10^{-10}, has been found to be the species involved.[2] Permanganate may be used as its own indicator, or, for a more sensitive end point, ferroin may be added. Whether phosphoric acid is present or not, the end point may be detected potentiometrically.

In many practical procedures, however, it is not convenient to titrate in sulfuric acid solution. For example, when stannous chloride or the silver reductor is used in the preliminary reduction of Fe(III) to Fe(II), hydrochloric acid is necessarily present. It has long been known that the iron-permanganate reaction gives high results in hydrochloric acid solution, the deviation increasing with increasing hydrochloric acid concentration. The error is relatively smaller the larger the amount of iron being titrated and the slower the titration.[3]

Zimmermann[4] showed that the error was decreased by the addition of manganese(II) sulfate, and Reinhardt[5] added phosphoric acid, primarily to decolorize the ferric iron. In present-day practice, the Zimmermann-Reinhardt "preventive solution" is prepared from manganese(II) sulfate, sulfuric acid, and phosphoric acid.

The mechanism of the corrective action has been a source of speculation for many years. Frequently, it is stated in elementary textbooks that the function of the Z-R reagent is to lower the oxidation potential of the $MnO_4^- $-Mn(II) couple, Eq. (19-1), to below the potential of the chlorine-chloride couple (1.36 volt), so that chloride cannot be oxidized. This explanation is clearly inadequate in view of the irreversible character of (19-1). Moreover, it fails to take into account the *induced* character of the chloride oxidation. For example, if 1 drop of permanganate is added to 100 ml of 1 N hydrochloric acid, a persistent permanganate color is observed. However, if a known amount of Fe(II) is present, the result is high by an amount that depends on the concentrations of reagents, the rate of addition of permanganate, and the rate of stirring.

To explain the induced oxidation, it appears necessary to postulate an active intermediate formed in the permanganate-iron titration that is not present in hydrochloric acid–permanganate mixtures. The active

[1] Kolthoff, I. M., and Smit, N., *Pharm. Weekblad*, **61**, 1082 (1924); *J. Chem. Soc.*, **126**, 786 (1924).
[2] Lanford, O. E., and Kiehl, S. J., *J. Am. Chem. Soc.*, **64**, 291 (1942).
[3] Kolthoff and Smit, *op. cit.*
[4] Zimmermann, C., *Ber. deut. chem. Ges.*, **14**, 779 (1881).
[5] Reinhardt, C., *Stahl u. Eisen*, **4**, 704 (1884); *Chemiker Ztg.*, **B**, 323 (1884).

intermediate could be either a higher oxidation state of iron or an intermediate oxidation state of manganese, which would oxidize hydrochloric acid.

An early explanation was that of Manchot,[1] who claimed that Fe(IV), (V), or (VI) was formed by various oxidants and that permanganate in particular oxidized Fe(III) to Fe(V). If Fe(II) is available, it reduces the Fe(V) back to (III), but, in regions of a local excess of permanganate, Fe(V) oxidizes chloride to chlorine. Bohnson and Robertson[2] offered optical evidence for Fe(VI) in solutions of hydrogen peroxide undergoing catalytic decomposition. Likewise, Bray and Gorin[3] postulated Fe(IV) as an intermediate in peroxide decomposition. However, later evidence for hydroxyl radical, HO, and perhydroxyl radical, HO$_2$, has adequately explained many phenomena related to the behavior of peroxides and strong oxidants. In any case, no convincing evidence has been set forth for higher oxidation states of iron in permanganate titrations.

On the other hand, several unstable intermediate oxidation states of manganese, namely (VI), (V), (IV), and (III) could be involved in the reduction of permanganate. Many years ago, Birch[4] suggested that manganese(III) chloride is formed in the absence of Mn(II) and that this intermediate could oxidize hydrochloric acid to chlorine. This suggestion was favored by Barneby,[5] who made the important observation that several alternative protective solutions could be used in place of the Z-R reagent. For example, sodium sulfate in high concentrations was effective; mixtures of sodium or potassium phosphates with phosphoric acid gave excellent results. Recently, various other reagents have been suggested,[6,7] including sodium acetate, borax, potassium pyrophosphate, manganese(II) acetate, and mixtures of alkali metal fluorides and sulfates. It was found[8] by measurement of potentials during the titration that successful addition agents caused the potential to be steady instead of fluctuating greatly after each addition of permanganate. The stabilization was attributed to speeding of attainment of the equilibrium between Mn(II) and permanganate. It appears, however, that the potential-determining system was actually the Mn(III)-Mn(II) couple and that stabilization was brought about largely by

[1] Manchot, W., *Ann. Chem. Liebigs*, **325,** 93 (1902); Manchot, W., and Wilhelms, O., *ibid.*, **325,** 105 (1902).

[2] Bohnson, V. L., and Robertson, A. C., *J. Am. Chem. Soc.*, **45,** 2493 (1923).

[3] Bray, W. C., and Gorin, M. H., *J. Am. Chem. Soc.*, **54,** 2124 (1932).

[4] Birch, W. C., *Chem. News*, **99,** 61 (1909); *Analyst*, **34,** 315 (1909).

[5] Barneby, O. L., *J. Am. Chem. Soc.*, **36,** 1429 (1914).

[6] Ishibashi, M., Shigematsu, T., and Shibata, S., *Bunseki Kagaku*, **5,** 636 (1956).

[7] Somasundaram, K. M., and Suryanarayana, C. V., *ActaC him. Acad. Sci. Hung.*, **8,** 423 (1956).

[8] *Ibid.*

complex formation between Mn(III) and various anions, including sulfate, acetate, phosphate, and fluoride.

Although there still is some uncertainty about the role of higher intermediate states of manganese, it now appears that Mn(III) is always involved in the reduction of permanganate to Mn(II). If it is not produced directly, it results from the interaction of Mn(VII) and (II). However, the potential corresponding to the half-reaction

$$Mn(III) + e^- \rightleftharpoons Mn(II) \qquad (19\text{-}28)$$

varies according to the nature of the Mn(III) species present.

For the aquated ions, the potential is high enough (1.5 to 1.6 volts) for oxidation of chloride. Taube[1] estimated the formation constant of the complex $MnCl^{++}$ to be 9 ± 3 at an ionic strength of 2. This relatively weak complex is converted readily to more stable complexes with a corresponding lowering of the potential. For example, with oxalic acid

$$MnCl^{++} + H_2C_2O_4 \rightarrow MnC_2O_4^+ + 2H^+ + Cl^- \qquad K = 5 \times 10^3 \quad (19\text{-}29)$$

There is considerable kinetic evidence for the formation of the ion Cl_2^-, which requires less activation energy than chlorine atoms.[2-4] A reasonable mechanism for the induced oxidation involves the reaction

$$MnCl^{++} + Cl^- \rightarrow Mn^{++} + Cl_2^- \qquad (19\text{-}30)$$

The Cl_2^- ion can readily be reduced back to chloride by ferrous iron

$$Fe^{++} + Cl_2^- \rightarrow Fe^{3+} + 2Cl^- \qquad (19\text{-}31)$$

or it may be oxidized to chlorine by Mn(III). Another plausible reaction involves the formation of hypochlorous acid from the reaction of Mn(IV)

$$MnO^{++} + Cl^- + H^+ \rightarrow Mn^{++} + HOCl \qquad (19\text{-}32)$$

Manganese(II) would prevent this reaction by reacting rapidly with Mn(IV), forming Mn(III).

Accordingly, the action of the Z-R reagent is first to supply an adequate concentration of Mn(II) to react with any local excess of permanganate, thus ensuring also the reduction of any intermediate oxidation states of manganese to Mn(III). Of course, the Mn(II) also exerts a depressing effect upon the potential of the *reversible* Mn(III)-Mn(II) couple. Phosphoric acid (and to a lesser extent, sulfuric acid) lowers the Mn(III)-Mn(II) potential, so that Mn(III) is reduced by Fe(II) rather than by chloride.

[1] Taube, *J. Am. Chem. Soc.*, **70**, 3928 (1948).
[2] Taube, *J. Am. Chem. Soc.*, **69**, 1418 (1947).
[3] Taube and Bray, *J. Am. Chem. Soc.*, **62**, 3357 (1940).
[4] Duke, F. R., and Borchers, C. E., *J. Am. Chem. Soc.*, **75**, 5186 (1952).

Schleicher[1] also has stressed the importance of the Mn(III)-Mn(II) couple and has maintained that *five* Mn(II) ions should be present locally for each one of Mn(VII), to be sure that no manganese oxidation state higher than (III) can exist. For this purpose *four* ions should suffice:

$$Mn(VII) + 4Mn(II) \rightarrow 5Mn(III) \qquad (19\text{-}33)$$

There remains to be considered the role of the reducing agent in the induced oxidation. Those reagents which yield appreciable concentrations of Mn(III) *without forming complexes with it* can be expected to induce the oxidation of chloride. Oxalate exerts its own protective action by forming Mn(III) complexes, as discussed above, until toward the end of the titration the decreasing oxalate concentration makes the system sensitive to the induced oxidation of chloride. It is interesting that the error is greatest at low temperatures. Apparently the rate of reduction of Mn(III) by oxalate (the rate-controlling step) is fast enough above 70°C to compete successfully against chloride as a reducing agent, but at lower temperatures appreciable amounts of chloride are oxidized. The error can be avoided by the addition of Mn(II) salts. In the case of arsenite, the oxidation product (arsenate) exerts protective action by stabilizing Mn(III).

In conclusion, it should be stressed that protective solutions for iron titrations are not completely effective and that the concentration of hydrochloric acid should be minimized. According to Kolthoff and Smit,[2] the error can be kept below 0.2 per cent for 0.1 N Fe(II) in 1 M HCl if enough protective solution is used and if the titration is not carried out too rapidly. The relative error is larger for lower concentrations of iron.

Dichromate and Ce(IV) have the advantage of permitting the accurate titration of Fe(II) in hydrochloric acid solutions without special precautions.

19-8. Determination of Hydrogen Peroxide

The mechanism of the reaction

$$5H_2O_2 + 2MnO_4^- + 6H^+ \rightarrow 2Mn^{++} + 5O_2 + 8H_2O \qquad (19\text{-}34)$$

cannot involve rupture of the O—O bond in hydrogen peroxide, because the oxygen atoms appearing as molecular oxygen have been shown to come cleanly from the hydrogen peroxide and not from the water.[3] The reaction, therefore, involves removal of protons and electrons (for

[1] Schleicher, A., *Z. anal. Chem.*, **135**, 258 (1952); **140**, 321 (1953); **144**, 100 (1955); **151**, 413 (1956).

[2] Kolthoff and Smit, *op. cit.*

[3] Cahill, A. E., and Taube, H., *J. Am. Chem. Soc.*, **74**, 2312 (1952).

instance, $H_2O_2 \rightarrow HO_2^- \rightarrow HO_2 \rightarrow O_2^- \rightarrow O_2$). The permanganate reaction shows an induction period similar to that observed in the oxalate reaction. However, there is no induced oxidation of hydrochloric acid, perhaps because of the formation of a peroxy complex of Mn(III), which stabilizes the acid.

An accurate comparison of the permanganate titration has been made[1] with the measurement of the oxygen produced by catalytic decomposition of hydrogen peroxide. It was concluded that the results are very accurate (within 1 part in 5,000) over a twofold range of concentration of sulfuric acid and a fivefold range of rate of addition of permanganate. However, it is good practice to use a fairly high acid concentration (15 to 20 per cent sulfuric acid) and a reasonably low rate of addition in order to minimize the danger of forming manganese dioxide, which is a very active catalyst for the decomposition of hydrogen peroxide.

The permanganate method suffers from the disadvantage, as compared with the Ce(IV) titration (cf. page 386), that organic substances are likely to interfere. A fading end point is an indication of the presence of organic matter or other reducing agents.[2] For colored solutions or for titrations with dilute permanganate, the use of ferroin as an indicator is advantageous.

19-9. Other Determinations with Permanganate

It is beyond the scope of the present treatment to make a comprehensive survey of the applications. For details, the reader is referred to the excellent treatment in the monograph by Kolthoff et al.[3] or to the original literature. However, the more important types of applications, both direct and indirect, will be outlined to provide an idea of the scope of permanganate methods.

Direct Titrations with Permanganate. Permanganate is, of course, useful for the determination of all of the substances mentioned above as primary standards. These include iodide, As(III), oxalate, Fe(II), and ferrocyanide.

Several other reactions, outlined in Table 19-1, can be carried out as direct titrations under the conditions specified.

Determination of Reductants through Iron(III) Reaction. A number of metals can be reduced readily to a lower oxidation state by passage through a suitable reductor but cannot be titrated conveniently because of the extreme sensitivity of the reduced solution to air oxidation. A technique involving rigid exclusion of dissolved oxygen from the titrant

---

[1] Huckaba, C. E., and Keyes, F. G., *J. Am. Chem. Soc.*, **70**, 1640 (1948).

[2] Reichert, J. S., McNeight, S. A., and Rudel, H. W., *Ind. Eng. Chem., Anal. Ed.*, **11**, 194 (1939).

[3] Kolthoff and Belcher (eds.), "Volumetric Analysis," vol. 3, Interscience, 1957.

can often be replaced by the simple operation of passing the reduced solution directly into an air-free solution of Fe(III), usually present as ferric alum. The Fe(II) thus produced is readily titrated with permanganate or, of course, Ce(IV) or dichromate.

TABLE 19-1. DIRECT TITRATIONS WITH PERMANGANATE

Reducing agent	Oxidation product	Conditions	Ref.
Sb(III)	Sb(V)	HCl or HCl + H_2SO_4, 2.5 to 3 N HCl, ICl end point	1, 2
Mn(II)	Mn(IV)	Neutral, ZnO + $ZnSO_4$, Volhard method	3
Mn(II)	Mn(III)	HCl, NH_4F, fluoride method, visual	4
Mn(II)	Mn(III)	Pyrophosphate method, potentiometric	5
V(IV)	V(V)	Bismuth reductor, titration at 80°C	6
V(IV)	V(V)	Acetate buffer, 50°C, ferroin	7
W(V)	W(VI)	Cd reductor, 1 M H_3PO_4, air-free	8
U(IV)	U(VI)	Zn reductor, air oxidation of U(III) to U(IV)	9
Tl(I)	Tl(III)	F^- present, $MnO_4^- \rightarrow$ Mn(III)	10
Cr(III)	Cr(VI)	Hot NaOAc solution, $MnO_4^- \rightarrow MnO_2$	11
Ce(III)	Ce(IV)	Pyrophosphate solution	12

1. Pugh, W., *J. Chem. Soc.*, **1933**, 1.
2. Hammock, E. W., Brown, R. A., and Swift, E. H., *Anal. Chem.*, **20**, 1048 (1948).
3. Kolthoff, I. M., *Pharm. Weekblad*, **61**, 1141 (1924).
4. Zvenigorodskaya, V. M., *Zavodskaya Lab.*, **12**, 152 (1947); *Chem. Abstr.*, **41**, 5662 (1946).
5. Lingane, J. J., and Karplus, R., *Ind. Eng. Chem., Anal. Ed.*, **18**, 191 (1946).
6. Someya, K., *Z. anorg. u. allgem. Chem.*, **138**, 291 (1924).
7. Willard, H. H., and Young, P., *Ind. Eng. Chem., Anal. Ed.*, **6**, 48 (1934).
8. Treadwell, W. D., and Nieriker, R., *Helv. Chim. Acta*, **24**, 1067, 1098 (1941).
9. Lundell, G. E. F., and Knowles, H. B., *J. Am. Chem. Soc.*, **47**, 2637 (1925).
10. Beale, R. S., Hutchison, A. W., and Chandlee, G. C., *Ind. Eng. Chem., Anal. Ed.*, **13**, 240 (1941).
11. Reinitzer, B., and Conrath, P., *Z. anal. Chem.*, **68**, 81 (1926).
12. Edwards, J. W., and Milner, G. W. C., *Analyst*, **82**, 593 (1957).

Common examples produced by means of the Jones reductor are Cr(II), V(II), Ti(III), Nb(III), Mo(III) and Re(-I). The final oxidation products are Cr(III), V(IV), Ti(IV), Nb(V), Mo(VI), and Re(VII).

Tin(II) is a special case, in which a pronounced air oxidation is induced by permanganate or dichromate oxidation (cf. page 467). The induced oxidation is prevented by using Fe(III) as an intermediate.

Copper(I) oxide[1] and chloride[2] react with ferric sulfate to form Cu(II).

[1] Köszegi, D., *Z. anal. Chem.*, **70**, 297 (1927).
[2] Hatch, L. F., and Estes, R. R., *Ind. Eng. Chem , Anal. Ed.*, **18**, 136 (1946).

Indirect Determinations Using Excess Permanganate. A number of reducing agents react too slowly to enable a direct titration to be performed but undergo stoichiometric reactions with excess permanganate.

The method of Stamm[1] involves the addition of excess permanganate in strongly alkaline solution in the presence of barium ion to form barium manganate. The excess permanganate is determined by titration with sodium formate. Examples of oxidation reactions are iodide to periodate, phosphite or hypophosphite to phosphate, cyanide to cyanate, thiocyanate to cyanate and sulfate, and formate or formaldehyde to carbonate.

Sulfide,[2] sulfite,[3,4] thiosulfate[3] and hyposulfite[3] are oxidized to sulfate by excess alkaline permanganate. The excess can be determined iodometrically.

Nitrite is not oxidized by permanganate in alkaline solution but is oxidized quantitatively to nitrate by excess permanganate in acid solution. After 15 min, the excess is determined iodometrically.[5,6]

Indirect Determinations Using Excess Reductant. A number of oxidizing agents that do not react rapidly enough to permit direct titration with a reductant can be determined by adding an excess of standard reductant and back-titrating the excess with permanganate [or Ce(IV) or, sometimes, dichromate].

Arsenite[7] and oxalate[8] are commonly used as reducing agents for "active oxygen" in higher oxides, e.g., MnO_2, PbO_2, or Pb_3O_4. Iron(II) is often used for the reduction of Cr(VI) to (III), V(V) to (IV), and Mn(VII) to (II). Titration of the excess Fe(II) can, in each case, be carried out without oxidizing the other metal. The prior oxidation steps have been considered in Chap. 18.

Peroxydisulfate, $S_2O_8^=$, is reduced to sulfate by excess ferrous iron. By adding phosphoric or hydrofluoric acid, the reduction becomes quantitative in a few minutes at room temperature.[9] The interference of organic matter, which undergoes induced oxidation, is discussed on page 467.

Nitrate is reduced to nitric oxide by ferrous iron. In acid solution,

[1] Stamm, *op. cit.*
[2] Kolthoff, *Pharm. Weekblad,* **61,** 841 (1924).
[3] *Ibid.*
[4] Murooka, T., *Bull. Inst. Phys. Chem. Research Tokyo,* **21,** 1150 (1942).
[5] Cool, R. D., and Yoe, J. H., *Ind. Eng. Chem., Anal. Ed.,* **5,** 112 (1933).
[6] Brasted, *Anal. Chem.,* **23,** 980 (1951).
[7] Cantoni, O., *Ann. chim. appl.,* **16,** 439 (1926).
[8] Fleischer, M., *Ind. Eng. Chem., Anal. Ed.,* **15,** 31 (1943).
[9] Kurtenacker, A., and Kubina, H., *Z. anal. Chem.,* **83,** 14 (1931).

molybdate acts as a catalyst;[1] in alkaline solution, silver diammine sulfate[2] is used. The latter conditions appear more favorable, for they avoid air oxidation, although Leithe[3] has obtained good results even in the presence of air, using molybdate catalyst at relatively high acidity.

Chlorate can be reduced either with Fe(II), using osmium tetroxide as a catalyst,[4] or with Sn(II), using molybdate as a catalyst.[5]

Indirect Determination of Metals Using Oxalate as a Precipitant. Many metals form insoluble oxalates and can, therefore, in principle be determined by titration of the precipitate, after it has been dissolved in acid.

Calcium oxalate is precipitated as in the gravimetric determination, washed, dissolved in hydrochloric or sulfuric acid, and titrated. Reprecipitation is necessary if the sample contains much magnesium.[6]

Magnesium oxalate is best precipitated from 85 per cent acetic acid.[7,8] Other metals that can be determined through oxalate precipitation include cadmium, zinc, lead, cobalt, nickel, thorium, and the rare earths. The precipitation reactions are, however, not at all specific, and preliminary separations are required.

PROBLEMS

19-1. From the pH-dependence of the potential of (19-3), calculate the standard potential of (19-4).

19-2. Combine (19-2) and (19-4) to derive the standard potential of (19-1).

19-3. Write balanced equations for the reactions in the following titrations with permanganate:

    a. Mn(II) to Mn(III) in the presence of pyrophosphate [cf. Eq. (19-8)]

    b. H_3AsO_3 to H_3AsO_4 in sulfuric acid solution

    c. Iodide to ICl, ICN, and CH_3COCH_2I, respectively

19-4. Confirm the value of ΔF° for reaction (19-7) by combining half-reactions (19-2) and (19-6).

19-5. Calculate the standard free energy change and the equilibrium constant of reaction (19-9). *Ans.* -64.4 kcal, $\log K = 47.2$.

19-6. Write balanced equations to describe the oxidation of the following substances with strongly alkaline permanganate in the presence of barium ion (Stamm reaction): iodide, phosphite (HPO_3^-), hypophosphite ($H_2PO_2^-$), cyanide, thiocyanate, formate.

[1] Kolthoff, I. M., Sandell, E. B., and Moskowitz, B., *J. Am. Chem. Soc.*, **55**, 1454 (1933).

[2] Szabó, Z. G., and Bartha, L., *Anal. Chim. Acta*, **5**, 33 (1951).

[3] Leithe, W., *Anal. Chem.*, **20**, 1082 (1948).

[4] Van der Meulen, J. H., *Chem. Weekblad*, **28**, 348 (1931).

[5] Haight, G. P., Jr., *Anal. Chem.*, **25**, 642 (1953).

[6] Kolthoff, I. M., and Sandell, E. B., "Textbook of Quantitative Inorganic Analysis," 3d ed., The Macmillan Company, New York, 1952.

[7] Elving, P. J., and Caley, E. R., *Ind. Eng. Chem., Anal. Ed.*, **9**, 558 (1937).

[8] Gordon, L., and Caley, E. R., *Anal. Chem.*, **20**, 560 (1948).

19-7. A 1.234-g sample, containing lead as PbO and PbO_2, is treated with 20 ml of 0.25 M oxalic acid, which reduces the PbO_2 to Pb^{++}. The resulting solution is neutralized with ammonia, thus precipitating all the lead as lead oxalate. The filtrate is titrated with standard permanganate, using 10.00 ml of 0.04 M $KMnO_4$. The precipitate, after acidification, requires 30.00 ml of permanganate for titration. Calculate the percentage of PbO and PbO_2 in the sample. *Ans.* 36.18, 19.38 per cent.

19-8. A sample containing V, Cr, and Mn is oxidized to yield a solution containing V(V), dichromate, and permanganate, which requires 40.00 ml of 0.1 N ferrous iron. The resulting vanadyl ion is titrated with permanganate, requiring 2.5 ml of 0.02 M reagent. After the addition of pyrophosphate, the resulting Mn(II) and the original Mn(II) are titrated to Mn(III), requiring 4.0 ml of the same permanganate solution. Calculate the milligrams of V, Cr, and Mn in the sample. *Ans.* 12.7, 41.5, 14.8 mg.

19-9. A 1.50-g sample containing MnO and Cr_2O_3 is fused with sodium peroxide, giving Na_2MnO_4 and Na_2CrO_4. After dissolution and decomposition of the excess peroxide, the solution is acidified, whereupon the manganate disproportionates to MnO_4^- and MnO_2, which is filtered off. The filtrate is heated with 50.0 ml 0.1 N ferrous sulfate. The excess ferrous iron requires 18.40 ml 0.01 M permanganate. The precipitate is treated with 10 ml 0.1 N ferrous sulfate, the excess requiring 8.24 ml $KMnO_4$. Calculate the percentage of MnO and Cr_2O_3 in the sample. *Ans.* 4.16, 3.41 per cent.

19-10. An 0.80-g steel sample containing Cr and Mn is dissolved and treated to yield Fe(III), Cr(VI) and Mn(II). The Mn(II) is titrated in the presence of fluoride with 0.005 M $KMnO_4$, requiring 20.0 ml. The resulting solution is titrated with 0.04 M ferrous sulfate, requiring 30.0 ml. Calculate the percentage of Cr and Mn in the sample. *Ans.* 0.0173, 2.75 per cent.

20. Cerium(IV) as an Oxidant

Although quadrivalent cerium has been known for a long time, it was first used as a titrimetric oxidizing agent in 1927 by Martin.[1] Systematic studies of its uses were begun soon thereafter by Furman[2] and Willard.[3]

20-1. Half-reactions and Electrode Potentials

In the early work Ce(IV) was used in sulfuric acid solution and was considered to exist as the aquated ion, which undergoes the simple half-reaction

$$Ce^{4+} + e^- \rightleftharpoons Ce^{3+}$$

Later, Smith and Getz[4] determined the formal oxidation potentials in various concentrations of perchloric, nitric, and sulfuric acids, with the results given in Table 20-1. Smith and Getz postulated that Ce(IV)

TABLE 20-1. FORMAL POTENTIALS OF CERIUM(IV)-CERIUM(III) COUPLE
Volts vs. saturated hydrogen electrode

Acid concentration, N	$HClO_4$	HNO_3	H_2SO_4
1	1.70	1.61	1.44
2	1.71	1.62	1.44
4	1.75	1.61	1.43
6	1.82	1.56	–
8	1.87	–	1.42

existed as anionic complexes $Ce(ClO_4)_6^=$, $Ce(NO_3)_6^=$, $Ce(SO_4)_3^=$, and $CeCl_6^=$ in perchloric, nitric, sulfuric, and hydrochloric acids, respectively. In

[1] Martin, J., *J. Am. Chem. Soc.*, **49**, 2133 (1927).
[2] Furman, N. H., *J. Am. Chem. Soc.*, **50**, 755 (1928).
[3] Willard, H. H., and Young, P., *J. Am. Chem. Soc.*, **50**, 1322 (1928).
[4] Smith, G. F., and Getz, C. A., *Ind. Eng. Chem., Anal. Ed.*, **10**, 191 (1938).

hydrochloric acid, Ce(IV) is not particularly stable, but a value of 1.28 volts in 1 N acid was reported.[1] It should be emphasized that the formal potentials of Smith and Getz were measured against a saturated calomel electrode. The measured values, therefore, include liquid-junction potentials that cannot be accurately estimated.

A careful study of the electrode potential of the Ce(IV)-Ce(III) couple in sodium perchlorate solutions was made by Sherrill, King, and Spooner,[2] who found that the potential varied with hydrogen ion concentration but was practically independent of perchlorate ion concentration. It was concluded that neither Ce(IV) nor Ce(III) reacts with perchlorate ion and that Ce(III) is not hydrolyzed in 0.2 to 2.4 M perchloric acid, but that Ce(IV) is hydrolyzed in two stages. The standard potentials were estimated as follows:

$$Ce(OH)^{3+} + H^+ + e^- \rightleftharpoons Ce^{3+} + H_2O \qquad E° = 1.7134 \text{ volts}$$
$$Ce(OH)_2^{++} + 2H^+ + e^- \rightleftharpoons Ce^{3+} + H_2O \qquad E° = 1.7265 \text{ volts}$$

Later Heidt and Smith[3] offered photochemical evidence for dimeric species of Ce(IV) in perchloric acid solutions and showed by recalculation of the Sherrill, King, and Spooner emf data that better consistency could be obtained there also by assuming dimeric species. They estimated the standard potentials:

$$Ce(OH)_2^{++} + 2H^+ + e^- \rightleftharpoons Ce^{3+} + 2H_2O \qquad E° = 1.7286 \text{ volts}$$
$$(CeOCe)^{6+} + 2H^+ + 2e^- \rightleftharpoons 2Ce^{3+} + H_2O \qquad E° = 1.6652 \text{ volts}$$
$$(HOCeOCeOH)^{4+} + 4H^+ + 2e^- \rightleftharpoons 2Ce^{3+} + 3H_2O \qquad E° = 1.6783 \text{ volts}$$
$$(CeOCeOH)^{5+} + 3H^+ + 2e^- \rightleftharpoons 2Ce^{3+} + 2H_2O \qquad E° = 1.6628 \text{ volts}$$

Supporting evidence for dimeric species was obtained by Hardwick and Robertson[4] from absorption spectra. They estimated that in 2 M perchloric acid, 28 per cent of the Ce(IV) is present as aquated Ce^{4+}, the remainder predominantly as $Ce(OH)^{3+}$ and as a dimer such as $(CeOCe)^{6+}$ or $(CeOCeOH)^{5+}$. Duke and Parchen[5] found that they could best explain the kinetics of electron exchange between Ce(IV) and Ce(III) in perchloric acid solutions by assuming that Ce(IV) is present as $Ce(OH)_2^{++}$, $Ce(OH)_3^+$, and $(CeOCeOH)^{5+}$ in 5 to 6 M perchloric acid. At lower acid concentrations, more highly hydrolyzed and polymerized species seemed to be involved. It is interesting that platinum was found not to catalyze the electron exchange reaction in 5 to 6 M perchloric acid, whereas at

[1] *Ibid.*
[2] Sherrill, M. S., King, C. B., and Spooner, R. C., *J. Am. Chem. Soc.*, **65**, 170 (1943).
[3] Heidt, L. J., and Smith, M. E., *J. Am. Chem. Soc.*, **70**, 2476 (1948).
[4] Hardwick T. J., and Robertson, E., *Can. J. Chem.*, **29**, 818, 828 (1951).
[5] Duke, F. R., and Parchen, F. R., *J. Am. Chem. Soc.*, **78**, 1540 (1956).

lower acidities, according to Fronaeus and Östman,[1] it did catalyze the electron exchange between Ce(III) and the *hydrolyzed dimer* of Ce(IV). This observation may be significant in connection with the reversibility of the Ce(IV)-Ce(III) electrode reaction. From Vetter's[2] studies of polarization curves, the potential-determining system in sulfuric or nitric acid appears to be the Ce^{4+}-Ce^{3+} couple modified by complex formation and hydrolysis. However, further work is necessary, particularly in view of more recent work on formation of oxide films at platinum surfaces (cf. page 334), to understand the electrode reaction of the Ce(IV)-Ce(III) couple.

In all the previous work, Ce(III) appeared to be present as the aquated ion Ce^{3+} in perchloric acid. However, an optical study of Ce(III)* has indicated the existence of a complex, $CeClO_4^{++}$. The value of the formation constant was evaluated at about 80 at ionic strength zero and was found to decrease rapidly with increasing ionic strength, in accordance with the Debye-Hückel theory. If this interpretation is correct, it would seem that Ce(IV) must also form a perchlorate complex of comparable stability to account for the lack of effect of perchlorate on the potential.

In nitric acid solution, Noyes and Garner[3] found standard potentials of 1.6085, 1.6096, and 1.6104 volts, respectively, for acid concentrations of 0.5, 1.0, and 2.0 M from measurements against a hydrogen electrode. From the slight variation with acid concentration Noyes and Garner concluded that neither hydrolysis nor complex formation was involved at the acid concentrations in question. Migration of Ce(IV) to the anode has been reported[4,5] in nitrate solutions under conditions that were not clearly specified. Garner[6] reported migration of Ce(IV) to the anode in 6 M nitric acid but to the cathode in 2 M nitric acid. There appears to have been no thorough spectrophotometric study of nitric acid solutions of Ce(IV), although, qualitatively, the deepening of color upon the addition of nitrate to a Ce(IV) perchlorate solution is an indication of complex formation. The low formal potential in nitric acid as compared with perchloric acid appears to indicate weak complex formation between Ce(IV) and nitrate ion. In summary, it appears that anionic complexes, perhaps $Ce(NO_3)_5^-$ and $Ce(NO_3)_6^=$, exist in nitric acid solutions of

[1] Fronaeus, S., and Östman, O., *Acta Chem. Scand.*, **10**, 769 (1956).

[2] Vetter, K. J., *Z. physik. Chem. Leipzig*, **196**, 360 (1951).

* Heidt, L. J., and Berestecki, J., *J. Am. Chem. Soc.*, **77**, 2049 (1955).

[3] Noyes, A. A., and Garner, C. S., *J. Am. Chem. Soc.*, **58**, 1265 (1936).

[4] Meyer, R. J., and Jacoby, R., *Z. anorg. u. allgem. Chem.*, **27**, 359 (1901).

[5] Duval, C., *Bull. soc. chim. France*, [5], **5**, 1021 (1938).

[6] Yost, D. M., Russell, H., Jr., and Garner, C. S., "The Rare Earth Elements and Their Compounds," John Wiley & Sons, Inc., New York, 1947.

concentrations greater than 6 M but that the interaction between aquated Ce(IV) and nitrate ions decreases rapidly at lower acidities.

Kunz[1] measured the Ce(IV)-Ce(III) potential in sulfuric acid solution against the hydrogen electrode and obtained standard-potential values of 1.4442 and 1.4435 volts, respectively, in 0.5 and 1.0 molal solutions of the acid. The fact that the potential is lower than it is with perchloric acid solutions is an indication of complex formation. Jones and Soper[2] found from electrical migration experiments that, in 0.5 N to 20 N sulfuric acid, Ce(IV) exists in the form of anionic complexes, which they believed to be largely $Ce(OH)(SO_4)_3^{3-}$. In a more extensive study, Hardwick and Robertson[3] observed both absorption spectra and electrical migration. In solutions of constant hydrogen ion concentration of 1 M (using perchloric acid) but variable sulfate concentration, they found that the electrical migration at a sulfate concentration of 0.01 M occurred mainly to the cathode. Migration occurred in both directions at 0.05 M sulfate, but at 0.5 M only migration to the anode occurred. From optical data they evaluated the constants:

$$Ce^{4+} + HSO_4^- \rightleftharpoons CeSO_4^{++} + H^+ \qquad K_1 = 3,500$$
$$CeSO_4^{++} + HSO_4^- \rightleftharpoons Ce(SO_4)_2 + H^+ \qquad K_2 = 200$$
$$Ce(SO_4)_2 + HSO_4^- \rightleftharpoons Ce(SO_4)_3^= + H^+ \qquad K_3 = 20$$

Cerium(III) also forms complexes with sulfate. Newton and Arcand[4] estimated the formation constant of the species $CeSO_4^+$ to be 2.4×10^3 at zero ionic strength and found that it decreased rapidly with increasing ionic strength. At unit ionic strength, the formation constant was estimated to be about 18.

In hydrochloric acid solutions, Ce(IV) is not stable but oxidizes chloride at a rate that increases with the concentrations of Ce(IV) and of hydrochloric acid. Duke and Borchers[5] studied the kinetics of the oxidation, which could be explained by the formation of a series of complexes, $CeCl^{3+}$, $CeCl_2^{++}$, and higher. The rate is controlled by reactions such as

$$CeCl^{3+} + Cl^- \rightleftharpoons Ce^{3+} + Cl_2^-$$
$$CeCl_2^{++} \rightleftharpoons Ce^{3+} + Cl_2^-$$

A complication is introduced by the hydrolysis of Ce(IV). Apparently the hydrolyzed ion $Ce(OH)^{3+}$ does not oxidize chloride at an appreciable rate.

[1] Kunz, A. H., *J. Am. Chem. Soc.*, **53**, 98 (1931).
[2] Jones, E. G., and Soper, F. G., *J. Chem. Soc.*, **1935**, 802.
[3] Hardwick and Robertson, *op. cit.*
[4] Newton, T. W., and Arcand, G. M., *J. Am. Chem. Soc.*, **75**, 2449 (1953).
[5] Duke, F. R., and Borchers, C. E., *J. Am. Chem. Soc.*, **75**, 5186 (1955).

Considering the reaction between Ce(IV) and chloride ion, it appears that the observed formal potential of 1.28 volts in 1 M hydrochloric acid is actually a mixed potential[1] determined partly by the chlorine-chloride couple. Consequently, measured values of the potential cannot be used to calculate the formation constants of Ce(IV)-chloride complexes. From a practical analytical viewpoint, however, it is important that Ce(IV) can be used as a titrant for solutions containing up to 3 M hydrochloric acid[2] without loss of chlorine.

Also, the wide available range of formal potentials (Table 20-1) renders Ce(IV) a versatile oxidant of wide applicability.

20-2. Preparation of Cerium(IV) Solutions

In the early work with Ce(IV), standard solutions were prepared from relatively crude preparations of cerium(IV) oxide, cerium(IV) sulfate, or cerium(IV) ammonium sulfate. Contamination from other rare earths and phosphate led to the gradual precipitation of rare earth phosphates from a sulfuric acid solution.

The preparation of Ce(IV) compounds free of foreign metals is greatly facilitated by the fact that, if ammonium nitrate is added to a concentrated nitric acid solution of Ce(IV), the compound $(NH_4)_2Ce(NO_3)_6$ is precipitated in relatively pure form.[3,4] In concentrated nitric acid, the Ce(IV) evidently exists as the complex ion $Ce(NO_3)_6^=$, and the ammonium salt is properly called ammonium hexanitratocerate(IV). In water and in dilute nitric acid, extensive dissociation occurs, as mentioned above.

Smith, Sullivan, and Frank[5] suggested the use of ammonium hexanitratocerate(IV) as a primary standard and recommended drying to a constant weight at 100°C. Later, it was recognized that slow decomposition occurs at this temperature, and Smith and Fly[6] recommended a procedure that involved drying a product of "primary standard" grade at 85°C for 1 to 6 hr. We[7] have confirmed the accurate results of Smith and Fly in using this procedure to prepare standard solutions directly by weight.[8]

[1] Wadsworth, E., Duke, F. R., and Goetz, C. A., *Anal. Chem.*, **29**, 1824 (1957).

[2] Tsubaki, I., *Buneski Kagaku*, **3**, 253 (1954).

[3] Meyer and Jacoby, *op. cit.*

[4] Smith, G. F., Sullivan, V. R., and Frank. G., *Ind. Eng. Chem.*, *Anal. Ed.*, **8**, 449 (1938).

[5] *Ibid.*

[6] Smith, G. F., and Fly, W. H., *Anal. Chem.*, **21**, 1233 (1949).

[7] Laitinen, H. A., and Burdett, L. W., *Anal. Chem.*, **23**, 1265 (1951).

[8] V. A. Fassel (private communication) has found that the product of "primary-standard" grade contains 0.08 to 0.2 per cent Th (expressed as ThO_2). The accurate results quoted above must arise from a compensating error, perhaps a deficiency of NH_3.

CERIUM(IV) AS AN OXIDANT 383

For special purposes it is desirable to avoid nitrate ions and ammonium ions. It is stated by Smith[1] that solutions of ammonium hexanitratocerate(IV) in 1 to 8 M perchloric acid are equivalent to similar solutions of cerium(IV) perchlorate in practically every respect and that the small amount of nitrate ion has no effect on the formal oxidation potential. However, for many purposes, such as kinetic studies, solutions free of ammonium nitrate are desirable. It might appear that a simple method would be to ignite ammonium hexanitratocerate(IV) to cerium(IV) oxide and dissolve it in the appropriate acid. Pure cerium(IV) oxide, however, is insoluble in acids in the absence of reducing agents. The crude oxide dissolves readily.

Electrolytic oxidations of Ce(III) in nitric, perchloric, or sulfuric acids can be carried out almost quantitatively using platinum electrodes.[2] Thus, cerium(IV) oxide can be dissolved with the addition of hydrogen peroxide to form a Ce(III) solution that is subsequently oxidized.[3]

A more convenient method is to precipitate hydrous cerium(IV) oxide by adding ammonia to ammonium hexanitratocerate(IV). The hydrous oxide is readily soluble in acids.[4]

20-3. Stability of Cerium(IV) Solutions

Cerium(IV) solutions in perchloric acid are sensitive to photochemical reduction by water. Weiss and Porret[5] postulated that the mechanism involves photochemical activation of the aquated Ce^{4+} ion to form an active species Ce^{4+*} that can react to form hydroxyl radical

$$Ce^{4+} + h\nu \rightarrow Ce^{4+*}$$
$$Ce^{4+*} + H_2O \rightarrow Ce^{3+} + H^+ + \cdot OH$$

The hydroxyl radical can reoxidize Ce(III) or it can react to release oxygen.

$$\cdot OH + Ce^{3+} \rightarrow Ce^{4+} + OH^-$$
$$\cdot OH + \cdot OH \rightarrow H_2O + O$$
$$O + O \rightarrow O_2$$

Hydrogen peroxide, formed from hydroxyl radicals, can also be involved. The ultraviolet-band spectra of aquated Ce(IV) ions have been inter-

[1] Smith, "Cerate Oxidimetry," G. Frederick Smith Chemical Co., Columbus, Ohio, 1942.
[2] Smith, G. F., Frank, G., and Kott, A. E., *Ind. Eng. Chem., Anal. Ed.*, **12**, 268 (1940).
[3] Smith, *Anal. Chem.*, **27**, 1142 (1955).
[4] Smith and Fly, *op. cit.*
[5] Weiss, J., and Porret, D., *Nature*, **139**, 1019 (1937).

preted[1] on the basis of electron transitions from the water of hydration to the Ce(IV) ion.

It is important that the photochemical reduction is negligible in sulfuric acid solution, because of the very low concentration of Ce^{4+} ions. Furman[2] has stated that 0.1 N solutions of Ce(IV) in sulfuric acid solutions are stable for at least 6 years, but he feels that the presence of nitrate and ammonium ions is not desirable. Smith has found that 0.1 N Ce(IV) in 0.5 to 1.0 N sulfuric acid is stable even upon boiling for several hours but that nitric and perchloric acid solutions decompose somewhat upon boiling. Stored at room temperature, 0.1 N Ce(IV) in nitric or perchloric acid solutions showed 0.01 to 0.03 per cent decrease in normality per day.[3] Nitric and perchloric acid solutions should be protected from light, but sulfuric acid solutions need no protection.

20-4. Standardization against Sodium Oxalate

Sodium oxalate was used by Willard and Young[4] as a primary standard substance for Ce(IV) in sulfuric acid. In the absence of a catalyst, a temperature of 70 to 75°C is necessary. The end point is best detected potentiometrically, although a visual titration utilizing the yellow color of Ce(IV) can be used with an appropriate blank correction. Using iodine monochloride as a catalyst, the reaction can be run at room temperature. However, if ferroin is to be used as an indicator, the temperature should be above 45°C, so that the locally oxidized indicator may be reduced rapidly; but it should not exceed 50°C, because the indicator is destroyed by excess Ce(IV). Wheatley[5] and Watson[6] used Mn(II) as the catalyst and ferroin as the indicator, titrating either at room temperature[7] or at 40 to 50°C. Smith and Getz[8] found that, in 1 to 2 M perchloric acid solution, sodium oxalate can be titrated at room temperature with cerium(IV) perchlorate or nitrate but not with the sulfate. More recently, Smith[9] has standardized electrolytically prepared cerium(IV) perchlorate using the oxalate titration at room temperature. Nitroferroin has the advantage over ferroin of being less subject to local oxidation, because of its higher potential.

[1] Schläfer, H. L., Z. physik. Chem. Frankfurt, [N.F.], **3**, 263 (1955).
[2] Furman, foreword to Smith, "Cerate Oxidimetry," Smith Chemical Co., 1942.
[3] Smith and Getz, Ind. Eng. Chem., Anal. Ed., **12**, 339 (1940).
[4] Willard and Young, J. Am. Chem. Soc., **50**, 1322 (1928); **55**, 3260 (1933).
[5] Wheatley, V. R., Analyst, **69**, 207 (1944).
[6] Watson, J. P., Analyst, **76**, 177 (1951).
[7] Wheatley, op. cit.
[8] Smith and Getz, Ind. Eng. Chem., Anal. Ed., **10**, 304 (1938).
[9] Smith, Anal. Chem., **27**, 1144 (1955).

20-5. Standardization against Arsenic(III) Oxide and Other Standards

Arsenic(III) oxide is especially favorable as a primary standard (cf. page 367). It may be titrated in hydrochloric acid solution using iodine monochloride as a catalyst and ferroin as the indicator. The results were originally thought to be 0.3 per cent low,[1] but Swift and Gregory[2] obtained excellent results by increasing the hydrochloric acid concentration to 4 M. The beneficial effect was found to be due to chloride ion, and good results could be obtained at lower acidities in the presence of sufficient chloride. The titration can be run at room temperature using the color of iodine in a carbon tetrachloride layer to indicate the end point. If ferroin is used the temperature must be raised to 50°C.

The most convenient method is to titrate in sulfuric acid solution at room temperature using osmium tetroxide as the catalyst.[3] Hydrochloric acid interferes, but not in the presence of excess mercuric perchlorate.[4] We have found that the visual end point using ferroin coincides within 0.01 per cent with the potentiometric end point.

The various forms of ferrous iron can be used for Ce(IV) as well as for permanganate, with the added advantage that hydrochloric acid solutions of iron can be titrated without difficulty.

Potassium ferrocyanide[5] and potassium iodide[6] can be used for Ce(IV) just as for permanganate. The results are not highly accurate unless specially purified potassium iodide is titrated potentiometrically.[7]

20-6. Determination of Iron

Cerium(IV) has the advantage of being applicable to a wide variety of solutions of Fe(II). Perchloric or sulfuric acid can be used[8] in concentrations of 0.5 to 8 M. Hydrochloric acid solutions are usually used in concentrations of 0.5 to 3 M, although even 6 M hydrochloric acid can be used with the iodine chloride end point (see page 429). Ferroin is most commonly used as the indicator, although Cagle and Smith[9] used 2,2'-dipyridyl in 1 M hydrochloric or sulfuric acids. A better indicator

[1] Willard and Young, *J. Am. Chem. Soc.*, **50**, 1322 (1928).

[2] Swift, E. H., and Gregory, C. H., *J. Am. Chem. Soc.*, **52**, 901 (1930).

[3] Gleu, K., *Z. anal. Chem.*, **95**, 305 (1933).

[4] *Ibid.*

[5] Claassen, A., and Visser, J., *Rec. trav. chim.*, **60**, 213 (1941).

[6] Kolthoff, I. M., and Laitinen, H. A., *J. Am. Chem. Soc.*, **61**, 1690 (1939).

[7] Kolthoff, I. M., Laitinen, H. A., and Lingane, J. J., *J. Am. Chem. Soc.*, **59**, 429 (1937).

[8] Smith and Getz, *Ind. Eng. Chem., Anal. Ed.*, **10**, 191 (1938).

[9] Cagle, F. W., and Smith, G. F., *Anal. Chem.*, **19**, 384 (1947).

in hydrochloric acid is 5,6-dimethylferroin,[1] which has a lower transition potential. Nitroferroin with its high potential may be used to advantage in nitric or perchloric acid solution.[2]

For many purposes, hydrochloric acid is the most convenient titration medium, as it permits the use of stannous chloride or the silver reductor as selective reducing agents (see pages 349 and 352). Cerium has the advantage over permanganate of not being subject to error due to induced oxidation of chloride. It has a sharper end point than dichromate. Lang and Fürstenau[3] used thiosulfate as a reducing agent for Fe(III) and removed the excess with selenious acid. Petzold[4] has titrated small amounts of Fe(II) in the presence of arsenic, antimony, and Sn(II). Iron(II) can be titrated in the presence of V(IV) by using a silver reductor with 1 M hydrochloric acid and making the solution 5 M in sulfuric acid to prevent the oxidation of V(IV) at the ferroin end point.[5]

Thiry[6] has studied the effect of various organic substances on the titration of Fe(II) with Ce(IV) in sulfuric acid, with particular reference to the analysis of pharmaceuticals. Most saturated aliphatic acids, benzoic acid, ethanol, sucrose, and lactose do not interfere. Oxalic and citric acids are oxidized, and salicyclic and gallic acids produce interfering colors.

20-7. Determination of Hydrogen Peroxide

The use of Ce(IV) for the titration of hydrogen peroxide

$$H_2O_2 + 2Ce(IV) \rightarrow 2Ce(III) + O_2 + 2H^+$$

was introduced by Atanasiu and Stefanescu,[7] and was shown to be applicable in sulfuric, hydrochloric, nitric, or acetic acid solutions.[8-10] Cerium(IV) has the advantage over permanganate of being less subject to interference from organic matter.

The mechanism of the reaction was studied by Baer and Stein,[11] who found that, in sulfuric acid in the pH range 0 to 1.4, the reaction can be

[1] Brandt, W. W., and Smith, G. F., *Anal. Chem.*, **21**, 1313 (1949).

[2] Smith, G. F., and Richter, F. P., *Ind. Eng. Chem., Anal. Ed.*, **16**, 580 (1944).

[3] Lang, R., and Fürstenau, I., *Z. anal. Chem.*, **133**, 163, 331 (1951).

[4] Petzold, A., *Z. anal. Chem.*, **149**, 258 (1956).

[5] Walden, H. G., Jr., Hammett, L. P., and Edmonds, S. M., *J. Am. Chem. Soc.*, **56**, 350 (1934).

[6] Thiry, G., *J. pharm. Belg.*, **2**, 121 (1947).

[7] Atanasiu, I. A., and Stefanescu, V., *Ber. deut. chem. Ges.*, **61**, 1343 (1928).

[8] Furman, N. H., and Wallace, J. H., Jr., *J. Am. Chem. Soc.*, **51**, 1449 (1929).

[9] Willard and Young, *J. Am. Chem. Soc.*, **55**, 3260 (1933).

[10] Reichert, J. S., McNeight, S. A., and Rudel, H. W., *Ind. Eng. Chem., Anal. Ed.*, **11**, 194 (1939).

[11] Baer, S., and Stein, G., *J. Chem. Soc.*, **1953**, 3176.

represented by the two processes:

(a) $\qquad H_2O_2 + Ce(IV) \rightleftharpoons HO_2 + H^+ + Ce(III)$
(b) $\qquad HO_2 + Ce(IV) \rightarrow O_2 + H^+ + Ce(III)$

From the fact that Ce(IV)–hydrogen peroxide reaction induces the electron exchange reaction between Ce(III) and Ce(IV) in sulfuric acid solution, Sigler and Masters[1] concluded that the first step, reaction (a), is reversible. No hydroxyl radicals are present in the system,[2] showing that the reaction

$$H_2O_2 + HO_2 \rightarrow H_2O + O_2 + \cdot OH$$

does not proceed at an appreciable rate in comparison with reaction (b). This mechanism is consistent with the findings of Cahill and Taube,[3] who found from tracer experiments that all the oxygen atoms set free as molecular oxygen were originally present in the hydrogen peroxide molecule and none in the water. Therefore, there is no rupture of the O—O bond, and the reaction is a stepwise removal of two hydrogen ions and two electrons. Again, there is no hydroxyl radical involved, for an exchange of oxygen atoms with water would be expected if there were.

An accurate comparison of the Ce(IV) method with the permanganate method and with an absolute gravimetric method based on the weight loss in catalytic decomposition was made by Hurdis and Romeyer.[4] Using Ce(IV) in 2 N nitric acid as the reagent and 1.2 N perchloric acid as the sample solvent, or Ce(IV) in 2 N sulfuric acid as the titrant and 0.6 N sulfuric acid as the sample solvent, the results agreed within 0.1 per cent with permanganate titrations and within 0.03 per cent with computations by the absolute method. Nitroferroin was better than ferroin in the titrations with nitric and perchloric acids, because it had less tendency to be oxidized locally by a transient excess of Ce(IV). The oxidized indicator was slow to return to its reduced state in the immediate vicinity of the end point. For the sulfuric acid solutions, nitroferroin changes color at too high a potential, and the slow fading of the ferroin color made the use of ferroin preferable to titration without an indicator, using the color of the Ce(IV) itself. Baer and Stein[2] also found an exact stoichiometry, using very pure Ce(IV). With ordinary reagent-quality Ce(IV), however, an error due to catalytic decomposition of hydrogen peroxide was observed when hydrogen peroxide was in excess, although the results were always exact when Ce(IV) was in excess.

Detailed studies of the determination of various peroxycompounds

[1] Sigler, P. B., and Masters, B. J., *J. Am. Chem. Soc.*, **79**, 6353 (1957).
[2] Baer and Stein, *op. cit.*
[3] Cahill, A. E., and Taube, H., *J. Am. Chem. Soc.*, **74**, 2312 (1952).
[4] Hurdis, E. C., and Romeyer, H., Jr., *Anal. Chem.*, **26**, 320 (1952).

alone and in mixtures with each other have been made by Csányi and Solymosi.[1]

20-8. Other Direct Titrations with Cerium(IV)

Oxalate, As(III), ferrocyanide, and iodide, which have been mentioned in connection with the standardization of Ce(IV), can, of course, be determined by direct titration. Various other reducing agents that react so rapidly and stoichiometrically that they can be titrated directly are listed in Table 20-2.

TABLE 20-2. DIRECT TITRATIONS WITH CERIUM(IV)

Reducing agent	Oxidation product	Conditions	Ref.
Sb(III)	Sb(V)	HCl, ICl catalyst, ferroin, 50°C	1, 2
Mo(V)	Mo(VI)	2 M HCl, Ag or Hg reductor, ferroin	3, 4, 5
Pu(III)	Pu(IV)	1 N H_2SO_4, Zn reductor, ferroin	6
Sn(II)	Sn(IV)	HCl, air-free	7, 8
$S_2O_3^=$	$S_4O_6^=$	Iodide-starch indicator	9
Tl(I)	Tl(III)	HCl + H_2SO_4, 80 to 90°C	10
U(IV)	U(VI)	4 M HCl, Ag reductor, 60 to 90°C, cool	11
U(IV)	U(VI)	3 M HCl, Pb reductor	12
V(IV)	V(V)	HCl, H_2SO_4, or $HClO_4$	13, 14, 15

1. Willard, H. H., and Young, P., *J. Am. Chem. Soc.*, **55**, 3260 (1933).
2. Přibil, R., *Chem. listy*, **39**, 19 (1945).
3. Furman, N. H., and Murray, W. M., *J. Am. Chem. Soc.*, **58**, 1689, 1843 (1936).
4. Birnbaum, N., and Walden, G. H., Jr., *ibid.*, **60**, 64, 66 (1938).
5. Hiskey, C. F., Springer, V. F., and Meloche, V. W., *ibid.*, **61**, 3125 (1939).
6. Koch, C. W., in Seaborg, Glenn T., *et al.* (eds.), "The Transuranium Elements," p. 1337, National Nuclear Energy Series, div. IV, vol. 14B, McGraw-Hill Book Company, Inc., New York, 1949.
7. Bassett, L. G., and Stumpf, L. F., *Ind. Eng. Chem., Anal. Ed.*, **6**, 477 (1934).
8. Lykken, L., and Tuemmler, F. D., *ibid.*, **14**, 68 (1942).
9. Furman, N. H., and Wallace, J. H., Jr., *J. Am. Chem. Soc.*, **53**, 1283 (1931).
10. Willard and Young, *ibid.*, **52**, 36 (1930).
11. Birnbaum, N., and Edmonds, S. M., *Ind. Eng. Chem., Anal. Ed.*, **12**, 155 (1940).
12. Fritz, I. S., Fulda, M. O., Margerum, S. L., and Lane, E. S., *Anal. Chim. Acta*, **10**, 513 (1954).
13. Willard and Young, *Ind. Eng. Chem.*, **20**, 972 (1928).
14. Furman, *J. Am. Chem. Soc.*, **50**, 755 (1928).
15. Smith, G. F., and Getz, C. A., *Ind. Eng. Chem., Anal. Ed.*, **10**, 191 (1938).

20-9. Indirect Determination of Peroxydisulfate

The direct titration of peroxydisulfate, $S_2O_8^=$, by ferrous iron is not possible because the reaction is too slow. Therefore, an excess of

[1] Csányi, L. J., and Solymosi, F., *Acta. Chim. Acad. Sci. Hung.*, **13**, 9, 19, 257, 275 (1957).

standard ferrous iron is added, and the excess is back-titrated with Ce(IV). Accurate results are possible under the proper conditions, but certain precautions have to be taken, as will be discussed below.[1]

Kolthoff, Medalia, and Raaen[2] postulated that the over-all reaction

$$2Fe^{++} + S_2O_8^= \rightarrow 2Fe^{3+} + 2SO_4^-$$

takes place through the steps

$$Fe^{++} + S_2O_8^= \rightarrow Fe^{3+} + SO_4^- + \cdot SO_4^-$$
$$Fe^{++} + \cdot SO_4^- \rightarrow Fe^{3+} + SO_4^=$$

where the first step is the rate-determining process that forms the radical ion SO_4^-. When ferrous iron was added slowly to peroxydisulfate, with or without oxygen, a mole ratio of iron to peroxydisulfate of less than 2 was found. Presumably, an induced decomposition similar to that observed for hydrogen peroxide (page 465) occurs, although the decomposition is much less extensive and no oxygen was actually detected.

If oxygen is present, induced air oxidation leads to the consumption of too much iron. The effect of oxygen is accentuated by the presence of organic matter. In the absence of oxygen, the induced oxidation of organic substances causes the consumption of too much peroxydisulfate. For further details, see the discussion of these induced reactions on page 466. From the analytical viewpoint it is important that bromide suppresses both induced reactions, presumably through the reaction

$$\cdot SO_4^- + Br^- \rightarrow SO_4^= + Br\cdot$$

forming a bromine atom which rapidly oxidizes ferrous iron

$$Br\cdot + Fe^{++} \rightarrow Br^- + Fe^{3+}$$

The bromine atom is no doubt stabilized by the formation of the bromine molecule ion Br_2^-.

Kolthoff and Carr[3] used the suppressing effect of bromide to permit the determination of peroxydisulfate even in the presence of organic matter. The optimum bromide concentration was of the order of 1 M; ferroin served as the indicator for the back-titration, which was carried out with Ce(IV) in a 0.5 M sulfuric acid.

20-10. Indirect Determinations Using Excess Cerium(IV)

A number of reducing agents react too slowly with Ce(IV) to be titrated directly; yet they react quantitatively with excess Ce(IV), which can be

---

[1] Kolthoff, I. M., and Carr, E. M., *Anal. Chem.*, **25**, 298 (1953).

[2] Kolthoff, I. M., Medalia, A. I., and Raaen, H. P., *J. Am. Chem. Soc.*, **73**, 1733 (1951).

[3] Kolthoff and Carr, *op. cit.*

back-titrated with a reducing agent such as ferrous sulfate or arsenite. Various examples are listed in Table 20-3.

TABLE 20-3. INDIRECT DETERMINATIONS USING EXCESS CERIUM(IV)

Reducing agent	Oxidation product	Conditions	Ref.
As(O)	As(V)	Ce(IV) in H_2SO_4, arsenite	1
Cr(III)	Cr(VI)	Ce(IV) in H_2SO_4, hot, oxalate or nitrite	2, 3
V(IV)	V(V)	Ce(IV) in H_2SO_4, hot, oxalate or nitrite	2, 3
HN_3	N_2	Ce(IV) nitrate in HNO_3, Fe(II)	4
NH_2OH	N_2O	Ce(IV) in H_2SO_4, arsenite	5
NO_2^-	NO_3^-	Ce(IV) nitrate in $HClO_4$, oxalate	6
H_3PO_2	H_3PO_4	Ce(IV) in H_2SO_4, Fe(II)	7, 8
H_3PO_3	H_3PO_4	Ce(IV) in H_2SO_4, boil, Fe(II)	7, 8
$H_4P_2O_6$	H_3PO_4	Ce(IV) in HNO_3, OsO_4, arsenite	9
Hg(I)	Hg(II)	Ce(IV) in H_2SO_4, Fe(II)	10
Re(III) or (IV)	Re(VII)	Ce(IV) in H_2SO_4, Fe(II)	11
Te(IV)	Te(VI)	Ce(IV) in H_2SO_4, Cr^{3+}, Fe(II)	12

1. Kolthoff, I. M., and Amdur, E., *Ind. Eng. Chem., Anal. Ed.*, **12**, 177 (1940).
2. Willard, H. H., and Young, P., *J. Am. Chem. Soc.*, **51**, 139 (1929).
3. Willard and Young, *Trans. Electrochem. Soc.*, **67**, 347 (1935).
4. Arnold, J. W., *Ind. Eng. Chem., Anal. Ed.*, **17**, 215 (1945).
5. Cooper, S. R., and Morris, J. B., *Anal. Chem.*, **24**, 1360 (1952).
6. Stubblefield, F. M., *Ind. Eng. Chem., Anal. Ed.*, **16**, 366 (1944).
7. Bernhart, D. N., *Anal. Chem.*, **26**, 1798 (1954).
8. Rao, K. B., and Rao, G. G., *Z. anal. Chem.*, **147**, 274, 279 (1955).
9. Moeller, T., and Quinty, G. H., *Anal. Chem.*, **24**, 1354 (1952).
10. Willard and Young, *J. Am. Chem. Soc.*, **52**, 557 (1930).
11. Geilmann, W., and Wrigge, F. W., *Z. anorg. u. allgem. Chem.*, **222**, 56 (1935).
12. Willard and Young, *J. Am. Chem. Soc.*, **52**, 553 (1930).

20-11. Indirect Determinations Using Iron(III)

In determining strong reducing agents that are sensitive to air oxidation, it is advantageous to pass the reduced solution directly into an excess of Fe(III). The equivalent amount of Fe(II) can readily be determined. Cerium(IV) has the advantage over permanganate of permitting the use of relatively concentrated solutions of hydrochloric acid as the reducing medium. Several applications are outlined in Table 20-4.

20-12. Determination of Organic Compounds

In the early work of Willard and Young,[1] various organic acids were heated at 90 to 95°C with an excess of Ce(IV) in relatively dilute sulfuric

[1] Willard and Young, *J. Am. Chem. Soc.*, **52**, 132 (1930).

TABLE 20-4. INDIRECT DETERMINATIONS USING EXCESS IRON(III)

Determination of	Reduction conditions	Reduced form	Oxidized form	Reference
Copper	2 M HCl, Ag reductor	Cu(I)	Cu(II)	1
Molybdenum	2 M HCl, Ag reductor	Mo(V)	Mo(VI)	2
Molybdenum	Th(MoO$_4$)$_2$ dissolved in HCl, Zn	Mo(III)	Mo(VI)	3
Thorium	Th(MoO$_4$)$_2$ dissolved in HCl, Zn	Mo(III)	Mo(VI)	3
Titanium	HCl, Cd reductor	Ti(III)	Ti(IV)	4
Niobium	Electrolytic	Nb(III)	Nb(V)	5

1. Birnbaum, N., and Edmonds, S. M., *Ind. Eng. Chem., Anal. Ed.,* **12**, 155 (1940).
2. Birnbaum, N., and Walden, G. H., Jr., *J. Am. Chem. Soc.,* **60**, 64 (1938).
3. Banks, C. V., and Diehl, H., *Anal. Chem.,* **19**, 222 (1947).
4. Claassen, A., and Vissev, J., *Rec. trav. chim.,* **60**, 213 (1941).
5. Tomiček, O., Spurny, K., Jerman, L., and Holoček, V., *Collection Czechoslov. Chem. Communs.,* **18**, 757 (1953).

acid. Tartaric, malonic, malic, glycolic, and citric acids were readily oxidized, but not with exact stoichiometry. Benzoic and salicylic acids were attacked slowly and incompletely, but fumaric, maleic, and phthalic acids were only very slightly affected. Formic, succinic, and acetic acids were not appreciably attacked. More recently, Takahashi et al.[1] have oxidized a wider variety of compounds, including alcohols, phenols, amines, amino acids, and carbohydrates. The reactions in general were not stoichiometric.

Sharma and Mehrotra[2] found that, by increasing the concentration of sulfuric acid to 50 to 66 per cent and refluxing, it was possible to oxidize all the acids studied by Willard and Young except succinic and acetic acids quantitatively to carbon dioxide. It was found later[3] that, with pure cerium(IV) sulfate, formic acid is not appreciably oxidized and that the catalytic effect of impurities as well as the high concentration of sulfuric acid had been responsible for the quantitative oxidation. By adding a small amount of Cr(III) as a catalyst, the results previously observed with impure cerium(IV) sulfate could be duplicated. This made it possible to determine glycerol and glycol in mixtures, oxidizing one aliquot to formic acid in the absence of catalyst and another aliquot to carbon dioxide in the presence of Cr(III). Similar procedures for mixtures of formic acid with formaldehyde or methanol were devised.

[1] Takahashi, T., Kimoto, K., and Sakurai, H., *Repts. Gov. Chem. Inst. Ind. Research Tokyo,* **5**, 121 (1955).
[2] Sharma, N. N., and Mehrotra, R. C., *Anal. Chim. Acta,* **11**, 417, 507 (1954).
[3] Sharma and Mehrotra, *Anal. Chim. Acta,* **13**, 419 (1955).

Sharma[1] also showed that Ce(IV) oxidation of aldoses in the absence of catalysts led to the formation of formic acid. In ketoses a molecule of carbon dioxide was formed. In the presence of Cr(III), complete oxidation to carbon dioxide and water was effected.

Smith and Duke[2] used cerium(IV) perchlorate in 4 M perchloric acid as the oxidant and found a stoichiometric oxidation of many compounds at room temperature. In general, compounds containing active methylene groups and polyhydroxy compounds containing hydroxyl groups on adjacent carbon atoms are oxidized to fatty acids, ketones, aldehydes (other than formaldehyde), and carbon dioxide. Glycerol was exceptional in that it required heating to 45°C for 15 min. Acetone, acetaldehyde, or compounds yielding them as oxidation products, showed appreciable oxidation upon standing more than 5 min at 10°C and, therefore, led to errors. Formaldehyde is quantitatively oxidized to carbon dioxide. The reaction conditions and products are given for several compounds in Table 20-5.

TABLE 20-5. OXIDATION WITH CERIUM(IV) IN 4 M PERCHLORIC ACID

Compound	Conditions		Products	Equivalents Ce(IV) per mole
	Temp, °C	Time, min		
Glycerol	45	15	$3HCOOH$	8
Glucose	26	45	$6HCOOH$	12
Sucrose	24	45	$11HCOOH + CO_2$	26
Cellulose	27	120	$6HCOOH$	12
Biacetyl	24	5	$2CH_3COOH$	2
Acetyl acetone	25	10	$2CH_3COOH + HCOOH$	6
Tartaric acid	26	10	$2HCOOH + 2CO_2$	6
Malonic acid	26	10	$HCOOH + 2CO_2$	6
Citric acid	10	30	$2HCOOH + 4CO_2$	14
Malic acid	25	15	$2HCOOH + 2CO_2$	8

[From Smith, G. F., and Duke, F. R., *Ind. Eng. Chem., Anal. Ed.*, **15**, 120 (1943).]

[1] Sharma, *Anal. Chim. Acta*, **14**, 423 (1956); *Z. anal. Chem.*, **154**, 340 (1957).
[2] Smith and Duke, *Ind. Eng. Chem., Anal. Ed.*, **15**, 120 (1943).

21. Methods Involving Iodine

The iodine-iodide couple may be characterized by the half-reaction

$$I_2(\text{solid}) + 2e^- \rightleftharpoons 2I^- \qquad E^\circ = 0.5345 \text{ volt} \qquad (21\text{-}1)$$

which shows that iodine is a relatively weak oxidant and iodide is a relatively weak reductant. Thus iodine is quantitatively reduced to iodide by moderately strong reductants [Sn(II), H_2SO_3, H_2S, or arsenite in neutral solution], and iodide is quantitatively oxidized to iodine by moderate or strong oxidants (H_2O_2, IO_3^-, $Cr_2O_7^=$, MnO_4^-, etc.).[1]

The behavior of iodine is complicated by the relatively low solubility of iodine in water (1.33×10^{-3} M at 20°C) and by the formation of the triiodide ion

$$I_2(\text{aq}) + I^- \rightleftharpoons I_3^- \qquad K = \frac{a_{I_3^-}}{a_{I_2}a_{I^-}} = 710 \qquad (21\text{-}2)$$

Equation (21-1) describes the behavior of a solution saturated with solid iodine. This half-reaction will occur, for example, toward the end of a titration of iodide with an oxidant such as permanganate, when the iodide ion concentration becomes relatively low. Near the beginning, or in most indirect determinations, an excess of iodide is present, and the half-reaction is better written

$$I_3^- + 2e^- \rightleftharpoons 3I^- \qquad E^\circ = 0.5355 \text{ volt} \qquad (21\text{-}3)$$

The relationship between (21-1) and (21-3) may be clarified by considering the half-reaction for a solution unsaturated with iodine:

$$I_2(\text{aq}) + 2e^- \rightleftharpoons 2I^- \qquad E^\circ = 0.6197 \text{ volt} \qquad (21\text{-}4)$$

---

[1] It is common practice to distinguish between *iodimetric* methods, involving direct titration with iodine, and *iodometric* methods, involving the indirect determination of oxidants by addition of excess iodide and titration of the resulting iodine with thiosulfate or arsenite.

Since the activity of solid iodine may be taken as unity, we may compare Eqs. (21-1) and (21-4) and write

$$E = E^{\circ}_{I_2(solid),I^-} + \frac{RT}{2F} \ln \frac{1}{a_{I^-}^2} = E^{\circ}_{I_2(aq),I^-} + \frac{RT}{2F} \ln \frac{a_{I_2(aq)}}{a_{I^-}^2} \qquad (21\text{-}5)$$

or

$$E^{\circ}_{I_2(aq),I^-} = E^{\circ}_{I_2(solid),I^-} - \frac{RT}{2F} \ln S = 0.5345 + 0.0852 = 0.6197 \text{ volt} \qquad (21\text{-}6)$$

where S is the molar solubility of iodine. Writing the Nernst equation for (21-4) and considering (21-2),

$$E = 0.6197 + \frac{RT}{2F} \ln \frac{a_{I_2(aq)}}{a_{I^-}^2} \qquad (21\text{-}7)$$

$$= 0.6197 - \frac{RT}{2F} \ln K + \frac{RT}{2F} \ln \frac{a_{I_3^-}}{a_{I^-}^3}$$

$$= 0.5355 + \frac{RT}{2F} \ln \frac{a_{I_3^-}}{a_{I^-}^3} \qquad (21\text{-}8)$$

which is the Nernst equation for reaction (21-3). The standard potentials of (21-1) and (21-3) happen to be only 1 mv apart because the concentration of triiodide ion happens to be about 1 M in a solution saturated with iodine and containing 1 M free iodide ion. The potential for a solution unsaturated with iodine may be calculated using either (21-7) or (21-8), taking care to use the actual equilibrium concentration of either triiodide ion or iodine. Often, for the sake of simplicity and in order to emphasize the stoichiometric relationships, we shall write a reaction showing the formation of iodine even in a solution containing excess iodide ion.

21-1. Sources of Error

Two common sources of error in the quantitative use of iodine are (1) loss of iodine owing to its volatility, and (2) air oxidation of iodide.

Losses due to volatility are most likely to be encountered if the concentration of iodide is so low that solid iodine is present. Sufficient iodide should be present to decrease the concentration of free iodine below the saturation value. Danger of loss of iodine is enhanced by evolution of gases (e.g., carbon dioxide generated for deaeration) and by elevated temperatures. The determinations should be carried out in cold solutions.

Air oxidation of iodide is negligible in neutral solutions in the absence of catalysts. However, the rate of air oxidation increases rapidly with increasing acidity. The reaction is catalyzed by metal ions of variable valence (particularly copper) and is photochemical in nature. Moreover, the air oxidation of iodide may be induced by the reaction between iodide and the oxidizing agent, especially when the main reaction is slow.[1] Solutions containing an excess of iodide and acid must, therefore, not be allowed to stand any longer than necessary before titration of the iodine. If prolonged standing is necessary, the air should be displaced by an inert gas such as carbon dioxide, and in extreme cases the solution should be protected from light. The formation of triiodide ions in extremely dilute aqueous solutions of iodine has been attributed to reduction of iodine by traces of impurities.[2]

21-2. Starch as an Indicator for Iodine

The characteristic deep blue color imparted to a dilute solution of iodine by soluble starch is used as a very sensitive indicator. Iodine at a concentration of 10^{-5} N is readily detected. The color intensity decreases with increasing temperature, being 10 times less sensitive[3] at 50 than at 25°C. The sensitivity decreases upon the addition of solvents such as alcohol. No color is observed in solutions containing 50 per cent ethanol or more.

The color is often described as being due to an adsorption complex, and this is partly true. Starches can be separated into two major fractions which exist in different proportions in various plants.[4] Amylose is a straight-chain fraction abundant in potato starch. Rundle[5] and others have shown by iodine titration and X-ray diffraction that amylose forms a definite blue complex with iodine. A particular form of amylose, prepared by alcohol precipitation, absorbed 26 per cent of its weight of iodine vapor, corresponding to one iodine molecule in six glucose units or in one unit of the helical starch structure. The other major fraction, amylopectin, is branched in structure, and interacts only loosely with iodine, probably by adsorption, to form a red-purple product.

The work of Lambert[6] indicates that the linear fraction of potato starch interacts with triiodide ion, rather than molecular iodine, in solution and that excess iodide is not required to produce the blue color. The fact that dilute iodine gives no color with starch in the presence of excess silver or Hg(II) is sometimes cited as evidence for the necessity

[1] Kolthoff, I. M., and Menzel, H., "Volumetric Analysis," translated by N. H. Furman, vol. 2, p. 346, John Wiley & Sons, Inc., New York, 1929.

[2] Wolfenden, J. H., *Anal. Chem.*, **29**, 1098 (1957).

[3] Kolthoff, I. M., and Sandell, E. B., "Textbook of Quantitative Inorganic Analysis," 3d ed., p. 589, The Macmillan Company, New York, 1952.

[4] Meyer, K. H., "Advances in Colloid Science," vol. 1, pp. 142–162, Interscience Publishers, Inc. New York, 1942.

[5] Rundle, R. E., *J. Am. Chem. Soc.*, **65**, 142, 1707 (1943).

[6] Lambert, J. L., *Anal. Chem.*, **23**, 1251 (1951).

of iodide. However, the reaction

$$5Ag^+ + 3I_2 + 3H_2O \rightarrow 5AgI + IO_3^- + 6H^+ \qquad \Delta F^\circ = -45.3 \text{ kcal}$$

$$(21\text{-}9)$$

proceeds to the right in the presence of silver ions. A similar reaction can be written for Hg(II). Upon addition of an excess of iodide, iodine is generated once more. This is the basis for the use of starch-iodine or Ce(IV)-starch as an indicator for the silver iodide titration.[1]

"Soluble starch," available from chemical supply houses, is readily dispersed in water. The iodine-starch complex has limited water solubility, and it is therefore important not to add the starch indicator until near the end point when the iodine concentration is very low. Because starch is subject to attack by microorganisms, the solution is usually prepared as needed. Among the products of hydrolysis is dextrose, which could cause large errors because of its reducing action. Various substances have been recommended as preservatives, including mercuric iodide,[2] thymol, and more recently glycerol[3] and formamide.[4] The latter forms a clear solution containing 5 per cent starch which is stable indefinitely.

Liggett and Diehl[5] recommended the amylose fraction of starch as a very sensitive iodine indicator. Lambert[6] and Lambert and Rhoads[7] have described simple methods for preparation of a linear starch fraction in 10 per cent acetic acid. Sodium starch glycollate[8,9] and polyvinyl-alcohol[10] have been suggested as being superior to starch in forming water-soluble complexes.

21-3. Primary Standards and Standard Solutions

Iodine can be purified by sublimation from potassium iodide and lime, and weighed as a primary standard. Because of the limited solubility and volatility of iodine, it is necessary to dissolve it in concentrated potassium iodide solution and dilute to volume. To avoid air oxidation of the iodide, the solution should be prepared using water free of heavy metal ions, and it should be stored in a cool, dark place. Because of the

[1] Bloom, A., and McNabb, W. M., *Ind. Eng. Chem., Anal. Ed.*, **8**, 167 (1936).

[2] Kolthoff and Sandell, *op. cit.*

[3] Nordling, W. D., *Chemist Analyst*, **42**, 70 (1953).

[4] Holler, A. C., *Anal. Chem.*, **27**, 866 (1955).

[5] Liggett, L. M., and Diehl, H., *Anachem News*, **6**, 9 (1946); *Chem. Abstr.*, **40**, 2757 (1946).

[6] Lambert, *Anal. Chem.*, **25**, 984 (1953).

[7] Lambert, J. L., and Rhoads, S. C., *Anal. Chem.*, **28**, 1629 (1956).

[8] Peat, S., Bourne, E. J., and Thrower, R. D., *Nature*, **159**, 810 (1947).

[9] Deibner, L., *Chim. Anal.*, **33**, 207 (1951).

[10] Miller, S. A., and Bracken, A., *J. Chem. Soc.*, **1951**, 1933.

inconvenience of weighing iodine accurately, its solutions are commonly standardized against arsenious oxide[1] (primary standard) or thiosulfate.

Thiosulfate solutions are generally prepared from sodium thiosulfate pentahydrate, $Na_2S_2O_3 \cdot 5H_2O$, which under ordinary conditions is not a primary standard. The pentahydrate, which is efflorescent, may be stored over a saturated solution of calcium chloride hexahydrate. Anhydrous sodium thiosulfate[2] and barium thiosulfate monohydrate[3,4] have been suggested as primary standard substances. The anhydrous sodium salt is somewhat hygroscopic, and the barium salt suffers from the disadvantage of limited water solubility. According to Ludekens and de Silva,[5] strontium thiosulfate can readily be prepared in 99.90 per cent purity and shows no absorption of moisture when exposed to the atmosphere at 80 to 96 per cent relative humidity.

Thiosulfate solutions should be prepared from water free of heavy metal impurities, to avoid "catalytic" air oxidation. Ordinary air oxidation is negligible in rate and proceeds through the slow decomposition of thiosulfate to sulfite, which is rapidly air-oxidized to sulfate. "Catalyzed" air oxidation, on the other hand, proceeds through the reduction of metals such as Cu(II) or Fe(III), present as thiosulfate complexes, followed by air oxidation of the lower oxidation state, e.g.,

$$2Cu(II) + 2S_2O_3^= \rightarrow S_4O_6^= + 2Cu(I) \qquad (21\text{-}10)$$
$$2Cu(I) + \tfrac{1}{2}O_2 + H_2O \rightarrow 2Cu(II) + 2OH^- \qquad (21\text{-}11)$$

Freshly boiled water is generally recommended, so as to avoid bacteria that decompose thiosulfate solutions. A few drops of chloroform[6] act as an effective preservative. Boiling also removes dissolved carbon dioxide, which is harmful unless neutralized, because of the decomposition of thiosulfate

$$HS_2O_3^- \rightarrow HSO_3^- + S \qquad (21\text{-}12)$$

to form sulfite and sulfur. A *small amount* (0.1 g liter^{-1}) of sodium carbonate may be added to advantage to ensure a slightly alkaline solution, but the addition of sodium hydroxide or large amounts of carbonate or borax should be avoided, because there is evidence that such solutions are actually less stable, especially at higher temperatures.[7] The detailed mechanism of decomposition is very complicated and involves the forma-

[1] Popoff, S., and Whitman, J. L., *J. Am. Chem. Soc.*, **47**, 2259 (1925).

[2] Tomlinson, H. M., and Ciapetta, F. G., *Ind. Eng. Chem., Anal. Ed.*, **13**, 539 (1941).

[3] MacNevin, W. M., and Kriege, O. H., *Anal. Chem.*, **25**, 767 (1953).

[4] Ludekens, W. L. W., and de Silva, N. R., *Chemist Analyst*, **45**, 77 (1956).

[5] Ludekens and de Silva, *Research Correspondence* [suppl. to *Research (London)*], **9**, no. 8, S31 (1956).

[6] Kassner, J. L., and Kassner, E. E., *Ind. Eng. Chem., Anal. Ed.*, **12**, 655 (1940).

[7] Rue, S. O., *Ind. Eng. Chem., Anal. Ed.*, **14**, 802 (1942).

tion of sulfide, sulfite, sulfate, tetrathionate, and perhaps trithionate.[1,2] If a turbidity develops, it is best to discard the solution and prepare a fresh one. Care must be taken to add an excess of acid, especially when titrating standard iodine solutions stored under neutral conditions.

Several primary standards are available for the standardization of thiosulfate solutions.[3,4] *Potassium dichromate* liberates iodine according to the equation

$$Cr_2O_7^= + 14H^+ + 6I^- \rightarrow 3I_2 + 2Cr^{3+} + 7H_2O \qquad (21\text{-}13)$$

The reaction is not instantaneous at moderate acidity, and a relatively high acidity is used, with the concomitant danger of air oxidation of iodide. By regulating the concentrations of acid and potassium iodide rather closely (for example, using 0.2 M hydrochloric acid and 2 per cent potassium iodide) and allowing the mixture to stand 10 min, accurate results are obtained. Some procedures call for displacement of the air by addition of sodium bicarbonate to evolve carbon dioxide and allowing the mixture to stand at moderate acid concentration for a few minutes. Copper(II) exerts a catalytic effect[5] on the reaction such that the reaction is instantaneous even in acetic acid solution. The acetic acid has the additional advantage of decreasing the intensity of the Cr(III) color by complex formation. For accurate work, the iodine can be distilled into a potassium iodide solution with the aid of a stream of carbon dioxide.[6]

Potassium iodate can be purified for use as a primary standard by recrystallization from water and drying at 180°C. It is useful not only as a titrant in the Andrews and related procedures (page 426) but also as a substitute for iodine solution as a titrant and as a source of iodine for the standardization of thiosulfate. The latter two uses are based on the rapid and stoichiometric formation of iodine in solutions that are even slightly acidic:

$$IO_3^- + 6H^+ + 5I^- \rightarrow 3I_2 + 3H_2O \qquad (21\text{-}14)$$

This reaction forms the basis for using potassium iodate as a primary standard for the standardization of strong acids (page 90) and also provides a sensitive test for the presence of iodide in iodate or the reverse.

Morgan *et al.*[7] have postulated that the mechanism of the iodate-

---

[1] Bassett, H., and Durrant, R. G., *J. Chem. Soc.*, **1927**, 1401.

[2] Kolthoff and Menzel, "Volumetric Analysis," vol. 1, pp. 231–238, Wiley, 1928.

[3] Popoff and Whitman, *op. cit.*

[4] Munday, W. H., *J. Assoc. Offic. Agr. Chemists*, **38**, 382 (1955).

[5] Sully, B. D., *J. Chem. Soc.*, **1942**, 366.

[6] Analytical Chemists Committee of Imperial Chemical Industries, *Analyst*, **75**, 577 (1950).

[7] Morgan, K. J., Peard, M. G., and Cullis, C. F., *J. Chem. Soc.*, **1951**, 1865.

iodide reaction involves the *basic* dissociation of iodic acid

$$HIO_3 \rightleftharpoons IO_2^+ + OH^-$$

with the formation of the cation IO_2^+, which interacts with iodide to form an intermediate $IO_2^+ \cdot I^-$. The latter can either decompose

$$IO_2^+ \cdot I^- \rightarrow IO^+ + IO^-$$

or react with iodide

$$IO_2^+ \cdot I^- + I^- \rightarrow I^+ + 2IO^-$$

The intermediate IO^+ can react with iodide

$$IO^+ + I^- \rightarrow I^+ + IO^-$$

Hypoiodite ion is in equilibrium with unipositive iodine ions

$$IO^- + H^+ \rightleftharpoons IOH$$
$$IOH + H^+ \rightleftharpoons IOH_2^+ (= I^+ \cdot H_2O)$$
$$I^+ + I^- \rightleftharpoons I_2$$

The reverse reaction, the formation of iodate by the reaction of iodine with hydroxyl ion, proceeds through the formation of hypoiodite

$$I_2 + 2OH^- \rightarrow I^- + OI^-$$

It has been postulated[1] that the disproportionation of hypoiodite is extremely complex, involving the reaction between IO^- and HOI to form $HI_2O_2^-$, which reacts with several other species.

Potassium bromate can, likewise, be purified by recrystallization and drying at 180°C. It is somewhat more stable than potassium iodate but reacts more slowly with iodide. The reaction rate can be increased by increasing the hydrogen ion concentration (to about 1 N) or by adding a small amount of ammonium molybdate as a catalyst. The reaction is

$$BrO_3^- + 6H^+ + 6I^- \rightarrow 3I_2 + Br^- + 3H_2O \qquad (21\text{-}15)$$

Potassium ferricyanide,[2] *metallic copper, potassium biiodate,*[3] and *iodine* are also useful primary standards for thiosulfate. Permanganate and Ce(IV) solutions, appropriately standardized, may be used as secondary standards, chiefly as a check on the separate standardizations.[4,5]

[1] Morgan, *Quart. Rev. Chem. Soc.,* **8,** 123 (1954).
[2] Kolthoff, *Pharm. Weekblad,* **59,** 66 (1922).
[3] Kolthoff, I. M., and van Beck, L. H., *J. Am. Chem. Soc.,* **48,** 2799 (1926).
[4] Bray, W. C., and Miller, H. E., *J. Am. Chem. Soc.,* **46,** 2204 (1924).
[5] Popoff and Whitman, *op. cit.*

21-4. The Iodine-Thiosulfate Reaction

When a neutral or slightly acidic solution of iodine in potassium iodide is titrated with thiosulfate, the following reaction occurs rapidly and stoichiometrically:

$$I_3^- + 2S_2O_3^= \rightarrow 3I^- + S_4O_6^= \tag{21-16}$$

Although the reaction is rapid and some tetrathionate is formed immediately upon mixing, it has been shown that a colorless intermediate, $S_2O_3I^-$, is formed by a rapid, reversible reaction

$$S_2O_3^= + I_3^- \rightleftharpoons S_2O_3I^- + 2I^- \tag{21-17}$$

The intermediate reacts with iodide,

$$2S_2O_3I^- + I^- \rightarrow S_4O_6^= + I_3^- \tag{21-18}$$

which accounts for the reappearance of iodine near the end point in the titration of very dilute iodine solutions.[1]   The intermediate also reacts with thiosulfate,[2,3] to provide the main course of the over-all reaction

$$S_2O_3I^- + S_2O_3^= \rightarrow S_4O_6^= + I^- \tag{21-19}$$

The rate law for the formation of tetrathionate turns out to involve the square of the concentration of the ion $S_2O_3I^-$.   At low concentrations of iodide (below $0.003\ M$) the stoichiometry is no longer exact, because some sulfate is formed by the reaction

$$S_2O_3I^- + 3I_3^- + 5H_2O \rightarrow 2SO_4^= + 10H^+ + 10I^- \tag{21-20}$$

which involves the first power of the $S_2O_3I^-$ concentration in the rate law.   Thus sulfate formation becomes more important toward the end of a titration, as the $S_2O_3I^-$ concentration becomes smaller.   Tetrathionate undergoes slow oxidation by excess iodine to form sulfate,[4] but the reaction is too slow to be of serious consequence under the usual analytical conditions.   However, the instability of tetrathionate must be considered if the solution is to be used for other determinations, because substances that consume iodine, such as thiosulfate and sulfite, may be slowly formed, particularly in neutral or alkaline solution.[5]

From a practical viewpoint, the iodine-thiosulfate reaction is accurate under the usual experimental conditions provided that the pH is less than 5.   In alkaline solution, (pH > 8) iodine reacts with hydroxyl ion

[1] Kolthoff, *Z. anal. Chem.*, **60**, 338 (1921).

[2] Dodd, G., and Griffith, R. O., *Trans. Faraday Soc.*, **45**, 546 (1949).

[3] Awtrey, A. D., and Connick, R. E., *J. Am. Chem. Soc.*, **73**, 1341 (1951).

[4] *Ibid.*

[5] Kolthoff and Menzel, *op. cit.*, p. 348.

to form hypoiodous acid $(K_a \cong 10^{-11})$

$$I_2 + OH^- \rightleftharpoons HOI + I^- \qquad (21\text{-}21)$$

or hypoiodite ion[1]

$$I_2 + 2OH^- \rightleftharpoons OI^- + I^- + H_2O \qquad (21\text{-}22)$$

either of which oxidizes thiosulfate partially to sulfate.[2] For example, Kolthoff[3] found that the consumption of thiosulfate was low by 2.5, 2.3, and 7.1 per cent, respectively, when equal volumes of 0.2 M $NaHCO_3$, Na_2HPO_4, and $Na_2B_4O_7$ were added to 0.1 N iodine solution prior to titration. However the same salts had no effect on the reverse titration, because the rapid thiosulfate reaction consumed the iodine before it could react with hydroxyl ions. In strongly alkaline solution, the reaction goes quantitatively to sulfate.[4] For this reason it is safe practice to ensure proper stoichiometry by acidification. In extremely acid solution, one must guard against exposure of thiosulfate (even a local excess) to acid, for fear of decomposition of thiosulfate to yield sulfurous acid and sulfur. Sulfurous acid reacts with 1 mole I_2 per mole as compared with $\frac{1}{2}$ mole I_2 per mole of thiosulfate.

$$S_2O_3^= + 2H^+ \rightarrow H_2SO_3 + S \qquad (21\text{-}23)$$
$$H_2SO_3 + I_2 + H_2O \rightarrow SO_4^= + 4H^+ + 2I^- \qquad (21\text{-}24)$$

Actually, a rather strongly acidic solution of iodine can be titrated if the thiosulfate is added slowly with vigorous stirring. However, in the reverse titration (thiosulfate with iodine), a very weakly acidic solution must be used to avoid decomposition. A minimum concentration of acid is favorable to avoid appreciable air oxidation of iodide.

It should be remembered that strong oxidants generally oxidize thiosulfate to a mixture of tetrathionate, sulfate, and sulfur. The reaction between the oxidant and excess iodide must, therefore, be allowed to go to completion before titration of the iodine with thiosulfate.

21-5. The Iodine-Arsenite Reaction

For an acid solution (pH < 2), we may write the equilibrium

$$H_3AsO_3 + I_3^- + H_2O \rightleftharpoons H_3AsO_4 + 3I^- + 2H^+ \qquad (21\text{-}25)$$

for which an equilibrium constant of 5.5×10^{-2} has been evaluated.[5]

At higher pH values, the ionization of arsenious acid ($pK_1 = 9.2$) and of arsenic acid ($pK_1 = 2.3$, $pK_2 = 4.4$, $pK_3 = 9.2$) must be considered.

[1] Allen, T. L., and Keefer, R. M., J. Am. Chem. Soc., **77**, 2957 (1955).
[2] Bradbury, J. H., and Hambly, A. N., Australian J. Sci. Research, **A5**, 541 (1952).
[3] Kolthoff, op. cit.
[4] Abel, E., Z. anorg. u. allgem. Chem., **74**, 395 (1912).
[5] Washburn, E. W., and Strachan, E. K., J. Am. Chem. Soc., **35**, 681 (1912).

Thus the half-reactions for oxidation of As(III) are properly written

$$H_3AsO_3 + H_2O \rightarrow H_3AsO_4 + 2H^+ + 2e^- \qquad pH < 2.3 \qquad (21\text{-}26)$$
$$H_3AsO_3 + H_2O \rightarrow H_2AsO_4^- + 3H^+ + 2e^- \qquad 2.3 < pH < 4.4 \qquad (21\text{-}27)$$
$$H_3AsO_3 + H_2O \rightarrow HAsO_4^- + 4H^+ + 2e^- \qquad 4.4 < pH < 9.2 \qquad (21\text{-}28)$$
$$H_2AsO_3^- + H_2O \rightarrow AsO_4^{3-} + 4H^+ + 2e^- \qquad 9.2 < pH \qquad (21\text{-}29)$$

The iodine-iodide half-reaction is independent of pH until a pH of 9 is reached. From pH 9 to 11, the formation of hypoiodite is appreciable, but hypoiodite oxidizes arsenite to arsenate stoichiometrically

$$H_2AsO_3^- + OI^- + 2OH^- \rightarrow AsO_4^{3-} + I^- + H_2O \qquad (21\text{-}30)$$

and so arsenite can be titrated successfully with iodine up to pH 11.* Above this pH value, the formation of iodate becomes appreciable, and iodate does not readily oxidize arsenite. The reverse titration of iodine with arsenite is not successful above a pH of 9, because of the formation of iodate.

The potential-pH diagram of the arsenate-arsenite system is shown in Fig. 21-1.

Arsenate is a stronger oxidant than iodine in strongly acidic solution and, indeed, can be determined quantitatively by addition of excess iodide at an acid concentration of about 4 N and titration of the resulting iodine. The more usual determination, however, is based on the direct titration of arsenite with iodine at a higher pH. To ensure adequate speed and quantitativeness, the titration should be carried out at pH values between 4 and 9.

Disodium phosphate or borax may be conveniently used to buffer a strongly acidic solution to the proper pH range. Sodium bicarbonate is less desirable because of the possible loss of iodine vapor with the escaping carbon dioxide.

21-6. Determination of Iodide

Iodide may be oxidized to iodine with sodium nitrite in acid solution

$$2I^- + 2HNO_2 + 2H^+ \rightarrow 2NO + I_2 + 2H_2O \qquad (21\text{-}31)$$

and $\qquad 4I^- + 2HNO_2 + 4H^+ \rightarrow N_2O + 2I_2 + 3H_2O \qquad (21\text{-}31a)$

Reaction (21-31) predominates in 10 to 12 N H_2SO_4; both (21-31) and (21-31a) occur in 2 to 7.5 N H_2SO_4. In hydrochloric acid similar reactions occur except at concentrations above 5 N; in that case ICl and NO are the primary products.[1]

$$I^- + 2HNO_2 + 2H^+ + Cl^- \rightarrow ICl + 2NO + 2H_2O \qquad (21\text{-}32)$$

---

* McAlpine, R. K., *J. Chem. Educ.*, **26**, 362 (1949).
[1] Britton, H. T. S., and Britton, H. G., *J. Chem. Soc.*, **1952**, 3892.

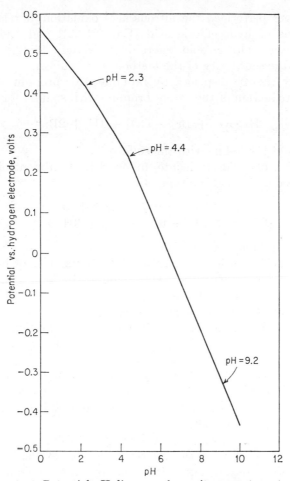

Fig. 21-1. Potential-pH diagram of arsenite-arsenate system.

The excess nitrite (and nitric oxide) can be destroyed by the addition of an excess of urea

$$2HNO_2 + CO(NH_2)_2 \rightarrow CO_2 + 2N_2 + 3H_2O \qquad (21\text{-}33)$$

Since the reaction between urea and nitrous acid (and nitric oxide) is slow compared with the rapid reaction between nitrite and iodide in acid solution, the urea may be added first to the acidified iodide solution. Then sodium nitrite is added, and then, allowing time for the reaction of excess nitrous acid and nitric oxide, the iodine is titrated with standard thiosulfate.[1]

[1] Kolthoff and Sandell, *op. cit.*, p. 599.

Johannesson[1] performed the nitrous acid oxidation at relatively high concentrations of hydrochloric acid [Eq. (21-32)] and added urea to remove the excess nitrous acid before diluting and adding excess iodide. In this way, the sensitivity of the method was doubled.

Iodine may also be displaced by bromine; this procedure is followed by selective reduction of the excess bromine with sodium formate

$$HCOO^- + Br_2 \rightarrow CO_2 + H^+ + 2Br^- \qquad (21\text{-}34)$$

and titration of the iodine with thiosulfate.[2]

By oxidation of iodide to iodate, followed by treatment of the iodate with excess iodide in acid solution,

$$I^- + 3H_2O \rightarrow IO_3^- + 6H^+ + 6e^- \qquad (21\text{-}35)$$
$$IO_3^- + 5I^- + 6H^+ \rightarrow 3I_2 + 3H_2O \qquad (21\text{-}36)$$

an amplification factor of 6 is achieved.

In weakly acid solution (pH 1.2 to 3.2), bromine may be used as a quantitative oxidant, the excess being removed by boiling or, more conveniently, by the addition of phenol to form mono-, di-, or tribromophenol depending upon the relative concentrations of bromine and phenol. The solution should be acidic, because in an alkaline solution some of the excess bromine is converted to bromate, which is not removed by boiling or phenol treatment. Bromate reacts relatively slowly with excess iodide and gives rise to a fleeting end point with high results in the thiosulfate titration.[3]

Sodium chlorite has been used to oxidize iodide to iodate in acetate or phosphate buffers of pH 5.3 to 5.7.[*]

The amplification factor may be increased to 36 or even to 216 by extracting the iodine with carbon tetrachloride, extracting back into aqueous solution, reoxidizing with bromine water, boiling to remove excess bromine, adding excess iodide and repeating the extraction.[4]

Chlorine may also be used to oxidize iodide to iodate. In the original method of Winkler,[5] chlorine was used in weakly acid solution (pH = 2), and the excess was removed by boiling. Phenol may also be used to remove excess chlorine.

Schulek and Endröi[6] studied the mechanism of the oxidation of iodide with chlorine and hypochlorite. In a neutral or acid solution in the

[1] Johannesson, J. K., *Anal. Chem.*, **30**, 1535 (1958).
[2] Spitzer, L., *Ind. Eng. Chem., Anal. Ed.*, **8**, 465 (1936).
[3] Jensen, P. W., and Crittenden, A. L., *Anal. Chem.*, **26**, 1373 (1954).
[*] Yntema, L. F., and Fleming, T., *Ind. Eng. Chem., Anal. Ed.*, **11**, 375 (1939).
[4] Spitzy, H., Skrube, H., and Sadek, F. S., *Mikrochim. Acta*, **1953**, 375.
[5] See von Weszelszky, J., *Z. anal. Chem.*, **39**, 81 (1900).
[6] Schulek, E., and Endröi, P., *Anal. Chim. Acta*, **5**, 252 (1951).

presence of bromide, bromine chloride is formed

$$Cl_2 + Br^- \rightarrow BrCl + Cl^-$$

and an excess of chlorine must be added to effect the complete oxidation of iodide to iodate. If the solution is too acidic, a loss of iodine may be experienced upon boiling; if it is too basic, bromate will be formed. Schulek and Endröi suggested the use of potassium cyanide to remove excess chlorine as cyanogen chloride, CNCl, which is inactive toward iodide. They found that the oxidation of iodide was speeded up enormously by bromide and suggested that the mechanism involves hypobromite, which oxidizes iodide to iodate:

$$BrCl + 2OH^- \rightarrow OBr^- + Cl^- + H_2O \qquad (21\text{-}37)$$
$$I^- + 3OBr^- \rightarrow IO_3^- + 3Br^- \qquad (21\text{-}38)$$

Hypochlorite oxidizes iodide to iodate (and bromide to bromate) quantitatively at pH 5.5 to 7.0.[1,2] In the original van der Meulen method, excess hypochlorite was removed by catalyzed reduction with hydrogen peroxide. A better method, introduced by D'Ans and Höfer,[3] involves the use of sodium formate. This reaction is catalyzed by a trace of ammonium molybdate.[4]

Iodate may be determined in the presence of bromate by taking advantage of its more rapid reaction with iodide. At a pH of 5, iodate reacts quantitatively, but bromate does not react. To determine the bromate, acid and molybdate catalyst are added to hasten the bromate-iodide reaction.[5]

21-7. Determination of Bromide

A variety of oxidants has been used to oxidize bromide to bromine, which is distilled or extracted and determined iodometrically. By proper choice of oxidant, bromide is oxidized selectively in the presence of chloride. Among the oxidants are permanganate with hydrochloric acid, phosphoric acid, or copper sulfate; chromic acid with sulfuric acid; and chromic acid with nitric acid. Using the latter oxidant with an extraction of bromine,[6] iodide was converted to iodate and did not interfere. Larger amounts of sodium chloride than 75 mg in 100 ml gave high results.

[1] Van der Meulen, J. H., *Chem. Weekblad*, **28**, 82, 238 (1931).

[2] Willard, H. H., and Heyn, A. H. A., *Ind. Eng. Chem., Anal. Ed.*, **15**, 321 (1943).

[3] D'Ans, J., and Höfer, P., *Angew. Chem.*, **47**, 73 (1934).

[4] Kolthoff, I. M., and Yutzy, H. C., *Ind. Eng. Chem., Anal. Ed.*, **9**, 75 (1937).

[5] Kolthoff, I. M., and Hume, D. N., *Ind. Eng. Chem., Anal. Ed.*, **15**, 174 (1943).

[6] Kapur, P. L., Verma, M. R., and Khosla, B. D., *Ind. Eng. Chem., Anal. Ed.*, **14**, 157 (1942).

Iodate can be used in acid solution to oxidize bromide to bromine which is removed by boiling. The excess iodate is determined iodometrically.[1] Large amounts of chloride cause high results.

Lang[2] used permanganate in the presence of cyanide to oxidize bromide to cyanogen bromide

$$Br^- + HCN \rightarrow CNBr + H^+ + 2e^- \qquad (21\text{-}39)$$

which is not reduced by acid solutions of reducing agents such as arsenite or ferrous iron. Thus the excess permanganate can be destroyed by the addition of Fe(II), and the iodine that is formed from the cyanogen bromide by the reaction

$$CNBr + H^+ + 2I^- \rightarrow I_2 + Br^- + HCN \qquad (21\text{-}40)$$

is titrated with thiosulfate. If the titration is carried out immediately after adding iodide, the excess ferrous iron does not interfere.

The oxidation of bromide by chlorine has been studied by Szabó and Csányi,[3] who stated that the oxidation occurs in two steps. At pH 6.5 to 7.5, hypobromous acid, HOBr, is formed, which yields bromate upon hydrolysis. At pH 8.5 to 9.0 the hydrolysis proceeds at a rate fast enough for analytical purposes.

According to Farkas and Lewin,[4] the mechanism of the oxidation of bromide by hypochlorite involves the formation of hypobromite:

$$OCl^- + Br^- \rightarrow OBr^- + Cl^- \qquad (21\text{-}41)$$

which is complete in several minutes at pH 9 to 10 or in several hours at pH 12 to 14. At lower pH values, bromate is formed by the reactions:

$$2OCl^- + OBr^- \rightarrow 2Cl^- + BrO_3^- \qquad (21\text{-}42)$$
and
$$2HOCl + OBr^- \rightarrow 2Cl^- + BrO_3^- + 2H^+ \qquad (21\text{-}43)$$

In addition, some chlorate is formed:

$$2HOCl + OCl^- \rightarrow 2Cl^- + ClO_3^- + 2H^+ \qquad (21\text{-}44)$$

By controlling the pH at 9.0 to 9.4, Farkas and Lewin[5] were able to produce hypobromite exclusively. By using a measured amount of hypochlorite and by taking advantage of the fact that alkaline phenol reduces hypobromite in the presence of hypochlorite, they were able to determine bromide in the presence of chloride. The excess hypochlorite was determined after the phenol reaction by adding an excess of arsenite and titrat-

[1] Kolthoff, *Z. anal. Chem.*, **60**, 344, (1921).
[2] Lang, R., *Z. anorg. u. allgem. Chem.*, **144**, 75 (1925).
[3] Szabó, Z. G., and Csányi, L. J., *Anal. Chim. Acta*, **6**, 208 (1952).
[4] Farkas, L., and Lewin, M., *Anal. Chem.*, **19**, 662, 665 (1947).
[5] *Ibid.*

ing the arsenite with iodine. For this procedure exact control of conditions is necessary to prevent the reduction of hypochlorite by phenol.

Another method for determination of hypobromite in the presence of hypochlorite is that of Schulek and Endröi,[1,2] who used the reaction with cyanide to form cyanogen bromide and chloride:

$$OX^- + CN^- + H_2O \rightarrow CNX + 2OH^- \qquad (21\text{-}45)$$

This reaction is rapid for both hypobromite and hypochlorite and is followed by the slow reaction

$$CNX + H_2O \rightarrow X^- + CNO^- + 2H^+ \qquad (21\text{-}46)$$

the rate of which depends upon the pH. For the determination, the hypohalite mixture is poured into a solution containing KH_2PO_4 and potassium cyanide. The solution is mixed, acidified, and treated with potassium iodide. After 30 min standing, the iodine is titrated with thiosulfate. Under proper conditions only the cyanogen bromide reacts with iodide.

21-8. Determination of Chloride

By treating a soluble chloride with the sparingly soluble iodate of silver, Hg(I), or Hg(II), an equivalent amount of iodate is released:

$$AgIO_3 + Cl^- \rightarrow AgCl + IO_3^- \qquad (21\text{-}47)$$

Belcher and Goulden[3] have proposed this reaction for the determination of organic chlorine. By determining the iodate iodometrically, an amplification factor of 6 is achieved.

21-9. Determination of Arsenic

The conventional method[4] consists of titrating As(III) in bicarbonate solution with standard iodine, using starch as the indicator. Arsenic(V) may be reduced to arsenic trichloride by cuprous chloride in hydrochloric acid solution and separated by distillation. If distillation is employed for separation, the Andrews titration to the iodine monochloride end point (page 428) is convenient.

Ion exchange is convenient as a separation method for arsenate.[5] Arsenic is oxidized by nitric acid and potassium bromate, and the excess oxidant is destroyed by evaporation to dryness. The residue is dissolved in dilute hydrochloric acid and passed through a column of cation

[1] Schulek and Endröi, op. cit.
[2] Schulek and Endröi, Anal. Chim. Acta, **5**, 252 (1951).
[3] Belcher, R., and Goulden, R., Mikrochim. Acta, **1953**, 290.
[4] Jamison, G. S., Ind. Eng. Chem., **10**, 290 (1918).
[5] Odencrantz, J. T., and Riemann, W., III, Anal. Chem., **22**, 1066 (1950).

exchange resin in the hydrogen form. The resin retains metallic ions and allows arsenic acid and hydrochloric acid to pass through. The hydrochloric acid concentration is adjusted to 4 N, an excess of iodide is added, and the liberated iodine is titrated with thiosulfate.

Arsenic may also be determined by preliminary reduction to elemental arsenic by means of hypophosphorous acid.[1-3] The arsenic is separated by filtration, treated with excess standard Ce(IV) in sulfuric acid,[4] bromate-bromide in hydrochloric acid,[5] or iodine in a bicarbonate medium[6] to oxidize the arsenic to As(V). The excess oxidant is determined with standard arsenite.

21-10. Determination of Nitrite

Several iodometric procedures have been proposed for nitrite.[7-9] The reaction

$$2HNO_2 + 2I^- + 2H^+ \rightarrow I_2 + 2NO + 2H_2O \qquad (21\text{-}48)$$

proceeds only in acid solution and is negligible in rate above pH 6.* Air must be carefully excluded, because the reactions:

$$NO + \tfrac{1}{2}O_2 \rightarrow NO_2 \qquad (21\text{-}49)$$
$$NO_2 + 2I^- + 2H^+ \rightarrow I_2 + NO + H_2O \qquad (21\text{-}50)$$

are rapid over a wide range of pH. At a pH above 6, nitrogen dioxide gives a high result, but it is consumed by the reaction

$$2NO_2 + 2OH^- \rightarrow NO_3^- + NO_2^- + H_2O \qquad (21\text{-}51)$$

and thereafter the air oxidation is not abnormally rapid.* A stream of carbon dioxide,*,[10] is usually recommended.

Because it is difficult to exclude air, the iodopermanganate method[11] is preferable. The oxidation of nitrite by permanganate is a slow reaction, not well suited to a direct titration. However, if an excess of acidified permanganate is added to a nitrite solution, the nitrite is quantitatively

[1] Kolthoff, I. M., and Amdur, E., *Ind. Eng. Chem., Anal. Ed.*, **12**, 177 (1940).

[2] Sloviter, H. A., McNabb, W. M., and Wagner, E. C., *Ind. Eng. Chem , Anal. Ed.*, **14**, 516 (1942).

[3] Haslam, J., and Wilkinson, N. T., *Analyst*, **78**, 390 (1953).

[4] Kolthoff and Amdur, *op. cit.*

[5] Sloviter, McNabb, and Wagner, *op. cit.*

[6] Haslam and Wilkinson, *op. cit.*

[7] Winograd, A., *Chemist Analyst*, **20**(3), 15 (1931).

[8] Lang, F. M., and Aunis, G., *Chim. anal.*, **32**, 139 (1950).

[9] Abeledo, C. A., and Kolthoff, I. M., *J. Am. Chem. Soc.*, **53**, 2893 (1931).

* *Ibid.*

[10] Winograd, *op. cit.*

[11] Brasted, R. C., *Anal. Chem.*, **23**, 980 (1951).

oxidized to nitrate. The permanganate is reduced in part to Mn(II) and in part to manganese(IV) oxide. An excess of iodide reduces the manganese quantitatively to Mn(II), and the resulting iodine is titrated in the usual way with thiosulfate.

Longstaff and Singer[1] suggested the use of bromine as an oxidant in acetic acid in the presence of pyridine as a catalyst. The excess bromine is determined iodometrically.

21-11. Determination of Hypophosphite and Phosphite

Wolf and Jung[2] showed that iodine in bicarbonate solution rapidly oxidizes phosphite to phosphate, whereas hypophosphite hardly reacts at all. On the other hand, in acid solution hypophosphite reacts quantitatively, and phosphite reacts only partially in 1 hr.

Jones and Swift[3] used a phosphate buffer to maintain an essentially neutral solution for the oxidation of phosphite, and 1.5 M HCl for the oxidation of hypophosphite. Both reactions are relatively slow. Total reducing power is determined by allowing iodine to react in acid solution for 3.5 hr, buffering to essential neutrality, and continuing the reaction for another hour. In a separate determination, the phosphite is determined by oxidation in neutral solution, and the hypophosphite is determined by difference.

21-12. Determination of Sulfide

The reaction

$$H_2S + I_2 \rightarrow S + 2H^+ + 2I^- \tag{21-52}$$

can be applied as a direct titration with iodine or with iodate-iodide or as an indirect determination by adding an excess of iodine followed by a back titration.[4,5] A source of error, in addition to the usual ones in iodine methods, is the loss of H_2S by volatility. The error is minimized by the use of a back-titration method, by using a closed system, or by using a solution such as ammoniacal cadmium chloride to collect the sulfide as CdS, which releases H_2S upon acidification. Occlusion of iodine with the precipitated sulfur is minimized by using starch as a dispersing agent.[6] Oxidation of sulfide to sulfate may occur in part in alkaline solution. Bethge[7] recommended the use of a phosphoric acid

[1] Longstaff, J. V. L., and Singer, K., *Analyst*, **78**, 491 (1953).

[2] Wolf, L., and Jung, W., *Z. anorg. u. allgem. Chem.*, **201**, 337 (1931); *Z. anal. Chem.*, **97**, 275 (1934).

[3] Jones, R. T., and Swift, E. H., *Anal. Chem.*, **25**, 1272 (1953).

[4] Luke, C. L., *Ind. Eng. Chem., Anal. Ed.*, **15**, 602 (1943); **17**, 298 (1945).

[5] Bethge, P. O., *Anal. Chim. Acta*, **9**, 129 (1953).

[6] Luke, *op. cit.*

[7] Bethge, *op. cit.*

solution in an evacuated flask to which the sulfide sample and an excess of iodine are added.

Horak[1] determined pyrite sulfur by distillation of hydrogen sulfide from a mixture of phosphoric acid and hypophosphorous acid. The H_2S was collected in cadmium acetate, which was boiled in a stream of CO_2 to remove phosphine. After acidification, the sample was titrated with iodate-iodide solution.

Luke[2] reduced sulfate to hydrogen sulfide by distillation from a mixture of hydriodic acid and hypophosphorous acid. The hydrogen sulfide was collected in ammoniacal cadmium solution. The method was devised for the determination of total sulfur in rubber; it involved a wet oxidation treatment to convert sulfur to sulfuric acid and the addition of zinc nitrate as a retainer to avoid loss of SO_3 during the oxidation.

21-13. Determination of Sulfurous Acid

The direct titration of sulfurous acid with iodine is subject to error due to air oxidation,[3] even in the presence of substances like mannitol, cane sugar, etc., which retard the air oxidation. Accurate results, however, can be obtained by adding the sample to a measured excess of iodine.

The reaction between sulfite and iodine can be retarded by the addition of an excess of formaldehyde, to permit the determination of thiosulfate in the presence of sulfite.[4]

21-14. Determination of Cyanide

Iodine reacts with hydrocyanic acid according to the equation[5,6]

$$I_2 + HCN \rightarrow ICN + I^- + H^+ \qquad K = 0.87 \qquad (21\text{-}53)$$

The magnitude of the equilibrium constant indicates that a quantitative reaction could be expected in alkaline solution. According to Kolthoff[7] the end point is sharpest in a carbonate-bicarbonate medium in the absence of starch, which slows the reaction between iodine and cyanide. An extraction indicator such as carbon tetrachloride is recommended.

21-15. Determination of Selenium

Selenite can be determined iodometrically, through the reaction

$$SeO_3^= + 4I^- + 6H^+ \rightleftharpoons Se + 2I_2 + 3H_2O \qquad (21\text{-}54)$$

[1] Horak, O., *Z anal. Chem.*, **139**, 196 (1953).
[2] Luke, *op. cit.*
[3] Kolthoff, *Z. anal. Chem.*, **60**, 448 (1921).
[4] Kurtenacker, A., and Wollack, R., *Z. anorg. u. allgem. Chem.*, **161**, 201 (1927).
[5] Kovách, L., *Z. physik. Chem. Leipzig*, **80**, 107 (1912).
[6] Bowersox, O. F., Butler, E. A., and Swift, E. H., *Anal. Chem.*, **28**, 221 (1956).
[7] Kolthoff and Menzel, "Volumetric Analysis," vol. 2, p. 402, Wiley, 1929.

The reaction is reversible but is practically complete at relatively high concentrations of iodide and acid.[1]

The reaction between selenite and thiosulfate to form selenopentathionate and tetrathionate:

$$SeO_3^= + 4S_2O_3^= + 6H^+ \rightarrow S_4SeO_6^= + S_4O_6^= + 3H_2O \qquad (21\text{-}55)$$

proceeds quantitatively[2] at 0°C with an excess of thiosulfate, which may be determined by iodine titration. McNulty[3,4] used a limited quantity of iodide to produce only a trace of elemental iodine and selenium; the bulk of the thiosulfate reacted directly to form selenopentathionate. Thus the back titration was avoided. The starch-iodine reaction served as the indicator. Selenium was separated by distillation of selenium tetrabromide, which was hydrolyzed to selenite.

Elemental selenium (produced from selenite by reduction with sulfur dioxide or hydrazine) reacts with cyanide to form selenocyanate:[5]

$$CN^- + Se \rightarrow SeCN^- \qquad (21\text{-}56)$$

The excess cyanide is removed as HCN by boiling with boric acid (a low pH must be avoided to prevent decomposition of selenocyanide to selenium and HCN). The selenocyanide can be determined by oxidation with bromine:

$$SeCN^- + 4Br_2 + 4H_2O \rightarrow BrCN + SeO_4^= + 8H^+ + 7Br^- \qquad (21\text{-}57)$$

The reaction proceeds satisfactorily at pH 2 to 8. In strongly acid solution, the reaction is reversed; and at high pH, bromate is formed. After removal of the excess bromine with phenol, iodide and acid are added to reduce the cyanogen bromide.

$$BrCN + 2I^- \rightarrow I_2 + Br^- + CN^- \qquad (21\text{-}58)$$

and the iodine is titrated with thiosulfate.

The selenate ion does not oxidize iodide under the usual iodometric conditions. Selenate may be reduced to selenite by boiling with concentrated hydrochloric acid.

21-16. Determination of Peroxides and Peroxy Compounds

Hydrogen peroxide is best determined by taking advantage of the catalytic effect of molybdate[6,7] on the reaction between hydrogen peroxide

[1] Muthmann, W., and Schäfer, J., *Ber. deut. chem. Ges.*, **26**, 1008, 1015 (1893).
[2] Norris, J. F., and Fay, H., *Am. Chem. J.*, **18**, 703 (1896); **23**, 119 (1901).
[3] McNulty, J. S., *Ind. Eng. Chem., Anal. Ed.*, **19**, 809 (1947).
[4] McNulty, J. S., Center, E. S., and MacIntosh, R. M., *Anal. Chem.*, **23**, 123 (1951).
[5] Schulek, E., and Koros, E., *Z. anal. Chem.*, **139**, 20 (1953).
[6] Kolthoff, *Z. anal. Chem.*, **60**, 393 (1921).
[7] Brode, J., *Z. physik. Chem. Leipzig*, **37**, 257 (1901).

and iodide in acid solution:

$$H_2O_2 + 2H^+ + 2I^- \rightarrow I_2 + 2H_2O \tag{21-59}$$

This method is preferable to the oxidimetric method using Ce(IV) and especially permanganate in the presence of organic substances that might undergo oxidation with strong oxidants.

Peroxydisulfate ("persulfate") is advantageously determined by iodometric means.[1] Good results were obtained in the presence of organic matter inert to iodine and iodide, over a wide pH range in acid solution. The ferrous iron method gives erroneous results in the presence of organic substances (cf. pages 466–467).

Peroxy acids may be determined by using cerium(IV) sulfate as a titrant to remove any hydrogen peroxide present and then determining the peroxy acids iodometrically.[2] This method gives more reliable values than the classical method of D'Ans and Frey,[3] based on permanganate. Failure to add potassium iodide immediately after reaching the permanganate end point results in a deep red-purple color, apparently from an interaction of Mn(II) (or III?) with the peroxy acid. Diacyl peroxides do not react at appreciable speed with cold aqueous hydrogen iodide and can be distinguished from peroxy acids such as peroxyformic and peroxyacetic acids.

21-17. Determination of Ozone

Ozone has been determined iodometrically for many years, utilizing the reaction

$$O_3 + H_2O + 2I^- \rightarrow I_2 + O_2 + 2OH^- \tag{21-60}$$

A more recent study of this reaction[4] has shown that correct results are obtained if the gas sample is passed into a neutral unbuffered 2 per cent potassium iodide solution. After acidification, the sample is titrated with thiosulfate. The use of boric acid is unnecessary and may lead to high results, owing to air oxidation of iodide.

21-18. Determination of Oxygen in Water

The classical method of determining dissolved oxygen in water is the Winkler[5] method, which is based on the reaction between oxygen and a suspension of manganese(II) hydroxide in a strongly alkaline solution.

---

[1] Kolthoff, I. M., and Carr, E. M., *Anal. Chem.*, **25**, 298 (1953).

[2] Greenspan, F. P., and MacKellar, D. G., *Anal. Chem.*, **20**, 1061 (1948).

[3] D'Ans, J., and Frey, W., *Ber. deut. chem. Ges.*, **45**, 1845 (1912); *Z. anorg. u. allgem. Chem.*, **84**, 145 (1913).

[4] Birdsall, C. M., Jenkins, A. C., and Spadinger, E., *Anal. Chem.*, **24**, 662 (1952).

[5] Winkler, A. W., *Ber. deut. chem. Ges.*, **21**, 2843 (1888).

Upon acidification in the presence of iodide, the oxidized manganese hydroxide is reduced back to Mn(II) with the titration of an amount of iodine equivalent to the dissolved oxygen present.

Potter and White[1,2] have discussed critically the sources of error in the original Winkler method and various modifications of this method, with special reference to the determination of very low concentrations (below 0.01 ppm) of dissolved oxygen.   The principal sources of error are the following:

1. Reducing agents, such as sulfite, thiosulfate, ferrous iron, and organic matter, which react with oxygen or oxidized manganese in alkaline solution or with iodine in acid solution.

2. Oxidizing agents, which react with suspended manganous hydroxide in alkaline solution or with iodide in acid solution.   Examples are chlorine, hypochlorite, nitrite, and peroxides.

3. Failure to compensate properly for any dissolved oxygen in the reagents.

4. Errors inherent in the final determination.

The Winkler method can be modified variously in the pretreatment of the sample to avoid interferences, in the method of running blanks, and in the final determination.   A few modifications are discussed in the following paragraphs.

Pretreatment.   A permanganate pretreatment is sometimes used to oxidize ferrous iron and nitrite.   This method fails if considerable amounts of organic matter are present.   Sodium azide prevents the interference of nitrite by reducing it to nitrogen.[3]   To remove sulfites, thiosulfate, polythionates, free chlorine, or hypochlorite from paper-mill sulfite wastes, an excess of alkaline hypochlorite can be added, followed by the addition of acid and iodide and by titration of the liberated iodine with sulfite.[4]

To remove ferrous iron, particularly when determining very low concentrations of oxygen, Potter and White[5] used a cation exchange resin, taking care to deoxygenate the resin bed before introducing the sample. The main difficulty in the use of ion exchange resin is the slow equilibrium of the oxygen between the sample and the water imbibed by the resin.

Use of Blanks.   In practical analysis, it is common to run a blank in which the usual order of adding reagents ($MnSO_4$, KOH and KI, H_2SO_4) is just reversed.   Potter[6] pointed out that the order to be preferred in

[1] Potter, E. C., *J. Appl. Chem. London,* **7,** 285, 297 (1957).

[2] Potter, E. C., and White, J. F., *J. Appl. Chem. London,* **7,** 309, 317, 459 (1957).

[3] Ruchhoft, C. C., Moore, W. A., and Placak, O. R., *Ind. Eng. Chem., Anal. Ed.,* **10,** 701 (1938).

[4] Theriault, E. J., and McNamee, P. D., *Ind. Eng. Chem., Anal. Ed.,* **4,** 59 (1932).

[5] Potter and White, *op. cit.*

[6] Potter, *op. cit.*

running the blank is KOH and KI, H_2SO_4, $MnSO_4$. Thus, if the blank is initially made alkaline, allowance is made for substances that interfere specifically in alkaline solution.

It is possible to have a "negative" blank if reducing substances such as sulfite are present in greater amounts than oxidants. In this case it is necessary to add iodine or iodate to both sample and blank in order to provide an excess of iodine after acidification. An important interference not corrected for by running a blank is ferrous iron, which leads to low results by forming ferrous hydroxide, which reacts with oxygen. The resulting ferric ion does not produce an equivalent amount of iodine upon acidification.

Final Determination. Pomeroy and Kirschman[1] recommended the use of a relatively high concentration of iodide ion to decrease the interference of reducing agents, particularly organic matter. Potter and White[2] showed that the Winkler method can be used for oxygen concentrations below 0.001 ppm if the starch end point is replaced by the more sensitive amperometric end point, which was successful for the titration of 10^{-7} N thiosulfate with 10^{-5} N iodate.

21-19. Determination of Copper

If a slightly acidic solution of Cu(II) is treated with an excess of iodide, a precipitate of cuprous iodide is formed, and an equivalent amount of iodine is released. The iodine is titrated with thiosulfate.

The reaction may be written

$$2Cu^{++} + 4I^- \rightarrow 2CuI + I_2 \tag{21-61}$$

or, better,

$$2Cu^{++} + 5I^- \rightarrow 2CuI + I_3^- \tag{21-62}$$

The iodide ion not only serves as a reducing agent but exerts an enormous influence on the potential of the Cu(II)-Cu(I) couple, because of the slight solubility of cuprous iodide ($K_{sp} = 10^{-12}$). Copper(I), which is not stable at appreciable concentrations, owing to its disproportionation into Cu(II) and metallic copper, is stabilized by the formation of cuprous iodide. The half-reaction

$$Cu^{++} + I^- + e^- \rightleftharpoons CuI(\text{solid}) \qquad E^\circ = +0.85 \text{ volt} \tag{21-63}$$

corresponds to a stronger oxidizing system than the iodine-triodide couple

$$I_3^- + 2e^- \rightleftharpoons 3I^- \qquad E^\circ = 0.536 \text{ volt} \tag{21-64}$$

Although hydrogen ions do not appear in Eq. (21-61) or in (21-62) the effect of pH on the experimental results is important. If the pH is

[1] Pomeroy, R., and Kirschman, H. D., *Ind. Eng. Chem., Anal. Ed.*, **17**, 715 (1945).
[2] Potter and White, *op. cit.*

above about 4, hydrolysis of cupric ion causes the reaction to become sluggish; a fleeting end point is then observed, owing to a shift in the equilibrium to release more iodine as it is removed by reaction with thiosulfate. Complexing agents also inhibit the reaction by decreasing the concentration of cupric ion. If the pH is below about 0.5, air oxidation of iodide becomes significant.[1] Actually, the lower limit of pH is often more severely limited by the presence of As(V) or Sb(V), which oxidize iodide in acid solution. If the pH is 3.2 or greater, no oxidation occurs.[2]

Generally, the pH is adjusted to the proper value with the aid of a suitable buffer. Ammonium bifluoride is especially advantageous because it acts as an equimolar buffer of HF and F^- ($K_a \cong 7 \times 10^{-4}$) of the proper pH value.[3] and also serves as a complexing agent to prevent the interference of ferric iron by its strong complexation.[4] The effects of various buffer components have been studied by Crowell,[5] who found that the permissible pH range depends on the nature of the buffer components as well as the expected impurities. He recommended formic acid buffers for solutions free of iron. Acetate and phthalate buffers are commonly used, with the addition of fluoride if iron is present.

A source of error is the adsorption of iodine by cuprous iodide. The adsorbed iodine imparts a buff color to the precipitate and interferes with the sharpness of the end point. In addition, the results may be as much as 0.3 per cent low,[6] and fleeting end points may be observed.

Foote and Vance[7] suggested the addition of thiocyanate just before the end point. Copper(I) thiocyanate is less soluble than the iodide, and it is to be expected that at least the surface layers of the CuI will be transformed into CuSCN, which will have less tendency to adsorb iodine (as triiodide ion). Also, the last of the Cu(II) should produce the thiocyanate rather than the iodide of Cu(I), and the greater insolubility should bring about a more favorable equilibrium near the end point. Less interference from the formation of Cu(II) complexes should be experienced, owing to the more favorable equilibrium. These expected advantages are actually experienced.[8,9]

If thiocyanate is not added, the thiosulfate should be standardized

[1] Hammock, E. W., and Swift, E. H., Anal. Chem., 21, 975 (1949).

[2] Park, B., Ind. Eng. Chem., Anal. Ed., 3, 77 (1931).

[3] Crowell, W. R., et al., Ind. Eng. Chem., Anal. Ed., 8, 9 (1936); 10, 80 (1938).

[4] Park, op. cit.

[5] Crowell, Ind. Eng. Chem., Anal. Ed., 11, 159 (1939).

[6] Hammock and Swift, op. cit.

[7] Foote, H. W., and Vance, J. E., J. Am. Chem. Soc., 57, 845 (1935); Ind. Eng. Chem., Anal. Ed., 8, 119 (1936).

[8] Winkler, op. cit.

[9] Ruchhoft, Moore, and Placak, op. cit.

with copper metal under the same conditions.[1,2] The thiocyanate should not be added until most of the iodine has been reduced by thiosulfate, because appreciable reduction of iodine by thiocyanate may occur.

The error due to adsorption of iodine may also be prevented by the use of sufficiently high concentrations of iodide to dissolve the copper(I) iodide as CuI_2^-:

$$CuI + I^- \rightleftharpoons CuI_2^- \qquad K = 6 \times 10^{-4} \qquad (21\text{-}65)$$

This method, described by Scott,[3] has been studied in detail and recommended by Meites.[4] A disadvantage is the consumption of relatively large amounts (25 g) of potassium iodide. Hahn[5] used only enough potassium iodide (5 g) to dissolve the precipitate initially. Although some cuprous iodide precipitated, it was white, and the adsorption error was negligible.

Oxidizing agents, especially oxides of nitrogen remaining from the dissolution of the sample, must be completely removed. Boiling is effective in removing oxides of nitrogen, but is inconvenient. Moreover, a boiled nitric acid solution may develop appreciable amounts of nitrous acid upon standing.[6] Urea, which is commonly used to remove nitrous acid, is effective in warmed solutions.[7] Brasted[8] recommended sulfamic acid as being more convenient. The reactions are

$$2HNO_2 + CO(NH_2)_2 \rightarrow 2N_2 + CO_2 + 3H_2O \qquad (21\text{-}66)$$
$$HNO_2 + HSO_3NH_2 \rightarrow N_2 + H_2SO_4 + H_2O \qquad (21\text{-}67)$$

The reaction between Cu(II) and iodide can be prevented or reversed by the addition of certain complexing agents. Kapur and Verma[9] used pyrophosphate to repress the reaction of copper, and determined iodate in the presence of Cu(II). The use of pyrophosphate is limited by the relatively high pH necessary for stable complex formation, with the consequence of a slow reaction between iodate and iodide. By adding citrate, Hume and Kolthoff[10] reversed the Cu(II)-iodide reaction and, therefore, were able to determine strong oxidants in the presence of

---

[1] Foote, *J. Am. Chem. Soc.*, **60**, 1349 (1938).

[2] Kolb, J. J., *Ind. Eng. Chem., Anal. Ed.*, **11**, 197 (1939).

[3] Scott, W. W., Furman, N. H. (ed.), "Scott's Standard Methods of Chemical Analysis," 5th ed., p. 368, D. Van Nostrand Company, Inc., Princeton, N.J., 1939.

[4] Meites, L., *Anal. Chem.*, **24**, 1618 (1952).

[5] Hahn, F. L., *Anal. Chim. Acta*, **3**, 65 (1949).

[6] Brasted, *Anal. Chem.*, **24**, 1040 (1952).

[7] Hill, L. O., *Ind. Eng. Chem., Anal. Ed.*, **8**, 200 (1936).

[8] Brasted, *op. cit.*

[9] Kapur, P. L., and Verma, M. R., *Ind. Eng. Chem., Anal. Ed.*, **13**, 338 (1941).

[10] Hume and Kolthoff, *Ind. Eng. Chem., Anal. Ed.*, **16**, 103 (1943).

Cu(II).   By adding excess mineral acid, the Cu(II)-citrate complex was destroyed, allowing the determination of copper in the same sample. An alternative method of destroying the citrate complex without the necessity of titrating at very low pH is to add cyanide, which also prevents the precipitation of copper(I) iodide.[1]

A similar use of complexing is made in the titration of As(III) with iodine in the presence of Cu(II).   Neutral tartrate is used to prevent the interaction of Cu(II) with iodide.   After the iodine titration, the copper may be determined by acidification to the proper pH and titration of the resulting iodine.[2]

Verma and Bhuchar[3] determined copper by reducing its tartrate complex with glucose to form insoluble Cu_2O, which was treated with an excess of standard iodine and back-titrated with standard arsenite. Oxalate was added as a complexing agent to aid in the oxidation of the Cu_2O, and precautions were taken to avoid air oxidation.   The method has the advantage of avoiding interference from V(V).

21-20. Determination of Iron

The reaction between Fe(III) and iodide

$$2Fe^{3+} + 2I^- \rightleftharpoons 2Fe^{++} + I_2 \tag{21-68}$$

is favored by high acidity (to prevent hydrolysis of ferric iron) and high iodide concentration.   Even moderate concentrations of sulfate are unfavorable, for they decrease the reaction rate and necessitate the use of such high concentrations of acid and iodide that fleeting end points are experienced.[4,5]   Hahn[6] suggested the addition of cuprous iodide as a catalyst, in the presence of sufficient iodide to dissolve the cuprous iodide. Hammock and Swift[7] found that satisfactory results were obtained even in the presence of relatively high concentrations of sulfate, if sufficient cuprous iodide was added.   The action is a homogeneous catalysis by the Cu(I)-Cu(II) couple, so the reaction rate increases with Cu(I) concentration until the saturation limit is reached.   A procedure for the determination of iron in the presence of copper is given by Brasted.[8]

[1] Scaife, J. F., *Anal. Chem.*, **29**, 1224 (1957).

[2] Kolthoff and Sandell, "Textbook of Quantitative Inorganic Analysis," 3d ed., p. 602, Macmillan, 1952.

[3] Verma, M. R., and Bhuchar, V. M., *J. Sci. Ind. Research India*, **15B**, 437 (1956).

[4] Kolthoff, *Pharm. Weekblad*, **58**, 1510 (1922).

[5] Swift, *J. Am. Chem. Soc.*, **51**, 2682 (1929).

[6] Hahn, *Anal. Chim. Acta*, **3**, 65 (1949).

[7] Hammock and Swift, *Anal. Chem.*, **25**, 1113 (1953).

[8] Brasted, *op. cit.*

21-21. Determination of Other Metals

The reaction of dichromate with iodide has already been described in connection with the standardization of thiosulfate against potassium dichromate. This reaction is useful for the determination of several metals. Kolthoff[1] discussed the optimum acid concentration to be used at various concentration levels of dichromate to obtain quantitative results.

Chromium can be oxidized to dichromate using perchloric acid either alone or in admixture with other acids.[2,3] The use of silver nitrate as a catalyst with mixed perchloric and sulfuric acids to ensure complete oxidation of small quantities of chromium has been recommended.[4]

Barium and *strontium* can be determined by precipitation of the chromates with potassium dichromate, filtration, and determination of the excess dichromate in an aliquot part of the filtrate.[5] By precipitating from an acetate buffer and restricting the excess dichromate, it is possible to precipitate barium in the presence of strontium. For quantitative precipitation of strontium chromate, an ammoniacal solution containing ethanol is necessary. Calcium does not interfere with the barium determination, but causes error due to coprecipitation with strontium chromate.

Lead may be determined either by titrating the excess dichromate or by dissolving the precipitate in dilute hydrochloric acid and determining the chromate in the precipitate.[6] Titration of the precipitate is recommended only for lead concentrations below 0.01 M. Lead iodide is precipitated during the titration, and exerts a catalytic effect on the air oxidation of iodide. A large quantity tends to obscure the end point.

Vanadium(V) reacts quantitatively with iodide in acid solution to form vanadyl ion and iodine.[7] Owing, however, to the pronounced induced air oxidation of iodide (cf. page 467), for accurate results it is essential to provide for complete exclusion of atmospheric oxygen.

A better method is that of Verma and Bhuchar,[8] in which citrate is used as the reducing agent and an excess of standard iodine is added and back-titrated with arsenite. This method is applicable even in the presence of copper.[9]

[1] Kolthoff, *Z. anal. Chem.*, **59**, 401 (1920).

[2] Smith, G. F., "Mixed Perchloric, Sulfuric and Phosphoric Acids and Their Application in Analysis," G. Frederick Smith Chemical Co., Columbus, Ohio, 1934.

[3] Smith, G. F., and Getz, C. A., *Ind. Eng. Chem., Anal. Ed.*, **9**, 378, 518 (1939).

[4] Lynn, S., and Mason, D. M., *Anal. Chem.*, **24**, 1855 (1952).

[5] Kolthoff, *Pharm. Weekblad*, **57**, 972 (1920).

[6] Kolthoff, *Pharm. Weekblad*, **57**, 934 (1920).

[7] Ramsey, J. B., *J. Am. Chem. Soc.*, **49**, 1138 (1927).

[8] Verma and Bhuchar, *J. Sci. Ind. Research India*, **14B**, 19 (1955).

[9] Verma and Bhuchar, *J. Sci. Ind. Research India*, **15B**, 437 (1956).

Lithium is precipitated as a complex periodate from a strongly alkaline solution of potassium periodate.[1] The precipitate is washed free of excess periodate using 4 N potassium hydroxide; after acidification the periodate is determined iodometrically. The method is applicable to milligram quantities of lithium in the presence of sodium and potassium. It is necessary to standardize the procedure by analysis of known lithium solutions. The method has been applied to the determination of lithium in silicates.[2]

Zinc is determined according to the method of Lang,[3,4] by addition of potassium ferricyanide to a slightly acid zinc solution containing excess iodide. Zinc is precipitated as potassium zinc ferrocyanide, and iodide is oxidized to iodine

$$3Zn^{++} + 2Fe(CN)_6^{3-} + 2I^- + 2K^+ \rightarrow K_2Zn_3\{Fe(CN)_6\}_2 + I_2 \quad (21\text{-}69)$$

because the oxidation potential of the ferricyanide-ferrocyanide couple is increased by the low prevailing concentration of ferrocyanide. However, the ferricyanide had to be added stepwise, followed by thiosulfate titration after each addition, to avoid an appreciable excess during the reaction. By controlling the pH with a phthalate or bisulfate-sulfate buffer, Maun and Swift[5] were able to avoid the stepwise addition and obtain precise results. However, an empirical correction factor of 1.019 was necessary.

Tin is commonly reduced to its divalent state using lead,[6] antimony[7] or nickel,[8,9] which is claimed[10] to give the sharpest end point upon titration back to Sn(IV) with standard iodine solution. It is unnecessary to remove the undissolved nickel. Powdered iron has also been used as a reductant for tin in the presence of Ti(IV), which is complexed by fluoride and, therefore, not reduced to Ti(III).*

Thorium may be separated from the rare earths by precipitation as the iodate from solutions of relatively high nitric acid concentration.[11] The iodate is determined iodometrically.

The precipitation of thorium selenite, followed by the Norris and Fay

[1] Rogers, L. B., and Caley, E. R., *Ind. Eng. Chem., Anal. Ed.*, **15**, 209 (1943).

[2] Bacon, F. R., and Starks, D. T., *Ind. Eng. Chem., Anal. Ed.*, **17**, 230 (1945).

[3] Lang, *Z. anal. Chem.*, **79**, 161 (1929); **93**, 21 (1933).

[4] Casto, C. C., and Boyle, A. J., *Ind. Eng. Chem., Anal. Ed.*, **15**, 623 (1943).

[5] Maun, E. K., and Swift, E. H., *Anal. Chem.*, **21**, 798 (1949).

[6] Lundell, G. E. F., and Scherrer, J. A., *Ind. Eng. Chem.*, **14**, 426 (1922).

[7] Stelling, E., *Ind. Eng. Chem.*, **16**, 346 (1924).

[8] Hallett, R. L., *J. Soc. Chem. Ind.*, **35**, 1087 (1916).

[9] McDow, T. B., Furbee, K. D., and Clardy, F. B., *Ind. Eng. Chem., Anal. Ed.*, **16**, 555 (1944).

[10] *Ibid.*

* Dupraw, W. A., *Anal. Chem.*, **26**, 1642 (1954).

[11] Moeller, T., and Fritz, N. D., *Anal. Chem.*, **20**, 1055 (1948).

determination of selenite, has been suggested as a means for thorium determination.[1]

Manganese is precipitated as the dioxide, with potassium bromate as the oxidant in dilute acid solution.[2] Bromate is not so easily decomposed by boiling as peroxydisulfate is, and the oxidation and precipitation are, therefore, more easily reproducible. The filtered manganese dioxide is determined iodometrically. The results are low by 2 per cent if iron or zinc are present and still lower if they are not. An empirical correction factor must be used.

Manganese(III) forms so stable a complex with acetylacetone that it does not release iodine from potassium iodide.[3] Manganese dioxide in the presence of hydrochloric acid and acetylacetone forms the stable Mn(III) complex and chlorinated acetylacetone, which evolves iodine from acidified potassium iodide:

$$CH_3COCHClCOCH_3 + H^+ + 2I^- \rightarrow CH_3COCH_2COCH_3 + I_2 + Cl^-$$

$$(21\text{-}70)$$

Thus, Mn(IV) releases an amount of iodine equivalent to its reduction to Mn(III), and it is possible to determine Mn(IV) in the presence of Mn(III).

Cobalt was determined by Metzl[4] by oxidation in bicarbonate solution with hydrogen peroxide to form a green cobalt(III) carbonate complex, which was decomposed to cobalt(III) hydroxide by boiling with sodium hydroxide. In this procedure nickel is not oxidized. After the excess peroxide was decomposed by boiling, an excess of iodide and acid were added, and the liberated iodine was titrated with thiosulfate.

Willard and Hall[5] preferred to precipitate cobalt(III) hydroxide directly by using perborate or hydrogen peroxide in strongly alkaline solution or to reduce the green cobalt(III) complex produced in bicarbonate solution with excess ferrous iron, which was back-titrated with permanganate. The same green complex can be used directly for an iodometric determination, simply by adding iodide and acid to the solution after the excess hydrogen peroxide has been decomposed.[6]

Gold in an *aqua regia* solution may be determined by adding sodium hypochlorite or potassium chlorate to ensure oxidation to Au(III). After dilution, chlorine is removed by boiling. The acid is neutralized by addition of sodium bicarbonate, and potassium iodide is added, reduc-

[1] Deshmukh, G. S., and Swamy, L. K., *Anal. Chem.*, **24**, 218 (1952).
[2] Kolthoff and Sandell, *Ind. Eng. Chem.*, *Anal. Ed.*, **1**, 181 (1929).
[3] Fyfe, W. S., *Anal. Chem.*, **23**, 174 (1951).
[4] Metzl, A., *Z. anal. Chem.*, **53**, 537 (1914).
[5] Willard, H. H., and Hall, D., *J. Am. Chem. Soc.*, **44**, 2237 (1922).
[6] Laitinen, H. A., and Burdett, L. W., *Anal. Chem.*, **23**, 1268 (1951).

ing the gold and releasing iodine:

$$Au(III) + 3I^- \rightarrow AuI + I_2 \qquad (21\text{-}71)$$

The iodine is titrated with sodium arsenite.[1]

21-22. The Karl Fischer Reagent for Water

In 1935, Karl Fischer[2] described a method for the direct titration of water. This method is widely applicable not only to the determination of water in organic and inorganic systems but also to many indirect determinations based on quantitative reactions that consume or produce water. Many of these methods are described in an important monograph by Mitchell and Smith.[3]

Stoichiometry. The Karl Fischer method usually consists of the titration of a sample in anhydrous methanol with a reagent composed of iodine, sulfur dioxide, and pyridine in methanol.[4] The end point corresponds to the appearance of the first excess of iodine detected visually or by electrical means.

Smith, Bryant, and Mitchell elucidated the reaction path, which was shown to involve two distinct steps. The iodine and sulfur dioxide were shown to be present as addition compounds with pyridine. The first step involves the reaction between iodine and sulfur dioxide, in the presence of pyridine and water to form an inner salt of pyridine-N-sulfonic acid. Pyridine acts as a base to form pyridinium iodide.

$$C_5H_5N{\cdot}I_2 + C_5H_5N{\cdot}SO_2 + C_5H_5N + H_2O \rightarrow$$

$$2C_5H_5NH^+I^- + C_5H_5N_+{\diagup}\overset{SO_2}{\underset{-O}{|}} \qquad (21\text{-}72)$$

This first step involves the reduction of iodine and the oxidation of sulfur dioxide, the water serving as a source of oxide ion. In the absence of methanol, the pyridine inner salt, "pyridine sulfur trioxide," could be isolated as a stable product. The second step of the reaction involves methanol, with the formation of pyridinium methyl sulfate:

$$C_5H_5N_+{\diagup}\overset{SO_2}{\underset{-O}{|}} + CH_3OH \rightarrow C_5H_5NHOSO_2OCH_3 \qquad (21\text{-}73)$$

The methanol plays an important role here, because without it the second step could involve water instead of methanol, with the formation

[1] Herschlag, V. E., *Ind. Eng. Chem.*, *Anal. Ed.*, **13**, 561 (1941).

[2] Fischer, K., *Angew. Chem.*, **48**, 394 (1935).

[3] Mitchell, J., Jr., and Smith, D. M., "Aquametry," Interscience Publishers, Inc., N.Y., 1948.

[4] Smith, D. M., Bryant, W. M. D., and Mitchell, J., Jr., *J. Am. Chem. Soc.*, **61**, 2407 (1939).

of pyridinium hydrogen sulfate:

$$C_6H_5N_+\diagup\overset{\displaystyle SO_2}{\underset{-O}{|}} + H_2O \rightarrow C_5H_5NHOSO_2OH \qquad (21\text{-}74)$$

This reaction, however, is not at all specific, because any active hydrogen compound could replace methanol. Therefore, practical titrations are always carried out in the presence of an excess of methanol. Under these conditions, the over-all reaction involves 1 mole of iodine per mole of water, and a simplified over-all equation can be written

$$I_2 + SO_2 + H_2O + CH_3OH + 3py \rightarrow 2pyH^+I^- + pyHOSO_2OCH_3$$
$$(21\text{-}75)$$

where py represents pyridine.

Preparation of Reagent. Smith, Bryant, and Mitchell[1] observed that, even in the absence of water, a reagent consisting of iodine, sulfur dioxide, pyridine, and methanol undergoes a rapid initial loss in strength, followed by a slower change. The reactions involve the formation of quaternary pyridinium salts and pyridinium iodide, for example,

$$I_2 + SO_2 + 2CH_3OH + 3py \rightarrow 2pyH^+I^- + py(CH_3)OSO_2OCH_3$$
$$(21\text{-}76)$$

Various procedures have been suggested to overcome at least partially the disadvantage of instability of the reagent. For a discussion, see Kolthoff and Belcher.[2] Of the various methods, the following are especially worthy of mention.

The *two-reagent method*[3,4] involves introduction of the sample into a reagent composed of pyridine, methanol, and sulfur dioxide. The titration reagent is iodine in methanol, which is relatively stable. This method is as precise as the usual one-reagent method, as long as no procedure involving the addition of excess iodine and back titration with water is employed.

A *stabilized reagent* using methyl cellosolve in place of methanol was proposed by Peters and Jungnickel.[5] A mixture of ethylene glycol and pyridine was recommended as the sample solvent. By avoiding the use of methanol, certain interferences were minimized or eliminated. Such a stabilized reagent is commercially available.

[1] *Ibid.*

[2] Kolthoff and Belcher, "Volumetric Analysis," vol. 3, pp. 413–417, Interscience Publishers, Inc., New York, 1957.

[3] Johannson, A., *Acta Chem. Scand.*, **3**, 1058 (1949).

[4] Seaman, W., McComas, W. H., and Allen, G. A., *Anal. Chem.*, **21**, 510 (1949).

[5] Peters, E. D., and Jungnickel, J. L., *Anal. Chem.*, **27**, 450 (1955).

Application to Determination of Water. The Karl Fischer reagent can be applied directly to the determination of water in a large variety of organic compounds,[1] including saturated or unsaturated hydrocarbons, alcohols, halides, acids, acid anhydrides, esters, ethers, amines, amides, nitroso and nitro compounds, sulfides, hydroperoxides, dialkyl peroxides, etc.

Active carbonyl compounds interfere by forming acetals or ketals by reaction with methanol. The interference can be avoided by adding hydrogen cyanide to form cyanohydrins that do not interfere. Other interfering substances include mercaptans and certain amines, which react with iodine, and various oxidizing substances such as peroxy acids, diacylperoxides, and quinones, which react with iodide to produce iodine.

With inorganic substances, a greater variety of interferences is encountered.[2] These may be classified as follows.

Oxidizing Agents. Both sulfur dioxide and iodide act as reducing agents in the Karl Fischer water determination. Hydrogen peroxide and its derivatives appear to react exclusively with sulfur dioxide, e.g.,

$$H_2O_2 + SO_2 \rightarrow H_2SO_4$$

and, therefore, do not interfere if a sufficient excess of sulfur dioxide is present. Some oxidants react exclusively with iodide, and a correction can be made for the amount of iodine produced. For example, if $CuSO_4 \cdot 5H_2O$ is to be analyzed for water of hydration, 5 moles of iodine are consumed per mole of pentahydrate by the water of hydration, but 0.5 mole is produced by the reduction of $Cu(II)$ to cuprous iodide, leaving a net consumption of 4.5 moles. Other oxidants react nonstoichiometrically, either because of limited solubility or because both sulfur dioxide and iodide are attacked. Dichromate causes serious interference, but potassium permanganate is relatively insoluble, thus almost unreactive.

Reducing Agents. Substances that reduce iodine will, of course, cause erroneously high values for the water content of the sample. Sodium thiosulfate, stannous chloride, and sulfides react to reduce iodine.

Basic Oxides, Hydroxides, and Salts. Oxides and hydroxides of several metals react to form iodides, and behave like water toward the Karl Fischer reagent. For example, the net effect of zinc oxide may be represented by the reaction

$$ZnO + 2pyH^+ \rightarrow Zn^{++} + 2py + H_2O \qquad (21\text{-}77)$$

where the zinc ions, no doubt, form coordination complexes with the pyridine that is present. Copper(I), silver, and mercury(II) oxides

---

[1] Mitchell and Smith, *op. cit.*

[2] Bryant, W. M. D., Mitchell, J., Jr., Smith, D. M., and Ashby, E. C., *J. Am. Chem. Soc.*, **63**, 2924, 2927 (1941).

react similarly, but copper(II), nickel(II), lead(II), and aluminum oxides do not react appreciably and remain as insoluble solids. Higher oxides may act both as oxidants and as basic oxides. Manganese dioxide reacts stoichiometrically:

$$MnO_2 + 4pyH^+ + 2I^- \rightarrow Mn^{++} + 4py + I_2 + 2H_2O \quad (21\text{-}78)$$

with the net effect of 1 mole of water per mole of MnO_2. Lead dioxide and iron(III) oxide react incompletely.

Alkali and alkaline earth metal salts of weak acids may react like basic oxides, e.g.,

$$NaHCO_3 + pyH^+ \rightarrow Na^+ + CO_2 + H_2O + py \quad (21\text{-}79)$$

Suter[1] used azeotropic distillation of water with xylene to separate it from alkaline materials, such as sodium hydroxide.

The Karl Fischer method has proved to be successful in the determination of water in a wide variety of materials.[2]

Application to Functional-group Determinations. In principle, the Karl Fischer reagent can be used for the determination of any organic functional group that will undergo a quantitative and stoichiometric reaction to produce or consume water under conditions that will not interfere with the titration. Through the pioneer work of Mitchell and his coworkers[3] and of other investigators, a considerable number of quantitative procedures have become available. Only the barest principles can be covered here. For details, the reader is referred to the Mitchell and Smith monograph and to the more recent literature.

Alcohols can be determined by quantitative esterification using a large excess of acetic acid with boron trifluoride as a catalyst:

$$ROH + CH_3COOH \rightarrow CH_3COOR + H_2O \quad (21\text{-}80)$$

Carboxylic acids are determined by making use of the same type of reaction, using an excess of methanol:

$$RCOOH + CH_3OH \rightarrow RCOOCH_3 + H_2O \quad (21\text{-}81)$$

Acid anhydrides are hydrolyzed quantitatively in acetic acid solution with boron trifluoride as the catalyst, or in pyridine with sodium iodide as the catalyst. A small excess of water is used and back-titrated.

$$(RCO)_2O + H_2O \rightarrow 2RCOOH \quad (21\text{-}82)$$

Carbonyl compounds are determined by making use of the familiar con-

---

[1] Suter, H. R., *Anal. Chem.*, **19**, 326 (1947).

[2] Mitchell, *Anal. Chem.*, **23**, 1069 (1951).

[3] Mitchell and Smith, *op. cit.*

densation reaction with hydroxylamine hydrochloride to form an oxime:

$$R_2CO + H_2NOH \cdot HCl \rightarrow R_2C = NOH + HCl + H_2O \quad (21\text{-}83)$$

The interference of excess hydroxylamine hydrochloride is prevented by adding an excess of sulfur dioxide and pyridine in methanol. The method is applicable to a wide variety of aldehydes and ketones.

Primary and secondary amines are acetylated by an excess of acetic anhydride in pyridine:

$$R_2NH + (CH_3CO)_2O \rightarrow CH_3CONR_2 + CH_3COOH \quad (21\text{-}84)$$

The excess anhydride is determined as described above.

Primary amines are determined by condensation with excess benzaldehyde to form the Schiff base:

$$RNH_2 + C_6H_5CHO \rightarrow RN = CHC_6H_5 + H_2O \quad (21\text{-}85)$$

The excess aldehyde is converted to the cyanohydrin by adding a solution of hydrocyanic acid in pyridine, and the water produced is titrated as usual.

Nitriles are quantitatively hydrolyzed by using boron trifluoride as a catalyst in acetic acid solution:

$$RCN + H_2O \rightarrow RCONH_2 \quad (21\text{-}86)$$

The excess water is determined.

Peroxides, including hydroperoxides and dialkyl peroxides, are reduced with zinc in acetic acid to form the corresponding alcohols which are determined by the esterification procedure described above. Diacyl peroxides do not react.

22. Oxyhalogen Compounds as Oxidants

Of the various oxyhalogen compounds, we consider here only those which are useful as standard solutions either in direct titrations (iodate, bromate) or when added in excess and determined by back titration (periodate, hypochlorite). Perchloric acid and potassium chlorate have been discussed as prior oxidants in Chap. 18.

22-1. Potassium Iodate

Andrews[1] introduced an important titration, further developed later by Jamieson,[2] in which potassium iodate is used as a titrating reagent. In 3 to 9 M hydrochloric acid, iodate is reduced to iodine monochloride:

$$IO_3^- + 6H^+ + Cl^- + 4e^- \rightarrow ICl + 3H_2O \qquad (22\text{-}1)$$

In hydrochloric acid solution, iodine monochloride forms a stable complex with chloride:[3-5]

$$ICl + Cl^- \rightleftharpoons ICl_2^- \qquad K = 1.7 \times 10^2 \qquad (22\text{-}2)$$

and the reduction half-reaction is more properly written

$$IO_3^- + 6H^+ + 2Cl^- + 4e^- \rightarrow ICl_2^- + 3H_2O \qquad E° = 1.23 \text{ volts}* \qquad (22\text{-}3)$$

During the course of the titration, when a reducing agent is present,

---

[1] Andrews, L. W., *J. Am. Chem. Soc.*, **25**, 756 (1903).

[2] Jamieson, G. S., "Volumetric Iodate Methods," Reinhold Publishing Corporation, New York, 1926.

[3] Swift, E. H., *J. Am. Chem. Soc.*, **52**, 894 (1930).

[4] Philbrick, F. A., *J. Am. Chem. Soc.*, **56**, 1257 (1934).

[5] Faull, J. H., Jr., *J. Am. Chem. Soc.*, **56**, 522 (1934).

* Calculated from data in Latimer, W. M., "Oxidation Potentials," 2d ed., p. 65, Prentice-Hall, Inc., Englewood Cliffs, N.J., 1952.

free iodine is present in the system. This can be regarded as being formed from the further reduction of the iodine monochloride complex:

$$2ICl_2^- + 2e^- \rightarrow I_2 + 4Cl^- \qquad E^\circ = 1.06 \text{ volts*} \qquad (22\text{-}4)$$

When the reducing agent has all been consumed, the free iodine is titrated to form the iodine monochloride complex

$$2I_2 + IO_3^- + 6H^+ + 1OCl^- \rightarrow 5ICl_2^- + 3H_2O \qquad (22\text{-}5)$$

and the end point is marked by the disappearance of the last of the iodine.

The role of hydrochloric acid has been the subject of some controversy. Lang[1] considered that hydrolysis of I^+ becomes important below a hydrochloric acid concentration of 3.5 to 4 N, resulting in the formation of free iodine and the consumption of too much iodate.

$$I^+ + H_2O \rightleftharpoons HOI + H^+ \qquad (22\text{-}6)$$
$$5HOI \rightarrow 2I_2 + IO_3^- + H^+ + 2H_2O \qquad (22\text{-}7)$$

Swift,[2] however, found that an iodine monochloride solution in 3.5 N hydrochloric acid could be diluted with an equal volume of water without forming any iodine. He showed that the important factor was the rate of reaction near the end point. Even in 1 M acid the correct end point was reached, but only after long standing. The results of Philbrick[3] also indicate that hydrolysis is unimportant under the usual conditions of titration.

The optimum acidity varies from one reductant to another. For example, with Sb(III), the acidity is rather critical, correct results being obtained only over the range 2.5 to 3.5 N hydrochloric acid.[4] At lower acidity, the rate of oxidation of iodine to iodine monochloride [Eq. (22-5)] is too low. The upper limit of acidity appears to be limited by the rate of reduction of iodine monochloride to iodine. For example, Penneman and Audrieth[5] found that, at excessively high concentrations of hydrochloric acid (above 9 N), no visual end point could be observed in the titration of hydrazine because no iodine was formed. Yet the oxidation proceeded smoothly, as evidenced by the formation of nitrogen. Arsenic(III) behaves similarly. Evidently the complex ICl_2^- reacts only slowly with certain reducing agents with which ICl reacts rapidly.

To detect the end point, Andrews used a few milliliters of an extraction solvent such as carbon tetrachloride or chloroform. Starch cannot be

* Latimer, *loc. cit.*
[1] Lang, R., *Z. anal. Chem.*, **106**, 12 (1936).
[2] Swift, *op. cit.*
[3] Philbrick, *op. cit.*
[4] Hammock, E. W., Brown, R. A., and Swift, E. H., *Anal. Chem.*, **20**, 1048 (1948).
[5] Penneman, R. A., and Audrieth, L. F., *Anal. Chem.*, **20**, 1058 (1948).

used, because the characteristic blue color of the starch-iodine complex is not formed at the high hydrochloric acid concentrations that are used. The extraction end point is highly sensitive. The main disadvantage is the inconvenience of shaking with the extraction solvent after each addition of reagent near the end point. Smith and his coworkers[1,2] studied several dyes as possible internal indicators. The best results were obtained with amaranth (BCI 184) and brilliant ponceau (BCI 185), which are destroyed by the first excess of oxidant. The indicator reaction is, therefore, irreversible. Belcher and Clark[3] found p-ethoxychrysoidin to be advantageous, because the end point could be traversed twice before the indicator was destroyed.

As well as iodine [Eq. (22-5)], several other reducing agents can be accurately titrated. The following over-all reactions indicate the stoichiometry of some of the more important applications. For simplicity, the product is written as ICl rather than ICl_2^-.

$$2I^- + IO_3^- + 6H^+ + 3Cl^- \rightarrow 3ICl + 3H_2O$$
$$2H_2SO_3 + IO_3^- + 2H^+ + Cl^- \rightarrow ICl + 2H_2SO_4 + H_2O$$
$$2H_3AsO_3 + IO_3^- + 2H^+ + Cl^- \rightarrow ICl + 2H_3AsO_4 + H_2O$$
$$2SbCl_4^- + IO_3^- + 6H^+ + 5Cl^- \rightarrow ICl + 2SbCl_6^- + 3H_2O$$
$$2Hg_2Cl_2 + IO_3^- + 6H^+ + 13Cl^- \rightarrow ICl + 4HgCl_4^- + 3H_2O$$
$$N_2H_4 + IO_3^- + 2H^+ + Cl^- \rightarrow ICl + N_2 + 3H_2O$$
$$2Tl^+ + IO_3^- + 6H^+ + 13Cl^- \rightarrow ICl + 2TlCl_6^{3-} + 3H_2O$$
$$2SCN^- + 3IO_3^- + 6H^+ + Cl^- \rightarrow ICl + 2ICN + 2H_2SO_4 + H_2O$$

The direct titration of thiocyanate with iodate gives erratic results, but, by adding the thiocyanate to an excess of iodine monochloride in hydrochloric acid and titrating back with iodate, quantitative determinations can be made.[4] An indirect determination of submilligram quantities of copper by precipitating copper(I) thiocyanate has been devised.[5] The Cu(I) is oxidized to Cu(II), and the thiocyanate reacts as above.

An indirect determination of iron was based similarly on the addition of Fe(II) from a reductor into a solution of iodine monochloride.[6] The main advantage is that many types of organic matter do not interfere.

Swift and Hoeppel[7] determined vanadium by adding a measured excess of iodide to a solution of V(V) strongly acidified with hydrochloric acid. The resulting iodine was titrated to iodine monochloride without oxidizing

[1] Smith, G. F., and May, R. L., *Ind. Eng. Chem., Anal. Ed.*, **13**, 460 (1941).

[2] Smith, G. F., and Wilcox, C. S., *Ind. Eng. Chem., Anal Ed.*, **14**, 49 (1942).

[3] Belcher, R., and Clark, S. J., *Anal. Chim. Acta*, **4**, 580 (1950).

[4] Hammock, E. W., Beavon, D., and Swift, E. H., *Anal. Chem.*, **21**, 970 (1949).

[5] Tantranon, K., and Cunningham, B. B., *Anal. Chem.*, **25**, 194 (1953).

[6] Heisig, G. B., *J. Am. Chem. Soc.*, **50**, 1687 (1928).

[7] Swift, E. H., and Hoeppel, R. W., *J. Am. Chem. Soc.*, **51**, 1366 (1929).

the vanadyl ion produced by reduction of V(V). The method has the advantage of being applicable in the presence of As(V), Fe(III), and phosphate. However, the solutions must be carefully deaerated to prevent induced air oxidation of iodide (see page 467).

Swift and his coworkers[1,2] showed that permanganate, Ce(IV), and dichromate can be used in place of iodate, if a small amount of iodine monochloride is added to provide an indicator. It is interesting that permanganate does not show the characteristic error due to oxidation of chloride, even at high acidities. Swift[3] surmised that any excess permanganate reacts to form iodine trichloride, because no permanganate color is visible after the end point.

Lang[4] found that, in the presence of cyanide, iodine is oxidized quantitatively to iodine cyanide. The standard potential of the half-reaction

$$2ICN + 2H^+ + 2e^- \rightleftharpoons I_2(solid) + 2HCN \qquad E^\circ = 0.711 \text{ volt} \qquad (22\text{-}8)$$

has been evaluated by Swift and his coworkers.[5] This method has the advantage over the iodine chloride end point that the acidity level is lower (1 N in hydrochloric acid or 2 N in sulfuric acid), so that starch can be used as the indicator. Some chloride should be present, because iodine monochloride evidently forms as an intermediate. Excessive concentration of hydrochloric acid must be avoided, because the rate of conversion of iodine chloride to iodine cyanide may occur too slowly. Extreme caution must be exercised to avoid the fumes of hydrogen cyanide. The applications are similar to those of the Andrews method. In place of iodate, other strong oxidants can be used, provided that iodine monochloride or iodine cyanide is added to serve as an indicator.

Berg[6] titrated iodide with iodate in the presence of acetone to form iodoacetone, which is analogous to iodine cyanide.

$$IO_3^- + 2I^- + 3(CH_3)_2CO + 3H^+ \rightarrow 3CH_3COCH_2I + 3H_2O \qquad (22\text{-}9)$$

The iodoacetone method is of some interest in connection with the use of potassium iodide as a primary standard for the standardization of Ce(IV) or permanganate[7] by a direct visual titration using ferroin as the indicator.

[1] Hammock, Brown, and Swift, *op. cit.*

[2] Swift, *op. cit.*

[3] *Ibid.*

[4] Lang, *Z. anorg. u. allgem. Chem.*, **122**, 332 (1922); **142**, 229, 280 (1925); **144**, 75 (1925).

[5] Bowersox, D. F., Butler, E. A., and Swift, E. H., *Anal. Chem.*, **28**, 221 (1956).

[6] Berg, R., *Z. anal. Chem.*, **69**, 369 (1926).

[7] Kolthoff, I. M., and Laitinen, H. A., *J. Am. Chem. Soc.*, **61**, 1690 (1939).

22-2. Potassium Bromate

Bromate is a strong oxidant, as indicated by the standard potential.[1]

$$BrO_3^- + 6H^+ + 5e^- \rightleftharpoons \tfrac{1}{2}Br_2 + 3H_2O \qquad E^\circ = 1.52 \text{ volts} \qquad (22\text{-}10)$$

During a titration, in the presence of excess reducing agent, bromine is further reduced to bromide:

$$Br_2 + 2e^- \rightleftharpoons 2Br^- \qquad E^\circ = 1.087 \text{ volts} \qquad (22\text{-}11)$$

With the first excess of bromate, free bromine appears in the solution, owing to the reaction

$$BrO_3^- + 5Br^- + 6H^+ \rightleftharpoons 3Br_2 + 3H_2O \qquad \Delta F^\circ = -52.2 \text{ kcal} \qquad (22\text{-}12)$$

In some cases, the reaction between the reducing agent and bromine is so slow that an excess of bromine must be added and then back-titrated after being allowed to stand. In this case bromate is essentially a convenient substitute for the less stable solution of elemental bromine.

Smith[2] showed that the addition of Hg(II) is beneficial in several direct bromate titrations, for it prevents the premature appearance of excess bromine. The effect is due to the formation of stable complexes between Hg(II) and bromide, with the result that the potential of the bromine-bromide couple is increased. From the solubility of mercury(II) bromide and the formation constants of $HgBr^+$ and $HgBr_2$ we estimate

$$Br_2(0.1\ M) + Hg^{++}(0.1\ M) + 2e^- \rightleftharpoons HgBr_2(\text{sat}) \qquad E = 1.591 \text{ volts} \qquad (22\text{-}13)$$

Several oxidation reactions, including nitrous acid to nitric acid, oxalic acid to carbon dioxide, manganese(II) to manganese(IV) oxide, and Cr(III) to Cr(VI) were quantitative only in the presence of excess Hg(II).

Detection of the End Point. If an excess of bromate is used, an iodometric determination of the excess is convenient. Alternatively, an excess of arsenite can be added and then titrated, as described below, with standard bromate.

Györy[3] described the first direct titrations using bromate, and used the bleaching of methyl orange by excess bromine to detect the end point. His method is used, with minor modifications, even today. Various other dyes that are irreversibly destroyed at the end point were studied by Smith and coworkers.[4,5] Of these, the most satisfactory proved to be

[1] Latimer, *op. cit.*, p. 61.

[2] Smith, *J. Am. Chem. Soc.*, **45**, 1115, 1417, 1667 (1923); **46**, 1577 (1924).

[3] Györy, S., *Z. anal. Chem.*, **32**, 415 (1893).

[4] Smith, G. F., and Bliss, H. H., *J. Am. Chem. Soc.*, **53**, 2091 (1931).

[5] Smith, G. F., and May, R. L., *Ind. Eng. Chem., Anal. Ed.*, **13**, 460 (1941).

brilliant ponceau 5R (BCI 185), Bordeaux (BCI 88), fuschsine (BCI 678), and naphthol blue-black (BCI 246). The main disadvantage of these indicators is that they are irreversibly oxidized, so that a local excess of reagent should be avoided during the titration. Addition of fresh indicator very near the end point is often recommended. The end point, of course, can be traversed only in one direction.

Various reversible indicators have been suggested. Of these, α-naphthoflavone,[1,2] p-ethoxychrysoidine,[3] and quinoline yellow[4] appear to be the most satisfactory.

Application of Bromination Reactions. The first use of a bromate-bromide mixture as a source of bromine was by Koppeschaar,[5] who devised the classical bromination method for phenol. The method is still in use today, and has been applied to a wide variety of organic compounds.

Francis and Hill[6] made a systematic study of the sources of error in bromination reactions. Three types of error can be recognized: (1) oxidation of readily oxidized substances, such as o- and p-aminophenols, o- and m-toluidines, and the phenylenediamines; (2) precipitation of incompletely brominated products, which occurs especially with para-substituted compounds such as p-nitroaniline and p-iodoaniline; and (3) replacement of certain groups such as —COOH, —CHO, or —SO$_3$H by bromine.

Day and Taggert[7] studied the quantitative bromination of phenol, aniline, and their derivatives, using an excess of bromate with bromide, followed by iodometric back titration. Procedures for a large number of such determinations have been reviewed by Kolthoff and Belcher.[8]

The bromination of 8-hydroxyquinoline (oxine) is especially important,[9] because of its application to the indirect determination of various metals. Each mole of oxine consumes 2 moles of bromine, or 4 equivalents of oxidant,

$$C_9H_7ON + 2Br_2 \rightarrow C_9H_5Br_2ON + 2H^+ + 2Br^- \qquad (22\text{-}14)$$

so the method is quite sensitive. Hollingshead[10] has presented a compre-

[1] Uzel, R., *Collection Czechoslov. Chem. Communs.*, **7**, 380 (1935).

[2] Schulek, E., *Z. anal. Chem.*, **102**, 111 (1935).

[3] Schulek, E., and Rózsa, P., *Z. anal. Chem.*, **115**, 185 (1939).

[4] Belcher, *Anal. Chim. Acta*, **5**, 30 (1951).

[5] Koppeschaar, W. F., *Z. anal. Chem.*, **15**, 233 (1876).

[6] Francis, A. W., and Hill, A. J., *J. Am. Chem. Soc.*, **46**, 2498 (1924).

[7] Day, A. R., and Taggert, W. T., *Ind. Eng. Chem.*, **20**, 545 (1928).

[8] Kolthoff and Belcher, "Volumetric Analysis," vol. 3, chap. 12, Interscience Publishers, Inc., New York, 1957.

[9] Berg, *Pharm. Ztg.*, **71**, 1542 (1926).

[10] Hollingshead, R. G. W., "Oxine and Its Derivatives," vols. 1–4, Butterworth & Co. (Publishers) Ltd., London, 1954–1956.

hensive treatment of the uses of oxine.   A brief review is given by Kolt-hoff and Belcher.[1]

Anthranilic acid (o-aminobenzoic acid) is another precipitant that can readily be brominated quantitatively.   Shennan, Smith, and Ward[2] found that the best results were obtained by adjusting conditions to produce the tribromo rather than the dibromo derivative.   Funk and coworkers[3,4] have described procedures for the determination of various metals that are precipitated in neutral or slightly acidic solution.

The addition of bromine to carbon-carbon double bonds is used for the determination of unsaturation.   Side reactions such as substitution and hydrolysis cause complications in many cases.   Polgar and Jungnickel[5] have reviewed this subject in detail.

Application of Oxidation Reactions.   The titration of As(III), originally described by Györy,[6] is carried out in hydrochloric acid[7-9] or sulfuric acid[10] solution.   The optimum acidity depends on which indicator is used.   Indirect determinations of many oxidants[11] have been based on the addition of excess arsenite followed by back titration.   Gleu[12] determined peroxysulfuric acid (Caro's acid, H_2SO_5) in the presence of hydrogen peroxide and peroxydisulfuric acid by utilizing the reaction

$$H_2SO_5 + 2HBr \rightarrow H_2SO_4 + H_2O + Br_2 \qquad (22\text{-}15)$$

which is hastened by the presence of excess arsenite.   After back titration of the arsenite, hydrogen peroxide is determined by titration with permanganate.   Finally, peroxydisulfate is determined by heating with an excess of arsenite and back-titrating with bromate.

To determine arsenic in organic compounds, Schulek and von Villecz[13] destroyed the organic matter by heating with hydrogen peroxide and concentrated sulfuric acid.   The As(V) was reduced to As(III) with hydrazine sulfate.   After the excess hydrazine sulfate was decomposed by

[1] Kolthoff and Belcher, op. cit.

[2] Shennan, R. J., Smith, J. H. F., and Ward, A. M., Analyst, **61**, 395 (1936).

[3] Funk, H., and Ditt, M., Z. anal. Chem., **91**, 332 (1933); **93**, 241 (1933).

[4] Funk, H., and Demmel, M., Z. anal. Chem., **96**, 385 (1934).

[5] Polgar, A., and Jungnickel, J. L., in "Organic Analysis," vol. 3, Interscience Publishers, Inc., New York, 1956.

[6] Györy, op. cit.

[7] Smith and May, op. cit.

[8] Uzel, op. cit.

[9] Schulek and Rózsa, op. cit.

[10] Schulek, op. cit.

[11] De Bacho, F., Ann. chim. appl., **12**, 153 (1919).

[12] Gleu, K., Z. anorg. u. allgem. Chem., **195**, 61 (1931).

[13] Schulek, E., and von Villecz, P., Z. anal. Chem., **76**, 81 (1929).

heating to give nitrogen and sulfur dioxide, the latter was removed by boiling, and the As(III) was titrated with bromate.

Sloviter, McNabb, and Wagner[1] reduced As(V) to elemental arsenic using sodium hypophosphite. The product was filtered off and treated with excess bromate, which was determined iodometrically.

Antimony(III) was titrated by Györy[2] in exactly the same way as As(III). The method has been widely applied. Various procedures differ in method of isolation and of prior reduction of the antimony. Luke[3] isolated arsenic, antimony, and tin from lead alloys by gathering with manganese dioxide. After reduction with hydrazine sulfate and expulsion of sulfur dioxide, the arsenic was removed by distillation of the trichloride. After the Sb(III) in the residue was titrated, tin was determined by reduction to the divalent state and titration with iodine. Luke[4] analyzed tin-base alloys by reducing Sb(V) to Sb(III) with sulfur dioxide. McKay[5] reduced Sb(V) with mercury in hydrochloric acid solution, leaving As(V) unattacked. The resulting calomel was filtered off, and the filtrate was titrated as usual. In McKay's procedure, any copper present is reduced to Cu(I), which is air-oxidized before the titration. In the air-oxidation step, some Sb(III) apparently undergoes induced air oxidation, for the results tend to be low. The use of a silver reductor, followed by a potentiometric titration to titrate both Cu(I) and Sb(III) and thereby avoid the air-oxidation step, would appear to be an improvement. Antimony is often isolated as the sulfide; the use of thioacetamide is noteworthy.[6]

Iron(II) can be titrated to iron(III) in the presence of organic substances, such as tartaric, citric, and succinic acids, which interfere with permanganate or dichromate titrations. Other organic substances, such as sugars, alcohol, acetone, and formic acid, interfere. Smith and Bliss[7] used copper(II) chloride to catalyze the slow oxidation of Fe(II). To prevent air oxidation, which is also catalyzed by copper salts, arsenate was added. Arsenate oxidizes Cu(I), preventing its air oxidation. The resulting As(III) is not subject to air oxidation and is rapidly oxidized by bromate. Phosphoric acid was added to lower the potential of the Fe(III)-Fe(II) couple.

Berg[8] used bromate for the successive determination of iodide, chloride,

[1] Sloviter, H. A., McNabb, W. M., and Wagner, E. C., *Ind. Eng. Chem., Anal. Ed.*, **14**, 516 (1942).

[2] Györy, *op. cit.*

[3] Luke, C. L., *Ind. Eng. Chem., Anal. Ed.*, **15**, 626 (1943).

[4] Luke, *Ind. Eng. Chem., Anal. Ed.*, **16**, 448 (1944).

[5] McKay, L. W., *Ind. Eng. Chem., Anal. Ed.*, **5**, 1 (1933).

[6] Flaschka, H., and Jakobljevich, H., *Anal. Chim. Acta*, **4**, 247 (1950).

[7] Smith, G. F., and Bliss, H. H., *J. Am. Chem. Soc.*, **53**, 4291 (1931).

[8] Berg, *Z. anal. Chem.*, **69**, 1, 342 (1926).

and bromide in mixtures. In the presence of hydrocyanic acid, iodide is oxidized to iodine cyanide.

$$BrO_3^- + 3I^- + 3CN^- + 6H^+ \rightarrow 3ICN + Br^- + 3H_2O \quad (22\text{-}16)$$

Starch can be used to detect the end point. To determine bromide, the titration is continued until an excess of bromine appears. After the excess bromine is removed with aniline, the resulting bromine cyanide is determined iodometrically. Chloride is determined by oxidation with a large excess of bromate in warm solution. The resulting solution is treated with aniline and analyzed iodometrically.

Various other determinations are reviewed by Kolthoff and Belcher.[1] We may mention the direct titrations of Cu(I) to (II), Tl(I) to (III), colloidal selenium to Se(IV), hydrogen peroxide to oxygen, and hydrazine to nitrogen. Using excess bromate, usually in the presence of bromide, oxidations of hydroxylamine to nitrate, Se(IV) to (VI), metallic mercury to Hg(II), and thiocyanate to sulfate and cyanide can be carried out quantitatively. Hypophosphite can be determined in the presence of phosphite by using bromate alone.[2] In the presence of bromide, both hypophosphite and phosphite are oxidized to phosphate.

22-3. Hypohalites

Hypochlorite is a strong oxidant in alkaline solution, as shown by the standard potential of the half-reaction

$$OCl^- + H_2O + 2e^- \rightleftharpoons Cl^- + 2OH^- \qquad E^\circ = 0.89 \text{ volt} \quad (22\text{-}17)$$

which is higher than those of the permanganate-manganate (0.56 volt) and manganate–manganese dioxide (0.60 volt) couples.

The mechanisms of hypohalite oxidations have been reviewed by Edwards[3] and by Taube.[4] From the lack of isotopic oxygen exchange it appears that hypochlorite occurs in solution as the discrete species OCl^- and not, for example, as the hydrate $Cl(OH)_2^-$. Many hypohalite oxidations proceed by direct oxygen atom transfer, but alternative reaction paths are often possible, and the reactions can become quite complicated.

Hypobromite, although a weaker oxidant than hypochlorite ($E^\circ = 0.76$ volt), often reacts more rapidly with reducing agents. Hypobromite solutions are relatively unstable,[5,6] and it is, therefore, advantageous to

[1] Kolthoff and Belcher, *op. cit.*

[2] Schwicker, A., *Z. anal. Chem.*, **110**, 161 (1937).

[3] Edwards, J. O., *Chem. Revs.*, **50**, 455 (1952).

[4] Taube, H., *Record Chem. Progr. Kresge-Hooker Sci. Lib.*, **17**, 25 (1956).

[5] Kolthoff, I. M., Stricks, W., and Morren, L., *Analyst*, **78**, 405 (1953).

[6] Tomiček, O., and Jašek, M., *Collection Czechoslov. Chem. Communs.*, **10**, 353 (1938).

produce hypobromite *in situ* by adding an excess of bromide to the sample[1] and then oxidizing with hypochlorite.

Farkas, Lewin, and Bloch[2] found that the rate of the reaction

$$OCl^- + Br^- \rightarrow OBr^- + Cl^- \qquad (22\text{-}18)$$

was proportional to the hydrogen ion concentration in the pH range 10 to 13. The mechanism involves the formation of HOCl, the rate-determining step being

$$HOCl + Br^- \rightarrow HOBr + Cl^- \qquad (22\text{-}19)$$

In mildly alkaline solutions, e.g., in sodium bicarbonate medium, the formation of hypobromite is so rapid that direct titrations of certain reducing agents are possible using hypochlorite as the titrant but hypobromite as the active oxidant.[3,4] In solutions of pH 12 to 14, reaction (22-18) is so slow that it takes several hours to go to completion.

At pH values appreciably below 9, side reactions lead to the formation of chlorate and bromate, in addition to hypobromite.[5] Bromate is also formed when hypobromite solutions are prepared by direct reaction of bromine and alkali.[6]

$$Br_2 + 2OH^- \rightarrow OBr^- + Br^- + H_2O \qquad (22\text{-}20)$$
$$Br_2 + 6OH^- \rightarrow BrO_3^- + 5Br^- + 3H_2O \qquad (22\text{-}21)$$

To minimize the formation of bromate, Tomiček and Jašek recommended cooling to $-4°C$ in a mixture of ice and salt and maintaining a sodium hydroxide concentration of 0.5 M. In more concentrated alkali, the bromate concentration becomes appreciable, and in more dilute alkali the rate of decomposition becomes excessive. Köszegi and Salgo[7] prepared hypobromite for each determination by treating a known amount of potassium bromate with an excess of potassium bromide and hydrochloric acid, followed by an excess of sodium hydroxide.

Bromate causes difficulties in certain applications of hypobromites, but chlorate appears to be without effect. For example, in the determination of ammonia, bromate causes high results owing to the formation of oxides of nitrogen,[8] whereas quantitative oxidation to nitrogen occurs if hypo-

[1] Kolthoff, I. M., and Stenger, V. A., *Ind. Eng. Chem., Anal. Ed.*, **7**, 79 (1935).

[2] Farkas, L., Lewin, M., and Bloch, R., *J. Am. Chem. Soc.*, **71**, 1988 (1949).

[3] Kolthoff and Stenger, *op. cit.*

[4] Laitinen, H. A., and Woerner, D. E., *Anal. Chem.*, **27**, 215 (1955).

[5] Farkas and Lewin, *Anal. Chem.*, **19**, 665 (1947).

[6] Tomiček and Jašek, *op. cit.*

[7] Köszegi, D., and Salgo, E., *Z. anal. Chem.*, **143**, 423 (1954); *Acta Chim. Acad. Sci. Hung.*, **7**, 333 (1955).

[8] Kolthoff, I. M., and Laur, A., *Z. anal. Chem.*, **73**, 177 (1928).

bromite is produced *in situ*.[1,2] Oxides of nitrogen are formed if hypochlorite is used without the addition of bromide. Bromate has also been found to cause high results in the determination of thiocyanate and thiosulfate.

To summarize, it appears that, whenever the reaction of hypobromite with the reducing agent occurs rapidly in mildly alkaline solutions, a solution of hypochlorite should be used in the presence of bromide. If the oxidation is not rapid enough to permit a direct titration, an excess of hypochlorite can be added and determined iodometrically. Alternatively, an excess of standard arsenite can be added and back-titrated with hypochlorite. If a strongly alkaline medium is necessary and the reaction of hypochlorite is too slow, a standard solution of hypobromite should be used, with due precautions to avoid the presence of bromates.

To determine the end point in direct titrations, Bordeaux can be used as an irreversible indicator,[1] quinoline yellow[3,4] or tartrazine[5] as a reversible indicator. Potentiometric[6] and amperometric[7,8] end points can also be used.

Various applications are illustrated by the equations listed below. Particularly when the reducing agent is volatile or unstable in acid solution, the use of hypohalite in alkaline solution may be advantageous. For the experimental conditions the monograph of Kolthoff and Belcher[9] or the original literature should be consulted. Hypobromite is written as the oxidant, even though a standard solution of hypochlorite may be used in some cases, as explained above.

$$H_2AsO_3^- + OBr^- + OH^- \rightarrow HAsO_4^- + Br^- + H_2O$$
$$2NH_3 + 3OBr^- \rightarrow N_2 + 3Br^- + 3H_2O$$
$$CO(NH_2)_2 + 3OBr^- \rightarrow N_2 + CO_2 + 3Br^- + 2H_2O$$
$$SO_3^= + OBr^- \rightarrow SO_4^= + Br^-$$
$$S^= + 4OBr^- \rightarrow SO_4^= + 4Br^-$$
$$S_2O_3^= + 4OBr^- + 2OH^- \rightarrow 2SO_4^= + 4Br^- + H_2O$$
$$SCN^- + 4OBr^- + 2OH^- \rightarrow CNO^- + 4Br^- + SO_4^= + H_2O$$
$$CN^- + OBr^- \rightarrow CNO^- + Br^-$$
$$NO_2^- + OBr^- \rightarrow NO_3^- + Br^-$$
$$HPO_3^= + OBr^- + OH^- \rightarrow PO_4^{3-} + Br^- + H_2O$$
$$SeO_3^= + OBr^- \rightarrow SeO_4^= + Br^-$$

[1] Kolthoff and Stenger, *op. cit.*
[2] Köszegi and Salgo, *op. cit.*
[3] Sinn, V., *Chim. anal.* **29,** 58 (1947).
[4] Belcher, *Anal. Chim. Acta,* **5,** 27 (1951).
[5] Belcher, *Anal. Chim. Acta,* **4,** 468 (1950).
[6] Tomiček and Jašek, *op. cit.*
[7] Kolthoff, Stricks, and Morren, *op. cit.*
[8] Laitinen and Woerner, *op. cit.*
[9] Kolthoff and Belcher, *op. cit.,* chap. 13.

Hypoiodite is of limited applicability because of its inherent instability and because many of its reactions are not stoichiometric.[1] Mention should be made, however, of the determination of formaldehyde[2] and acetaldehyde.[3] The primary reaction of formaldehyde is an oxidation to formate ion

$$HCHO + OI^- + OH^- \rightarrow HCOO^- + I^- + H_2O$$

For acetaldehyde, the iodoform reaction

$$CH_3CHO + 3I_2 + 4OH^- \rightarrow CHI_3 + HCOO^- + 3I^- + 3H_2O$$

is favored relative to the oxidation reaction (to form acetate) by low concentrations of iodine and acetaldehyde and by a high concentration of hydroxyl ion. The method is essentially quantitative (within 2 per cent) for 1 mg or less of acetaldehyde in very dilute solution.

22-4. Periodate

The equilibria existing in solutions of periodic acid and its salts have been thoroughly investigated by Crouthamel and coworkers.[4,5] Of the possible hydrates of iodine(VII) oxide, only paraperiodic acid, H_5IO_6, exists as a solid in equilibrium with its aqueous solutions.

Potentiometric titrations[6] of the acid with base reveal two distinct end points: a sharp end point at pH 5.5 and a less distinct one at pH 10.0. From spectrophotometric data, there is evidence of a third ionization step. The ionization equilibria are complicated by a dehydration step; the following thermodynamic equilibrium constants have been evaluated:[7]

$$H_5IO_6 \rightleftharpoons H^+ + H_4IO_6^- \qquad K_1 = 5.1 \times 10^{-4} \qquad (22\text{-}22)$$
$$H_4IO_6^- \rightleftharpoons IO_4^- + 2H_2O \qquad K = 40 \qquad (22\text{-}23)$$
$$H_4IO_6^- \rightleftharpoons H^+ + H_3IO_6^{=} \qquad K_2 = 2.0 \times 10^{-7} \qquad (22\text{-}24)$$

The apparent dissociation constants for the first two steps are given by[6,7]

$$K_1' = \frac{a_{H^+}(a_{IO_4^-} + a_{H_4IO_6^-})}{a_{H_5IO_6}} = 2.3 \times 10^{-2} \qquad (22\text{-}25)$$

$$K_2' = \frac{a_{H^+}a_{H_3IO_6^-}}{a_{IO_4^-} + a_{H_4IO_6^-}} = 4.35 \times 10^{-9} \qquad (22\text{-}26)$$

[1] Mitchell, J., Jr., Kolthoff, I. M., Proskauer, E. S., and Weissberger, A. (eds.), "Organic Analysis," vol. 1, p. 268, Interscience Publishers, Inc., New York, 1953.

[2] Romijn, G., Z. anal. Chem., **36**, 18 (1897).

[3] Bose, S., Anal. Chem., **30**, 1526 (1958).

[4] Crouthamel, C. E., Meek, H. V., Martin, D. S., Jr., and Banks, C. V., J. Am. Chem. Soc., **71**, 3031 (1949).

[5] Crouthamel, C. E., Hayes, A. M., and Martin, D. S., Jr., J. Am. Chem. Soc., **73**, 82 (1951).

[6] Crouthamel, Meek, Martin, and Banks, op. cit.

[7] Crouthamel, Hayes, and Martin, op. cit.

The third step of ionization is so weak ($pK_3 = 15$) that it does not give an end point in aqueous titrations.

Periodic acid is a very strong oxidant in acid solution, as shown by the estimated standard potential:[1]

$$H_5IO_6 + H^+ + 2e^- \rightleftharpoons IO_3^- + 3H_2O \qquad E^\circ \cong 1.6 \text{ volts} \qquad (22\text{-}27)$$

Potassium periodate has been used in place of iodate for various titrations involving the iodine chloride, iodine bromide, or iodine cyanide end points.[2] There seems, however, to be no particular advantage in using periodate.

The Malaprade[3] reaction represents an important application of periodate to the determination of α-diols and α-carbonyl alcohols. If two adjacent carbon atoms have hydroxyl groups, periodate causes a cleavage of the carbon-carbon bond, with the formation of carbonyl groups:

$$\begin{array}{ccc} \text{H} & \text{H} & \\ \text{R—C} & \text{—C—R}' \end{array} \rightarrow \text{RC}{=}\text{O} + \text{R}'\text{C}{=}\text{O} + 2\text{H}^+ + 2e^- \qquad (22\text{-}28)$$
$$\begin{array}{cc} \text{OH} & \text{OH} \end{array}$$

If an alcohol has an α-carbonyl group, the carbonyl acts as though it were hydrated, with the formation of a carboxyl group:

$$R\text{—C—C—R}' \xrightarrow{H_2O} R\text{——C——C—R}' \rightarrow$$

$$R\text{—C}{=}\text{O} + R'\text{C}{=}\text{O} + 2\text{H}^+ + 2e^- \qquad (22\text{-}29)$$

Polyhydroxy compounds can be considered to be oxidized stepwise, the first step giving an α-hydroxy carbonyl compound, which is oxidized to a carboxylic acid. If each carbon atom has a hydroxyl group, the final products are formic acid and formaldehyde:

$$CH_2OH\text{—}(CHOH)_n\text{—}CH_2OH \rightarrow 2HCHO + nHCOOH$$
$$+ 2(n+1)H^+ + 2(n+1)e^- \qquad (22\text{-}30)$$

Periodate also oxidizes α-amino alcohols in which the amino group is primary or secondary.[4] Ammonium ion is produced according to the

[1] Latimer, "Oxidation Potentials," p. 66, Prentice-Hall, 1952.

[2] Singh, B., and Singh, A., *J. Indian Chem. Soc.*, **29**, 34 (1952); **30**, 143, 786 (1953); *Anal. Chim. Acta*, **9**, 22 (1953).

[3] Malaprade, L., *Compt. rend.*, **186**, 382 (1928); *Bull. soc. chim. France*, [4], **43**, 683 (1928).

[4] Nicolet, B. H., and Shinn, L. A., *J. Am. Chem. Soc.*, **61**, 1615 (1939).

reaction

$$R-\underset{\underset{OH}{|}}{\overset{\overset{H}{|}}{C}}-\underset{\underset{NH_2}{|}}{\overset{\overset{H}{|}}{C}}-R' + H_2O \rightarrow R\overset{H}{C}=O + R'\overset{H}{C}=O + NH_4^+ + H^+ + 2e^-$$

(22-31)

Other related compounds, such as α-diamines, α-amino acids, and acetylated α-amino alcohols, react only very slowly. Hydroxycarboxylic acids, such as glycolic acid or lactic acids, are not oxidized.

Based upon the above reactions, in which periodate is reduced to iodate, several approaches to the determination of single compounds and the analysis of mixtures are possible. The oxidations are usually carried out at room temperature, with an excess of periodic acid or its salts. One or more of the following types of determination are then carried out.

Alkalimetric Determination. The sample and a blank are treated with periodic acid and are back-titrated with standard base. At the first end point (pH = 5.5), periodic acid, iodic acid, and formic acid act as monobasic acids. Since formic acid is weaker than the other two, the pH at the first end point is slightly higher if formic acid is present.[1] Methyl red indicator or a potentiometric end point can be used. If both end points of periodic acid are potentiometrically determined, the difference gives a measure of the excess periodate in the presence of iodic and formic acids.

Iodometric Determination of Periodate plus Iodate.[2] After the periodate oxidation is completed, an excess of potassium iodide and acid are added, and the resulting iodine is titrated with thiosulfate. This method has the disadvantage that iodate produces three-fourths as much iodine as an equimolar amount of periodate. The result in terms of periodate consumption is, therefore, the difference between two relatively large numbers.

Determinations of Periodate in the Presence of Iodate. In a slightly alkaline solution, buffered with borate, periodate is reduced to iodate by excess potassium iodide.[3] The resulting iodine is titrated with standard arsenite. Alternatively, a slight excess of standard arsenite can be added to reduce periodate to iodate; then the excess arsenite can be titrated with iodine.[4]

Iodimetric Determination of Aldehyde. The aldehydes formed by periodic acid oxidation are distilled into a sodium bisulfite solution.[5] The excess bisulfite is oxidized with iodine solution; the excess iodine is just

[1] Allen, N., Charbonnier, H. Y., and Coleman, R. M., *Ind. Eng. Chem., Anal. Ed.*, **12**, 384 (1940).

[2] *Ibid.*

[3] Willard, H. H., and Greathouse, L. H., *J. Am. Chem. Soc.*, **60**, 2869 (1938).

[4] Fleury, P., and Lange, J., *J. pharm. chim.*, [8], **17**, 107 (1933).

[5] Johnson, M. J., *Ind. Eng. Chem., Anal. Ed.*, **16**, 626 (1944).

decolorized with thiosulfate. Sodium bicarbonate is added to dissociate the bisulfite-aldehyde compound, and the liberated bisulfite is titrated with standard iodine.

Shinn and Nicolet[1] and Martin and Synge[2] showed that acetaldehyde and higher aldehydes can be removed by aeration while formaldehyde is retained in a neutral buffer solution in the presence of an amino acid. The higher aldehyde is caught in a bisulfite solution and determined as above. Formaldehyde can be determined in the residue. Colorimetric and polarographic methods can also be applied.

Determination of Ammonia. Van Slyke and coworkers[3] developed a procedure for the determination of α-hydroxyamino acids by determining the ammonia produced by oxidation with periodate in a carbonate medium. Of the amino acids occurring in proteins, only serine, thalomine, hydroxylysine, and α-hydroxyglutamic acid have adjacent hydroxy and amino groups. Various other amino acids react with periodate, but only those with the α-hydroxyamino structure yield ammonia. The ammonia can be removed by aeration and determined acidimetrically or manometrically.

PROBLEMS

22-1. Write an equation for the oxidation of copper(I) thiocyanate in the Andrews titration.

22-2. Write equations for the titration of iodine to iodine monochloride, using permanganate, dichromate, and periodate as oxidants.

22-3. From the standard potential of half-reaction (22-1) and the equilibrium constant of (22-2), calculate the standard potential of (22-3).

22-4. From the standard potentials of (22-3) and (22-4), calculate the equilibrium constant of (22-5).

22-5. Given the standard potential of the half-reaction $Br_2(aq) + 2e^- \rightleftharpoons 2Br^-$, $E° = 1.087$ volts; the formation constants $k_1 = 10^9$, $k_2 = 10^{8.3}$ for $HgBr_2$; and the solubility of $HgBr_2$, $1.7 \times 10^{-2} M$; verify the potential given for (22-13).

22-6. Calculate the equilibrium constant of reaction (22-18) from the standard potentials of the half-reactions.

22-7. Write equations for the periodic acid oxidation of glycerol, 1,2-propylene glycol, and 2,3-butylene glycol. If A moles of formaldehyde, B moles of acetaldehyde, and C moles of formic acid are produced by periodic acid oxidation, how many moles of each of the three compounds were present, and how many moles of periodic acid were reduced? *Ans.* C; $(A - 2C)$; $(B - A + 2C)/2$; $A/2 + B/2 + C$.

[1] Shinn and Nicolet, *J. Biol. Chem.*, **138**, 91 (1941).

[2] Martin, A. J. P., and Synge, R. L. M., *Biochem. J.*, **35**, 294 (1941).

[3] Van Slyke, D. D., Hiller, A., MacFadyen, D. A., Hastings, A. B., and Klemperer, F. W., *J. Biol. Chem.*, **133**, 287 (1940).

23. Other Oxidants and Reductants

The purpose of this chapter is to review several reagents of lesser importance. Dichromate is included in this category even though it is used in many routine determinations, because most of its applications center around a single reaction, the oxidation of ferrous iron.

23-1. Dichromate as an Oxidant

Potassium dichromate is available as a primary-standard-grade product from the National Bureau of Standards. Its standard solutions, usually prepared by direct weight, are extraordinarily stable. Carey[1] found that a 0.1 N solution did not change appreciably in titer in 24 years.

From the standard potential of the half-reaction

$$Cr_2O_7^= + 14H^+ + 6e^- \rightarrow 2Cr^{3+} + 7H_2O \qquad E^\circ = 1.36 \text{ volts} \qquad (23\text{-}1)$$

it is apparent that dichromate is a weaker oxidant in acid solution than either permanganate or Ce(IV). Two fundamental points should be borne in mind in considering the strength of dichromate as an oxidant. (1) The formal potential varies widely with the nature and concentration of acid (see Table 23-1). (2) Dichromate can bring about induced oxidation reactions that would be considered thermodynamically impossible on the basis of the standard potential of Eq. (23-1). This apparently paradoxical behavior, which occurs because of the transitory existence of active intermediates, is discussed in detail in Chap. 24.

The Iron(II)-Dichromate Reaction. By far the most important analytical reaction of dichromate is the oxidation of Fe(II):

$$6Fe^{++} + Cr_2O_7^= + 14H^+ \rightarrow 6Fe^{3+} + 2Cr^{3+} + 7H_2O \qquad (23\text{-}2)$$

which has been the subject of a number of mechanism studies. Benson[2]

[1] Carey, W. M., *J. Am. Pharm. Assoc.*, **16**, 115 (1920).
[2] Benson, C., *J. Phys. Chem.*, **7**, 1, 356 (1903).

long ago studied the rate equation for the disappearance of Cr(VI):

$$-\frac{d[\mathrm{Cr(VI)}]}{dt} = k\,\frac{[\mathrm{Cr(VI)}]^{1.7}[\mathrm{Fe(II)}]^2[\mathrm{H^+}]^2}{[\mathrm{Fe(III)}]}$$

The rate increases with the square of the hydrogen ion concentration and varies *inversely* with the ferric ion concentration. The importance of the ferric ion concentration is further illustrated by the fact that fluoride, which forms stable complexes with Fe(III), *increases* the reaction rate.[1] Wagner and Preiss[2] interpreted the inverse effect of Fe(III) on the basis that the first step is a reversible reaction, involving the formation of Cr(V):

$$\mathrm{Cr(VI)} + \mathrm{Fe(II)} \rightleftharpoons \mathrm{Cr(V)} + \mathrm{Fe(III)}$$

Either of the following two schemes for the subsequent reactions would account for the dependence of the rate on the square of the concentration of Fe(II):

$$\mathrm{Cr(V)} + \mathrm{Fe(II)} \rightarrow \mathrm{Cr(IV)} + \mathrm{Fe(III)} \qquad \text{rate-controlling} \qquad (23\text{-}4)$$
$$\mathrm{Cr(IV)} + \mathrm{Fe(II)} \rightarrow \mathrm{Cr(III)} + \mathrm{Fe(III)}$$

$$\mathrm{Cr(V)} + \mathrm{Fe(II)} \rightarrow \mathrm{Cr(III)} + \mathrm{Fe(IV)} \qquad \text{rate-controlling} \qquad (23\text{-}5)$$
$$\mathrm{Fe(IV)} + \mathrm{Fe(II)} \rightarrow 2\mathrm{Fe(III)}$$

Although there seems to be no experimental basis at present for a choice,[3] the first alternative appears intuitively more acceptable, because it calls for two single-electron transfer steps and just two "unusual" oxidation states, Cr(V) and Cr(IV), which also occur in other reduction schemes. Although Fe(IV) cannot be regarded as an impossible intermediate, its formation would require a two-electron transfer step.[4]

The curious dependence of the rate upon the Cr(VI) concentration has been considered by Westheimer.[5] In an acidic dichromate solution we have the equilibria[6,7]

$$\mathrm{HCrO_4^-} \rightleftharpoons \mathrm{H^+} + \mathrm{CrO_4^=} \qquad K_2 = 3.2 \times 10^{-7} \qquad (23\text{-}6)$$
$$2\mathrm{HCrO_4^-} \rightleftharpoons \mathrm{Cr_2O_7^=} + \mathrm{H_2O} \qquad K = 98 \qquad \mu = 0 \qquad (23\text{-}7)$$
$$K = 35.5 \qquad \mu = 1$$

If $\mathrm{Cr_2O_7^=}$ is the active oxidant, its concentration varies as the square of

[1] Gortner, R. A., *J. Phys. Chem.*, **12**, 632 (1908).

[2] Wagner, C., and Preiss, W., *Z. anorg. u. allgem. Chem.*, **168**, 265 (1928).

[3] Westheimer, F. H., *Chem. Revs.*, **45**, 419 (1949).

[4] An oxygen atom transfer reaction would also give Fe(IV) in a single particle-transfer step.

[5] *Ibid.*

[6] Neuss, J. D., and Rieman, W., III, *J. Am. Chem. Soc.*, **56**, 2238 (1934).

[7] Tong, J. Y., and King, E. L., *J. Am. Chem. Soc.*, **75**, 6180 (1953).

the total Cr(VI) concentration at low values of the latter. At higher concentrations, dichromate becomes the dominant form of Cr(VI), and the second-order dependence should, therefore, approach first-order dependence.

The initial rapid equilibrium may be written

$$Cr_2O_7^- + Fe(II) \rightleftharpoons Cr_2O_7^{3-} + Fe(III) \qquad (23\text{-}8)$$

where, strictly speaking, $Cr_2O_7^{3-}$ is merely an example of a 1:1 complex of Cr(VI) and Cr(V). There seems to be no independent evidence for such a complex.

Duke[1] has proposed an alternative mechanism that does not call for an equilibrium in which Cr(V) must act as a *reductant*. In this mechanism, the forward rate would be determined by internal oxidation and reduction in a complex ion $Fe_2Cr_2O_7^{+}$, involving two Fe(II) ions and one $Cr_2O_7^-$ ion. A plausible reaction to form Cr(V) is

$$Fe_2Cr_2O_7^{+} + 2H^+ \rightarrow 2Fe^{3+} + 2CrO_3^- + H_2O$$

To account for the inverse first-order dependence on Fe(III), Duke assumed that Fe(III) forms one-to-one complexes of comparable stability with both $HCrO_4^-$ and $Cr_2O_7^-$. The reaction order in Cr(VI) then would depend upon the relative amounts of $Cr_2O_7^-$ and $HCrO_4^-$ in all forms, including the complexes with Fe(II) and Fe(III).

It is evident that more research is needed to elucidate the mechanism; in particular, the complex species formed by the interaction of non-oxidizable metal ions with Cr(VI) as a function of hydrogen ion concentration should be examined.

The potentiometric titration curves and indicators for the Fe(II)-dichromate reaction have been discussed in Chap. 17.

Values of the formal potentials of the Fe(III)-Fe(II) couple and the Cr(VI)-Cr(III) couple, as determined from potentiometric titration curves, are listed in Table 15-2. In general, the dichromate potential increases as expected with increasing acidity. However, the variations with the nature of the acid cannot be explained at present. In particular, the dichromate potential is so low in 0.1 M perchloric acid that the potential break is barely discernible.[2] Further research on this point is desirable, particularly with reference to the role of oxide films on the "inert" electrode surface. From the practical viewpoint it should be emphasized that the rate of attainment of electrode equilibrium, particularly near the end point and beyond it, becomes slower with increasing dilution. Nevertheless, the reaction itself proceeds quantitatively and reasonably rapidly

[1] Duke, F. R., in Kolthoff, I. M., and Elving, P. J. (eds.), "Treatise on Analytical Chemistry," part I, vol. 1, p. 653, Interscience Publishers, Inc., New York, 1959.
[2] Smith, G. F., *Anal. Chem.*, **23**, 925 (1951).

even at extreme dilution.   We[1] have successfully titrated as little as 1 μg of chromium in 100 ml solution ($\sim 10^{-7}$ M dichromate) with an accuracy of the order of ± 1 per cent, using an amperometric end point such as that described by Kolthoff and May.[2]

Applications of Dichromate.   The most important applications involve either directly or indirectly the titration of Fe(II).   An excess of standard Fe(II) can be added to determine oxidants, or an excess of Fe(III) can be added to determine reductants.   These determinations could usually be carried out equally well or better with Ce(IV).   However, for routine applications, the low cost and ease of preparation of standard solutions and the great stability of dichromate offer some advantages.   Permanganate is at a disadvantage especially if hydrochloric acid solutions are to be used.   According to Tsubaki,[3] hydrochloric acid concentrations up to 3.5 N can be tolerated with dichromate.

Dichromate reacts too slowly with several reducing agents to permit a direct titration.   If the reductant does not react rapidly and quantitatively with Fe(III), excess dichromate can be added and back-titrated with Fe(II).   According to Rao and Rao,[4] sulfite is cleanly oxidized by excess dichromate in 1 to 3 N acetic acid or 0.5 to 1.0 N hydrochloric acid, even in the absence of catalysts.   In sulfuric acid or at higher concentrations of hydrochloric acid, a catalyst such as iodine monochloride is necessary in order to avoid errors due to the formation of dithionate.   Dithionate is oxidized quantitatively to sulfate by boiling for 1 hr in sulfuric acid solution with excess dichromate.[5]   Other examples are discussed by Kolthoff and Belcher.[6]

Many organic compounds can be oxidized to carbon dioxide and water by heating with excess dichromate in strongly acid solutions.   The reactions are often complicated by side reactions such as the formation of carbon monoxide and are, therefore, of limited use.

23-2. Vanadium(V) as an Oxidant

The standard potential of the V(V)-V(IV) couple is given by[7]

$$VO_2^+ + 2H^+ + e^- \rightleftharpoons VO^{++} + H_2O \qquad E^\circ = 1.00 \text{ volt} \qquad (23\text{-}9)$$

The formal potential, according to Willard and Manalo,[8] is 1.02 volts in

---

[1] Laitinen, H. A., and O'Brien, A. S., unpublished experiments.

[2] Kolthoff, I. M., and May, D. R., *Ind. Eng. Chem., Anal. Ed.*, **18**, 208 (1946).

[3] Tsubaki, I., *Bunseki Kagaku*, **3**, 253 (1954).

[4] Rao, K. B., and Rao, G. G., *Anal. Chim. Acta*, **13**, 313 (1955).

[5] Glasstone, S., and Hickling, A., *J. Chem. Soc.*, **1933**, 5.

[6] Kolthoff, I. M., and Belcher, R., "Volumetric Analysis," vol. 3, Interscience Publishers, Inc., New York, 1957.

[7] Carpenter, J. E., *J. Am. Chem. Soc.*, **56**, 1847 (1934).

[8] Willard, H. H., and Manalo, G. D., *Ind. Eng. Chem., Anal. Ed.*, **19**, 462 (1947).

1 M sulfuric acid. According to Syrokomskii and Antropov,[1] the formal potential varies with sulfuric acid concentration according to

$$E^{\circ\prime} = 0.97 + 0.0173 \times (N \; H_2SO_4)$$

As an oxidant, V(V) is comparable with dichromate. Ferrous iron can be titrated in solutions containing up to 4 N hydrochloric acid or 13.5 N sulfuric acid.[2] Suitable indicators are diphenylamine and its derivatives in relatively dilute acid solution containing phosphoric acid,[3] and N-phenyl-anthranilic acid in concentrated solutions of acids.[4]

Vanadium(V) has the advantage over dichromate or Ce(IV) of being less subject to interference from organic compounds. Thus phenol and o-, m-, and p-cresols interfere with the titration of hydroquinone with Ce(IV), but V(V) gives the correct result.[5]

Vanadium(V) has been used as a substitute for iodate in the Andrews titration (see Sec. 22-1) in 7.0 to 7.5 N hydrochloric acid, in the presence of iodine monochloride.[6] A number of other determinations involve addition of an excess of V(V), followed by back titration with ferrous iron. Reducing agents include oxalate, sulfite, thiosulfate, phosphite, and hypophosphite. Direct titrations include Mo(V) to (VI) and U(IV) to (VI). For details, the reader is referred to the treatise of Kolthoff and Belcher[7] and to the original literature.

23-3. Chloramine-T as an Oxidant

Chloramine-T (sodium salt of p-toluenesulfochloramide) behaves much like hypochlorite; indeed both may be considered to be derivatives of unipositive chlorine. Chloramine-T, however, has the advantages of being applicable both in acid and in alkaline solution[8] and of being more stable,[9] especially if prepared in a state of high purity and stored in a brown glass bottle.

The reagent is used directly as a titrant in hydrochloric acid solutions with the Andrews iodine monochloride end point. In these applications it appears to offer little advantage over iodate. In many other applications, an excess of reagent is added and determined iodometrically. An

[1] Syrokomskii, V. S., and Antropov, L. I., *Zavodskaya Lab.*, **9**, 818 (1940).

[2] *Ibid.*

[3] Bishop, E., and Crawford, A. B., *Analyst*, **75**, 273 (1950).

[4] Syrokomskii and Antropov, *op. cit.*

[5] Rao, G. G., Rao, V. P., and Sastri, M. N., *Current Sci. India*, **18**, 381 (1949).

[6] Singh, B., and Singh, R., *Anal. Chim. Acta*, **10**, 408 (1954); **11**, 412 (1954); **13**, 405 (1955).

[7] Kolthoff and Belcher, *op. cit.*

[8] Tomiček, O., and Suckarda, B., *Collection Czechoslov. Chem. Communs.*, **4**, 285 (1932).

[9] Poethke, W., and Wolf, F., *Z. anorg. u. allgem. Chem.*, **268**, 244 (1952).

interesting example is the determination of nitrite,[1] which is oxidized to nitrate in an acetic acid solution. Sulfite is determined similarly. According to Leonhardt and Moeser,[2] the titration of ascorbic acid with chloramine-T is preferable to the iodine titration because of a faster reaction rate also and to the Ce(IV) titration, which tends to give high results due to overoxidation.

23-4. Miscellaneous Oxidants

Ferricyanide is of some interest because it can be applied in alkaline solutions. Willard and Manalo[3] found that the formal potential of the ferri-ferrocyanide couple was essentially constant at 0.45 volt in neutral or alkaline media. The same authors[4] oxidized As(III), Sb(III), Cr(III), and hydrazine with excess ferricyanide and back-titrated with vanadyl sulfate. Sulfide is oxidized quantitatively to sulfur at pH 9.4; at higher pH values some sulfate is formed.[5]

Manganese(III) is a strong oxidant that must be stabilized by complex formation. Belcher and West[6] found that even the pyrophosphate complex, which is a relatively weak oxidant, is not very stable if it stands. The reagent, therefore, is of limited use.

Copper(III), stabilized by the formation of periodate or tellurate complexes, has been applied as an analytical reagent, especially by Beck.[7] The sparingly soluble sodium diperiodatocuprate(III) has the formula[8] $Na_7\{Cu(IO_6)_2\}$. The reagent is used as the potassium salt, prepared by the oxidation of an alkaline mixture of potassium iodate or periodate and copper(II) sulfate with potassium peroxydisulfate.[9] The tellurate complex is prepared in a similar way. Beck has described a number of oxidation reactions in alkaline solutions, including the oxidation of As(III), Sb(III), thiosulfate, metallic sulfides, cyanide, and glucose. In these reactions, Cu(III) had been regarded as the active oxidant with the periodate or tellurate acting only as complexing agent. However, Keyworth and Stone[10] found that periodate or tellurate may also undergo reduction. Kolthoff and Belcher[11] warn against errors due to undecom-

[1] Van Eck, P. N., *Pharm. Weekblad*, **63**, 1117 (1926).

[2] Leonhardt, H., and Moeser, W., *Z. anal. Chem.*, **122**, 3 (1941).

[3] Willard and Manalo, *Ind. Eng. Chem., Anal. Ed.*, **19**, 167 (1947).

[4] *Ibid.*

[5] Charlot, G., *Bull. cot. chim. France*, [5], **6**, 1447 (1939).

[6] Belcher, R., and West, T. S., *Anal. Chim. Acta*, **6**, 322 (1955).

[7] Beck, G., *Mikrochemie*, **35**, 169 (1950); **36**, 245 (1950); **38**, 1, 152 (1950); **39**, 22, 147 (1952); **40**, 258 (1953).

[8] Malaprade, L., *Compt. rend.*, **204**, 979 (1937).

[9] Beck, *op. cit.*

[10] Keyworth, D. A., and Stone, K. G., *Anal. Chem.*, **27**, 833 (1955).

[11] Kolthoff and Belcher, *op. cit.*, p. 651.

posed peroxydisulfate. The procedures, therefore, are empirical in nature and appear to be applicable mainly to micro-scale determinations of limited accuracy.

Cobalt(III) sulfate was studied by Bricker and Loeffler[1] as a possible titrimetric reagent. Although it could be stored at $-7°C$ with no apparent decomposition for 3 months, the reagent decomposed so rapidly at room temperatures (20 per cent loss in 24 hr) that its usefulness appears to be quite limited.

23-5. Titanium(III) as a Reductant

Titanium(III) is a moderately strong reducing agent, as shown by the formal potential of 0.056 volt reported by Diethelm and Foerster[2] for 0.5 M total titanium in 4 N sulfuric acid. Upon tenfold dilution with the same acid, the formal potential changed to 0.12 volt. Upon tenfold dilution of both titanium and sulfuric acid, the formal potential became -0.01 volt, showing roughly a pH-dependence of $2 \times 2.3RT/F$ or 0.12 volt per pH unit. Latimer[3] wrote the half-reaction

$$TiO^{++} + 2H^+ + e^- \rightleftharpoons Ti^{3+} + H_2O \qquad E° \cong 0.1 \text{ volt} \qquad (23\text{-}10)$$

According to Kolthoff,[4] the potential of the couple is given by

$$E = 0.03 + 0.061 \log \frac{[Ti(IV)][H^+]}{[Ti(III)]} \qquad \text{at } 18°C \qquad (23\text{-}11)$$

in 0.72 N hydrochloric acid solution. The pH-dependence suggests a half-reaction such as

$$TiO^{++} + H^+ + e^- \rightleftharpoons TiOH^{++} \qquad E°' = 0.03 \text{ volt} \qquad (23\text{-}12)$$

Mixtures of high ratio [Ti(III)]/[Ti(IV)] showed a tendency toward hydrogen evolution, catalyzed by a platinum surface, as would be expected from the negative value of the potential calculated from Eq. (23-11). Any potential measured under such conditions is a mixed potential (cf. page 295) and, therefore, of no precise thermodynamic significance. Kolthoff[5] found also that the formal potential became more negative with increasing chloride concentration at a constant hydrogen ion concentration, showing that Ti(IV) has some tendency to form chloride complexes. Kolthoff and Robinson[6] used citrate or tartrate as complexing

[1] Bricker, C. E., and Loeffler, L. J., *Anal. Chem.*, **27**, 1419 (1955).

[2] Diethelm, B., and Foerster, F., *Z. physik. Chem. Leipzig*, **62**, 129 (1908).

[3] Latimer, W. H., "Oxidation Potentials," 2d ed., p. 268, Prentice-Hall, Inc., Englewood Cliffs, N.J., 1952.

[4] Kolthoff, *Rec. trav. chim.*, **43**, 768 (1924).

[5] *Ibid.*

[6] Kolthoff, I. M., and Robinson, C., *Rec. trav. chim.*, **26**, 169 (1926).

agent to lower the potential of the Ti(IV)-Ti(III) couple, thereby making Ti(III) act as a stronger reductant. With citrate or tartrate, in spite of this change in potential, there is less danger of reduction of hydrogen ion, because of the higher pH. A method for the determination of nitro compounds was based on the use of citrate solutions. It would appear that ethylenediaminetetraacetate solutions might possess advantages because of the enormous stability of the Ti(IV)-EDTA complex. (Compare Fe(III)-EDTA complex, page 243.)

Standard solutions of titanium(III) chloride and sulfate must be stored under an inert atmosphere, because they are very sensitive to air oxidation. Commercial titanous chloride usually contains considerable quantities of ferrous iron; therefore titanium hydride is advantageous as a source of Ti(III).[*] Standardization is conveniently carried out against dichromate.[1]

Ferric iron can be titrated accurately with thiocyanate as an indicator if the reagent is added very slowly near the end point[2] or if the temperature is raised to 50 to 60°C. Dissolved air should be removed with a stream of carbon dioxide.

Copper(II) can be titrated in the presence of thiocyanate to give a white precipitate of cuprous thiocyanate.[3] A little ferrous iron is added as an indicator. The end point is detected by the disappearance of the red Fe(III)-thiocyanate color from the solution. If ferric iron is present, it is, of course, titrated also. Kolthoff[4] has described a method for selectively reducing Fe(III) in the presence of copper and other metals.

Knecht and Hibbert[5] have given details for the determination of many oxidants, usually by adding an excess of Ti(III) and back-titrating with Fe(III), with thiocyanate as the indicator. Potentiometric end points are often used.

23-6. Chromium(II) as a Reductant

Chromium(II) is so strong a reducing agent that it is theoretically unstable with respect to hydrogen ions:

$$Cr^{++} + 2H^+ \rightarrow Cr^{3+} + H_2 \tag{23-13}$$

It is, therefore, important to realize that measurements with an electrode of low hydrogen overpotential are subject to error due to mixed potential

---

[*] Wagner, C. D., Smith, R. H., and Peters, E. D., *Anal. Chem.*, **19**, 982 (1947).
[1] Pierson, R. H., and Gantz, E. St. C., *Anal. Chem.*, **26**, 1809 (1954).
[2] Kolthoff, *Rec. trav. chim.*, **43**, 816 (1924).
[3] Rhead, E. L., *J. Chem. Soc. London*, **89**, 1491 (1906).
[4] Kolthoff, *op. cit.*
[5] Knecht, E., and Hibbert, E., "New Reduction Methods in Volumetric Analysis," 2d ed., Longmans, Green & Co., New York, 1925.

behavior. Grube and Schlecht,[1] who made systematic studies of the Cr(III)-Cr(II) couple, used an electrolytic tin electrode because a platinum electrode gave erroneous results. They preferred tin to mercury, which had previously been used by Forbes and Richter[2] and later by Lingane.[3] The values of the formal potential, according to Grube and Schlecht, are -0.411 volt in 0.003 N H_2SO_4 and -0.386 to -0.373 volt in 0.2 N to 2 N H_2SO_4. In 0.1 N HCl, Forbes and Richter found $E^{\circ\prime} = -0.400$.

Solutions of chromium(II) chloride or sulfate are readily prepared by reduction of Cr(III) with zinc. Lingane and Pecsok[4] prepared determinate solutions by reducing weighed quantities of potassium dichromate to Cr(III), using hydrogen peroxide. The resulting solution was reduced to Cr(II) and stored over amalgamated zinc.

Chromium(II) is the strongest reducing agent that is used as a titrating reagent. Its strongly reducing properties are illustrated by the fact that Lingane[5] was able to carry out automatic potentiometric titrations of Ti(IV) with Cr(II). Solutions of Cr(II) must, of course, be rigorously protected from atmospheric oxygen. In fact, a quantitative determination of dissolved oxygen[6] is based on the reaction

$$O_2 + 4Cr^{++} + 4H^+ \rightarrow 4Cr^{3+} + 2H_2O \qquad (23\text{-}14)$$

A variety of direct titrations with Cr(II) is described in the literature. The end points are almost always detected potentiometrically. Brintzinger and Rodis,[7] for example, performed successive titrations of antimony, iron, copper, tin, and bismuth in various combinations. Reviews of the literature have been given by Brennecke[8] and, more recently, by Jerschkewitz and Rienacker.[9]

Special mention should be made of the reduction of nitrate to ammonium ion by excess Cr(II) in sulfuric acid solution.[10] The reduction is catalyzed by Ti(IV), which is rapidly reduced to Ti(III). Since the latter reduces nitrate only to nitric oxide in acid solution, it appears that the rate of the chromous ion reduction must be determined by the rate of its initial reaction with nitrate.

[1] Grube, G., and Schlecht, L., *Z. Elektrochem.*, **32**, 178 (1926).

[2] Forbes, G. S., and Richter, H. W., *J. Am. Chem. Soc.*, **39**, 1140 (1917).

[3] Lingane, J. J., *Anal. Chem.*, **20**, 797 (1948).

[4] Lingane, J. J., and Pecsok, R. L., *Anal. Chem.*, **20**, 425 (1948).

[5] *Ibid.*

[6] Stone, H. W., and Eichelberger, R. L., *Anal. Chem.*, **23**, 868 (1951).

[7] Brintzinger, H., and Rodis, F., *Z. Elektrochem.*, **34**, 246 (1928).

[8] Brennecke, E., in Bottger, W. (ed.), "Newer Methods of Volumetric Chemical Analysis," p. 129, Chapman and Hall, Ltd., London, 1938.

[9] Jerschkewitz, H. C., and Rienacker, G., in Jander, G. (ed.), "Neuere Massanalytischen Methoden," 6th ed., Enke Ferd. Verlag, Stuttgart, 1956.

[10] Lingane and Pecsok, *Anal. Chem.*, **21**, 622 (1949).

Bottei and Furman[1] studied the reduction of a number of organic compounds with an excess of Cr(II), followed by back titration with ferric alum. Various nitro and nitroso compounds were reduced to amines; diazonium compounds gave hydrazine derivatives; an azo compound was reduced to the amines resulting from a cleavage of the azo linkage. The monopotassium salt of acetylene dicarboxylic acid was reduced to the corresponding ethylenic compound.

To summarize the behavior of Cr(II), all the reactions of Ti(III) can be carried out, usually under milder conditions. For example, most of the nitro compounds studied by Bottei and Furman were quantitatively reduced after 1 to 2 min of standing with a moderate excess of Cr(II) at room temperature. The usual technique with Ti(III) involves heating with a larger excess of reductant.

23-7. Miscellaneous Reductants

Mercurous nitrate was introduced as a reagent for ferric iron by Bradbury and Edwards,[2] who used thiocyanate as an indicator. A number of other investigators, notably Belcher and West,[3] have studied the Fe(III)-Hg(I) reaction for the direct determination of iron and the indirect determination of oxidants that react quantitatively with ferrous iron. An interesting example is the reduction of Cu(II) to Cu(I) by ferrous iron in the presence of thiocyanate. In this reaction, complex formation causes the normal direction of reaction to be reversed. Certain reducing agents, such as hydroxylamine and Hg(I) can be determined by adding an excess of ferric iron and back-titrating the excess.

Mercurous perchlorate has also been used as a reductant[4] in conjunction with alkaline ferricyanide as an oxidant. Reducing agents such as Cr(III), hydrogen peroxide, hydrazine, and arsenite are treated with an excess of standard ferricyanide and back-titrated.

Vanadium(II) is intermediate between Ti(III) and Cr(II) as a reductant, the standard potential of the V(III)-V(II) couple being -0.25 volt. Although it can be used for many reduction reactions,[5,6] it does not appear to offer any notable advantages.

[1] Bottei, R. S., and Furman, N. H., *Anal. Chem.*, **27**, 1182 (1955); **29**, 119 (1957). Furman and Bottei, *ibid.*, **29**, 121 (1957).

[2] Bradbury, F. R., and Edwards, E. G., *J. Soc. Chem. Ind.*, **59**, 96T (1940).

[3] Belcher and West, *Anal. Chim. Acta*, **5**, 260, 268, 360, 472, 546 (1951).

[4] Burriel-Marti, F., Lucena-Conde, F., and Arribas-Jimeno, S., *Anal. Chim. Acta*, **10**, 301 (1954); **11**, 214 (1954).

[5] Maass, K., *Z. anal. Chem.*, **97**, 241 (1934).

[6] Vanerjee, P. C., *J. Indian Chem. Soc.*, **12**, 198 (1935); **13**, 301 (1936); **15**, 475 (1938); **19**, 30, 35 (1942).

Several mild reducing agents, including Sn(II),* U(IV),† Mo(V),‡ and W(V),§ have been applied in relatively high concentrations of hydrochloric acid. None appears to have notable advantages over more common reagents. Tungsten(III) is unusual in that it is readily prepared in the form of the stable salt $K_3W_2Cl_9$, which can be dissolved in 1 N hydrochloric acid.[1]

Two organic reducing agents are worthy of mention. *Ascorbic acid* has been studied extensively, especially by Erdey and coworkers.[2,3] Ferric iron is titrated in 0.1 N to 0.2 N hydrochloric acid solution using thiocyanate or, better, variamine blue (4-amino-4'-methoxydiphenylamine) as the indicator.[4] Silver, gold, platinum, and mercury salts are determined by reduction to the metals.[4-6] Chlorate is reduced to chloride in the presence of Se(IV) as a catalyst.[7]

Hydroquinone is of interest mainly as a reductant for Au(III) to the metal using *o*-dianisidine[8] or 3-methylbenzidine[9] as indicators. Potentiometric titrations of various oxidants have been described.[10]

* Szabó, Z. G., and Sugár, E., *Anal. Chem.*, **22**, 361 (1950); *Anal. Chim. Acta*, **6**, 295 (1952).

† Belcher, R., Gibbons, D., and West, T. S., *Anal. Chem.*, **26**, 1025 (1954).

‡ Tourky, A. R., Farah, M. Y., and El Shamy, H. K., *Analyst*, **73**, 258, 262, 266 (1948); *J. Chem. Soc.*, **1949**, 140.

§ Tourky, A. R., Issa, I. M., and Amin, A. M., *Anal. Chim. Acta*, **10**, 168 (1954).

1 Uzel, R., and Přibil, R., *Collection Czechoslov Chem. Communs*, **10**, 330 (1938).

2 Erdey, L., and Bodor, E., *Anal. Chem.*, **24**, 418 (1952); *Z. anal. Chem.*, **133**, 265 (1951); **137**, 410 (1953).

3 Erdey, L., and Buzas, I., *Acta Chim. Acad. Sci. Hung.*, **4**, 195 (1954); **8**, 263 (1955).

4 Erdey and Bodor, *op. cit.*

5 Erdey and Buzas, *op. cit.*

6 Rao and Rao, *Z. anal. Chem.*, **150**, 29 (1956).

7 Erdey and Bodor, *Z. anal. Chem.*, **133**, 265 (1951).

8 Pollard, W. B., *Analyst*, **62**, 597 (1937).

9 Belcher, R., and Nutten, A. J., *J. Chem. Soc.*, **1951**, 550.

10 Simon, V., and Zýka, J., *Collection Czechoslov. Chem. Communs.*, **21**, 571 (1956).

24. Reaction Rates in Chemical Analysis

Reaction rates are of importance in several aspects of chemical analysis. (1) The slowness of a stoichiometric reaction may be a serious obstacle to its use in analysis, particularly in titrimetry. (2) Quantitative determinations can be based on measurements of reaction rate, as in the analysis of a mixture containing two closely related compounds that undergo the same type of reaction at different rates. (3) The rates of catalyzed homogeneous reactions are often proportional to the concentration of catalyst and can, therefore, be used in the estimation of catalyst concentration. (4) Through the measurement of kinetic constants, it is often possible to elucidate reaction mechanisms and thereby explain the causes of nonstoichiometry.

Induced reactions, which are usually annoying sources of error but which occasionally can be made to proceed as useful quantitative reactions, can be understood only through a detailed study of reaction mechanisms.

To illustrate several causes of nonstoichiometry, let us consider the familiar air oxidation of iodide ion in an iodometric determination. In the absence of catalysts, the air oxidation rate depends upon the concentrations of hydrogen ion and iodide ion, but it is not affected by the iodine-thiosulfate reaction. This is a typical *side reaction*, for which a correction can be made by running a suitable blank. Certain substances that are present in the sample, e.g., traces of oxides of nitrogen, can act as *catalysts*, which undergo either no chemical change or a cyclic change such that no permanent alteration occurs. A blank is ineffective in correcting for catalyzed air oxidation except in the impractical case of equal amounts of catalyst in the unknown and the blank. A third type of air oxidation is through an *induced reaction*, as, for example, in the iodometric determination of vanadium. The oxidation of iodide ion by V(V) induces the air oxidation of iodide by a mechanism that will be discussed below. Quantitative results can be obtained only by rigorous exclusion of atmospheric oxygen.

24-1. Slow Stoichiometric Reactions

Particularly in titrimetry, the reaction rate is often an important limitation on the possible use of a given reaction for quantitative purposes. Especially near the equivalence point, where the reactants are present in very low concentration, the reaction rate may become a limiting factor.

Of the common analytical reactions, ion-combination reactions (acid-base, complex formation, and precipitation) are usually relatively rapid. Slow reactions are most frequently encountered in redox reactions and in molecular reactions, including many reactions of organic compounds.

Several expedients are commonly used to overcome the difficulty of a slow reaction. These include (1) use of elevated temperatures, (2) addition of catalysts, (3) change of solvent, (4) addition of excess reagent, followed by back titration, and (5) use of an end-point detection technique that does not require observations in the immediate vicinity of the equivalence point. Examples of such techniques are conductometric, amperometric, and photometric titrations involving an extrapolation procedure to detect the end point.

In principle, the determination of reaction rate during the early stages of a reaction should permit a quantitative determination in situations where a stoichiometric reaction may not persist to the equivalence point because of reversibility or because of the intervention of consecutive reactions. To be applicable, this method requires a sensitive means for the accurate detection of the change in concentration near the beginning of a reaction. Blaedel and Pettijean[1] made an elegant application of this principle in determining ethyl acetate by observing the rate of its alkaline hydrolysis. The reaction involves the substitution of acetate ions for an equivalent number of hydroxyl ions. The corresponding decrease in conductance could be followed in a sensitive way by a high-frequency oscillator method. By using a working curve based on calibration with knowns, the rate of reaction can be accurately translated into concentration *even if the rate law for the reaction is unknown.* In systems free from interferences, the method of Blaedel and Pettijean was found to give a relative precision and accuracy of about 0.3 per cent.

[1] Blaedel, W. J., and Pettijean, D. L., *Anal. Chem.*, **30**, 1958 (1958).

24-2. Reaction Rates for Analysis of Mixtures

Lee and Kolthoff,[1] Lee,[2] and Fritz and Hammond[3] have considered the principles underlying the analysis of mixtures by taking advantage of differences in the rates of reaction of the components. A particularly favorable case, which may be extremely difficult to handle by conventional methods, is represented by a sample containing two organic compounds with the same functional group. It is often possible to find a reagent that reacts with both compounds by the same mechanism but with different reaction rates.

We shall consider here only the simplest case of a reaction that is kinetically a first-order reaction with respect to the two sample constituents A and B.   This could be either a reaction involving no other reactant (e.g., decomposition of an aldehyde-bisulfite addition compound) or a pseudomonomolecular reaction of A and B with a reactant R that is present at a relatively large and therefore constant concentration:

$$A + R \rightarrow products$$
$$B + R \rightarrow products$$

The kinetic order with respect to the reagent R is of no consequence, as long as the concentration of R is held constant in all experiments.

If k_A and k_B are the first-order or pseudomonomolecular rate constants for the two reactions, the rate of disappearance of A is given by

$$- \frac{d[A]}{dt} = k_A[A] \qquad (24\text{-}1)$$

or, in the integrated form,

$$\ln [A]_t = \ln [A]_0 - k_A t \qquad (24\text{-}2)$$

where $[A]_t$ = concentration of A at time t
  $[A]_0$ = initial concentration of A
Similar expressions can be written for the concentration of B.

Several methods for determining concentrations from rate determinations have been proposed.

Neglect of Reaction of Slower-reacting Component.[4]   If component A is the faster-reacting component, we can calculate the ratio k_A/k_B such that the reaction of A is essentially complete (say, 99 per cent) in a period

---

[1] Lee, T. S., and Kolthoff, I. M., *Ann. N.Y. Acad. Sci.*, **53**, 1093 (1951).

[2] Lee, in "Organic Analysis," vol. 2, p. 237, Interscience Publishers, Inc., New York, 1954.

[3] Fritz, J. S., and Hammond, G. S., "Quantitative Organic Analysis," chap. 9, John Wiley & Sons, Inc., New York, 1957.

[4] *Ibid.*, p. 150.

of time necessary for the reaction of a negligible amount (say, 1 per cent) of B. From Eq. (24-2) and the analogous equation for B,

$$\frac{\ln [A]_0/[A]_t}{\ln [B]_0/[B]_t} = \frac{k_A}{k_B} \tag{24-3}$$

For the example chosen,

$$\frac{k_A}{k_B} = \frac{\log 100}{\log 1.01} = 465$$

Thus, if the ratio of rate constants is at least 465:1, it is possible to find a reaction time such that the faster reaction is within 1 per cent of completion when the slower reaction has proceeded to less than 1 per cent of completion. An obvious limitation is that the reaction rates must be within certain limits and should, preferably, be controllable by simple means. For example, if even the faster reaction does not reach 99 per cent completion in a matter of minutes, the slower reaction will be impracticably slow unless it can be speeded up by a simple change such as raising the temperature.[1] At the other extreme, if even the slower reaction goes nearly to completion in a matter of minutes, it is usually impossible to make concentration determinations rapidly enough to take advantage of the difference in reaction rates.

According to Fritz and Hammond, the solvolysis rates of tertiary halides are so much higher than those of secondary halides that simple methods based on this principle should be possible. On the other hand, the differences between secondary and primary halides are usually so small that a more elegant procedure is required.

Logarithmic Extrapolation Method. The total initial concentration $[A]_0 + [B]_0$ and the total concentration at any time t, $[A]_t + [B]_t$, can readily be determined by titration or by instrumental means.

Now, if the rates of reactions A and B are independent of the presence of the other component, the total concentration C_t at time t is given by

$$C_t = [A]_t + [B]_t = [A]_0 e^{-k_A t} + [B]_0 e^{-k_B t} \tag{24-4}$$

If log C_t is plotted against t, a curve in general results, unless $k_A = k_B$. However, as time goes on, the contribution of the first term of Eq. (24-4) becomes progressively smaller (we again consider A to be the faster-reacting component), and the semilogarithmic plot eventually becomes linear. By extrapolation of the linear plot to $t = 0$, the value of log $(C_B)_0$ is determined.

This method is actually identical with the common procedure used in radiochemical analysis, in which a short-lived component is allowed to

---

[1] It is assumed here that the slower-reacting component is also to be determined. If not, this limitation does not exist.

decay to a negligible concentration and a longer-lived component is determined by extrapolation.

The advantage of this procedure is that a smaller ratio of k_A to k_B can be exploited. On the other hand, a sufficient number of determinations is necessary to assure a definition of the linear portion of the curve.

Example 24-1. As an example, a calculated curve for the case $k_A/k_B = 10$, $[A]_0/[B]_0 = 1$, is shown in Fig. 24-1. At $t = 5/k_A$, the concentration of component A

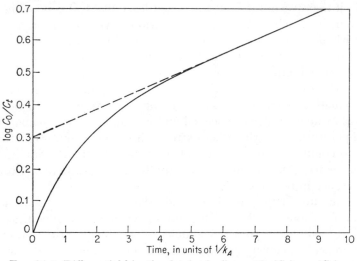

FIG. 24-1. Differential kinetic plot for $k_A/k_B = 10$, $(C_A)_0 = (C_B)_0$.

is only 0.67 per cent of its initial value, whereas 55 per cent of component B remains. Beyond that point, component A makes a negligible contribution to the total concentration. The situation, of course, becomes less favorable with increasing ratio of $[A]_0$ to $[B]_0$.

Determination of Rate of Change of Concentration. A method which does not depend on a linear extrapolation but which requires more observations is to determine the rate of change of total concentration dC_t/dt, which approaches $k_B[B]_t$ as the concentration of A approaches zero:

$$-\frac{dC_t}{dt} = k_A[A]_t + k_B[B]_t \tag{24-5}$$

By plotting C_t as a function of time, the rate of change can be determined from the slope of the curve. As constituent A disappears, the ratio of the (negative) slope to the concentration approaches a constant value of k_B:

$$-\frac{dC_t}{dt}\frac{1}{C_t} = k_B \qquad \text{for } [A]_t = 0$$

The initial concentration of B is then calculated from points late in the run, where $C_t = [B]_t$, using the equation

$$\ln [B]_0 = \ln [B]_t + k_B t$$

This method appears to be particularly useful when a continuous curve of concentration against time is available, for example, from an automatically recorded instrumental determination.

Example 24-2. For the same case as that of Example 24-1, $[C_A]_0 = [C_B]_0 = C_0/2$, $k_A/k_B = 10$, a calculated curve of C_t against t is shown plotted in Fig. 24-2, where

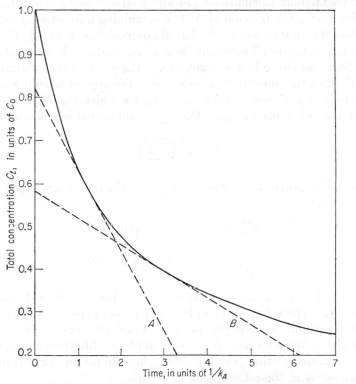

Fig. 24-2. Analysis by determination of total concentration as a function of time. Straight lines are tangents at $t = 1.25/k_A$ and $3.0/k_A$.

concentration is expressed in units of C_0 and time in units of $1/k_A$. The tangent is drawn at the point $t = 1.25/k_A$. The corresponding ratio of negative slope to concentration at that point is $-C_0/C_t\{\Delta(C_t/C_0)/\Delta(t/k_A)\} = -(1/0.585)\{(0.820 - 0.200)/(0 - 3.31)\} = 0.320$. Similarly, at the points $t = 2.3/k_A$, $3.0/k_A$, $4.6/k_A$, $6.9/k_A$, and $9.2/k_A$, the ratios are 0.201, 0.157, 0.114, 0.102, and 0.100. In this case, it is necessary to wait until a time $t = 6.9/k_A$ for the ratio of slope to concentration to approach within 2 per cent of the value for component B alone. A simple calculation shows that at that instant there remain 0.1 per cent of the initial amount of component A and 50 per cent of component B.

Single-point Method. Lee and Kolthoff[1] made an important contribution to analysis by kinetic measurements when they devised a procedure based on determination of the total concentration of the mixture after a single optimum time interval.

Referring to Eq. (24-4), it is evident that, if k_A and k_B are known from a study of the rates of reaction of the individual components, the individual initial concentrations $[A]_0$ and $[B]_0$ can be determined in principle by measuring the total initial concentration C_0 and the total concentration C_t at any known time t.

To avoid tedious calculations, Lee and Kolthoff used a calibration curve in which C_t/C_0, the fraction of A + B remaining unreacted at some time t, is plotted as a function of the initial composition ratio $[A]_0/C_0$. Since k_A, k_B, t, and C_0 are all constant for a given analysis, it is apparent that the calibration curve is a straight line. The slope of the calibration line depends upon the time interval t selected. For any set of values of k_A and k_B, there is an *optimum reaction period* t_{opt} for which the slope of the calibration curve is a maximum. This optimum period is given by

$$t_{opt} = \frac{\ln (k_A/k_B)}{k_A - k_B} \tag{24-6}$$

By combination of Eqs. (24-4) and (24-6), the following expressions are easily derived:

$$\frac{[A]_{t_{opt}}}{[A]_0} = \alpha^{1/(1-\alpha)} \qquad [B]_0 = 0 \tag{24-7}$$

$$\frac{[B]_{t_{opt}}}{[B]_0} = \alpha^{\alpha/(1-\alpha)} \qquad [A]_0 = 0 \tag{24-8}$$

where $\alpha = k_B/k_A$, the ratio of the rate constants, taken so that α is less than unity. The values given in Eqs. (24-7) and (24-8) correspond to the ends of the calibration line (100 per cent A and 100 per cent B), which are joined with a straight line to form the complete calibration curve. Thus, if the optimum reaction period is used, the calibration curve is uniquely determined by α, the ratio of rate constants.

Several values of the calibration points, calculated from Eqs. (24-5) and (24-6) by Lee and Kolthoff,[2] are given for illustrative purposes in Table 24-1. The corresponding calibration curves are shown in Fig. 24-3.

For second-order reactions, the relationships are much more complicated,[2] and it is beyond the scope of the present treatment to discuss their application. Suffice it to say that it is advantageous if possible to select conditions and reagent such as to permit the use of a relatively large

[1] Lee and Kolthoff, *Ann. N.Y. Acad. Sci.*, **53**, 1093 (1951).
[2] *Ibid.*

TABLE 24-1. CALIBRATION POINTS FOR FIRST-ORDER REACTIONS AT OPTIMUM
REACTION PERIOD

α	$\alpha^{1/(1-\alpha)}$	$\alpha^{\alpha/(1-\alpha)}$
$\frac{1}{3}$	0.19	0.57
$\frac{1}{5}$	0.135	0.675
$\frac{1}{10}$	0.08	0.78
$\frac{1}{25}$	0.035	0.875

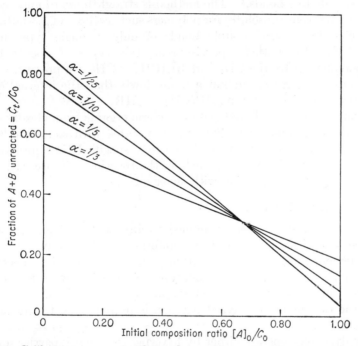

FIG. 24-3. Calibration curves for first-order reactions at optimum reaction period.

excess of reagent and thereby reduce the problem to the simpler pseudo-monomolecular case.

Lee and Kolthoff[1] concluded that, if the rate constants for the reactions of the two components differ by at least a factor of 4, it is practicable to carry out quantitative determinations of the two components. For example, they succeeded in determining closely related pairs of esters, e.g., ethyl acetate and isopropyl acetate, by use of their saponification rates, which at 25°C are in the ratio 4.2:1. The average error was 2 per cent (absolute). Various pairs of carbonyl compounds were analyzed

[1] *Ibid.*

by taking advantage of differences in the rates of decomposition of the bisulfite addition products. For formaldehyde and acetaldehyde at 25°C and pH 3.4, the rates were in the ratio 1:60.

Another interesting example is the determination of various types of carbon-carbon double bonds by the differences in their rates of reaction with peroxybenzoic acid to form epoxides. Thus, the rates of reaction of olefins of the types $RCH=CH_2$, $RC(CH_3)=CH_2$, $RCH=CHR$, and $RC(CH_3)=CHR$ were found to be in the ratio 1:25:30:400. On this basis polymers were analyzed for the relative amounts of "internal" and "external" double bonds.[1] The method is straightforward and accurate to about 1 per cent (absolute) for polymers such as those of 1,3-butadiene, which contain external double bonds of only a single type, namely $RCH=CH_2$. In synthetic polyisoprene, two types of double bonds, corresponding to $RCH=CH_2$ and $RC(CH_3)=CH_2$ are present. These react at different rates, but much more slowly than the internal double bonds that are all of the type $RC(CH_3)=CHR$.

Fetizon[2] has analyzed mixtures of isomeric organic bromides by taking advantage of differences in their reaction rates with sodium ethoxide. The amount of bromide ion produced in a specified time interval was determined conveniently by quenching the reaction mixture with water and titrating the bromide ion with silver nitrate.

24-3. Catalyzed Reactions

A catalyst may be broadly defined as an agent that alters the rate of a reaction without shifting the equilibrium. The catalyst undergoes no permanent change, although it may enter the reaction mechanism in a cyclic manner. From the analytical viewpoint, we are interested primarily in homogeneous catalysis of redox reactions, particularly where the rate of the catalyzed reaction is proportional to the catalyst concentration.

A catalyst may operate either by lowering the energy barrier for both the forward and backward reactions or by introducing an alternative reaction path.[3]

A redox reaction is particularly apt to be slow when unequal numbers of electrons are involved in the two half-reactions.[4] In that case, the reaction cannot proceed through a single bimolecular step and, therefore, involves either a succession of steps or a higher-order reaction. A suc-

[1] Kolthoff, I. M., Lee, T. S., and Mairs, M. A., *J. Polymer Sci.*, **2**, 199, 206, 220 (1947).

[2] Fetizon, M., *Compt. rend.*, **245**, 188 (1957).

[3] Laidler, Keith J., "Chemical Kinetics," chap. 10, McGraw-Hill Book Company, Inc., New York, 1950.

[4] Schaffer, P. A., *J. Am. Chem. Soc.*, **55**, 2169 (1933).

cession of steps generally involves an unstable intermediate oxidation state; a higher-order reaction involves a highly improbable higher-order collision.

As an example, consider the reaction between Ce(IV) and As(III), which is slow because the over-all reaction

$$2Ce(IV) + As(III) \rightarrow 2Ce(III) + As(V) \tag{24-9}$$

cannot proceed through a single bimolecular step.

There is some disagreement about the exact mechanism. Stefanofskii and Gaukhman[1] postulated the rate-determining step to be a one-electron transfer process,

$$Ce(IV) + As(III) \rightarrow Ce(III) + As(IV)$$

forming the unstable As(IV). However, according to Moore and Anderson,[2] the reaction follows third-order kinetics in sulfuric acid solution. Moore and Anderson's mechanism accounts nicely for the catalytic effect of Mn(II), which can be written in terms of the following bimolecular steps and which requires no postulation of As(IV):

$$Ce(IV) + Mn(II) \rightarrow Ce(III) + Mn(III) \tag{24-10}$$
$$Ce(IV) + Mn(III) \rightarrow Ce(III) + Mn(IV) \tag{24-11}$$
$$Mn(IV) + As(III) \rightarrow Mn(II) + As(V) \tag{24-12}$$

In the presence of iodide or iodine a pronounced catalysis occurs, probably through the sequence:[3]

$$Ce(IV) + I^- \rightarrow I^\circ + Ce(III) \tag{24-13}$$
$$2I^\circ \rightarrow I_2 \tag{24-14}$$
$$I_2 + H_2O \rightleftharpoons HOI + H^+ + I^- \tag{24-15}$$
$$H_3AsO_3 + HOI \rightarrow H_3AsO_4 + H^+ + I^- \tag{24-16}$$

because all the reactions involving iodine are known to be rapid. Dubravčić[4] found that, if only very small amounts of iodide are present, no catalysis is observed unless chloride is present. Evidently, in the absence of chloride, a side reaction occurs with the formation of iodate. Iodate is ineffective as a catalyst. In the presence of chloride, unipositive iodine is stabilized as iodine monochloride rather than as hypoiodous acid.

Sandell and Kolthoff[5] based a microdetermination of iodide on the

[1] Stefanofskii, V. F., and Gaukhman, M. S., *J. Gen. Chem. U.S.S.R.*, *Eng. Transl.*, **11**, 970 (1941).

[2] Moore, J. W., and Anderson, R. C., *J. Am. Chem. Soc.*, **66**, 1476 (1944).

[3] Bray, W. C., *Chem. Revs.*, **10**, 161 (1932).

[4] Dubravčić, M., *Analyst*, **80**, 146, 295 (1955).

[5] Sandell, E. B., and Kolthoff, I. M., *J. Am. Chem. Soc.*, **56**, 1426 (1934); *Mikrochim. Acta*, **1**, 9 (1937).

catalysis of the Ce(IV)-arsenite reaction. The rate of the over-all reaction (24-9) is determined by that of (24-13), which is proportional to the steady-state concentration of iodide ion. The method is extremely sensitive, because each iodide ion enters the catalytic cycle many times. Osmium tetroxide is also commonly used for the Ce(IV)-As(III) reaction (page 385). The exact mechanism is obscure, but it no doubt involves a cyclic oxidation of a lower oxidation state of osmium by Ce(IV) in two successive one-electron steps, followed by reduction of the higher oxidation state by As(III) in 1 two-electron step.

Another interesting example of homogeneous catalysis is the catalysis of the decomposition of hydrogen peroxide by bromide ion. Here hydrogen peroxide acts both as an oxidant and as a reductant, with two different reactions proceeding at characteristic rates under a given set of conditions:

$$H_2O_2 + 2Br^- + 2H^+ \xrightarrow{k_1} Br_2 + 2H_2O \qquad (24\text{-}17)$$

$$H_2O_2 + Br_2 \xrightarrow{k_2} O_2 + 2H^+ + 2Br^- \qquad (24\text{-}18)$$

If bromide or bromine is added to hydrogen peroxide, the reaction mixture reaches a steady state such that the rates of the two reactions are equal. If the reaction rates are initially unequal, either bromide or bromine will accumulate until the unequal concentrations cause the reaction rates to become equal. Then the only observable reaction is the sum of (24-17) and (24-18), or

$$2H_2O_2 \rightarrow 2H_2O + O_2 \qquad (24\text{-}19)$$

A number of procedures based on the catalysis of various redox reactions have been devised, especially by Goto, Shiokawa, and their coworkers. A summary is given in Table 24-2. In general, such procedures are very sensitive. The main disadvantage is the lack of specificity of most catalytic reactions and the consequent necessity for special precautions to avoid interferences.

An even more indirect use of reaction rates is in the determination of an inhibitor through its retarding effect on a catalytic reaction. An example is the determination of silver and mercury through their inhibitory effect on the catalysis of the Ce(IV)-As(III) reaction by iodide ion.[1]

24-4. Induced Reactions

The phenomenon of "chemical induction" has been recognized for over a century.[2-4] Discussions of the role of induced reactions in analytical

[1] Braun, T., *Magyar Kém. Folyóirat*, **63**, 39 (1957).

[2] Kessler, F., *Poggendorf's Ann.*, **95**, 224 (1855); **119**, 218 (1863).

[3] Lenssen, E., and Löwenthal, J., *J. prakt. Chem.*, **87**, 193 (1862).

[4] Schönbein, C. F., *Poggendorf's Ann.*, **100**, 34 (1857); *J. prakt. Chem.*, **75**, 108 (1858).

TABLE 24-2. DETERMINATION OF CATALYST BY REACTION RATE

Oxidant	Reductant	Catalysts	References
Cerium(IV)	Arsenic(III)	I^-, Os	1, 2, 3, 4
Permanganate	Arsenic(III)	Os	5
Cerium(IV)	Chloride	Ag	6
Peroxydisulfate	Manganese(II)	Ag	7
Iron(III)	Thiosulfate	Cu	8, 9
Iodine	Azide	$S^=$, $S_2O_3^=$, SCN^-	10, 11
Chlorate	Iodide	Os, Ru, V	12
Malachite green	Titanium(III)	Mo, W	13, 14
Methylene blue	Sulfide	Se	15
Oxygen	Ascorbic acid	Cu	16
Oxygen	Resorcinol	Cu	17
Hydrogen peroxide	Hydrogen peroxide	Mn, Pd, Cu	18
Hydrogen peroxide	p-Phenylenediamine	Cu, Fe, Os	19
Hydrogen peroxide	Iodide	Mo, W, V	20
Iron(III)	p-Phenylenediamine	$S_2O_3^=$	21

1. Goto, H., and Sudo, E., *Sci. Repts. Research Insts. Tohoku Univ.*, **1,** 37 (1949).
2. Shiokawa, T., *ibid.*, **2,** 443 (1950).
3. Lein, A., and Schwartz, N., *Anal. Chem.*, **23,** 1507 (1951).
4. Rogina, B., and Dubravćić, M., *Analyst*, **78,** 594 (1953).
5. Shiokawa, *Sci. Repts. Research Insts. Tohoku Univ.*, **2,** 446 (1950).
6. Goto and Shiokawa, *ibid.*, **1,** 41 (1949).
7. Underwood, A. L., Burrill, A. M., and Rogers, L. B., *Anal. Chem.*, **24,** 1597 (1952).
8. Goto and Sudo, *Sci. Repts. Research Insts. Tohoku Univ.*, **1,** 39 (1949); Goto H., and Suzuk, S., *ibid.*, **4,** 35 (1952).
9. Yatsimirskii, K. B., *Zhur. Anal. Khim.*, **10,** 339, 344 (1955).
10. Goto and Shiokawa, *Sci. Repts. Research Insts. Tohoku Univ.*, **1,** 179 (1949).
11. Shiokawa and Suzuki, *ibid.*, **3,** 413 (1951).
12. Shiokawa, *ibid.*, **2,** 290, 613 (1950); **3,** 424 (1951).
13. Shiokawa, *ibid.*, **2,** 287, 770 (1950).
14. Goto, H., and Ikeda, S., *ibid.*, **5,** 37 (1953).
15. Goto, H., Ikeda, S., and Hirayama, T., *ibid.*, **5,** 34 (1953).
16. Goto and Ikeda, *ibid.*, **7,** 301 (1955).
17. Lambert, R. H., *Anal. Chem.*, **24,** 868 (1952).
18. Shiokawa and Suzuki, *Sci. Repts. Research Insts. Tohoku Univ.*, **3,** 419 (1951).
19. Shiokawa, *ibid.*, **2,** 293 (1950); Goto and Suzuki, *ibid.*, **3,** 429, 335 (1951).
20. Yatsimirskii, K. B., and Afaneseva, L. P., *J. Anal. Chem. U.S.S.R., English Transl.*, **11** (3), 327 (1956); Yatsimirskii, K. B., and Rigin, V. I., *Zhur. Anal. Khim.*, **13,** 112 (1958).
21. Risk, J. B., and Strickland, J. H. D., *Anal. Chem.*, **29,** 434 (1957).

chemistry have been presented by Skrabal[1] and, more recently, by Kolthoff and Stenger[2] and by Medalia.[3]

A reaction between A and B is said to *induce* a reaction between A and C if the latter reaction under a given set of conditions does not occur at all or proceeds only very slowly unless it is caused to proceed by the simultaneous occurrence of the reaction between A and B. The substance B is called the *inductor*, C the *acceptor*, and A the *actor*, since it acts upon both B and C. The reaction between A and B is the *primary reaction;* that between A and C is the *induced* reaction.

A distinction should be made between an induced reaction and a catalyzed reaction. A catalyst is not altered permanently and, therefore, enters into a cyclic reaction or no reaction, whereas an inductor must take part in the primary reaction. A *side reaction* is distinguished from an induced reaction by the fact that its rate is unaffected by the occurrence of the primary reaction.

It was recognized long ago by Schilow[4] and by Luther and Schilow[5] that induced reactions fall into two classes. The first class, in which a primary reaction causes a relatively large amount of induced reaction to occur, was designated originally as "catalysis with destruction of the catalyst"[6] and later as "induced catalysis."[7] More recently, Livingston[8] has suggested the term "induced chain reaction," which emphasizes the nature of the reaction mechanism. The other class is the *coupled reaction*, which can be distinguished from an induced chain reaction by the behavior of the *induction factor* F_i, which is defined by the equation[9]

$$F_i = \frac{\text{equivalents of induced reaction}}{\text{equivalents of primary reaction}}$$

In an induced chain reaction the induction factor increases without limit as the ratio of acceptor to inductor is increased. In a coupled reaction, the induction factor approaches some definite small value such as 1, 2, or $\frac{1}{2}$.

[1] Skrabal, A., "Die induzierten Reaktionen; ihre Gesichte und Theorie," Ferd. Enke Verlag, Stuttgart, 1908.

[2] Kolthoff, I. M., and Stenger, V. A., "Volumetric Analysis," vol. 1., Interscience Publishers, Inc., New York, 1942.

[3] Medalia, A. I., *Anal. Chem.*, **27,** 1678 (1955).

[4] Schilow, N., *Z. physik. Chem. Leipzig*, **42,** 641 (1903).

[5] Luther, R., and Schilow, N., *Z. physik. Chem. Leipzig*, **46,** 777 (1903); *Z. anorg. u. allgem. Chem.*, **54,** 1 (1907).

[6] *Ibid.*

[7] Bray, W. C., and Ramsey, J. B., *J. Am. Chem. Soc.*, **55,** 2279 (1933).

[8] Livingston, R. L., in Friess, S. L., and Weissberger, A. (eds.), "Technique of Organic Chemistry," vol. 8, Interscience Publishers, Inc., New York, 1953.

[9] Lang, R., and Zweřina, J., *Z. anorg. u. allgem. Chem.*, **170,** 389 (1928).

In general, an induced reaction involves the formation, in the primary reaction, of an active intermediate[1] which reacts with the acceptor. The active intermediate may be formed from either the actor or the inductor, and it may be either a free radical or a species of intermediate oxidation state.

Induced Chain Reactions.   To illustrate an induced chain reaction, we consider the oxidation of ferrous iron by hydrogen peroxide, which induces a chain decomposition reaction. The primary reaction is generally accepted as proceeding through the Haber-Weiss mechanism,[2] which involves the hydroxyl free radical,

$$H_2O_2 + Fe^{++} \rightarrow Fe^{3+} + OH^- + \cdot OH \qquad (24\text{-}20)$$
$$\cdot OH + Fe^{++} \rightarrow Fe^{3+} + OH^- \qquad (24\text{-}21)$$

The two steps add to give the expected stoichiometric reaction

$$H_2O_2 + 2Fe^{++} \rightarrow 2Fe^{3+} + 2OH^- \qquad (24\text{-}22)$$

The hydroxyl radical can initiate a chain reaction causing the decomposition of hydrogen peroxide

$$\cdot OH + H_2O_2 \rightarrow HO_2 + H_2O \qquad (24\text{-}23)$$
$$HO_2 + H_2O_2 \rightarrow O_2 + H_2O + \cdot OH \qquad (24\text{-}24)$$

Reactions (24-23) and (24-24) add to give the induced reaction

$$2H_2O_2 \rightarrow 2H_2O + O_2 \qquad (24\text{-}25)$$

The induction factor is determined by the number of times the chain reaction is propagated before it is terminated by reaction (24-21). The induction factor, therefore, increases without limit as the ratio of hydrogen peroxide concentration to ferrous iron concentration is increased.

Other types of induced reaction are also encountered in the hydrogen peroxide–ferrous iron system.[3]   Suppose that an organic substance RH, e.g., ethyl alcohol, is present.   Reaction of RH with hydroxyl free radical produces a new free radical R·

$$\cdot OH + RH \rightarrow R\cdot + H_2O \qquad (24\text{-}26)$$

which reacts with ferric iron:

$$R\cdot + H_2O + Fe^{3+} \rightarrow RHO + H^+ + Fe^{++} \qquad (24\text{-}27)$$

[1] Duke [Duke, F. R., in Kolthoff, I. M., and Elving, P. J. (eds.), "Treatise on Analytical Chemistry," part I, vol. 1, p. 637, Interscience Publishers, Inc., New York, 1959] has proposed the name *reactates* for the active intermediates which are present only while a reaction is proceeding.

[2] Haber, F., and Weiss, J., *Naturwissenschaften*, **20**, 948 (1932); *Proc. Roy. Soc. London*, **A147**, 332 (1934).

[3] Kolthoff and Medalia, *J. Am. Chem. Soc.*, **71**, 3777, 3784, 3789 (1949).

If reactions (24-20), (24-26), and (24-27) are added, the result is the induced oxidation of organic substance by hydrogen peroxide:

$$H_2O_2 + RH \rightarrow RHO + H_2O \tag{24-28}$$

Ethyl alcohol, for example, is oxidized to acetaldehyde. The length of the chain depends on the relative rates of (24-21) and (24-26), since the reaction of hydroxyl radical with ferrous iron terminates the chain.

Another complication is introduced if oxygen is present. Oxygen reacts with the free radicals $R\cdot$ produced in reaction (24-26) to give a peroxide free radical

$$R\cdot + O_2 \rightarrow ROO\cdot \tag{24-29}$$

which reacts with ferrous iron to give the hydroperoxide

$$ROO\cdot + Fe^{++} + H^+ \rightarrow ROOH + Fe^{3+} \tag{24-30}$$

The hydroperoxide formed in reaction (24-30) reacts with ferrous iron by a reaction analogous to (24-20), that is,

$$ROOH + Fe^{++} \rightarrow RO\cdot + Fe^{3+} + OH^- \tag{24-31}$$

The reduction reactions of hydroperoxides are subject to the same types of chain mechanism as the reduction of hydrogen peroxide, and in addition the radical $RO\cdot$ can undergo various rearrangement reactions.

From the analytical viewpoint, the important point is that either low or high results for peroxide can be observed in the presence of organic matter and oxygen, depending upon the relative rates of the competing reactions (24-27) and (24-29). Reaction (24-27) leads to the induced reduction of peroxide and, therefore, to low results; reaction (24-29) leads to an induced air oxidation of ferrous iron

$$O_2 + 4Fe^{++} + 4H^+ \rightarrow 4Fe^{3+} + 2H_2O \tag{24-32}$$

and, therefore, to high results. Medalia[1] has cited examples in which the apparent peroxide content of organic hydroperoxides determined by ferrous iron methods varied from 17 to 690 per cent of the true peroxide content. The iodometric method (page 411), on the other hand, has been found to yield reliable results even in the presence of organic substances.

Similar induced reactions have been found in the reduction of peroxydisulfate by ferrous iron. Kolthoff and Carr[2] wrote a mechanism involving the free radical ion $\cdot SO_4^-$ as follows:

$$Fe^{++} + S_2O_8^= \rightarrow Fe^{3+} + SO_4^= + \cdot SO_4^- \tag{24-33}$$

$$Fe^{++} + \cdot SO_4^- \rightarrow Fe^{3+} + SO_4^= \tag{24-34}$$

[1] Medalia, op. cit.
[2] Kolthoff, I. M., and Carr, E. M., Anal. Chem., 25, 298 (1953).

In the presence of an organic substance RH (e.g., ethyl alcohol), a free radical can form by a reaction analogous to (24-26):

$$\cdot SO_4^- + RH \rightarrow HSO_4^- + R\cdot \qquad (24\text{-}35)$$

The free radical $R\cdot$ can then undergo reaction (24-27) with ferric iron, leading to an induced oxidation of the organic substance. Various other induced reactions, including the induced air oxidation of ferrous iron, can take place. From the analytical viewpoint it is of interest that the induced reactions are suppressed to some extent by the addition of bromide. Kolthoff and Carr interpreted the effect of bromide by assuming that bromide destroys the free radical ion $\cdot SO_4^-$ by the reaction

$$\cdot SO_4^- + Br^- \rightarrow SO_4^= + Br\cdot \qquad (24\text{-}36)$$

in which bromine free radicals (atoms) are formed. These are reduced to bromide ions:

$$Fe^{++} + Br\cdot \rightarrow Fe^{3+} + Br^- \qquad (24\text{-}37)$$

Various other induced air-oxidation reactions are of importance in analytical chemistry. A classic example, among the earliest ever observed,[1] is the air oxidation of Sn(II), which is induced by the reaction between Sn(II) and dichromate. Up to 98.3 per cent of the oxidation of Sn(II) was found to be due to oxygen and as little as 1.7 per cent to dichromate. Several other examples of induced air oxidation, reported by Lenssen and Löwenthal and by other early investigators, have been discussed by Bray and Ramsey.[2] In each of the following reactions, an induced reaction occurs between the reductant and atmospheric oxygen: $SnCl_2 + KMnO_4$, O_3, H_2O_2 or ClO_2; $H_2SO_3 + K_2Cr_2O_7$, $KMnO_4$, $K_2S_2O_8$ or H_2O_2.

Boyer and Ramsey[3] found that the air oxidation of iodide is induced by the reaction of iodide with peroxydisulfate, ferric iron, ferricyanide, or V(V). The latter reaction was investigated in detail and was found to behave as a typical induced chain reaction. The proposed mechanism involves the formation of atomic iodine $I°$ or the ion I_2^-, as an intermediate that reacts with oxygen. The chain is carried by the sequence:

$$I_2^- + O_2 + H^+ \rightarrow I_2 + HO_2 \qquad \text{rate-determining} \qquad (24\text{-}38)$$
$$H^+ + HO_2 + I^- \rightarrow I° + H_2O_2 \qquad (24\text{-}39)$$
$$I° + I^- \rightleftharpoons I_2^- \qquad (24\text{-}40)$$

The hydrogen peroxide formed in (24-39) is reduced by iodide:

$$H_2O_2 + 2I^- + 2H^+ \rightarrow I_2 + 2H_2O \qquad (24\text{-}41)$$

---

[1] Lenssen and Löwenthal, *op., cit.*
[2] Bray and Ramsay, *op. cit.*
[3] Boyer, M. H., and Ramsey, J. B., *J. Am. Chem. Soc.*, **75**, 3802 (1953).

The chain is initiated by the reaction

$$V(OH)_4^+ + I^- + 2H^+ \rightarrow VO^{++} + I^\circ + 3H_2O \qquad (24\text{-}42)$$

and terminated by the reaction

$$I_2^- + I_2^- \rightarrow I_3^- + I^- \qquad (24\text{-}43)$$

In accordance with this mechanism, an induced air oxidation of iodide is to be expected whenever I° or I_2^- is formed as the primary oxidation product of iodine. The induction factor and, therefore, the relative error due to air oxidation are decreased by an increasing concentration of iodide and oxidant, because of the increasing importance of the termination reaction (24-43).

From the viewpoint of analytical chemistry, induced chain reactions usually represent serious sources of error. In principle, such reactions can be used as the basis of sensitive qualitative tests, but it is difficult to control conditions so closely that useful quantitative results can be obtained.

Coupled Reactions. In the classical terminology, as described above, a *coupled reaction* is one in which the induction factor approaches some definite small value. Medalia[1] has suggested that it would be preferable to speak of the *over-all induced reaction* (sum of primary reaction and induced reaction) as the *coupled reaction*. This terminology has the advantage of emphasizing the stoichiometric relationship between the two reactions, particularly when the induced reaction taken by itself is thermodynamically unfavorable.

This point is well illustrated by the oxidation of Mn(II) by dichromate[2,3] to give manganese dioxide:

$$2Cr(VI) + 3Mn(II) \rightarrow 2Cr(III) + 3Mn(IV) \qquad (24\text{-}44)$$

This reaction is thermodynamically unfavored in the forward direction; in fact, the reverse reaction proceeds slowly. Yet, if the reaction of arsenious acid with dichromate is allowed to proceed in the presence of Mn(II), it is found that, for every equivalent of Cr(VI) reduced by As(III), 0.5 equivalent is reduced by Mn(II), at least under suitable conditions of concentration.[4]

The relationship observed is satisfactorily accounted for by the following mechanism for the primary reaction between Cr(VI) and As(III) in

[1] Medalia, *op. cit.*
[2] Westheimer, F., *Chem. Revs.*, **45**, 419 (1949).
[3] Lang and Zweřina, *op. cit.*
[4] *Ibid.*

the absence of Mn(II):

$$Cr(VI) + As(III) \rightarrow Cr(IV) + As(V) \qquad (24\text{-}45)$$
$$Cr(VI) + Cr(IV) \rightarrow 2Cr(V) \qquad (24\text{-}46)$$
$$Cr(V) + As(III) \rightarrow Cr(III) + As(V) \qquad (24\text{-}47)$$

The sum of (24-45), (24-46), and twice (24-47) is the primary reaction

$$2Cr(VI) + 3As(III) \rightarrow 2Cr(III) + 3As(V) \qquad (24\text{-}48)$$

In the presence of Mn(II), the unstable Cr(IV) formed in reaction (24-45) reacts according to

$$Cr(IV) + Mn(II) \rightarrow Mn(III) + Cr(III) \qquad (24\text{-}49)$$

The resulting Mn(III) is the final product if it is stabilized by the formation of a fluoride[1] or metaphosphate[2] complex. In the absence of such stabilizing reagents, the Mn(III) disproportionates to give Mn(IV), which precipitates as MnO_2.

$$2Mn(III) \rightarrow Mn(II) + Mn(IV) \qquad (24\text{-}50)$$

If every Cr(IV) ion produced in reaction (24-45) is used in reaction (24-49), the over-all induced reaction is the sum of twice (24-45) plus twice (24-49) plus (24-50), or

$$2Cr(VI) + 2As(III) + Mn(II) \rightarrow 2Cr(III) + 2As(V) + Mn(IV) \qquad (24\text{-}51)$$

which is the sum of the primary reaction (24-48) and the apparent induced reaction (24-44) taken in the ratio 2:1. It is evident that reaction (24-44) alone does not occur and that the paradoxical observation of a thermodynamically impossible reaction is due to the fact that this reaction is coupled with an energetically favorable reaction so that the over-all induced reaction has a negative free energy change.

Medalia[3] has suggested the use of the term *coupling factor*, defined by

$$F_c = \frac{\text{equivalents of coupled reaction}}{\text{equivalents of primary reaction}}$$

which expresses the amount of reaction (24-51) in relation to (24-48). If, in the above example, every Cr(IV) is reduced by Mn(II), so that reaction (24-51) proceeds exclusively, the coupling factor becomes infinite. To focus attention on the coupled reaction, another term, the

---

[1] Lang, R., and Kurtz, F., *Z. anorg. u. allgem. Chem.*, **181**, 111 (1929); **86**, 288 (1931).

[2] Lang, *Z. anal. Chem.*, **102**, 8 (1935).

[3] Medalia, *op. cit.*

coupling index CI, is defined by

$$CI = \frac{\text{equivalents of acceptor reacting in coupled reaction}}{\text{equivalents of inductor reacting in coupled reaction}}$$

The coupling index is *the limiting value of the induction factor* as the ratio of acceptor to inductor is increased. In the above example, Mn(II) is the acceptor and As(III) is the inductor. According to Eq. (24-51), the coupling index is 0.5, which is the limiting value of the induction factor.

Examples of the use of the dichromate-arsenite reaction to induce other oxidations, notably V(IV) to (V) and Ce(III) to (IV) are given in Chap. 18.

In alkaline solution, the reaction between Cr(VI) and As(III) induces the air oxidation of arsenite. This reaction was studied by Kolthoff and Fineman,[1] who found a coupling index of $\frac{4}{3}$. They postulated the scheme

$$Cr(VI) + As(III) \rightarrow Cr(IV) + As(V) \qquad (24\text{-}52)$$
$$Cr(IV) + As(III) \rightarrow Cr(II) + As(V) \qquad (24\text{-}53)$$
$$Cr(VI) + Cr(II) \rightarrow Cr(III) + Cr(V) \qquad (24\text{-}54)$$
$$Cr(V) + As(III) \rightarrow Cr(III) + As(V) \qquad (24\text{-}55)$$

as operating in alkaline solution in place of the sequence (24-45), (24-46), (24-47). The coupling index of $\frac{4}{3}$ corresponds to the reduction of 1 mole of oxygen per mole of Cr(VI). This is accounted for by assuming a 1:1 reaction between Cr(II) and oxygen to form a peroxide. The original paper should be consulted for details.

Other coupled reactions involving Cr(VI) have been discussed by Westheimer[2] and Medalia.[3] If a one-electron reductant such as Fe(II) reacts with Cr(VI), the first step presumably involves the formation of Cr(V)

$$Cr(VI) + Fe(II) \rightarrow Cr(V) + Fe(III) \qquad (24\text{-}56)$$

If iodide ion is present, an induced oxidation occurs, with a coupling index of 2.* The reaction probably proceeds through the following steps:[4]

$$Cr(V) + I^- \rightarrow Cr(III) + OI^- \qquad (24\text{-}57)$$
$$OI^- + I^- + H^+ \rightarrow I_2 + H_2O \qquad (24\text{-}58)$$

Reaction (24-57), however, is in competition with the reaction between

[1] Kolthoff, I. M., and Fineman, M. A., *J. Phys. Chem.*, **60**, 1383 (1956).

[2] Westheimer, *op. cit.*

[3] Medalia, *op. cit.*

* Manchot, W., and Wilhelms, O., *Ann. Chem. Liebig*, **325**, 105 (1902).

[4] Luther, R., and Rutter, T. F., *Z. anorg. u. allgem. Chem.*, **54**, 1 (1907).

Cr(V) and Fe(II):

$$\text{Cr(V)} + \text{Fe(II)} \rightarrow \text{Cr(IV)} + \text{Fe(III)} \qquad (24\text{-}59)$$
$$\text{Cr(IV)} + \text{Fe(II)} \rightarrow \text{Cr(III)} + \text{Fe(III)} \qquad (24\text{-}60)$$

so it would seem that the induction factor could approach 2 only if the ratio of iodide ion to ferrous ion concentration were very large. It happens, however, that the rate constant of reaction (24-57) is about 6 times greater than that of (24-59),* so that the limiting value of the induction factor can readily be approached.

In summary, it may be stated that coupled reactions can be used in some cases to bring about induced reactions that, taken alone, would be thermodynamically impossible. In many cases, determination of the coupling index affords important clues to the mechanisms of complex redox reactions.

PROBLEMS

24-1. Calculate the ratio of first-order rate constants k_A/k_B necessary if 99.9 per cent of A is to react in a time interval such that only 0.1 per cent of B reacts. *Ans.* 6,920.

24-2. Plot log C_t/C_0 as a function of time in units of $1/k_A$ for the case $k_A/k_B = 10$, $[A]_0/[B]_0 = 10$. At the times when (a) 1 per cent and (b) 0.1 per cent of A remains, what percentage of D is left? *Ans.* (a) 63.0 per cent; (b) 50.1 per cent.

24-3. For the case of Prob. 2, plot C_t in arbitrary units as a function of time (in units of $1/k_A$). For various arbitrary times, determine the ratio of slope to concentration, and show that it approaches the value k_B as t increases.

24-4. Derive Eqs. (24-7) and (24-8) by combining Eqs. (24-4) and (24-6).

24-5. For the case $k_A = 10^{-3} \text{ sec}^{-1}$, $k_B = 10^{-4} \text{ sec}^{-1}$, calculate (a) the value of t_{opt} and (b) the ends of the calibration curve, using Eqs. (24-6) to (24-8). (c) For $t = 10^3 \text{ sec}$ and (d) for $t = 5 \times 10^3 \text{ sec}$, calculate the ends of the calibration curve. *Ans.* (a) $2.56 \times 10^3 \text{ sec}$; (b) 0.0775, 0.775; (c) 0.368, 0.904; (d) 0.0067, 0.606.

* Wagner, C., and Preiss, W., *Z. anorg. u. allgem. Chem.*, **168**, 265 (1928).

25. Multistage Separation Methods

The analytical chemist makes use of a number of separation methods based upon transfer of matter from one phase into another. In earlier chapters, we have considered several methods sufficiently efficient to bring about a quantitative separation in a single stage of material transfer. Included in this category are all those precipitation reactions, volatilization or thermal decomposition reactions, liquid-liquid extraction separations, and electrodeposition reactions selective and complete enough to accomplish the desired separation in a single stage.

A second level of complexity is encountered when a single separation stage is not sufficiently selective or quantitative but the first phase can be brought repeatedly into contact with fresh portions of the second. Such a repetitive technique is applicable whenever one of the components to be separated remains quantitatively in one phase whereas the other is distributed between the phases. Thus, in precipitation separations, the amount of coprecipitation can usually be diminished by redissolving the precipitate in fresh solvent and repeating the process. Similarly, if, in an extractive separation, one component remains quantitatively in one of the two phases, say, the aqueous phase, while another is distributed between the two phases, then a repetitive extraction process can be used to advantage. The well-known Soxhlet extractor is an example in common use. Other applications of the same principle are encountered in the use of fresh batches of mercury as a cathode in controlled-potential electrolytic separations of metals, and in the use of ion exchange columns for the quantitative retention of ions from a solution. In Sec. 25-2, under Exhaustive Extraction, the theory of multiple extraction with finite batches of fresh solvent is formulated. The same concept can be extended to other examples of the same type, if it can be assumed that equilibrium involving a constant partition coefficient is reached at each stage.

The third level of complexity is reached when a moving phase containing the components to be separated is brought into contact with a stationary phase and when both components are distributed between the two phases. The two phases may be divided into discrete units, as in the Craig "countercurrent distribution" method of extraction, in which one of the two phases remains fixed in a number of extraction vessels and the other phase is moved stepwise from one vessel to the next. Strictly speaking, this method as usually applied is not a true countercurrent process, because one phase remains fixed. In most applications, the two phases are actually continuous, as in column techniques of chromatography. Even here, the stationary phase may be regarded as composed of a number of stages, or theoretical plates, for purposes comparing the efficiency of a column with that of a single equilibrium stage.

The fourth and final level of complexity is represented by the true countercurrent method, in which both phases are moving, but in opposite directions. The Craig multiple extraction method can be made into a true batch-type countercurrent method by moving both the solvents through the apparatus instead of leaving one phase fixed. Another example is the distillation column, which may be either continuous or divided into physically discrete stages or plates. A continuous column, once again, may be regarded as composed of a number of theoretical plates.

We choose to discuss distillation methods first, because from distillation theory comes the important concept of the theoretical plate, which represents a portion of a multistage device accomplishing the same amount of separation as a single equilibrium stage of phase distribution. Next, it is convenient to consider liquid-liquid extraction, in which the separate equilibrium stages can readily be identified. After examining the problem of exhaustive extraction, we proceed to the very important Craig multiple-extraction scheme with one mobile phase and consider the distribution of solute among the various portions of fixed phase. An extension of the technique of the liquid-liquid partition chromatography column is readily made by adding the theoretical-plate concept, as was first done by Martin and Synge.[1] The other types of chromatographic and ion exchange column separation processes are handled in a similar fashion.

At the outset, we should recognize that the theoretical-plate concept does not provide a mechanistic picture of the phase-distribution process. The interpretation begins from the viewpoint of equilibrium, but, since the number of theoretical plates is not known, the degree of departure from equilibrium can only be inferred from indirect observations. In some instances (e.g., paper chromatography) it is not always even possible to decide with certainty what type of phase distribution is involved. Generally, it is assumed as a first approximation that the phase-distribution equilibrium constant is independent of concentration. Departures

[1] Martin, A. J. P., and Synge, R. L. M., *Biochem. J.*, **35**, 1358 (1941).

from ideal behavior may then be ascribed to lack of equilibrium or to variation of equilibrium constant (nonlinear isotherm).

Other theoretical approaches to chromatographic separations are more fundamental from the viewpoint of mechanism. Thus adsorption kinetics,[1] diffusion and mass transfer between phases,[2] and statistics[3] have been used as the basis for recent theories. As will be pointed out later, a combination of the theoretical-plate concept with mechanistic theories[4] is valuable in predicting the effects of column variables.

25-1. Distillation

Although column distillation techniques are of less importance to the analytical chemist than to the preparative chemist, they are classic examples of multistage separations. The terminology applied to distillation columns is often extended to other column separation methods, and fruitful analogies may often be drawn. It is therefore worth while to examine the theory of column distillation, at least in an elementary way.

The Theoretical Plate. The effectiveness of a particular distillation column is often expressed in terms of the number of *theoretical plates*. A theoretical plate is defined by analogy to a plate column, which is divided physically into separate stages of vaporization and condensation. If, in an actual distillation, the same difference in composition is achieved between a liquid mixture and its vapor as would have been observed between these two phases at equilibrium, the distillation is said to involve one theoretical plate.

The most familiar representation of the vapor-liquid equilibrium of binary mixtures is by means of the boiling point–composition diagram. For a mixture that does not exhibit azeotropic behavior, such a diagram consists of two curves, representing the compositions of liquid and vapor in equilibrium at each temperature.

Referring to Fig. 25-1, suppose that the composition of a liquid mixture of A and B is represented by l_0. At its boiling point t_0, the composition of vapor in equilibrium with l_0 is d_1. The first drop of distillate would have the same composition, represented by l_1. Likewise, a liquid of composition l_1 is in equilibrium with vapor d_2, which has the same composition as the liquid l_2. A theoretical plate in column distillation is represented by the length of column required to produce a change in composition corresponding to the horizontal line connecting the equilibrium compositions of liquid and vapor. Thus three theoretical plates are necessary to effect the change in composition from l_0 to l_3 in Fig. 25-1.

[1] Giddings, J. C., and Eyring, H., *J. Phys. Chem.*, **59**, 416 (1955).

[2] Van Deemter, J. J., Zuiderweg, F. J., and Klinkenberg, A., *Chem. Eng. Sci.*, **5**, 271 (1956).

[3] Klinkenberg, A., and Sjenitzer, F., *Chem. Eng. Sci.*, **5**, 258 (1956).

[4] Glueckauf, E., *Trans. Faraday Soc.*, **51**, 34 (1955).

It is more common in distillation practice to use a similar stepping-off process with a vapor-liquid composition diagram such as that shown in Fig. 25-2. The mole fraction of the more volatile component A in the vapor is plotted against the corresponding equilibrium mole fraction in the liquid. Beginning with a liquid of composition l_0, the corresponding equilibrium vapor composition is d_1, which condenses to give a minute amount of liquid of the same composition. To transpose this composition to the same liquid composition, use is made of the 45° line, which of course corresponds to equal compositions of liquid and vapor. The process is repeated until the desired final composition (say, l_3) is reached. The

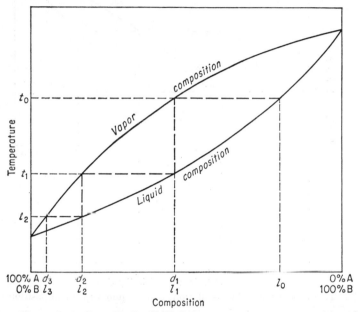

Fig. 25-1. Theoretical plates in distillation, from temperature-composition diagram.

effectiveness of a column is often expressed by the HETP, or *height equivalent to a theoretical plate*. The HETP is obtained by dividing the height of a column by the number of theoretical plates. A laboratory distillation column may have an HETP of the order of 1 to 10 cm; the exact value depends on the type of column packing and construction and on the manner in which it is operated. Having evaluated the HETP of a given type of column, it is possible to estimate the length of column necessary to effect a particular degree of separation.

The procedure outlined above is idealized in several respects. (1) It is assumed that the complete equilibrium diagram is known. In practice, it is desirable to be able to estimate the number of theoretical plates without having detailed phase diagrams. (2) The HETP of a particular type of column is not necessarily independent of the length of the column and of the materials being distilled, but depends to some extent on the conditions of its operation. (3) The equilibrium diagrams can be used, strictly speaking, only under conditions of total reflux. The composition of each liquid and vapor stage is altered somewhat by drawing distillate at a finite rate, so the actual separation is less complete than that calculated from the diagrams. (4) Finally, a batch distillation involves a

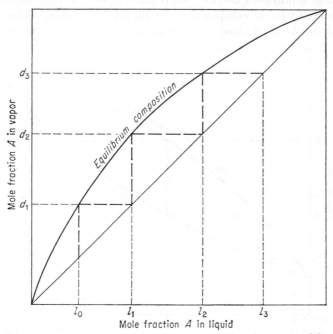

FIG. 25.2. Theoretical plates in distillation, from liquid-vapor composition diagram.

gradually changing composition of both distillate and residue, and the composition of a finite volume of distillate is actually an average one.

We shall now consider these problems in a little more detail.

The Relative Volatility. If we consider a binary liquid mixture, the volatility v_1 of the first component is defined by the ratio of its partial vapor pressure $\overline{p_1}$ to its mole fraction x_1 in the liquid,

$$v_1 = \frac{\overline{p_1}}{x_1} \qquad (25\text{-}1)$$

If Raoult's law holds (ideal mixture), $\overline{p_1} = x_1 p_1$, where p_1 is the vapor pressure of the pure liquid. Thus, for an ideal mixture, the volatility of a component is simply the vapor pressure of the pure component.

The *relative volatility* is the ratio of the two volatilities, or

$$\alpha = \frac{v_1}{v_2} = \frac{\overline{p_1}x_2}{\overline{p_2}x_1} \qquad (25\text{-}2)$$

Normally, the ratio of partial vapor pressures $\overline{p_1}/\overline{p_2}$ can be replaced by the ratio of mole fractions y_1/y_2 in the vapor (Dalton's Law); so

$$\frac{y_1}{y_2} = \alpha \frac{x_1}{x_2} \qquad (25\text{-}3)$$

where α is conventionally set greater than 1 by choosing the components so that $v_1 > v_2$.

For a binary mixture, $x_2 = 1 - x_1$ and $y_2 = 1 - y_1$. It is customary to use x and y as mole fractions of the more volatile component in the liquid and vapor, respectively, so that

$$\frac{y}{1 - y} = \alpha \frac{x}{1 - x} \qquad (25\text{-}4)$$

Equation (25-4) is often found extremely useful in practice, particularly for pairs of liquids that are chemically similar. If x is plotted against y, a curve similar to the "equilibrium composition" curve of Fig. 25-2 is obtained. The amount of curvature depends on the value of α. For the limiting case where $\alpha = 1$, a straight line of 45° slope results.

For an ideal liquid mixture, $\alpha = p_1/p_2$. Therefore, it is possible to plot the liquid-vapor composition diagram for closely similar liquids (e.g., benzene-toluene) without further ado. It should be noted that the value of α is not strictly constant over the whole composition range, even for an ideal mixture, because p_1 and p_2 do not necessarily vary similarly with temperature (Clausius-Clapeyron equation).

By applying the Clapeyron equation and Trouton's rule to the case of an ideal binary mixture, Rose[1] derived the relationship

$$\log \alpha = 8.9 \frac{T_2 - T_1}{T_2 + T_1} \qquad (25\text{-}5)$$

which is useful for estimating α from the absolute normal boiling points T_1 and T_2 of the pure components. Of course, Eq. (25-5) can be expected to hold only for chemically similar, normal liquids, to which Trouton's rule can be applied.

Example 25-1. The normal boiling points of chlorobenzene and bromobenzene are 132°C and 156°C, respectively. Estimate the relative volatility from Eq. (25-5), and compare this with the ratio of vapor pressures at 140°C (939.5 to 495.8 mm).

Answer. From Eq. (25-5), $\log \alpha = 8.9(429 - 405)/(429 + 405) = 0.256$, or $\alpha = 1.80$ as compared with $\alpha = 939.5/495.8 = 1.89$.

[1] Rose, A., *Ind. Eng. Chem.*, **33**, 594 (1941).

For nonideal liquid mixtures, more complex relationships involving activity coefficients are available.[1,2] It is always necessary, however, to obtain the vapor-pressure data from experimental measurements. Plots of vapor-liquid equilibrium composition can then be made for graphic interpretation.

The Fenske Equation. Fenske[3] and, independently, Underwood[4] derived an equation of the form

$$\frac{y_n}{1 - y_n} = \alpha^{n+1} \frac{x_s}{1 - x_s} \tag{25-6}$$

which holds for distillation with a column of n theoretical plates, if the relative volatility α can be regarded as independent of composition [Eq. (25-4)]. The mole fraction of the more volatile component is x_s in the still and y_n in the distillate, under conditions of total reflux. The exponent $n + 1$ occurs instead of n, because one theoretical plate is involved in passing from the still pot to the base of the column. The number of theoretical plates calculated from Eq. (25-6) is of course identical with the number obtained from the graphic procedure, provided that, in the latter procedure also, allowance is made for the additional theoretical plate involved in reaching the column.

Example 25-2. Using the data of Example 25-1, estimate the number of theoretical plates required to produce a vapor containing 99.9 mole per cent chlorobenzene at the top of a column under total reflux, if the still pot contains a 50:50 mole ratio mixture of chlorobenzene and bromobenzene.

Answer. From Eq. (25-6), taking $y_n = 0.999$, $x_s = 0.50$, and $\alpha = 1.89$, we calculate $(n + 1) \log 1.89 = \log 999$, or $n = 9.8$ or 10 plates.

Distillation under Partial Reflux: The Sorel-Lewis Method. Practical distillation processes cannot, of course, be operated under total reflux. Some sacrifice of completeness of separation must be made in order to obtain a finite rate of removal of distillate; or, what amounts to the same thing, a more efficient column must be used to achieve the desired degree of separation.

If L represents the moles of reflux and D the moles of distillate per unit time, L/D is the *reflux ratio* R_D. The total number V of moles of vapor leaving the top plate per unit time is then

$$V = L + D \tag{25-7}$$

By applying a material and thermal balance between two adjacent plates

[1] Carlson, H. C., and Colburn, A. P., *Ind. Eng. Chem.*, **34**, 581 (1942).

[2] Clark, A. M., *Trans. Faraday Soc.*, **41**, 718 (1945).

[3] Fenske, M. R., *Ind. Eng. Chem.*, **24**, 482 (1932).

[4] Underwood, A. J. V., *Trans. Inst. Chem. Engrs. London*, **10**, 112 (1932).

under equilibrium conditions, Sorel[1] derived equations permitting a plate-by-plate calculation of the composition down the column.

In its more modern form, due to Lewis,[2] the procedure of applying a thermal and material balance has led to an *operating-line equation* of great practical value. With certain simplifying assumptions (no heat loss, negligible heat of mixing, similar latent heats and specific heats of components), Lewis showed that the conditions of material balance also lead to conditions of thermal balance when a column is operating under steady-state conditions. Under these conditions, the quantities V, L, and D in Eq. (25-7) may be applied to each component at every point along the column.

From the material balance applied between the nth and the $(n-1)$st plates for the more volatile component, we have

$$V y_{n-1} = L x_n + D x_d \tag{25-8}$$

where $V y_{n-1}$ = moles of the component leaving the $(n-1)$st plate
  $L x_n$ = moles returning by reflux
  $D x_d$ = moles leaving as distillate
The operating-line equation is usually written

$$y_{n-1} = \frac{L}{V} x_n + \frac{D}{V} x_d \tag{25-9}$$

For conditions of total reflux, $D = 0$ and $L/V = 1$; so

$$y_{n-1} = x_n$$

which corresponds to the 45° line of Fig. 25-2.

Example 25-3. Calculate the number of theoretical plates required to produce a distillate containing 99.0 mole per cent chlorobenzene from a 50:50 mole ratio mixture of chlorobenzene and bromobenzene, if the reflux ratio is 9.

Answer. The operating-line equation is $y_{n-1} = 0.9x_n + 0.1x_d$, where $x_d = y_n = 0.990$. From Eq. (25-4), x_n is calculated by setting $y_n/(1-y_n) = 1.89x_n/(1-x_n)$, giving $x_n = 0.9812$. From Eq. (25-9), $y_{n-1} = 0.9821$. From the equation $y_{n-1}/(1-y_{n-1}) = \alpha x_{n-1}/(1-x_{n-1})$, taking $1/\alpha = 0.5227$, calculate $x_{n-1} = 0.9666$. From the operating-line equation, $y_{n-2} = 0.9699$. Continue the calculation until x reaches 0.50, which occurs at $x_{n-8} = 0.434$. Therefore, eight theoretical plates are required.

The McCabe-Thiele Operating-line Procedure. Equation (25-9) is useful in permitting a plate-by-plate calculation of composition, starting with the distillate composition and reflux ratio. However, for columns of large numbers of theoretical plates, a graphic procedure due to McCabe and Thiele[3] is often used. In Fig. 25-3, an operating line is drawn to

[1] Sorel, E., *Compt. rend.*, **108**, 1128, 1204, 1317 (1889).
[2] Lewis, W. K., *Ind. Eng. Chem.*, **1**, 522 (1909); **14**, 492 (1922).
[3] McCabe, W. L., and Thiele, E. W., *Ind. Eng. Chem.*, **17**, 605 (1925).

intersect the 45° line corresponding to the composition of distillate, x_d. The intercept of the operating line on the y axis is given by $y_0 = Dx_d/V$. It is a simple matter to step off the compositions of vapor and liquid for the various plates until the composition of the still pot has been reached.

It is clear from Fig. 25-3 that, for each original still composition and desired distillate composition, there is a *minimum reflux ratio* below which the desired separation could never be achieved even with an infinite number of theoretical plates. The minimum reflux ratio is readily calculated

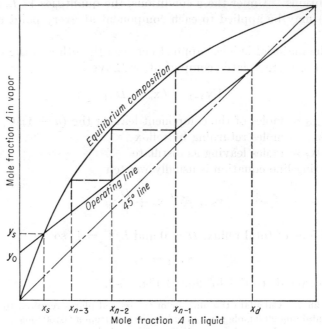

FIG. 25-3. Theoretical plates by McCabe-Thiele method.

from the fact that the slope of the operating line is L/V [Eq. (25-9)], which for the minimum reflux ratio (Fig. 25-3) is

$$\left(\frac{L}{V}\right)_{\min} = \frac{x_d - y_s}{x_d - x_s} \frac{L_{\min}}{L_{\min} + D} \qquad (25\text{-}10)$$

Since the minimum reflux ratio is $R_{D\min} = (L/D)_{\min}$, the right-hand term of Eq. (25-10) is $R_{D\min}/(R_{D\min} + 1)$, from which it is readily found that

$$R_{D\min} = \frac{x_d - y_s}{y_s - x_s} \qquad (25\text{-}11)$$

Example 25-4. Calculate the minimum reflux ratio for the separation required in Example 25-3.

Answer. From Eq. (25-4), $y_s = 0.655$. From Eq. (25-11), $R_{D_{min}} = (0.99 - 0.655)/$
$(0.655 - 0.50) = 1.52$.

Evaluation and Use of HETP Data. The performance of a column is evaluated experimentally by means of test mixtures, such as n-heptane-methylcyclohexane[1] or methylcyclohexane-toluene,[2] for which accurate vapor-liquid equilibrium data are available. Measurement of refractive index serves conveniently to establish the composition.

Comparison of the HETP values for various conditions, such as type of column packing, reflux ratio, or throughput, constitutes a reasonably reliable basis of choice of a suitable column for a given separation. HETP data are not, however, highly reproducible, and they vary somewhat with the type of material being distilled and with the height of the column. For example, it usually turns out that the number of theoretical plates is more than doubled by doubling the length of a column. However, for many practical purposes, a rough knowledge of the number of theoretical plates is entirely sufficient, and a crude estimate of the HETP is of considerable value.

Batch Distillation : The Rayleigh Equation. The discussion above has been restricted to continuous distillation processes, in which the composition at each point may be regarded as constant. In batch distillation, the composition varies continuously with the quantity of distillate.

The Rayleigh equation[3] is based on a material balance on the more volatile component. At any instant, S total moles remain in the still, and x_s is the mole fraction of the more volatile component in the still. After the removal of dS moles of distillate, the amount remaining in the still is $S - dS$, and the composition has changed to $x_s - dx_s$. The mole fraction in the distillate is x_d. Then a material-balance equation is

$$Sx_s = (S - dS)(x_s - dx_s) + x_d \, dS \tag{25-12}$$

Simplifying and dropping the second-order differential $dS \, dx_s$, we obtain

$$\frac{dS}{S} = \frac{dx_s}{x_d - x_s} \tag{25-13}$$

The integrated form

$$\ln \frac{S_1}{S_2} = \int_{x_{s_2}}^{x_{s_1}} \frac{dx_s}{x_d - x_s} \tag{25-14}$$

is the usual form of the Rayleigh equation. A graphic integration is performed by plotting $1/(x_d - x_s)$ versus x_s and determining the area under the resulting curve between the two limits corresponding to S_1 and S_2.

[1] Bromiley, E. C., and Quiggle, D., *Ind. Eng. Chem.*, **25**, 1136 (1933).
[2] Quiggle and Fenske, *J. Am. Chem. Soc.*, **59**, 1829 (1937).
[3] Rayleigh, Lord, *Phil. Mag.*, **8**, 534 (1904).

A common practice is to plot a graph of the distillate composition as a function of the quantity of distillate. The boiling point is an index of composition, which may be plotted; but usually the refractive index or density is a more accurate estimate of composition. The completeness of separation may be gauged from the sharpness with which various components give plateaus.

The shapes of the curves become too complex to be expressed in general algebraic form. However, by applying Fenske's equation [Eq. (25-6)] for total reflux as an approximation, it is possible to integrate Eq. (25-12)* for various values of α and n. A result of such a calculation is given in Fig. 25-4. The calculated curves, representing conditions of total reflux and

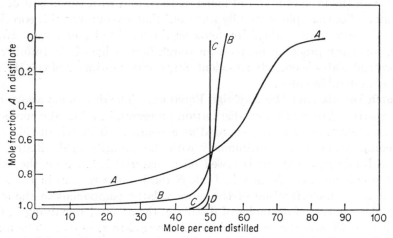

FIG. 25-4. Calculated effect of number of theoretical plates at total reflux on efficiency of separation. $\alpha = 1.25$. A, B, C, D: $n = 10, 20, 30, 40$ plates. [*With permission from Rose, A., and Welshans, L. M., Ind. Eng. Chem.*, **32**, 668 (1940).]

no holdup, represent the best possible separation to be obtained with the particular mixture and column. It is interesting that an increase in the total number of plates from 30 to 40 has little effect on the sharpness of separation. It is also true in practice that there is an optimum number of plates beyond which no appreciable improvement is achieved.

According to Rose,[1] the optimum number of plates should be about equal to the reflux ratio, and this number may be estimated from the equation

$$n = R_D = \frac{2.85}{\log \alpha} = \frac{T_2 + T_1}{3(T_2 - T_1)} \qquad (25\text{-}15)$$

where T_2 and T_1 are the absolute boiling points. Over a relatively narrow

* Rose, A., and Welshans, L. M., *Ind. Eng. Chem.*, **32**, 668 (1940).
[1] Rose, A., *Ind. Eng. Chem.*, **33**, 594 (1941).

range, it is possible to compensate for a smaller number of plates by a larger reflux ratio. These relationships and the limitations on the use of Eq. (25-15) are discussed by Rose and Rose.[1]

Applications. The construction and operation of several types of distillation columns suitable for laboratory-scale analytical distillation have been described by Winters and Dinerstein.[2] In small-scale operations, the proper design of a receiver system to avoid mixing of fractions and to allow accurate measurement of distillation volumes is particularly important. Performance data for several types of analytical columns are listed by Nerheim and Dinerstein.[3,4]

The Podbielniak[5] automatic distillation apparatus is designed to record boiling point as a function of volume of distillate automatically over a temperature range from -190 to $300°C$. The low-temperature apparatus has been described by Rose[6] as "a masterpiece of automatic and efficient separation of all except the closest-boiling components, such as the group of C_4 hydrocarbons boiling near $0°C$."

A number of useful practical working instructions are given in an industrial booklet by Todd.[7]

25-2. Liquid-Liquid Extraction

Extraction procedures based on the distribution of solutes between immiscible solvents are carried out for two purposes. *Exhaustive extraction* involves the quantitative removal of one solute; *selective extraction* involves the separation of two solutes. In considering the theory of extraction procedures, it is useful to consider first the behavior of a single solute, then to extend the treatment to separations by assuming that two or more solutes undergo no interaction. Although this assumption may be unwarranted in certain cases, it is usually valid, and we shall not consider this complication.

Exhaustive Extraction: Successive Extraction with Fresh Solvent. For the sake of convenience, we shall consider the distribution of a solute between an organic liquid and water, although of course any two immiscible liquids could be used. The distribution equilibrium for the simplest

[1] Rose, A., and Rose, E., in Weissberger, A. (ed.), "Technique of Organic Chemistry," vol. 4, pp. 1–174, Interscience Publishers, Inc., New York, 1951.

[2] Winters, J. C., and Dinerstein, R. A., *Anal. Chem.*, **27**, 546 (1955).

[3] Nerheim, A. G., and Dinerstein, R. A., *Anal. Chem.*, **28**, 1029 (1956).

[4] Nerheim, *Anal. Chem.*, **29**, 1546 (1957).

[5] Podbielniak, W. J., *Ind. Eng. Chem., Anal. Ed.*, **13**, 639 (1941); *Bulletin A-2*, Podbielniak, Inc., Chicago, 1953.

[6] Rose, A., *Anal. Chem.*, **21**, 81 (1949).

[7] Todd, F., "Modern Fractional Distillation Equipment for Your Laboratory," Todd Scientific Co., Springfield, Pa., 1953.

case (same molecular species in each phase) is described by the partition coefficient (or distribution coefficient) P:

$$\mathrm{x}_w \rightleftharpoons \mathrm{x}_o \qquad P = \frac{(a_\mathrm{x})_o}{(a_\mathrm{x})_w} \cong \frac{[\mathrm{x}]_o}{[\mathrm{x}]_w} \tag{25-16}$$

where the subscripts w and o refer to water and the organic liquid, respectively. Strictly speaking, the partition coefficient is given by the ratio of activities in the two phases; but normally the ratio of concentrations may be used, because extractions usually involve molecular rather than ionic species and dilute solutions may be regarded as ideal. If polymerization occurs in one phase but not in the other, the partition coefficient varies with concentration, and the treatment becomes much more complicated, particularly for multistage separations. This complication will not be considered here.

Consider an extraction of X moles of solute x dissolved in V_w ml water, with V_o ml organic solvent. From Eq. (25-16),

$$P = \frac{[\mathrm{x}]_o}{[\mathrm{x}]_w} = \frac{(X - Y)/V_o}{Y/V_w} \tag{25-17}$$

if Y moles remain in the water phase after a single extraction. From (25-17), the fraction remaining unextracted is

$$\frac{Y}{X} = f = \frac{1}{1 + P(V_o/V_w)} = \frac{V_w}{V_w + PV_o} \tag{25-18}$$

The fraction remaining unextracted is independent of the initial concentration. Therefore, if n successive extractions are performed with fresh portions of solvent, the fraction remaining unextracted is

$$f_n = \left(1 + P\frac{V_o}{V_w}\right)^{-n} \tag{25-19}$$

The question of the limiting amount of solute remaining unextracted after n extractions as n approaches infinity has been considered by Griffin.[1,2] Clearly, the limit of f_n in Eq. (25-19) is zero for a finite value of V_o/V_w. However, such an extraction does not represent a practical case, because the volume of extracting solvent would approach infinity.

For a finite volume V_o of extracting solvent divided into n portions, Eq. (25-19) becomes

$$f_n = \left(1 + P\frac{V_o}{nV_w}\right)^{-n} \tag{25-20}$$

[1] Griffin, C. W., *Ind. Eng. Chem., Anal. Ed.*, **6**, 40 (1934).
[2] Griffin, C. W., and von Saaf, M., *Ind. Eng. Chem., Anal. Ed.*, **8**, 358 (1936).

which, in the limit as $n \to \infty$, approaches the value

$$f_\infty = e^{-V_oP/V_w} \qquad (25\text{-}21)$$

As the number of extractions approaches infinity, the volume of the organic phase for each extraction approaches zero. In practice, little is gained by dividing the volume of extractant into more than four or five portions, because f_∞ is approached asymptotically. Equation (25-21) is useful in determining whether a given extraction is practicable, with a reasonable value of V_o/V_w, or whether an extractant with a more favorable partition coefficient should be sought.

Example 25-5. For a system with a partition coefficient $P = 2$, compare the fraction of solute remaining unextracted for the following situations: (a) single extraction with equal volume of organic solvent, (b) five extractions with the same total amount of organic solvent, (c) limiting case of infinite extractions with same total amount of solvent.

Answer. (a) $f_1 = \frac{1}{3} = 0.333$; (b) $f_5 = (1/1.4)^5 = 0.186$; (c) $f_\infty = e^{-2} = 0.135$.

Application of Exhaustive Extraction. The classical application of an exhaustive analytical separation is the ether extraction of ferric chloride from hydrochloric acid solutions.[1] The extraction is not strictly quantitative; an amount of 1 to 2 mg remains unextracted in the usual procedures. Therefore the method is best suited to the removal of large amounts of iron (several grams) from small amounts of such metals as nickel, cobalt, manganese, chromium, titanium, aluminum, etc.[2] It is of interest that ferrous iron remains completely unextracted.[3] Certain metals, e.g., nickel and copper, are extracted to a slight extent if present in high concentration. The usual procedure involves recovery of such metals by shaking the combined ether extracts with dilute hydrochloric acid. Swift and coworkers have found isopropyl ether[4] and β,β'-dichloroethyl ether[5] to be preferable to ethyl ether. Amyl acetate has been used by Wells and Hunter.[6]

Antimony(V) is extracted quantitatively from 6.5 to 8.5 M hydrochloric acid into isopropyl ether in two extractions.[7] Antimony(III) is extracted only to the extent of 2 per cent under the same conditions, so reextraction with hydrochloric acid permits the quantitative recovery of Sb(III) in the aqueous layer.

[1] Rothe, J. W., *Stahl u. Eisen*, **12**, 1052 (1892).

[2] For a discussion, see Hillebrand, W. F., Lundell, G. E. F., Bright, H. A., and Hoffman, J. I., "Applied Inorganic Analysis," 2d ed., John Wiley & Sons, Inc., New York, 1953.

[3] Swift, E. H., *J. Am. Chem. Soc.*, **46**, 2378 (1924).

[4] Dodson, R. W., Forney, G. J., and Swift, E. H., *J. Am. Chem. Soc.*, **58**, 2573 (1936).

[5] Axelrod, J., and Swift, E. H., *J. Am. Chem. Soc.*, **62**, 33 (1940).

[6] Wells, J. E., and Hunter, D. P., *Analyst*, **73**, 671 (1948).

[7] Edwards, F. C., and Voigt, A. F., *Anal. Chem.*, **21**, 1204 (1949).

The equilibria involved in solvent-extraction behavior of metal halides have been considered in a comprehensive way by Diamond,[1] who considered the various cationic, anionic, and polymeric species present in both phases at various concentrations of hydrogen halide. The equations were tested by studying the distribution of molybdenum(VI) halides between various solvents.

An important class of exhaustive extraction procedures involves the use of organic reagents, which are discussed separately in Chap. 14. Numerous examples, with references, are given in a review article by Morrison and Freiser.[2]

Countercurrent Distribution.   Craig[3,4] has devised an ingenious method for carrying out multiple liquid-liquid extractions, which he has termed *countercurrent distribution*.   An automatic apparatus permits the equilibration of two immiscible liquid phases in a series of specially designed tubes so arranged that one phase (say, the organic phase) is transferred from each tube to the next tube in sequence.   After equilibrium is reached again, another transfer occurs in the same direction.   By adding fresh solvent, it is possible to carry out as many transfers as needed.

Distribution of a Single Solute.   Consider a series of tubes, numbered $0, 1, 2, \ldots, r$, each containing (for the sake of simplicity) equal volumes of two immiscible liquids.   A solute is placed in the lower phase of tube 0. After equilibrium is reached, the top layer of tube 0 is transferred to tube 1.   The process is repeated n times; each time, all top layers are transferred to the next higher tube in sequence.

After the first transfer ($n = 1$), the fraction of solute remaining in tube 0 is $1/(P + 1)$, since V_o/V_w was taken equal to unity [Eq. (25-18)]. Upon equilibration, the second tube (tube 1; $r = 1$) contains

$$\left(\frac{1}{P+1}\right)\left(\frac{P}{P+1}\right) = \frac{P}{(P+1)^2}$$

in the bottom phase and $\left(\dfrac{P}{P+1}\right)\left(\dfrac{P}{P+1}\right) = \dfrac{P^2}{(P+1)^2}$ in the top phase. In the second transfer the top phase is moved to tube 2.   Tube 1 then contains $\dfrac{P}{(P+1)^2}$ transferred from tube 0 and an equal amount remaining after the second transfer, to give a total of $\dfrac{2P}{(P+1)^2}$.   The distribution of solute during four extractions is shown in Table 25-1.

[1] Diamond, R. M., *J. Phys. Chem.*, **61**, 69, 75 (1957).
[2] Morrison, G. H., and Freiser, H., *Anal. Chem.*, **30**, 632 (1958).
[3] Craig, L. C., *J. Biol. Chem.*, **155**, 519 (1944).
[4] Craig, L. C., and Post, O., *Anal. Chem.*, **21**, 500 (1949).

TABLE 25-1. FRACTION OF SOLUTE IN SUCCEEDING TUBES IN CRAIG COUNTER-
CURRENT DISTRIBUTION

No. of extractions n \ Tube no.	0	1	2	3	4
0	1	0	0	0	0
1	$\dfrac{1}{P+1}$	$\dfrac{P}{P+1}$	0	0	0
2	$\dfrac{1}{(P+1)^2}$	$\dfrac{2P}{(P+1)^2}$	$\dfrac{P^2}{(P+1)^2}$	0	0
3	$\dfrac{1}{(P+1)^3}$	$\dfrac{3P}{(P+1)^3}$	$\dfrac{3P^2}{(P+1)^3}$	$\dfrac{P^3}{(P+1)^3}$	0
4	$\dfrac{1}{(P+1)^4}$	$\dfrac{4P}{(P+1)^4}$	$\dfrac{6P^2}{(P+1)^4}$	$\dfrac{4P^3}{(P+1)^4}$	$\dfrac{P^4}{(P+1)^4}$

Williamson and Craig[1] showed that the fraction of solute remaining in the various tubes can be expressed by the terms of the binomial expansion

$$\left(\frac{1}{P+1} + \frac{P}{P+1} \right)^n$$

A similar expansion had been used earlier by Martin and Synge[2] to represent the amounts of sample in succeeding theoretical plates in partition chromatography.

The second term of the binomial corresponds to the fraction of solute transferred in each movement of the upper phase, and the first term corresponds to the fraction remaining unextracted.

According to the general expression for the terms of a binomial expansion, the fraction f in tube r after n extractions is given by

$$f(n,r) = \frac{n!}{r!(n-r)!} \left(\frac{1}{P+1} \right)^{n-r} \left(\frac{P}{P+1} \right)^r \tag{25-22}$$

In order to simplify the estimation of the partition coefficient from experimental values of the distribution of solute among a series of tubes, Lieberman[3] has listed a series of calculated values of $f(n,r)$ for $n = 8$ and $n = 24$ for various values of P.

Martin and Synge[2] pointed out that the successive terms of the binomial

[1] Williamson, B., and Craig, L. C., *J. Biol. Chem.*, **168**, 687 (1947).
[2] Martin and Synge, *op. cit.*
[3] Lieberman, S. V., *J. Biol. Chem.*, **173**, 63 (1948).

expansion approximate more and more closely to the normal error curve of statistics (cf. Sec. 26-2) as the number of terms increases. Craig[1] wrote the normal error curve

$$f(n,r) = \frac{1}{\sqrt{2\pi nP/(P+1)^2}} \exp\left\{\frac{-(r_{max}-r)^2}{2nP/(P+1)^2}\right\} \qquad (25\text{-}23)$$

which is a good approximation for $n > 25$. The quantity $r_{max} - r$ represents the number of tubes that a particular tube r is removed from the tube of maximum concentration. Equation (25-23) can be written in the form[2]

$$f(n,r) = \frac{1}{\sqrt{2\pi nXY}} \exp\left\{\frac{-(nX-r)^2}{2nXY}\right\} \qquad (25\text{-}24)$$

where $X = P/(P+1)$ = fraction transferred in the moving phase
$\qquad Y = 1/(P+1)$ = fraction remaining in the stationary phase

Note that, whereas Eq. (25-23) pertains to equal volumes of the two phases, Eq. (25-24) is valid regardless of their relative volumes.

The approximation $r_{max} = nX$ was first proposed by Craig[3] and derived by Nichols,[4] who pointed out that it is a valid approximation if n is large compared with r_{max}. This equation is analogous to the normal error curve [Eq. (26-1), Sec. 26-2], where the population mean μ is replaced by nX, x is replaced by r, and the standard deviation σ is replaced by $\sqrt{nXY}$.

The fraction of solute in the tube of maximum concentration is

$$f(n,r_{max}) = \frac{1}{\sqrt{2\pi nXY}} \qquad (25\text{-}25)$$

Thus the maximum concentration to be found in any one tube varies *inversely* with $\sqrt{n}$, where n is the number of transfers. As is evident from Fig. 25-5, the absolute spread of solute among the tubes increases with $\sqrt{n}$. However, the *relative* sharpness of the peak increases with increasing numbers of transfers, as is clearly shown in Fig. 25-6. It is assumed that the total amount of solute has increased with the increased number of transfers in order to give the same amount in the tube corresponding to r_{max}.

Separation of Two Solutes. According to Eq. (25-24), the peak of a distribution curve moves along the tubes at a rate proportional to the fraction extracted in each step ($r_{max} = nX$). In general, two or more

[1] Craig, *Anal. Chem.*, **22**, 1346 (1950).
[2] Nelson, E., *Anal. Chem.*, **28**, 1998 (1956).
[3] Craig, *J. Biol. Chem.*, **155**, 519 (1944).
[4] Nichols, P. L., Jr., *Anal. Chem.*, **22**, 915 (1950).

solutes act independently of each other, so that each will move according to its value of X.

Nichols[1] pointed out that the degree of overlap of two distribution curves can be determined by locating the tube corresponding to the intersection of the distribution curves. The area under the intersected portions of the distribution curves is a quantitative estimate of the degree of nonseparation. The area under any portion of a distribution curve can

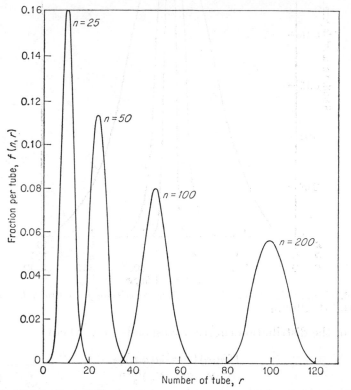

FIG. 25-5. Distribution of single solute, among tubes with increasing number n of transfers. [*With permission from Craig, L. C., Anal. Chem.*, **22**, 1346 (1950).]

be determined readily from appropriate statistical tables, since the shapes of the curves are closely approximated by the normal curve of error.

Nelson[2] wrote Eq. (25-22) in terms of X and Y as follows:

$$f(n,r) = \frac{n!}{r!(n-r)!} X^r Y^{n-r} \tag{25-26}$$

Now, if X_1, Y_1 refer to solute 1 and X_2, Y_2 to solute 2, the point of inter-

[1] Nichols, *op. cit.*

[2] Nelson, *op. cit.*

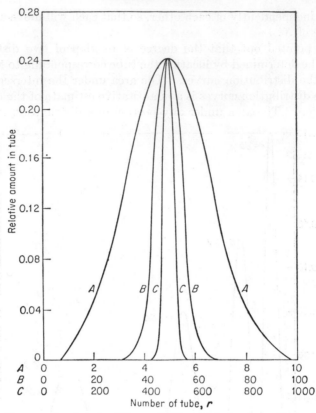

Fɪɢ. 25-6. Comparative band widths. [*With permission from Craig, L. C., Anal. Chem.*, **22**, 1346 (1950).]

section of the distribution curves corresponds to r_i, where

$$\{f(n,r_i)\}_1 = \{f(n,r_i)\}_2$$

or
$$X_1^{r_i} Y_1^{n-r_i} = X_2^{r_i} Y_2^{n-r_i} \qquad (25\text{-}27)$$

Equation (25-27), when solved for r_i, yields

$$r_i = \frac{n \log Y_2/Y_1}{\log X_1 Y_2/X_2 Y_1} = nA \qquad (25\text{-}28)$$

where A is defined by Eq. (25-28).

The normal curve of error [Eq. (26-1)] can now be used to estimate the fraction of solute between the peak r_{max} and the point of intersection r_i of the distribution curve (see Fig. 25-7). From Eqs. (25-24) and (25-27),

$$f(n,r_i) = \frac{1}{\sqrt{2\pi n XY}} \exp\left\{\frac{-(nX - nA)^2}{2nXY}\right\} \qquad (25\text{-}29)$$

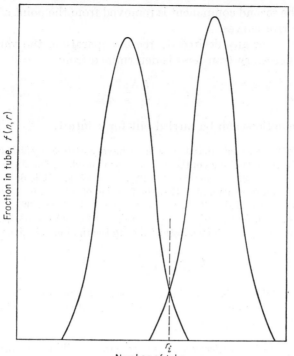

FIG. 25-7. Separation of two solutes in countercurrent distribution. $X_1 = 0.50$; $X_2 = 0.667$; $n = 132$. [*With permission from Nelson, E., Anal. Chem.*, **28**, 1998 (1956).]

which can be compared with the expression for the area under the tail of a normal error curve (cf. Sec. 26-2),

$$A_t = \frac{1}{\sqrt{2\pi}} \int_{-\infty}^{t} \exp\left(-y^2/2\right) dy$$

where A_t is the area under the tail of the error curve from $-\infty$ to t. The total area, corresponding to $t = \infty$, is normalized to unity by the factor $1/\sqrt{2\pi}$.

From a table of areas under the normal curve of error (cf. Table 26-1) corresponding to the variable

$$t_2 = \frac{nX_2 - nA}{\sqrt{nX_2Y_2}} \tag{25-30}$$

the fraction of solute 2 between the tube r_i and $r_{\max}$ can be determined directly. The quantity t_2 corresponds to the number of standard deviations along the normal error curve that the position of maximum concentration of the second component is removed from the point of intersection of the two error curves.

Conversely, for any desired degree of separation, the value of n (the number of necessary transfers) is determined from

$$n = \frac{t_2^2 X_2 Y_2}{(X_2 - A)^2} \tag{25-31}$$

Similar calculations can be carried out for solute 1.

Example 25-6. Suppose that two solutes have partition coefficients $P_1 = 1$ and $P_2 = 2$ and that equal volumes of the two phases are used. Then $X_1 = 0.5$, $Y_1 = 0.5$, $X_2 = 0.667$, $Y_2 = 0.333$. From Eq. (25-28), $A = 0.585$. It is desired to calculate the number of transfers required so that the fraction of solute 2 to the left of tube r_i is 2.5 per cent. From Table 26-3, this corresponds to $t_2 = 1.96$. Then $n = 127$, the number of transfers required. Now $nX_2 = 84.5$, $nX_1 = 63.5$, and $r_i = 74.3$. The fraction of solute 1 contained in the tubes to the right of r_i is given by calculating

$$t_1 = \frac{nX_1 - r_i}{\sqrt{nX_1Y_1}} = -1.81$$

From statistical tables, it is found that 3.5 per cent of solute 1 is to be found at $r > r_i$. The purity to be expected of either solute if the separation is made at $r = r_i$ can now be calculated readily.

Applications of Countercurrent Distribution. The countercurrent-distribution technique is of particular value whenever it is desired to follow in detail the progress of a separation. Thus, in the resolution of a complex mixture, an initial extraction may be performed using relatively few tubes of large size. Any desired fraction from the initial separation may then be subjected to further fractionation, using if necessary an apparatus of a large number of tubes, and performing a large number of transfers. A good example of such a separation is given by Bell,[1] who used up to 10,000 transfers in a 200-tube apparatus to isolate large peptide fragments from the degradation of ACTH.

Another special feature of countercurrent distribution is that it can be scaled up to permit the isolation of small quantities of components from large amounts of starting material. For example, Patterson et al.[2] used a 40-tube apparatus consisting of stages with 1 liter in each phase, to isolate protogen from 4 tons of mixed beef and pork liver.

25-3. Liquid-Liquid Partition Chromatography

Although historically adsorption chromatography was the earliest of the various packed-column chromatographic techniques, here liquid-

[1] Bell, P. H., *J. Am. Chem. Soc.*, **76**, 5565 (1954).

[2] Patterson, E. L., Pierce, J. V., Stokstad, E. L. R., Hoffman, C. E., Brockman, S. A., Day, F. P., Macchi, M. E., and Jukes, T. H., *J. Am. Chem. Soc.*, **76**, 1823 (1954).

liquid partition chromatography will be considered first, for the following reasons: (1) The technique can be regarded as closely analogous to Craig's countercurrent extraction; so we can show clearly the relationship between a column technique and one that consists of physically discrete equilibrium stages.[1] (2) The derivation by Martin and Synge,[2] involving the theoretical-plate concept, has become classic, because it can also be used to interpret various other multistage-separation methods.

The experimental method introduced by Martin and Synge involves a column packed with an inert filling, which firmly adsorbs a solvent (the *nonmobile, or stationary phase*). Another solvent (the *mobile phase*), immiscible with the first, is passed through the column. A solute is added to the top of the column, and pure mobile-phase solvent (the *eluting agent, or eluant*) is made to flow through the column. The solute, in distributing itself between the mobile and nonmobile solvents, proceeds down the column in a *band* or *zone*, the rate of motion of which is slower than that of the mobile solvent and dependent on the partition coefficient of the solute. In some cases, adsorption of solute on the supposedly inert filling may be a complicating factor, which will not be considered in detail here. Suffice it to say that, if the amount adsorbed is proportional to the concentration (linear isotherm), the same theory will hold in any case. It will be recalled that the Langmuir isotherm (page 168) approaches a linear form in very dilute solution; so that the theory to be given will apply in that case even if adsorption is playing a role. In the more general case of a nonlinear isotherm, the elution bands undergo distortion, as will be discussed below.

Theory. The following derivation is based on that originally given by Martin and Synge.[3] However, in place of the quantity R defined by Martin and Synge, the quantity R_F defined later by Consden, Gordon, and Martin[4] for paper chromatography is used. The quantity R_F is defined as the ratio of the rate of movement of a band of solute down the column to the rate of movement of the eluting solvent in the packed column. Originally Martin and Synge had defined R as a similar ratio, but the movement of solvent was measured in the empty tube above the column packing. The R_F value is more generally applicable, e.g., in paper chromatography, and is therefore preferred.

LeRosen,[5] in discussing adsorption chromatographic techniques, used R in the sense of R_F as defined here, and has further designated R_l to

[1] An extraction process involving the introduction of sample all at once but with a continuously flowing countercurrent liquid system has been discussed in detail by Johnson, J. D. A., *J. Chem. Soc.*, **1950**, 1743.

[2] Martin and Synge, *op. cit.*

[3] *Ibid.*

[4] Consden, R., Gordon, A. H., and Martin, A. J. P., *Biochem. J.*, **38**, 224 (1944).

[5] LeRosen, A. L., *J. Am. Chem. Soc.*, **64**, 1905 (1942); **67**, 1683 (1945); **69**, 87 (1947).

describe the motion of the leading edge and R_t that of the trailing edge of a zone. Other authors[1] use R_f to designate the position of the leading edge, particularly when it is sharp and the position of maximum concentration cannot be precisely located. The trailing edges of zones are seldom sharp enough to permit exact evaluation. We shall confine our attention to the position of the point of maximum concentration, as did Martin and Synge, because this point has the most fundamental significance.

Let h = HETP

A = cross-sectional area of column

A_m = cross-sectional area of mobile phase

A_s = cross-sectional area of stationary (nonmobile) phase

A_i = cross-sectional area of inert solid. Accordingly,

$$A = A_m + A_s + A_i$$

V = volume of solvent

P = partition coefficient = $\dfrac{\text{concentration in stationary phase}}{\text{concentration in mobile phase}}$ at equilibrium

V_h = effective plate volume = $h(A_m + PA_s)$

R_F = ratio of rate of movement of position of maximum concentration of solute to rate of movement of developing liquid

r = serial number of plate measured from top of column downward

$f(n,r)$ = fraction of solute in plate r after n extractions

Suppose that successive increments δV of mobile phase are considered to pass down the column $r = 0, 1, 2, \ldots$. If all of the solute is initially at $r = 0$, then, after one extraction with a volume δV, the amount extracted is the fraction $\delta V / A_m h$ of the equilibrium amount in the mobile phase of one theoretical plate.

From Eq. (25-18), taking $V_o = hA_s$ and $V_w = hA_m$, we have

$$f = \frac{1}{1 + PA_s/A_m} = \frac{A_m}{A_m + PA_s} \tag{25-32}$$

for the total equilibrium amount in the mobile phase. Then the fraction extracted by a volume δV is

$$f(1,1) = \frac{\delta V}{(A_m + PA_s)} = \frac{\delta V}{V_h} \tag{25-33}$$

and the fraction remaining unextracted is

$$1 - \frac{\delta V}{V_h}$$

[1] Strain, H. H., Sato, T. R., and Engelke, J., *Anal. Chem.*, **26**, 90 (1954).

The general expression for the fraction in plate r after the nth extraction is given by the binomial expansion

$$\left\{\left(1 - \frac{\delta V}{V_h}\right) + \frac{\delta V}{V_h}\right\}^n$$

or

$$f(n,r) = \frac{n!}{r!(n-r)!}\left(1 - \frac{\delta V}{V_h}\right)^{n-r}\left(\frac{\delta V}{V_h}\right)^r \qquad (25\text{-}34)$$

When $n \gg r \gg 1$, it can be shown that $n!/r!(n-r)!$ approaches $n^r/r!$ Also, since $\delta V/V_h \ll 1$, the approximation $(1 - x)^n = e^{-nx}$ enables us to replace $(1 - \delta V/V_h)^{n-r}$ by $\exp\{-(n-r)(\delta V/V_h)\}$ and approximately by $\exp(-n\,\delta V/V_h)$, since $n - r \cong n$ for $n \gg r$. Equation (25-34) then becomes

$$f(n,r) = \frac{1}{r!}\left(\frac{n\,\delta V}{V_h}\right)^r \exp\left(-n\,\delta V/V_h\right) \qquad (25\text{-}35)$$

The quantity $n\,\delta V$ is the total volume V of solvent that has been added; so[1]

$$f(n,r) = \frac{1}{r!}\left(\frac{V}{V_h}\right)^r \exp\left(-V/V_h\right) \qquad (25\text{-}36)$$

By Sterling's approximation,[2]

$$r! = e^{-r}r^r\sqrt{2\pi r}$$

so

$$f(n,r) = \frac{1}{\sqrt{2\pi r}}\left(\frac{V}{rV_h}\right)^r \exp\left(r - \frac{V}{V_h}\right) \qquad (25\text{-}37)$$

Thus, as in Craig's countercurrent liquid extraction, the maximum concentration of solute in the elution band varies inversely with the square root of the number of extractions. The band therefore broadens as it proceeds down the column.

Equation (25-37) is closely approximated by the error function when r is large. The corresponding Gaussian error curve is[3]

$$f(n,r) = \frac{1}{\sqrt{2\pi r}}\exp\left\{\frac{-(V/V_h - r)^2}{2r}\right\} \qquad (25\text{-}37a)$$

[1] Equation (25-36) is of the form $f = e^{-z}z^r/r!$, where $z = V/V_h$, and is an example of the *Poisson distribution*, which is characteristic of a continuous flow process, in contrast to the *binomial distribution* obtained by a batch process, such as Craig's extraction. Both are approximated by the Gaussian error curve when the number of stages becomes large. For a discussion, see Keulemans, A.I.M., "Gas Chromatography," edited by C. G. Verver, p. 110 *et seq.*, Reinhold Publishing Corporation, New York, 1957.

[2] Sterling's approximation is quite accurate even for moderate values of r, e.g. within 1 per cent for $r = 9$, 0.1 per cent for $r = 83$.

[3] Keulemans, *op. cit.*, p. 117.

which reaches a maximum value of f when $V/rV_h = 1$, the maximum value being $1/\sqrt{2\pi r}$. The same result is apparent by inspection of Eq. (25-37). Thus the solute-band maximum reaches the rth plate when r effective plate volumes of eluant have passed through the column.

Since h is the HETP, $rh = hV/V_h$ is the distance that the position of maximum concentration has moved down the column upon the addition of V ml of solvent. The relative rate of band movement (compared with the movement of the mobile liquid) is given by

$$R_F = \frac{hV/V_h}{V/A_m} = \frac{A_m h}{V_h} = \frac{A_m}{A_m + PA_s} = f \qquad (25\text{-}38)$$

The value of R_F can thus be interpreted as being equal to *the fraction of solute that is present at equilibrium in the mobile phase* at any cross section of the column. If all the solute is present in the mobile phase, $R_F = 1$, and the solute simply moves with the mobile phase.

Example 25-7. In a given partition column the volumes of mobile phase, stationary phase, and inert phase are in the ratio $A_m:A_s:A_i = 0.33:0.10:0.57$. If the partition coefficient of solute between stationary phase and mobile phase is $P = C_2/C_1 = 5$, calculate the value of R_F.

Answer. From Eq. (25-38), $R_F = 0.33/(0.33 + 0.10 \times 5) = 0.40$.

The Martin-Synge theory of column separations has proved generally applicable to the various techniques to be described below. It is of interest, therefore, to consider the conditions under which it can be expected to be valid. In the derivation, it is assumed that equilibrium exists at each theoretical plate. Qualitatively, it is clear that, the slower the flow rate, the more nearly equilibrium conditions are maintained. However, diffusion from plate to plate tends to decrease the efficiency of separation, so there would seem to be an optimum flow rate.[1] In practice, the slow step usually appears to be diffusion within the pores of the sorbent, and diffusion along the column is relatively unimportant. Therefore, the efficiency increases with decreasing rate of flow. For efficient separations, the use of sorbents of very small particle size or sorbents that exert only surface action is advantageous. The HETP increases with the square of the particle diameter[2] and proportionally with the rate of flow of the liquid. However, the HETP is often determined by channeling effects within the column. Glueckauf[3] concludes that, although nonequilibrium conditions cause a lack of symmetry of elution bands, this effect becomes less significant as the number of plates increases and is of relatively little consequence in most practical separations involving columns of more than 100 theoretical plates. An important effect is that

[1] Martin and Synge, *op. cit.*

[2] *Ibid.*

[3] Glueckauf, *loc. cit.*

the HETP varies with the distribution coefficient, so that a given column has different numbers of theoretical plates for the various species being separated. This, of course, affects the calculation of the degree of separation to be expected. To a first approximation, however, it can be assumed that h is a constant characteristic of a particular column.

If two substances of partition coefficients P_A and P_B are to be separated, the relative motion of the bands down the column is given by

$$\frac{(R_F)_A}{(R_F)_B} = \frac{A_m + P_B A_s}{A_m + P_A A_s} \tag{25-39}$$

Example 25-8. For the column described in Example 25-7, what is the relative rate of motion of the bands for two solutes for which $P_A = 2$, $P_B = 4$?

Answer. From Eq. (25-39), $(R_F)_A/(R_F)_B = (0.33 + 0.10 \times 4)/(0.33 + 0.10 \times 10)$ = 1.4.

The question of importance from the analytical viewpoint is whether the two bands have an appreciable overlap. As the number of theoretical plates approaches infinity, the shape of each band approaches the normal curve of error. Martin and Synge[1] found that the HETP of a partition chromatographic column is of the order of 0.002 cm, so that a column of even moderate length has a very large number of theoretical plates.

If the Gaussian error curve is expressed

$$\frac{f}{f_{max}} = e^{-t^2/2} \tag{25-40}$$

the quantity t, where $t = V/V_h \sqrt{r} - \sqrt{r}$ from Eq. (25-37a) corresponds to the number of "standard deviations" that a particular point on the elution band is removed from the point of maximum concentration.

The quantity of solute is proportional to the area under the error curve (Table 26-1, Sec. 26-2). Therefore, for $t = 1$, 2, and 3, respectively, it can be expected that 31.7, 4.54, and 0.26 per cent of the solute will be found in the "tails" of the band. In each case half will be in the leading tail and half in the following tail.

Example 25-9. Using the column described in Example 25-7 and assuming $h = 0.002$ cm and length of column = 10 cm, calculate the fraction of the first component not recovered if the eluant is cut midway between the peaks of the bands, taking $P_A = 2.0$ and $P_B = 2.2$.

Answer. Taking for convenience a cross-sectional area of 1 cm², we find $(V_h)_A = 0.002(0.33 + 2.0 \times 0.10) = 0.00106$ and, similarly, $(V_h)_B = 0.00110$ cm³. The value of $(R_F)_A/(R_F)_B = {}^{110}\!/_{106} = 1.037$. If the point of cut is to occur at 10 cm, the peaks must occur at 9.81 and 10.19 cm.

To bring the peak of solute A to 10.19 cm requires a volume of eluant equal to

[1] Martin and Synge, *op. cit.*

$V = r(V_h)_A = (10.19/0.002) \times 0.00106 = 5.40 \text{ cm}^3$.   The value of t [Eq. (25-40)] at 10 cm is calculated to be $t = 5.40/0.00106 \times \sqrt{5,000} - \sqrt{5,000} = 1.34$.   From tables of the area under the error curve, it is found that $t = 1.34$ corresponds to 9 per cent in the leading tail and 9 per cent in the following tail.

The problem of the completeness of separation has been considered in a more general way by Glueckauf.[1]   If the fractional impurity η_1 is defined as the mole fraction of component 2 in essentially pure component 1 and, similarly, η_2 is the mole fraction of component 1 in essentially pure

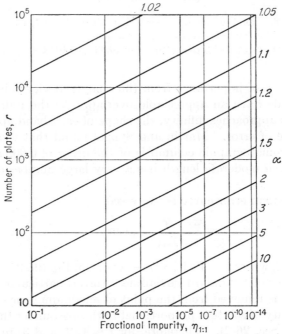

Fig. 25-8. Relation between number of plates r, fractional impurity η, and separation factor α. [*Simplified from Glueckauf, E., Trans. Faraday Soc.*, **51**, 34 (1955); *cf. Keulemans, A. I. M., in Verver, C. G. (ed.), "Gas Chromatography," p. 118, Reinhold Publishing Corporation, New York*, 1957.]

component 2, the cut is normally made so that $\eta_1 = \eta_2 = \eta$.   For any desired fractional impurity η and any desired separation factor α (equal to the ratio of partition coefficients, identical with the relative volatility in distillation), the number of theoretical plates may be read off from a graph.   A simplified version of Glueckauf's graph is shown in Fig. 25-8. The graph can be used directly only if the amounts of the two components are equal.   If the amounts are unequal, the fractional impurity $\eta_{1:1}$

---

[1] Glueckauf, *op. cit.*

for equal amounts is first calculated from the equation

$$\eta_{1:1} = \eta \, \frac{M_1^2 + M_2^2}{2M_1 M_2}$$

where M_1 and M_2 are the amounts of components 1 and 2 in moles.

Example 25-10. To illustrate the use of the graph, suppose that two components of $\alpha = 1.2$ are present in equal amounts and are to be separated to contain 0.1 per cent of impurity in each band. Then, corresponding to $\eta = 10^{-3}$, we find that somewhat more than 1,000 plates are required. If the amounts M_1 and M_2 are in the ratio 1:10, $\eta_{1:1} = \eta 101/20 = 5 \times 10^{-3}$, corresponding to less than 1,000 plates.

This result is at first surprising, for it shows that a smaller number of plates is required for an unequal mixture than for an equimolar mixture. It should be kept in mind, however, that the number of plates is calculated for an equal absolute (not relative) amount of cross contamination. Thus the major component is initially at a higher purity level and the minor component is finally at a lower purity level in the unequal mixture than in the equal mixture.

Applications. An important characteristic of liquid-liquid partition chromatography is that the partition coefficient ideally is independent of concentration. As will be discussed in further detail below, the elution bands are therefore more symmetrical and less subject to "tailing" than those usually observed in adsorption columns. Cleaner separations are therefore possible.

In the original development of the method, Martin and Synge[1] effected a separation of acetylated amino acids by using silica gel as the support for an aqueous stationary phase. The mobile phase was a mixture of chloroform, butanol, and water. The method was used for the analysis of the amino acids of various proteins.[2] Free amino acids were separated on columns of starch, using water as the stationary phase and mixed organic solvents, saturated with water, as the mobile phase.[3-5]

A number of workers have described methods for the separation of fatty acids. Fairbairn and Harpur[6] used a series arrangement of two columns, retaining the C_2 and C_3 acids in the first and C_4 to C_8 in the second.

[1] Martin and Synge, *op. cit.*

[2] Gordon, A. H., Martin, A. J. P., and Synge, R. L. M., *Biochem. J.*, **37**, 78, 86, 92, 313 (1943).

[3] Synge, *Biochem. J.*, **38**, 285 (1944).

[4] Stein, W. H., and Moore, S., *J. Biol. Chem.*, **176**, 337 (1948); **178**, 79 (1949).

[5] Moore and Stein, *J. Biol. Chem.*, **178**, 53 (1949).

[6] Fairbairn, D., and Harpur, R. P., *Nature*, **166**, 789 (1950).

Separation of sugar derivatives has been accomplished on columns of silica gel[1,2] and powdered cellulose.[3]

White and Vaughan[4] made a quantitative separation of the three isomeric cresols and also of phenol from coal tar acid mixtures.

Martin and Porter[5] were able to separate a crystalline enzyme, ribonuclease, into two enzymatically active components on a silica gel column. Boon et al.[6] showed that crude penicillin could be separated into five separate penicillins.

25-4. Gas-Liquid Partition Chromatography (GLPC)

Although Martin and Synge,[7] as long ago as 1941, had suggested the possible use of partition chromatography to separate components present in the gas phase, it remained for James and Martin[8] to make the first analytical applications of this method in 1952. Because of the very rapid development of this subject it is not surprising that some confusion of terminology and notation has arisen. We shall follow the recommendations of Johnson and Stross,[9] except that the symbol P will be used for the partition coefficient instead of H, which will be reserved for the heat content, as is customary in thermodynamics.

The term *gas chromatography* describes all chromatographic methods in which the mobile phase is a gas. *Gas-liquid partition chromatography* (GLPC) or gas-liquid chromatography (GLC) involves the use of a liquid distributed on a solid support as the stationary phase. *Gas-solid chromatography* describes all gas chromatographic methods in which the stationary phase is a solid. This method has proved to be of much less analytical value than GLPC, and will not be considered further.

James and Martin[12] used a column packed with kieselguhr, which was impregnated with a silicone preparation containing 10 per cent stearic acid to act as a stationary solvent. A small quantity of volatile sample

[1] Bell, D. J., *J. Chem. Soc.*, **1944**, 473.

[2] Bell, D. J., and Palmer, A., *J. Chem. Soc.*, **1949**, 2522.

[3] Hough, L., Jones, J. K. N., and Wadman, W. H., *J. Chem. Soc.*, **1949**, 2511.

[4] White, D., and Vaughan, G. A., *Anal. Chim. Acta*, **16**, 439 (1957).

[5] Martin, A. J. P., and Porter, R. R., *Biochem. J.*, **49**, 215 (1951).

[6] Boon, W. R., Calam, C. T., Gudgeon, H., and Levi, A. A., *Biochem. J.*, **43**, 262 (1948).

[7] Martin and Synge, *op. cit.*

[8] James, A. T., and Martin, A. J. P., *Analyst*, **77**, 915 (1952); *Biochem. J.*, **50**, 679 (1952).

[9] Johnson, H. W., and Stross, F. H., *Anal. Chem.*, **30**, 1586 (1958). Compare the footnotes below.[10,11]

[10] Ambrose, D., Keulemans, A. I. M., and Purnell, J. H., *Anal. Chem.*, **30**, 1582 (1958).

[11] Jones, W. L., and Kieselbach, R., *Anal. Chem.*, **30**, 1590 (1958).

[12] James and Martin, *op. cit.*

was passed through the column with a relatively large amount of an inert carrier gas. A mixture of fatty acids was successfully separated in this fashion, the effluent stream containing a series of "elution bands" of solute. The acids were determined by a manual and, later, by an automatic titration procedure that gave the total amount of acids as a function of time. The upper graph of Fig. 25-9 represents a series of "integral" elution bands. By taking the slope of the upper curve, the lower curve, representing "differential" elution bands, is obtained. In most analytical applications, the differential elution bands are observed directly. In principle, the determination of differential bands requires the continuous

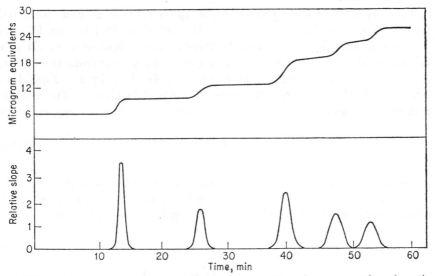

FIG. 25-9. Integral and differential elution bands. Gas chromatography of acetic, propionic, isobutyric, *n*-butyric, and α,α-dimethyl propionic acid. [*With permission from James, A. T., and Martin, A. J. P., Analyst,* **77**, 915 (1952).]

measurement of a property (such as thermal conductivity) that is a measure of the concentration of sample component in the inert gas stream.

Theory. James and Martin[1] showed that the Martin-Synge theory of liquid-liquid partition chromatography can readily be extended to cover GLPC. It is necessary only to take into account the compressibility of the mobile phase, which introduces a gradient of gas velocity down the column.

A carrier gas enters the column at inlet pressure p_i and leaves at the outlet pressure p_o. The gas flow rate F_c is expressed in cm³ sec⁻¹, corrected to correspond to the column temperature T and outlet pressure p_o.

---

[1] *Ibid.*

A sample is injected at one end of the column at time zero and emerges from the other end at a time t_R, the *retention time*. In the James-Martin theory it is presumed that all of the sample is introduced into the first plate of the column and that the center of the zone emerges at time t_R. The theory therefore pertains to very small samples; the necessary correction for larger sample sizes is described by Porter, Deal, and Stross.[1]

The *retention volume* V_R is the volume of gas measured at the column temperature and outlet pressure required to sweep the sample through the column. It is related to the retention time by the equation $V_R = t_R F_c$. A small correction may be necessary to take into account the finite volume of the detector.

The *corrected retention volume* V_R° is the retention volume corrected for the compressibility of the gas. The relationship between V_R° and V_R was derived by James and Martin[2] in the following way. If p is the pressure at a point in the column at a distance x from the outlet, then the linear gas velocity v at the point x is given by $v = F_c p_o/A_m p$, where A_m is the cross-sectional area of the mobile phase. The volume rate of flow of gas is proportional to the pressure gradient at any point, or

$$A_m v = K\frac{dp}{dx} = \frac{F_c p_o}{p} \tag{25-41}$$

where K is a proportionality constant that depends upon the viscosity of the gas and the tightness of the column packing. The pressure p along the column is obtained by integrating Eq. (25-41) to give

$$\frac{Kp^2}{p_o} = 2F_c x + Kp_o \tag{25-42}$$

or

$$F_c = \frac{p_o K}{2x}\left\{\left(\frac{p}{p_o}\right)^2 - 1\right\} \tag{25-43}$$

The time dt required for the solute to move a distance dx is given by $dt = dx/vR_F$. Therefore the retention time is given by

$$t_R = \int_0^l \frac{dx}{vR_F} = \int_0^l \frac{A_m p\, dx}{R_F p_o F_c} \tag{25-44}$$

where l is the length of the column.

In view of Eq. (25-41), substituting $dx = Kp\, dp/F_c p_o$, we express t_R in terms of pressures:

$$t_R = \int_{p_o}^{p_i} \frac{A_m K p^2\, dp}{R_F p_o^2 F_c^2} = \frac{KA_m(p_i^3 - p_o^3)}{3R_F p_o^2 F_c^2} \tag{25-45}$$

[1] Porter, P. E., Deal, C. H., and Stross, F. H., *J. Am. Chem. Soc.*, **78**, 2999 (1956).
[2] James and Martin, *op. cit.*

The retention volume is

$$V_R = t_R F_c = \frac{KA_m p_o}{3R_F F_c}\left\{\left(\frac{p_i}{p_o}\right)^3 - 1\right\} \tag{25-46}$$

or, in view of Eq. (25-43) applied at distance $x = l$,

$$V_R = \frac{2}{3}\frac{A_m l}{R_F}\left\{\frac{(p_i/p_o)^3 - 1}{(p_i/p_o)^2 - 1}\right\} \tag{25-47}$$

It can be shown that, as p_i/p_o approaches unity, V_R approaches the limiting value $A_m l/R_F$, which by definition is called V_R°, the retention volume corrected for pressure drop. Thus

$$V_R^\circ = V_R\left\{\frac{3}{2}\frac{(p_i/p_o)^2 - 1}{(p_i/p_o)^3 - 1}\right\} \tag{25-48}$$

Example 25-11. For the same pressure drop of 0.20 atm, how does the retention volume compare for outlet pressure of ∞, 1.0, and 0.1 atm?

Answer. For $p_o = \infty$, $V_R = V_R^\circ$. For other pressures p_o,

$$V_R = \frac{2}{3} V_R^\circ \frac{(p_i/p_o)^3 - 1}{(p_i/p_o)^2 - 1}$$

which, for $p_o = 1.0$, $p_i = 1.2$, gives $V_R = 1.10\ V_R^\circ$, and, for $p_o = 0.10$, $p_i = 0.30$ gives $V_R = 2.16\ V_R^\circ$.

Using the corrected retention volume, it is a simple matter to adapt the equations of liquid-liquid partition chromatography to GLPC.

Again using the notation of Johnson and Stross, we define

$V_G^\circ = A_m l$ = total gas volume in column, corrected to outlet pressure and column temperature

$V_L = A_s l$ = total volume of liquid phase

And we saw above that

$$V_R^\circ = \frac{A_m l}{R_F} = \frac{V_G^\circ}{R_F}$$

From Eq. (25-38),

$$R_F = \frac{A_m}{A_m + PA_s} = \frac{V_G^\circ}{V_G^\circ + PV_L} = \frac{V_G^\circ}{V_R^\circ} \tag{25-49}$$

The relative retention volume for two substances A and B in the same column [compare Eq. (25-39)] is

$$\frac{(V_R^\circ)_A}{(V_R^\circ)_B} = \frac{V_G^\circ + P_A V_L}{V_G^\circ + P_B V_L} \tag{25-50}$$

The quantity V_G° can be determined readily by evaluating the retention volume for a gas (such as oxygen) that is not absorbed appreciably by the column liquid ($P = 0$).

There have been suggestions that the quantity $(V_R^\circ)' = V_R^\circ - V_G^\circ$, which is a retention volume corrected both for compressibility of the gas phase and for dead-column volume, could easily be measured by taking retention-time measurements from the emergence of the "air peak" instead of from the time of sample injection. From Eq. (25-49),

$$(V_R^\circ)' = PV_L \tag{25-51}$$

which shows that such a corrected retention volume depends on the volume of the liquid phase in the column. $(V_R^\circ)'$ is, therefore, a property not of the sample alone but of the column as well. The column variables could be eliminated by taking ratios, such that $(V_R^\circ)'_A/(V_R^\circ)'_B = P_A/P_B$. This procedure, however, requires the use of a reference compound, and the relative values would depend to some extent on the nature of the reference compound chosen, because of failures of the simple theory.

A better way to eliminate column variables was suggested by Littlewood, Phillips, and Price,[1] who defined a quantity V_g, which has been called[2,3] *the specific retention volume.*

The specific retention volume V_g is obtained by calculating $(V_R^\circ)'$ to correspond to the retention volume *per unit weight of liquid phase* and then corrected to correspond to a temperature of 273°K and the outlet pressure. Thus

$$V_g = \frac{273(V_R^\circ)'}{W_L T} \tag{25-52}$$

where W_L = total weight of liquid phase

T = absolute temperature of column

Littlewood, Phillips, and Price found the quantity V_g convenient in the study of column temperature effects, because W_L remains constant irrespective of the temperature.

Porter, Deal, and Stross advocated the direct use of the partition coefficient, which is a fundamental constant at a given temperature. The general adoption of these practices would do much to render the experimental data of each investigator more useful to others. The partition coefficient has the same meaning in GLPC as in liquid-liquid extraction and represents the ratio of concentration (in weight or mole units per unit volume of solvent) in the liquid phase to the concentration in the same units in the gas phase. To calculate P, Eq. (25-49) can be used directly, giving

$$P = \frac{V_R^\circ - V_G^\circ}{V_L} = \frac{(V_R^\circ)'}{V_L} \tag{25-53}$$

[1] Littlewood, A. B., Phillips, C. S. G., and Price, D. T., *J. Chem. Soc.*, **1955**, 1480.

[2] Johnson and Stross, *op. cit.*

[3] Ambrose, Keulemans, and Purnell, *op. cit.*

It is also convenient to have a relationship between P and V_g. This is obtained readily, by replacing W_L in Eq. (25-52) by $\rho_L V_L$, where ρ_L is the density of the liquid phase. Then

$$P = \frac{V_g T \rho_L}{273} \qquad (25\text{-}54)$$

To use Eq. (25-53) or (25-54), it is necessary to know the density of the liquid phase at the column temperature. Ambrose, Keulemans, and Purnell[1] suggest that for many purposes it is adequate to estimate ρ_L at temperature T by using the density at room temperature and a cubic coefficient of expansion of 10^{-3} per degree centigrade, which is a value within a factor of 2 of the actual value of this coefficient for most organic liquids.

The effect of column temperature can be expressed by plotting log V_g against $1/T$, the slope of the line being $\Delta H_s/2.3R$, where ΔH_s is the partial molar heat of vaporization of the solute.[2] In view of Eq. (25-54), the effect of column temperature can also be portrayed by plotting log $P/T\rho_L$ against $1/T$, the slope again being $\Delta H_s/2.3R$. If the variation in ρ_L is neglected and log P/T is plotted, the curvature is less than the normal experimental error. A straight-line plot, therefore, means constant ΔH_s over the temperature range. The experimental curves are often linear over a moderate temperature range, although pronounced curvature is sometimes observed.[2]

The effects of nonideality of the liquid solution have been considered by Porter, Deal, and Stross.[3] If the activity coefficient of the solute varies with concentration (as it will, in general, except for an ideal solution), the effect is a nonlinear dependence of concentration in the liquid phase upon concentration in the gaseous phase. This type of effect is analogous to a nonlinear isotherm in adsorption chromatography (see Sec. 25-5) and leads to asymmetrical elution bands. The direction of asymmetry depends on the direction of the deviation from linearity. Both types of asymmetry (trailing front and trailing rear) have actually been observed in practice.[3]

For small samples, corresponding to dilute solutions in the liquid phase, symmetrical elution bands closely conforming to the theoretical shapes have often been observed. As in liquid-liquid partition chromatography, the band width increases and the band height decreases with the square root of the number of theoretical plates or the distance along the column.

The *efficiency* of a column is expressed conveniently in terms of the

[1] Ambrose, Keulemans, and Purnell, *op. cit.*
[2] *Ibid.*
[3] Porter, Deal, and Stross, *op. cit.*

number of theoretical plates, which in turn can be estimated from the amount of band broadening that has occurred. In GLPC, the band width is measured conveniently in the same units as the retention time (for example, in distance of recorder-chart travel). The retention time, in a given experiment, is proportional to the retention volume, which in turn is proportional to the length of the column or the number of theoretical plates. Now, in the same experiment, the broadening of the band is proportional to the square root of the number of theoretical plates. Keulemans[1] has pointed out that the band width is best measured as the base of a triangle obtained by drawing two tangents at the inflection points of the elution band.

The band width thus measured is, for a band following the Poisson distribution [cf. Eq. (25-36), Sec. 25-3], equal to $4\sqrt{r}$. If the distance along the recorder chart to the peak maximum is d and if the width of the peak in the same units is w, we have $d = kr$ and $w = k4\sqrt{r}$, where the same proportionality constant k holds for both equations. Thus

$$r = 16\left(\frac{d}{w}\right)^2 \qquad\qquad (25\text{-}55)$$

Once the number of theoretical plates has been evaluated, the procedure described under Liquid-Liquid Partition Chromatography can be used to calculate the degree of separation.

It should be noted that the number of theoretical plates determined from Eq. (25-55) is not necessarily the same for all sample components[2] and that the compound used in determining r should be specified.

Van Deemter, Zuiderweg, and Klinkenberg[3] compared the number of theoretical plates required to effect a given degree of separation in a countercurrent process such as batch distillation with the number required in a chromatographic column operation. They pointed out that in a countercurrent process all the plates are in use during the entire operation, whereas in the chromatographic column only plates that contain appreciable quantities of solute contribute to the separation. The comparison is evident in Fig. 25-10. However, the greater number of plates necessary for a chromatographic separation is much more easily achieved in practice than the smaller number required for a batch distillation.

The same authors considered the theory of the chromatographic column in terms of the kinetics of transport processes. As the supporting gas passes through an element of distance dx, it transports solute in and

[1] Keulemans, *op. cit.*, p. 113.

[2] Johnson and Stross, *op. cit.*

[3] Van Deemter, Zuiderweg, and Klinkenberg, *Chem. Eng. Sci.*, **5**, 271 (1956).

out of the volume element $A\,dx$ by convection in proportion to its local concentration. Longitudinal diffusion causes a spreading of the band. This type of diffusion is considered to consist of two parts: (1) molecular diffusion, in proportion to local concentration gradients, and (2) "eddy diffusion," which takes into account the various different paths taken by various gas molecules through the column packing. Another transport process is that of mass transfer of solute between the gas phase and the

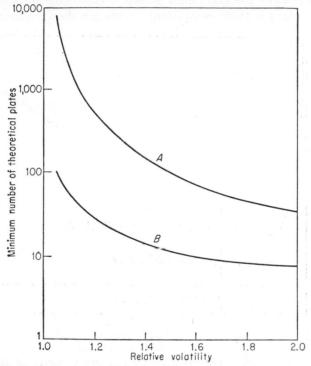

Fig. 25-10. Comparison of theoretical plates needed in gas chromatography (A) and batch distillation (B). Based on separation of equimolar mixture into two fractions of 97.7 per cent purity. [*From van Deemter, J. J., Zuiderweg, F. J., and Klinkenberg, A., Chem. Eng. Sci.*, **5**, 271 (1956).]

liquid phase. By considering the effects of these rate processes, the shape of the elution band of a single solute was shown to be approximated by a Gaussian error curve of the same type as that derived from the plate theory. Now by comparing the result of either of these theories with that derived from the plate theory, it is possible to arrive at an expression for the HETP as a function of linear gas velocity.

The van Deemter equation, which is discussed in detail by Keulemans,[1]

[1] Keulemans, *op. cit.*, pp. 125–127, 138.

may be written in the form

$$h = A + \frac{B}{v} + Cv \qquad (25\text{-}56)$$

where h = HETP

$\qquad v$ = linear gas velocity

The term A represents amount of eddy diffusion, B/v molecular diffusion, and Cv the departure from equilibrium, or resistance to mass transfer of solute between the gas and liquid phases. This equation has the shape of a hyperbola; the three component effects are shown schematically in

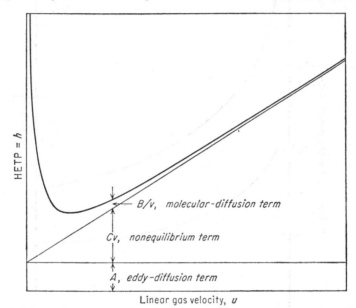

Linear gas velocity, v

FIG. 25-11. Schematic representation of the van Deemter equation $h = A + B/v + Cv$.

Fig. 25-11. Evidently there is a particular gas velocity at which h is a minimum and at which the column is operating at maximum efficiency. However, from Eq. (25-42), it is apparent that the pressure along the column varies in a nonlinear fashion. It follows, therefore, that a gas-liquid chromatographic column cannot be equally efficient throughout its entire length. The closest approach to ideal behavior is achieved by making conditions such that the *ratio* of pressures at the inlet and outlet is near unity[1] and such that the linear gas velocity corresponds to the minimum of the curve. The position of the minimum varies with a large number of column parameters, including the nature of the carrier gas, the solute, and the stationary liquid, the particle size of the packing, the

[1] For p_i/p_o less than about 1.5, the pressure gradient can be considered constant without introducing any serious error (Keulemans, *op. cit.*, p. 134).

length of the column, etc., and in general is not known. However, it is clear from the shape of the curve that an error is less serious in the direction of fast velocities than in the direction of slow velocities. In practice, it is often advantageous to work at considerably higher velocity than the optimum and to increase the column length slightly to offset the decreased efficiency, thus achieving an equally good separation in considerably shorter time. For critical separations, however, it is advisable to vary the rate of gas flow to determine whether the efficiency of separation shows an appreciable change.

Applications. The field of gas-liquid chromatography has enjoyed a phenomenal growth since its introduction late in 1952. Factors that have contributed to this rapid development are (1) the success of the method in performing quantitative separations even of closely related substances, (2) the ease with which the operation can be made automatic, (3) the speed, precision, and accuracy with which quantitative determinations can be made, and (4) the small quantities of sample required. The principal limitation of the method is that it is applicable only to gases or samples that exert vapor pressures of at least 10 mm Hg at the temperature of the column, which can be 300°C or higher. At the other extreme, low-molecular-weight gases of vapor pressure above about 1,000 mm Hg at the temperature of operation are better handled by adsorption chromatography, because of the difficulty of finding a suitable stationary liquid.

The effect of the nature of the stationary solvent on a particular separation has been considered by Keulemans, Kwantes, and Zaal.[1] These authors pointed out that GLPC is more nearly analogous to extractive distillation than to ordinary distillation. The partition coefficient, which determines the order of elution and the degree of separation, is related to the Henry coefficient (proportionality constant between the partial pressure of a gas and its concentration in the stationary phase) rather than to the relative vapor pressures of the components. Only if an ideal solution is formed will the Henry coefficient be proportional to the vapor pressures. Ideal solutions are very rare in GLPC, because the stationary phase must be of very low volatility. Nevertheless, Henry's law is often obeyed because the solutions are dilute.

Pierotti and coworkers[2] have considered solute-solvent interactions in terms of the activity coefficient of the solute in the stationary phase. For various homologous series of solutes, it was shown that, if the first few members of a homologous series are excluded, the logarithms of the partition coefficient is a linear function of the number of carbon atoms per molecule in the solute. This observation corresponds to a constant

[1] Keulemans, A. I. M., Kwantes, A., and Zaal, P., *Anal. Chim. Acta*, **13**, 357 (1955).

[2] Pierotti, G. J., Deal, C. H., Derr, E. L., and Porter, P. E., *J. Am. Chem. Soc.*, **78**, 2989 (1956).

increment of free energy of vaporization per added methylene group. Similar regularities of contribution to log P were found for other structural groups, e.g., methyl-group additions or hydroxyl-group additions to paraffin hydrocarbons. Likewise, if the solute is held constant and if the solvent is varied but kept within a particular homologous series, the partition coefficient varies systematically with the carbon number of the solvent. Such relationships are obviously of great help in selecting a solvent for a particular separation.

An interesting modification of the stationary phase is that made by Eggertsen and coworkers,[1] who replaced the usual inert supporting solid with one possessing adsorptive properties. In this way the pronounced "tailing" of chromatographic peaks due to nonlinear adsorption isotherms is minimized; yet the adsorptive properties enhance the usual separations possible with an inert solid. For example, by using carbon black impregnated with 1.5 per cent of its weight of hydrogenated squalene (a paraffin of empirical formula $C_{30}H_{60}$), separations of isomeric C_5-saturated hydrocarbons could be made that had not proved possible with the ordinary GLPC techniques.

Several commercial automatically recording pieces of equipment are available. In general, the differential elution bands are recorded directly as a function of time at a constant rate of flow of carrier gas. The thermal conductivity of the effluent gas, measured against the conductivity of the pure carrier gas, serves to indicate the concentration of various solutes in the elution bands. Under a given set of operating conditions, the retention time (proportional to retention volume) serves as a method of qualitative identification. The height, or area, of an elution band in comparison with that of a standard is used for quantitative purposes.

The peak height is more simply measured than the area, but it is necessary to keep constant all experimental variables that affect the retention volume or peak shape, namely, the column temperature, amount of liquid phase, volume of detector, and sample injection, etc. This means in practice a calibration with a known weight of sample under conditions identical with those to be used in the analysis. The main advantage of a peak-height measurement is that *it is not affected by errors in flow rate;*[2] it is therefore to be recommended when provisions for rigidly controlled flow rate are not available. On the other hand, the peak area is subject to the same relative error as the flow rate, because the recorder-chart rate is constant. However, the peak area is insensitive to the variables that affect retention volume (column efficiency, column temperature) and to the volume of detector and sample injector, because *the*

---

[1] Eggertsen, F. T., Knight, H. S., and Groennings, S., *Anal. Chem.*, **28**, 303 (1956).
[2] Johnson and Stross, *op. cit.*

peak area theoretically remains constant and proportional to sample size as the zone moves down the column. Usually it is more satisfactory to measure peak areas than peak heights, because it is advantageous to be able to vary the temperature without affecting the calibration. Of course, the detector must be insensitive to changes in column temperature. In summary, it may be concluded that peak areas are more reliable, but peak heights are more easily measured.[1]

The analysis of a mixture of several components can, typically, be carried out in 15 to 30 min on a sample of 1 to 10 mg of gas or volatile liquid. For quantitatively reproducible results, careful control must be maintained over operating variables such as column temperature and flow rate. A frequent source of error is inaccuracy in the measurement of the small samples. This error can be avoided by special internal-standardization techniques, which are described, e.g., by Keulemans.[2]

In the field of hydrocarbon analysis, gas-liquid chromatography has become a serious competitor of low-temperature fractional distillation (the Podbielniak apparatus) and of mass spectrometry and is rapidly displacing these methods in many applications. As an example of the separation of an extremely complex mixture, the quantitative analysis of a 19-component hydrocarbon mixture in a single experiment may be cited.[3] Many other examples of the separation of closely related compounds could be mentioned, but the field is being developed so rapidly that it is best to consult the current literature for examples of applications in any particular field.

25-5. Adsorption Chromatography

Historically, adsorption chromatography is the oldest of the chromatographic techniques, having originated in 1903 with the Russian botanist Tswett.[4] The method escaped notice until 1931;[5] a number of applications were made in the 1930s. In its original form, the method consisted of placing a solid adsorbent, e.g., alumina, in a tube, saturating the column with solvent, adding a small quantity of sample to the top of the column, and washing with solvent until colored bands of the solute components appeared. The column was then pushed out of the tube and cut to separate the colored bands. This method was limited to

[1] Keulemans, A. I. M., Kwantes, A., and Rijnders, G. W. A., *Anal. Chim. Acta*, **16**, 29 (1957).

[2] Keulemans, *op. cit.*, pp. 32–34.

[3] Fredericks, E. M., and Brooks, F. R., *Anal. Chem.*, **28**, 297 (1956).

[4] Tswett, M., *Trav. soc. naturalistes Varsovic*, **1903**, 14; *Ber. deut. botan. Ges.*, **24**, 384 (1906).

[5] Kuhn, R., and Lederer, E., *Naturwissenschaften*, **19**, 306 (1931); *Ber. deut. chem. Ges.*, **64**, 1349 (1931).

colored substances or to materials that could be observed in ultraviolet light or converted with suitable reagents to give colored bands.

Koschara[1] made the important contribution of continuing the washing procedure until each adsorbed substance in turn was removed from the column. This method, although a great improvement, still suffered from lack of a convenient analytical method of detecting colorless solutes as they emerged from the column. Tiselius[2] introduced the continuous measurement of refractive index for the detection of elution bands and thereby enormously extended the usefulness of the method. In a series of later papers, Tiselius and coworkers described refinements in the technique involving interferometric methods for detecting small changes of refractive index and for automatically registering the changes as a function of volume of solvent. Adsorption chromatography was also applied to gases, using thermal conductivity or gas density as the analytical method. Claesson[3] has written an excellent summary of the Tiselius procedures.

Three fundamental methods, which in principle can be applied to liquid solutions or to gases, have been found useful: (1) frontal analysis, (2) displacement development, and (3) elution analysis. A modification of the latter, gradient elution analysis, was introduced later. The principles underlying each of these methods will be discussed in turn.

Frontal Analysis. The column with adsorbent is saturated with the solvent and washed continuously with a relatively large volume of the solution to be analyzed.

If we consider a case in which three solutes are contained in the sample, the frontal-analysis curve can be represented by Fig. 25-12a. Until volume $(V_R)_1$ has been passed, the column retains all solutes completely. At this point, the least strongly adsorbed component comes through until volume $(V_R)_2$ has been passed, when the second component emerges, etc. The volumes $(V_R)_1$, $(V_R)_2$, etc., are called the *retention volumes* of solutes 1, 2, etc.

The retention volume must be corrected for the volume necessary to displace the solvent between the adsorbent particles in the column at the beginning of the experiment and also for any holdup between the end of the column and the point of analysis. The corrected retention volume divided by the weight of adsorbent is called the *specific retention volume* V_R'.

If $a°$ is the amount of solute adsorbed per gram of adsorbent, the corrected specific retention volume is

$$a° = V_R'C \tag{25-57}$$

[1] Koschara, W., *Z. physiol. Chem. Hoppe-Seyler's*, **239**, 89 (1936).
[2] Tiselius, A., *Arkiv Kemi Mineral. Geol.*, **14B**, 22 (1940).
[3] Claesson, S., *Arkiv Kemi Mineral. Geol.*, **23A**, 1 (1946).

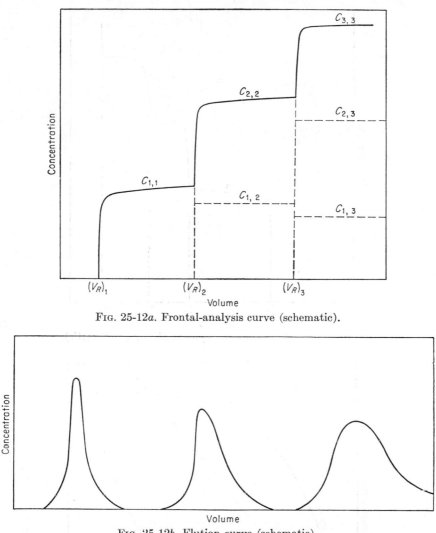

FIG. 25-12a. Frontal-analysis curve (schematic).

FIG. 25-12b. Elution curve (schematic).

where the concentration C is expressed in appropriate units (g/ml or millimoles/ml, etc.) to correspond with the units of a° and V'_R.

The amount of adsorbed substance per gram of adsorbent is related to the concentration by the adsorption isotherm

$$a^\circ = f(C) \qquad (25\text{-}58)$$

(Fig. 25-13) where a° normally approaches a limiting saturation value at sufficiently high solute concentrations. However, at very low concentrations, the isotherm may be regarded as linear. In some cases the isotherm

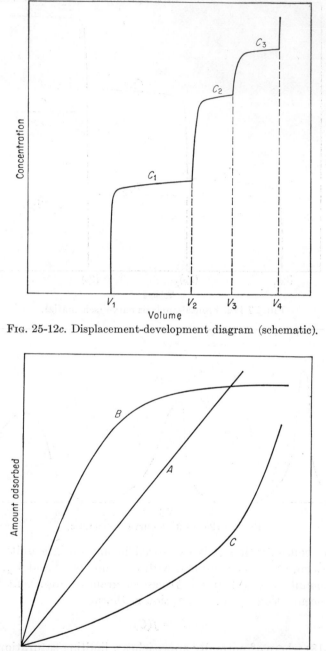

FIG. 25-12c. Displacement-development diagram (schematic).

FIG. 25-13. Schematic representation of adsorption isotherms.   A, Linear; B, Langmuir; C, abnormal (concave upward).

may even be concave upward (line C). For a linear isotherm $a° = kC$, the specific retention volume is independent of concentration, since $V'_R = a°/C = k$. For the normal (Langmuir) isotherm, the value of V'_R decreases with increasing concentration, whereas, for the abnormal concave isotherm, V'_R increases with increasing concentration.

For the normally curved isotherm, the frontal-analysis bands tend to be sharpened at their leading fronts and to trail at the rear edges. This can readily be understood by noting that an increasing value of V'_R corresponds to a slower movement along the column. Thus, if the leading front is disturbed to give a diffuse region of lower concentration, its rate of motion is slowed until the following region of higher concentration catches up. On the other hand, disturbances of the tail tend to be enhanced as the band moves along.

Just the inverse effect (diffuse front and sharp rear edge) would be expected for the abnormal isotherm of Fig. 25-13, line C.

It is important to realize that, in the frontal analysis of a mixture, the successive step heights *cannot be used directly as a measure of the concentration of any component*. Thus, with reference to Fig. 25-12a, the concentration $C_{1,1}$ of component 1 in the first band, is higher than the original solution concentration, because component 2 as it moves along displaces some of component 1 from the column. The third step (or, in general, the final step) corresponds to the original solution concentrations of all components, because the entire column is in equilibrium with the sample solution. However, since $C_{1,3}$ and $C_{2,3}$ are not directly known, the height of the third band cannot give C_1, C_2, or C_3 directly.

The concentrations $C_{1,1}$ $C_{1,3}$, etc., can be calculated by means of a recursion formula, which has been given for the general case of n solutes by Claesson.[1] By means of this formula, the concentration of the ith component in the $(m + 1)$st step can be calculated from its concentration in the mth step, if the equation of its adsorption isotherm is known. Claesson showed that, if the Langmuir isotherm is written

$$a_i° = \frac{k_i C_i}{1 + l_i C_i} \tag{25-59}$$

for the ith component, it becomes

$$a_i° = \frac{k_i C_i}{1 + \sum_n l_i C_i} \tag{25-60}$$

when applied to a mixture of n components. The quantity l_i does not appear in the recursion formula, and the quantity k_i, which is the limiting

[1] Claesson, *op. cit.*

slope of the isotherm at low concentrations, can easily be determined by experiment.

To illustrate the use of a recursion formula, we shall consider the simple case of two components, for which the formula can be derived as follows.

When $(V'_R)_2$ ml of a solution containing only components 1 and 2 have been passed per gram of adsorbent, the amount of component 1 adsorbed is given by

$$a_1^\circ = (V'_R)_2 C_1 - \{(V'_R)_2 - (V'_R)_1\} C_{1,1} = \frac{k_1 C_1}{1 + l_1 C_1 + l_2 C_2} \qquad (25\text{-}61)$$

since $(V'_R)_2 C_1$ is the initial amount in solution and $\{(V'_R)_2 - (V'_R)_1\}$ $C_{1,1}$ is the amount recovered in the first band. Since all of component 2 has been adsorbed up to this point,

$$a_2^\circ = (V'_R)_2 C_2 = \frac{k_2 C_2}{1 + l_1 C_1 + l_2 C_2} \qquad (25\text{-}62)$$

Taking the ratio of Eq. (25-61) to (25-62) we have

$$C_1 - \left\{1 - \frac{(V'_R)_1}{(V'_R)_2}\right\} C_{1,1} = \frac{k_1}{k_2} C_1$$

or, since, in the case of a two-component sample $C_{1,2} = C_1$, we have

$$C_{1,2} = C_{1,1} \frac{1 - (V'_R)_1/(V'_R)_2}{1 - k_1/k_2} \qquad (25\text{-}63)$$

Similar recursion formulas are available to relate the concentration of ith component between bands m and $m + 1$. In this way, knowing that the last band contains the various solutes at their original concentrations, it is possible to determine each of the concentrations, beginning with $C_{1,1}$.

Example 25-12. A mixture of two carboxylic acids in solution is subjected to frontal-analysis chromatography. The ratio k_1/k_2 between the slopes of the isotherms has the value 0.80, and the ratio $(V'_R)_1/(V'_R)_2$ between specific retention volumes is found to be 0.84. The concentrations of acid in the two bands are 0.010 M and 0.020 M, respectively. What are the concentrations of the two acids in the original solution?

Answer. From Eq. (25-63), $C_{1,2} = 0.8 C_{1,1} = 0.008$ M. The total initial concentration is 0.02 M; hence $C_1 = 0.008$ M, $C_2 = 0.012$ M.

Displacement Development.[1] In this method, as in elution analysis, a small quantity of sample is introduced at the top of a column saturated with solvent. However, the sample is not washed with pure solvent; instead, a substance more strongly adsorbed than any component of the

[1] Tiselius, *Arkiv Kemi Mineral. Geol.*, **16A**, no. 18 (1943).

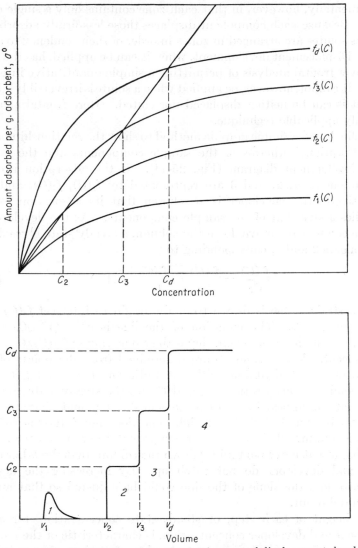

FIG. 25-14. Relationship between adsorption isotherms and displacement-development diagram. [*Tiselius, A., Arkiv Kemi Mineral. Geol.,* **16A,** *no.* 18 (1943).]

mixture is added to the solvent. The adsorbed components are successively displaced and moved along the column. The displacing reagent was called a "displacement developer" by Tiselius. We shall, however, use the name "displacer," reserving the term "developer" for an elution agent that causes the components to move as *separated* bands down the column. Superficially, the curve (Fig. 25-14) resembles that of frontal analysis in that it has a series of horizontal plateaus. It differs fundamentally, however, in that each zone contains only a single component. Because each component displaces those less firmly adsorbed, the various solutes are arranged in zones in order of their tendency to adsorption. Displacement development, when it can be applied, has the advantage over frontal analysis of permitting a simple quantitative interpretation. It cannot, however, be applied when a solute is irreversibly adsorbed so that it can be neither displaced nor eluted. Here frontal analysis is the only applicable technique.

Tiselius[1] used a simple graphic method to show the relationship between the adsorption isotherms of the sample components and the displacement-development diagram (Fig. 25-14). If the adsorption isotherms of components 1, 2, and 3 are represented by $f_1(C)$, $f_2(C)$, and $f_3(C)$, respectively, the developer is so chosen that its adsorption isotherm $f_d(C)$ lies above that of the sample components. As the developer and sample components move down the column, a steady state is reached for components 2 and 3, corresponding to

$$\frac{f_2(C)}{C_2} = \frac{f_3(C)}{C_3} = \frac{f_d(C)}{C_d} = (V'_R)_d \qquad (25\text{-}64)$$

Now, a straight line is drawn from the origin to intersect $f_d(C)$ at the concentration C_d. The equation of the line is $a° = (V'_R)_d C_d = f_d(C)$. But, since all the components have the same value of $f(C)/C = (V'_R)_d$, the concentrations C_2 and C_3 are determined from the points of intersection of the straight line with the isotherms $f_2(C)$ and $f_3(C)$. The corresponding concentrations C_2 and C_3 are the steady-state concentrations that will appear in the displacement-development diagram.

It will be noted that the straight line does not intersect $f_1(C)$, the lowest isotherm. This means that component 1 does not reach a steady state because it moves so rapidly down the column that the other components and developer do not catch up. By increasing the developer concentration, the slope of the line could be adjusted so that an intersection did occur.

The height of each step, or steady-state concentration, for a given adsorbent and developer concentration, is characteristic of the particular substance. In principle, the step heights therefore, give a basis for qualitative identification of sample constituents.

The length of the step is proportional to the quantity present. The *specific length*, or length of step per gram of substance, is determined as a calibration. The quantity present in an unknown is then obtained by dividing the length of the step by the specific length.

In principle, displacement-development chromatography accomplishes a physical separation of the constituents of the sample. In practice,

[1] *Ibid.*

however, a difficulty is observed in carrying out separations because the zones are in close contact and the boundary lines are not so sharp as Fig. 25-14 would indicate. To facilitate quantitative separations, Tiselius and Hagdahl[1] introduced the technique of *carrier displacement*. A substance of intermediate adsorption tendency (carrier) is interposed between two adjacent components to permit a quantitative separation. The carrier is chosen to be readily separated from the sample components. Examples are aliphatic alcohols, used as carriers for the separation of amino acids,[2] and methyl esters, as carriers for the separation of fatty acids.[3]

Elution Analysis. In elution analysis, the column once more is saturated with pure solvent. A *small* volume of sample solution is introduced into the top of the column, followed by a large volume of eluting solvent.

The components of the sample move as separate zones along the column (25-12b). The quantity of each component is given directly by the area under its elution peak.

Under idealized column conditions (adsorption equilibrium, linear adsorption isotherm), the elution bands can be described by equations analogous to those used for partition chromatography. However, adsorption equilibrium is much more likely to deviate from a linear isotherm than is partition equilibrium.[4] Since most adsorption isotherms are of the Langmuir type and since the R_F value increases with decreasing tendency for adsorption, it follows that R_F increases with increasing concentration. The effect is to cause a "tailing" of the band, which has a sharp forward edge but a diffuse trailing edge. The shapes of the elution bands cannot, therefore, be adequately approximated by the Gaussian error curve. The factor that limits completeness of separation is often the length of the diffuse tail.

The effect of nonequilibrium conditions is to cause an additional diffuseness. In practice, the zones become sharper with decreasing rate of flow even to the very slowest rates,[5] indicating that diffusion along the column is relatively unimportant in causing band spreading as compared with lack of equilibrium.

Gradient Elution Analysis. Alm, Williams, and Tiselius[6] introduced the technique of gradient elution in an effort to decrease the tendency to tailing in the ordinary elution procedure. In principle, the "strength" of the eluant is gradually increased by changing the composition so as

[1] Tiselius, A., and Hagdahl, L., *Acta Chem. Scand.*, **4**, 394 (1950).
[2] *Ibid.*
[3] Holman, R. T., *J. Am. Chem. Soc.*, **73**, 1261 (1951).
[4] Strain, *Anal. Chem.*, **22**, 41 (1950).
[5] Glueckauf, E., and Coates, J. I., *J. Chem. Soc.*, **1947**, 1315.
[6] Alm, R. S., Williams, R. J. P., and Tiselius, A., *Acta Chem. Scand.*, **6**, 826 (1952).

to favor desorption. This is accomplished by a continuous mixing process in an external mixing chamber. A large number of procedures are possible, depending upon the exact method of mixing.

The theory has been considered by Drake[1] and by Freiling.[2] Freiling's treatment is based on the Mayer-Tompkins. batch-equilibrium model (page 528), assuming a constant number of theoretical plates, and is therefore of limited applicability. We shall consider here only the general conclusions reached by Drake. Drake concluded that the sharpening of the elution zones must always be accompanied by a relative pushing together of the zones, so that an improvement of separation cannot be guaranteed. The factors that affect the degree of separation include the shape of the gradient (variation of concentrations with volume of eluant), the motion of the gradient through the column, the variation of partition coefficient with concentration of eluant, and the shape of the adsorption isotherm.

To illustrate applications of gradient elution, we may mention the separation of amino acids, peptides, and sugars by Tiselius and his coworkers[3-6] and the separation of organic acids by Donaldson, Tulane, and Marshall.[7]

Applications. Adsorption chromatography has been applied to many different organic separations since 1931. Quite a variety of adsorbents (alumina, carbon, calcium hydroxide, calcium carbonate, magnesia silica gel, etc.), and eluants have been applied. Although much of the work has been highly empirical in nature, a number of authors have formulated rules that aid in the selection of suitable adsorbents and eluants and in the prediction of the order of appearance of a related series of compounds on an adsorption column.

Lederer[8] observed that the tendency toward adsorption in a related series of compounds increased with increasing numbers of double bonds and hydroxyl groups. A rough classification of organic compounds in decreasing order of adsorption tendency is acids > alcohols, aldehydes, ketones > esters > unsaturated hydrocarbons > saturated hydrocarbons. Strain[9] has stressed the importance of the nature of the adsorbent, the composition of the solvent, and the temperature in determining the relative order of adsorption zones. As a criterion of homogeneity,

[1] Drake, B., *Arkiv Kemi*, **8**, 1 (1955).

[2] Freiling, E. C., *J. Am. Chem. Soc.*, **77**, 2067 (1955).

[3] Alm, Williams, and Tiselius, *op. cit.*

[4] Tiselius, *Endeavour*, **11**, 5 (1952).

[5] Hagdahl, Williams, and Tiselius, *Arkiv Kemi*, **4**, 193 (1952).

[6] Alm, *Acta Chem. Scand.*, **6**, 1186 (1952).

[7] Donaldson, K. O., Tulane, V. J., and Marshall, C. M., *Anal. Chem.*, **24**, 185 (1952).

[8] Lederer, *Bull. soc. chim. France*, [5], **6**, 897 (1939).

[9] Strain, *Ind. Eng. Chem., Anal. Ed.*, **18**, 605 (1946).

chromatography can give conclusive evidence only when a number of adsorbents and solvents have been tried.[1]

LeRosen and coworkers[2,3] carried out calculations of R_F values in terms of bond energies of interaction between the adsorbent, the solute, and the eluant. For each substance, the tendencies toward donation of electron pairs and acceptance of electron pairs and the hydrogen donor and acceptor behavior in hydrogen bond formation were considered. The various eluting solvents were compared with petroleum ether taken as a standard; the various adsorbents were evaluated by experiment. Then the behavior of the solutes could be predicted by a summation of the effects of its functional groups, together with a weighting factor taking into account the sum of the molecular weights of all the side chains. The success of this approach in the examples cited appears to signify an important step toward placing adsorption chromatography on a more fundamental footing.

It is beyond the scope of this discussion to consider specific applications, which are described in various monographs and in the original literature.

25-6. Paper Chromatography

The technique of paper chromatography was first described by Consden, Gordon, and Martin[4] in 1944. In its original form, the method consisted of applying a small drop of solution near the top of a long strip of filter paper, which was suspended in a closed container at liquid-vapor equilibrium to prevent drying of the spot. The chromatogram was developed by dipping the top end of the filter paper in a solvent only slightly miscible with water. As the developing solvent descended down the paper, the components of the sample were carried down the paper at different rates. The spots corresponding to the constituents of the sample could be observed by treatment with suitable color-producing reagents.

Various other experimental procedures have been used. Williams and Kirley[5] simplified the technique by allowing the developing solvent to proceed up the column by capillary action, a method known as *ascending development*. The important method of *two-dimensional development* was also described by Consden, Gordon, and Martin.[6] After developing a paper chromatogram in one direction, the paper was dried and developed with a different solvent in a direction at right angles to the

[1] Strain, *J. Am. Chem. Soc.*, **70**, 588 (1948).

[2] LeRosen, A. L., Monaghan, P. H., Rivet, C. A., and Smith, E. D., *Anal. Chem.*, **23**, 730 (1951).

[3] Smith and LeRosen, *Anal. Chem.*, **23**, (1951).

[4] Consden, Gordon, and Martin, *Biochem. J.*, **38**, 224 (1944).

[5] Williams, R. I., and Kirley, H., *Science*, **107**, 481 (1948).

[6] Consden, Gordon, and Martin, *op. cit.*

first development. In this way, taking advantage of a different sequence of separations with the two solvents, a mixture of 20 amino acids was separated. *Circular development*, in which the solvent is applied to the center of a circular disc of filter paper, was introduced by Rutter.[1]

Theory. The mechanism of paper chromatography has been the subject of controversy. Consden, Gordon, and Martin[2] considered paper chromatography to be simply a form of liquid-liquid partition chromatography in which the filter paper acts as the inert support of a stationary aqueous phase. Later authors criticized this view, the most important objection being that many separations have been carried out using water-soluble solvents such as ethanol, propanol, acetone, pyridine, or even pure water. Martin,[3] however, considers that the water retained by cellulose is comparable to a concentrated solution of glucose or of some soluble polysaccharide rather than to water saturated with the organic phase. Similarly, Hanes and Isherwood[4] regard the nonmobile phase as a water-cellulose complex. The problem has been reviewed by Moore and Stein.[5] It appears likely that both adsorption and partition are involved; in fact, Stamm and Zollinger have definitely established that this is the case for azo dyes.[6]

From the viewpoint of interpretation, an analogy with liquid-liquid partition chromatography is fruitful. The movement of a band of solute is usually described in terms of its R_F value, defined as the ratio of the distance traveled by the solute band to the distance traveled by the solvent. Generally, the leading edge of the band is used, because of the diffuse nature of the trailing edge. According to the theory of Martin and Synge,[7] [Eq. (25-38)] the R_F value depends on the relative amounts of the two phases in contact and on the partition coefficient of the solute. For a given paper and solvent, it should therefore be a distinctive property of each solute. For some mixed solvents, two solvent fronts are observed, a "wet" front and a "dry" front. The R_F value may be calculated with respect to either front, but of course the method must be specified.

Paper Electrophoresis. The application of an electric field in the direction of zone movement during the development of a paper chromatogram has been found in many instances to improve the separations that can be achieved. The method was developed in its present form in several laboratories during the period 1947–1949, although similar principles

[1] Rutter, L., *Nature*, **163**, 487 (1949); *Analyst*, **75**, 37 (1950).
[2] Consden, Gordon, and Martin, *op. cit.*
[3] Martin, *Ann. Rev. Biochem.*, **19**, 517 (1950).
[4] Hanes, C. S., and Isherwood, F. A., *Nature*, **164**, 1107 (1949).
[5] Moore and Stein, *Ann. Rev. Biochem.*, **21**, 521 (1952).
[6] Stamm, O. A., and Zollinger, H., *Helv. Chim. Acta*, **40**, 1105 (1957).
[7] Martin and Synge, *op. cit.*

had been introduced in 1937.[1] Various terms, including "zone electrophoresis," "ionophoresis," and "electrochromatography" have been applied to this method.

Although many different experimental arrangements have been used and several pieces of commercial equipment are available, they can all be classified into three groups[2] that involve (1) a vertical suspension, (2) a taut horizontal form, and (3) a horizontal paper between pressure plates of glass. The last method, in which evaporation is prevented, is especially suited to accurate measurement of solute mobilities.[3] In the open-strip techniques evaporation occurs to some extent, because of the generation of heat accompanying the passage of the electric current. The ends of the paper are immersed in electrolyte solution, which flows in to compensate for evaporation.

An important development, which enables the use of paper separation as a preparative separation method and which utilizes to advantage the combined effects of paper chromatography and paper electrophoresis, is the method of *continuous paper electrophoresis*.[4-6] It is a two-dimensional technique in which a sample to be separated is applied by a wick to a point at the top of a vertical sheet of filter paper. The top edge of the sheet is immersed in an electrolyte reservoir, so that paper chromatography brings the components downward as zones. At right angles, across the paper, an electric field is applied. The zones therefore proceed downward in paths which ideally should be straight but which in practice are somewhat curved. The zones reach the bottom edge at various points, depending on the relative rates of chromatographic migration and electrophoresis. By cutting pointed notches along the bottom edge of the paper, a series of samples can be caught in a row of vessels. Commercial equipment is available from several sources.

Applications. A large number of applications have been reviewed in the monographs cited at the end of this chapter. To indicate the scope of the subject, it is sufficient to mention the following classes of compounds, which have been separated under suitable conditions: alcohols, phenols, aldehydes, ketones, fatty acids, hydroxyacids, ketoacids, esters, amines, alkaloids, dyestuffs, sugars, carbohydrates, glycerides, steroids, amino acids, peptides, proteins, purines and pyrinidines, flavonoids, porphyrins,

[1] For a historical review and general discussion, see Block, R. J., Durrum, E. L., and Zweig, G., "A Manual of Paper Chromatography and Paper Electrophoresis," Academic Press, Inc., New York, 1955.

[2] Duggan, E. L., *Anal. Chem.*, **28**, 714 (1956).

[3] Kunkel, H. G., in Glick, D. (ed.), "Methods of Biochemical Analysis," vol. 1, pp. 141–170, Interscience Publishers, Inc., New York, 1954.

[4] Haugaard, G., and Kroner, T. D., *J. Am. Chem. Soc.*, **70**, 2135 (1948).

[5] Grassmann, W., and Hannig, K., *Naturwissenschaften*, **37**, 397, 496 (1950).

[6] Svensson, H., and Brattsten, I., *Arkiv Kemi*, **1**, 401 (1949).

vitamins, hormones, sulfonamides, antibiotics. Inorganic separations have been described especially by Burstall *et al.*,[1] Lederer,[2] and Pollard *et al.*[3,4] Systematic separation procedures are available, particularly for small groups of metal ions that have been separated by classical qualitative methods.

Quantitative estimations of substances separated by paper chromatography are made by two general types of techniques. (1) The most direct method involves the examination of spots on the paper. (2) A less direct but often more accurate method is to dissolve the separated material from the paper and to determine it by standard analytical techniques. Methods for the evaluation of spots on the paper include (*a*) measurement of the area of a spot,[5] (*b*) measurement of the length of oval spots,[6,7] (*c*) observation of transmitted or reflected light by spectrophotometric techniques,[8] (*d*) *retention* analysis. [This technique, devised by Wieland,[9] involves a two-dimensional technique in which the second dimension is provided by a continuous band of reagent. Wherever the reagent interacts with the spots of the separate constituents, its progress is retarded, with the formation of a V-shaped notch in the reagent front. Copper(II), for example, is used as a reagent for amino acids.[10]] (*e*) *Use of radioactive isotopes.* Lissitzky and Michel[11] have reviewed applications of paper chromatography to organic compounds labeled with radioactive isotopes. Quantitative results may be obtained by direct counting techniques applied to the spots. Another technique involves the use of a radioactive reagent to react with the developed chromatogram or the development of radioactive isotopes in the spots by neutron activation techniques.[12]

[1] Burstall, F. H., Davies, G. R., Lustead, R. P., and Wells, R. A., *J. Chem. Soc.*, **1950**, 516.

[2] Lederer, M., *Anal. Chim. Acta.*, **5**, 185 (1951).

[3] Pollard, F. H., McOmie, J. F. W., and Elbeih, I. I. M., *J. Chem. Soc.*, **1951**, 466, 470.

[4] Pollard, F. H., McOmie, J. F. W., and Stevens, H. M., *J. Chem. Soc.*, **1951**, 771.

[5] Fisher, R. B., Parsons, D. S., and Morrison, G. A., *Nature*, **161**, 764 (1948); Fisher, R. B., Parsons, D. S., and Holmes, R., *ibid*, **164**, 183 (1949).

[6] *Ibid.*

[7] Fowler, H. D., *Nature*, **168**, 1123 (1951).

[8] Müller, R. H., and Clegg, D. L., *Anal. Chem.*, **21**, 1123 (1949); Müller, R. H., *ibid*, **22**, 72 (1950); Müller, R. H., and Wise, E. N., *ibid*, **23**, 207 (1951); Block, R. J., *ibid*, **22**, 1327 (1950); **23**, 298 (1951). For an excellent discussion, see Block, Durrum, and Zweig, "A Manual of Paper Chromatography and Paper Electrophoresis," Academic Press, 1955.

[9] Wieland, T., *Angew. Chem.*, **60**, 313 (1948).

[10] Wieland, T., and Wirth, L., *Angew. Chem.*, **63**, 171 (1951).

[11] Lissitzky, S., and Michel, R., *Bull. soc. chim. France*, **1952**, 891.

[12] Winteringham, F. P. W., Harrison, A., and Bridges, R. G., *Nature*, **166**, 999 (1950); *Analyst*, **77**, 19 (1952).

25-7. Ion Exchange

An ion exchange medium consists essentially of a solid, insoluble phase that contains a number of positively or negatively charged sites. Adjacent to each site, in the liquid phase, is an equivalent amount of opposite charge as counter ions. The ion exchange equilibrium may be written

$$B^+ + A^+R^- \rightleftharpoons A^+ + B^+R^- \qquad \text{cation exchange} \qquad (25\text{-}65)$$
$$B^- + R^+A^- \rightleftharpoons A^- + R^+B^- \qquad \text{anion exchange} \qquad (25\text{-}66)$$

where R^+ or R^- represents the ion exchange medium.

The most important types of ion exchange materials are the synthetic resins, which are composed of networks of relatively loosely cross-linked polymers with attached cationic or anionic groups. A copolymer of styrene and p-divinyl benzene is conveniently cross-linked to the desired extent by regulating the fraction of divinyl benzene. The preparation of sulfonated cation exchange resins of this type is discussed by Pepper.[1] Wheaton and Bauman[2] have described anion exchange resins of the quaternary ammonium salt type, based on the same polymer network.

Cation exchange resins may be classified into the strong acid (RSO_3H) and weak acid ($RCOOH$ and ROH) types. A strong acid type (Dowex 50 or Amberlite IR-120) is greatly advantageous for most analytical applications, because its exchange capacity does not vary with pH if the pH is above 3 or 4. The weak acid types may be advantageous in certain specific situations, such as selective takeup of strongly basic substances in the presence of weak bases.

Anion exchange resins may likewise be classified into the strong base (quaternary ammonium salt) and weak base (primary, secondary, or tertiary amines). Once again, the strong base type (Dowex 1 or 2, Amberlite IRA-400) is preferable to the weak base type (Dowex 3, Amberlite IR-45) for most analytical applications. The exchange capacity of the weak base types decreases with increasing pH. The weakly basic resins become inert at high pH values, whereas the strongly basic resins can be used even at high pH values in the hydroxyl ion form. Weakly basic resins can be used to retain strong acid anions in the presence of weak acids, but this application is of limited use in analysis.

Ion Exchange Equilibria. Two different theoretical approaches have been used to describe ion exchange equilibria. The simplest approach[3] is to apply the mass-action law to Eqs. (25-65) and (25-66); that is,

$$\frac{a_A a_{BR}}{a_B a_{AR}} = K \qquad (25\text{-}67)$$

[1] Pepper, K. W., *J. Appl. Chem. London*, **1**, 124 (1951).

[2] Wheaton, R. M., and Bauman, W. C., *Ind. Eng. Chem.*, **43**, 1088 (1951).

[3] Boyd, G. E., Schubert, J., and Adamson, A. W., *J. Am. Chem. Soc.*, **69**, 2818 (1947).

where a_A and a_B represent the activities of ions in solution and a_{AR} and a_{BR} represent the activities in the solid state.

If the activities a_{AR} and a_{BR} are replaced by the products of mole fractions and activity coefficients, we have

$$\frac{a_A}{a_B} \frac{X_{BR}}{X_{AR}} = K'_{eq} = K \frac{\gamma_{AR}}{\gamma_{BR}} \tag{25-68}$$

where K'_{eq} is the "apparent equilibrium constant," which is experimentally determinable but which will be constant with variations in composition of the solid phase only if the ratio γ_{AR}/γ_{BR} is constant. There is no direct and independent experimental approach to a measurement of γ_{AR}/γ_{BR}, so that all deviations from a constancy of K_{eq} are, on this interpretation, ascribed to a variation of that ratio. Boyd, Schubert, and Adamson[1] determined K'_{eq} for various ion exchange reactions of the type

$$M^+ + HR \rightleftharpoons H^+ + MR \qquad K'_{eq} \tag{25-69}$$

and defined a series of relative equilibrium constants K'_{rel} for half-reactions

$$M^+ + R^- \rightleftharpoons MR \qquad K'_{rel} \tag{25-70}$$

by arbitrarily taking K'_{rel} for the hydrogen ion to be unity. On this basis, they showed a correlation between the values of K'_{rel} for the various alkali metal ions and the values of the Debye-Hückel ion size parameter a. Other listings of equilibrium data for ion exchange reactions are given by Ketelle and Boyd,[2] Bauman and Eichhorn,[3] Kressman and Kitchener,[4] Davidson and Argersinger,[5] Diamond,[6] and Gregor, Belle, and Marcus.[7]

The other approach to ion exchange equilibria is that based on the Donnan theory.[8,9] In its simplest form, the Donnan theory is identical with that used for membrane equilibria. If a salt A^+R^- is separated by a membrane from another salt A^+B^- of the same cation and if the membrane is defined as one permeable to A^+ and B^- but not to R^-, the condition of equilibrium is

$$(a_{A^+}a_{B^-})_1 = (a_{A^+}a_{B^-})_2 \tag{25-71}$$

[1] *Ibid.*

[2] Ketelle, B. H., and Boyd, G. E., *J. Am. Chem. Soc.*, **69**, 2800 (1947).

[3] Bauman, W. C., and Eichhorn, J., *J. Am. Chem. Soc.*, **69**, 2830 (1947).

[4] Kressman, T. R. E., and Kitchener, J. A., *J. Chem. Soc.*, **1949**, 1190, 1201, 1208, 1211.

[5] Davidson, A. W., and Argersinger, W. J., *Ann. N.Y. Acad. Sci.*, **57**, 105 (1953).

[6] Diamond, *J. Am. Chem. Soc.*, **77**, 2978 (1955).

[7] Gregor, H. P., Belle, J., and Marcus, R. A., *J. Am. Chem. Soc.*, **77**, 2713 (1955).

[8] Bauman and Eichhorn, *op. cit.*

[9] Gregor, *J. Am. Chem. Soc.*, **70**, 1293 (1948); **73**, 642 (1951).

where the subscripts 1 and 2 refer to the solutions on the two sides of the membrane.

Now, if the ion exchange resin is considered to consist of two phases such that the resin phase has an immobilized ion R^-, an analogy exists with Donnan membrane theory. Suppose that to a resin A^+R^- is added an electrolyte B^+C^-; the Donnan equilibrium conditon may be applied to the salts A^+C^- and B^+C^- in the two phases:

$$(a_{A^+}a_{C^-})_r = (a_{A^+}a_{C^-})_w \qquad (25\text{-}72)$$

and
$$(a_{B^+}a_{C^-})_r = (a_{B^+}a_{C^-})_w \qquad (25\text{-}73)$$

where the subscripts r and w refer to resin and water phase, respectively. Dividing,

$$\frac{(a_{A^+})_r}{(a_{B^+})_r} = \frac{(a_{A^+})_w}{(a_{B^+})_w} \qquad (25\text{-}74)$$

Representing activities in the resin phase by the products of mole fractions and activity coefficients and dropping the subscripts w,

$$\frac{a_{A^+}}{a_{B^+}}\frac{X_{BR}}{X_{AR}} = \frac{\gamma_{AR}}{\gamma_{BR}} = K'_{eq} \qquad (25\text{-}75)$$

which is an expression for the apparent equilibrium constant K'_{eq} identical with Eq. (25-68) except that the K of Eq. (25-68) here is equal to 1.

From a theoretical viewpoint, the Donnan theory has the advantage of permitting a more elegant interpretation of the thermodynamic behavior of ion exchange resins. However, from a practical viewpoint, the mass-action approach is simpler, and is adequate if we keep in mind that K'_{eq} may be regarded as constant only over a limited range. If the ions differ considerably in their properties, the variation of K'_{eq} can become very large.[1] An empirical equation due to Rothmund and Kornfeld,[2]

$$\frac{X_{BR}}{X_{AR}}\left(\frac{[A]}{[B]}\right)^p = k \qquad (25\text{-}76)$$

works in many such cases.[3] The quantities p and k are experimental parameters. The Rothmund-Kornfeld equation in general corresponds to a partition coefficient that varies with concentration or to a nonlinear isotherm.

An important characteristic of ion exchange equilibria is that, according to Eq. (25-68) or (25-75), *the ratio between the amounts of an ion in the*

---

[1] Högfeldt, E., Ekedahl, E., Sillén, L. G., *Acta Chem. Scand.*, **4**, 828, 1471, (1950).

[2] Rothmund, V., and Kornfeld, G., *Z. anorg. u. allgem. Chem.*, **103**, 129 (1918); **108**, 215 (1919).

[3] Walton, H. F., *J. Franklin Inst.*, **232**, 305 (1941); *Trans. Illinois State Acad. Sci.*, **34**, no. 2, 124 (1941).

*resin and in solution is independent of concentration, as long as two ions
are of the same charge.* On the other hand, if an ion exchange reaction
involves ions of different charges, it follows from either the mass-action
law or the Donnan theory that the resin phase becomes increasingly
selective toward higher-charged ions as the dilution is increased.[1]

Another characteristic is that, if one ionic species is present at very
low concentration and another ionic species in large excess, *the equilibrium
for the dilute species can be represented by a constant partition coefficient
regardless of the charges of the ions.*[2,3] This of course means that the
concentration of dilute species in the resin phase is proportional to its
concentration in the solution phase. Thus, in elution experiments where
the eluant is present at relatively high concentrations, a theory analogous
to that applied to other column techniques involving linear isotherms
should be valid.

Theory of Ion Exchange Columns. Mayer and Tompkins[4] applied a
plate-column concept to ion exchange separations. Although analogous
to the treatment of Martin and Synge for partition chromatography, it is
based on a batch-equilibrium theory in which it is assumed that all the
liquid in a theoretical plate comes to equilibrium with the solid before
it moves to the next plate. It is supposed that all of the solute is initially
present in plate 0 and that an eluting solvent moves the solute progressively down the column. We shall not reproduce the derivation here
but merely express the final results using a notation consistent with that
used above for other types of column separations. To simplify the
final expressions, Mayer and Tompkins expressed the volume of solution
that has passed through the column in terms of N_F, the number of
free-column volumes. If r is the number of theoretical plates and hA_m
the liquid volume in a theoretical plate, then rhA_m is the free-column
volume, and $N_F = V/rhA_m = n/r$, where V is the total volume of
eluting solution and n is the number of plate volumes that have eluted
a given plate. β is the equilibrium ratio of the fraction of solute in the
resin phase to the fraction in solution in a given column plate. Evidently
β is analogous to but not identical with a partition coefficient, because it
expresses the equilibrium ratio not considering the relative volumes of the
two phases.[5]

Now, when N_F free volumes of eluate have passed the column, the
location of the elution peak turns out to correspond to $N_{max} = \beta$. The

[1] Bauman and Eichhorn, *op. cit.*

[2] Tompkins, E. R., and Mayer, S. W., *J. Am. Chem. Soc.*, **69**, 2859 (1947).

[3] Samuelson, O., "Ion Exchangers in Analytical Chemistry," p. 37, John Wiley &
Sons, Inc., New York, 1953.

[4] Mayer and Tompkins, *J. Am. Chem. Soc.*, **69**, 2866 (1947).

[5] The relation between P and β is $P = \beta i/(1 - i)$, where i is the fraction of voids,
or the ratio of pore volume to column volume.

fraction of solute in solution at plate r (corresponding to the concentration at the elution peak) is given by

$$f_{max} = \frac{1}{\sqrt{2\pi r\beta(1 + \beta)}} \qquad (25\text{-}77)$$

which indicates that the peak height varies inversely with the square root of the distance down the column.

As in other column separation techniques, the shape of the elution peak is approximated by the normal error curve. The spread of a peak is represented by the value of t, where

$$t = \frac{\sqrt{r}\,(N_F - \beta)}{\sqrt{\beta(1 + \beta)}} \qquad (25\text{-}78)$$

By plotting the original elution data on probability paper (cf. page 555), the closeness of fit of the elution peak to the normal error curve can be judged, and the t values can readily be obtained. Since $(N_F)_{max} = \beta$, t is zero at the elution peak and, in general, represents the number of standard deviations σ that N_F is removed from the peak of the elution band.

Freiling[1] showed that a convenient method of portraying an elution peak is by plotting t as a function of N_F. Such a curve, for the ion exchange separation of gadolinium and europium, is shown in Fig. 25-15. The value of $(N_F)_{max}$ and therefore of β is determined directly from the point corresponding to $t = 0$. The number r of theoretical plates may then be calculated from Eq. (25-78).

Example 25-13. Freiling (see Fig. 25-15) found $\beta = 21.4$ for Gd and 25.4 for Eu, corresponding to $t = 0$. At the point corresponding to $t = \sqrt{2}$ on the Gd curve, N_F was found to be 22.3. From Eq. (25-78), at this point $r = 2\beta(1 + \beta)/(N_F - \beta)^2$, from which $r = 1,170$ theoretical plates.

From the point corresponding to $N_F = 23.0$, $t = 2.8$ for the Gd curve, corresponding to 0.28 per cent of the Gd remaining on the column. Similarly, from the point $N_F = 23.0$, $t = -2.9$ for the Eu curve, corresponding to 0.20 per cent Eu having been eluted. This gives an indication of the degree of separation that is possible.

An indication of the conformance of the shape of the elution peaks to the normal error curve is obtained by taking the point $N_F = 23.0$ and using Eq. (25-78) to calculate r, which turns out to be 1,470 and 1,000 calculated from the Gd and Eu curves, respectively. That these values are even in approximate agreement is gratifying.

Glueckauf[2] has criticized the Mayer and Tompkins theory on the basis that the physical model of a batch-equilibrium process is inadequate. By deriving appropriate equations based on the transfer of infinitesimal solution increments from plate to plate, as was done by Martin and

---

[1] Freiling, *J. Am. Chem. Soc.*, **77**, 2067 (1955).

[2] Glueckauf, *Trans. Faraday Soc.*, **51**, 34 (1955).

Synge, but expressing the results in terms similar to those used by Mayer and Tompkins, the magnitude of the discrepancy could be estimated. It turns out that the Mayer and Tompkins model predicts a more complete separation than it should. The discrepancy becomes more important for small separation factors P_1/P_2 and short columns; it is negligible only if the plate equilibrium greatly favors the solid. According to Glueckauf, for a column of 1,000 theoretical plates, a separation factor of 1.2, and a ratio of solute in the pore spaces to solute

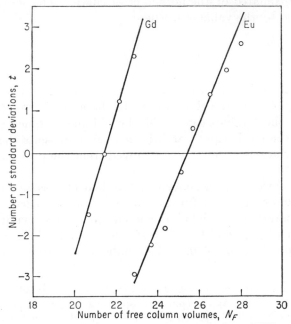

Fig. 25-15. Ion exchange elution curves of rare earths. [*With permission from Freiling, E. C., J. Am. Chem. Soc., 77, 2067 (1955).*]

in the solid phase of 1:5, the impurity level caused by contamination from an adjoining band is 3 times greater than that calculated from the Mayer-Tompkins theory. For a column of 160 theoretical plates, the same discrepancy occurs for a separation factor of 1.5. Evidently the Mayer-Tompkins theory must be regarded as an approximation valid only under special conditions.

Another way of describing the motion of an elution band is that of Kraus and Moore,[1] who defined the elution constant E as $E = dA/V$, where d is the distance in centimeters that a band maximum travels during the passage of V cm³ of eluant through a column of total area A.

[1] Kraus, K. A., and Moore, G. E., *J. Am. Chem. Soc.*, **73**, 9 (1951).

The relationship between the elution constant and the R_F value can be derived as follows.

Referring to Eq. (25-38) and applying it to the case of ion exchange, where the inert-phase area $A_i = 0$, we have $A_m + A_s = A$. If we represent the fraction of voids in the column by i, following Ketelle and Boyd,[1] we have

$$i = \frac{A_m}{A} \quad \text{and} \quad 1 - i = \frac{A_s}{A}$$

From Eq. (25-38),

$$R_F = \frac{A_m}{A_m + PA_s} = \frac{i}{i + P(1 - i)} = \frac{i}{i + D} \tag{25-79}$$

where $D = P(1 - i)$ = ratio of amount of solute in resin per unit volume of resin bed to amount of solute per unit volume of liquid at equilibrium

Now, in the time it takes for the band maximum to move a distance $d = EV/A$, the solvent moves a distance V/iA, so that $R_F = Ei$, or

$$E = \frac{R_F}{i} = \frac{1}{i + D} = \frac{1}{i + P(1 - i)} \tag{25-80}$$

The fraction of voids i can be determined readily for an ion exchange column by determining the elution constant for a substance not retained by the solid $(P = 0)$. For example, Kraus and Moore[2] used a solution of radioactive cation to evaluate i for an anion exchange column. Once i is known, the elution constant can be used to evaluate the partition coefficient P. If $P \gg i$, then $E \cong 1/P$, showing that, for strongly sorbed species, the rate of elution is inversely proportional to the partition coefficient.

Example 25-14. Kraus and Moore[2] found $i \cong 0.33$ for an anion exchange column. Thus the maximum value that E can reach (corresponding to $P = 0$), by Eq. (25-80), is $E_{max} = 1/i = 3$. Such a value was found for Zr(IV) in 3 M or 9 M HCl, at various concentrations of HF, indicating no formation of anionic complexes that would have been retained by the resin. On the other hand, for Nb(V), E was much smaller and varied with HCl and HF concentrations. In 9 M HCl, 1 M HF, E_{Nb} was found to be 2.7×10^{-2}, corresponding to $D = 37$ or $P = 55$.

Analytical Applications. Samuelson[3] has summarized a large number of analytical applications of ion exchange separations. In general, column techniques are used, both because of the favorable feature of multiplication of equilibrium stages and also because of their experimental

[1] Ketelle and Boyd, *J. Am. Chem. Soc.*, **69**, 2800 (1947).
[2] Kraus and Moore, *op. cit.*
[3] Samuelson, *op. cit.*

convenience. As mentioned previously, the strongly acidic cation exchangers and the strongly basic anion exchangers are generally advantageous. Only a few illustrative examples of various types of applications will be mentioned here.

Conversion of Salt to Acid. If a salt solution is passed through a cation exchange column in the hydrogen ion form, a quantitative reaction occurs:

$$M^+ + A^- + H^+R^- \rightleftharpoons M^+R^- + H^+ + A^- \qquad (25\text{-}81)$$

The acid HA that is formed can be titrated with standard base. The column is regenerated by washing with 3 to 4 N hydrochloric acid and washing with water. This procedure is applicable to the general determination of total salt concentration, provided that the acid HA can be washed from the column and titrated. Samuelson[1] applied this method to the determination of nitrate, with results agreeing within ± 0.2 per cent. Likewise, if only a single anion is present, sulfate, perchlorate, acetate, halides, etc., can be determined. This method affords a simple standardization of solutions of salts that are not conveniently prepared by direct weight, owing to hygroscopic behavior or to an uncertain degree of hydration. Another application is the preparation of standard solutions of acids by weighing an appropriate salt (HNO_3 from $AgNO_3$, HCl from NaCl, etc.).

Limitations are encountered, for example, with carbonates, bicarbonates, or bisulfites that form gaseous products or with salts of acids that are adsorbed on the column. Some organic acids tend to be retained on the column but can be washed off with alcohol. Phosphoric acid requires an abnormal amount of washing, and must be concentrated by evaporation before it can be titrated.[2]

An interesting application was made by Weisenberger[3] to the determination of saponification equivalent of esters. The ester can saponified with an excess of base, which is neutralized upon passage through an acidic resin bed. The organic acid is titrated with standard base. In this way, a relatively large excess of base can be used to ensure quantitative saponification. The determination is a direct titration; therefore, only one standard solution is required, rather than two, as in the customary indirect determination.

Conversion of Salt to Hydroxide. Using a strongly basic anion exchange resin, Samuelson and Schramm[4] converted various alkali metal salts to the hydroxides, which could then be titrated with standard acid. In general, however, the resin-regeneration technique was found to be less

---

[1] Samuelson, *op. cit.*, p. 116.

[2] Samuelson, *Z. anal. Chem.*, **116**, 328 (1939).

[3] Weisenberger, E., *Mikrochem. ver. Mikrochim. Acta*, **30**, 241 (1942).

[4] Samuelson, O., and Schramm, K., *Svensk Kem. Tidskr.*, **63**, 307 (1951).

convenient than the corresponding cation exchange method. Therefore the anion exchange method is preferable only in special circumstances, for example, in the determination of alkali metal phosphates or sulfites.

Removal of Interfering Ions. An important application of ion exchange is in the conversion of alkali metal sulfates or phosphates to the chlorides. Runeberg[1] used cation exchange for separating potassium from sulfate, and Runeberg and Samuelson[2] applied a similar method for separating alkali metals from phosphate. The procedure is to hold the alkali metals on a hydrogen ion column, washing out the sulfuric or phosphoric acid. The alkali metal is then eluted from the column with hydrochloric acid. Similar separations are readily made with strongly basic anion exchange resins.[3] The anion exchange method requires no elution to recover the alkali metal ion.

Another important example is in the separation of sulfate and phosphate from various cations.[4] Samuelson devised a method for sulfur in pyrites, which is based on the retention of Fe(III) on a cation exchange resin. The sulfuric acid passing through the column can be readily determined in the usual gravimetric manner as barium sulfate. In a similar way, phosphate can be determined in phosphate rock by retaining calcium, magnesium, iron, and aluminum on a cation exchange resin and determining the phosphate with high accuracy as magnesium pyrophosphate. The metal ions can be eluted from the column with $4 N$ hydrochloric acid.

Separations Based on Complex Formation. The separation factor for closely similar metal ions may often be enhanced by taking advantage of differences in formation constants of the complexes with a suitable reagent. A classic example is the separation of rare earths by using a buffered citrate solution as the eluting agent.

An analogous separation of various metal ions can be made on anion exchange columns by taking advantage of variations in the stabilities of chloro complexes. Jentsch[5] has summarized the behavior of 25 metals in various concentrations of hydrochloric acid. He distinguished four classes of metal ions, differing in the stabilities of their anionic chloro complexes, on the basis of the variation of elution behavior with acid concentration.

Especially effective separations are possible when one metal is converted into an anionic complex while another is present as a cation. Teicher and Gordon[6] separated iron and aluminum by retaining the iron

[1] Runeberg, G., *Svensk Kem. Tidskr.*, **57**, 114 (1945).

[2] Runeberg and Samuelson, *Svensk Kem. Tidskr.*, **57**, 91 (1945).

[3] Gabrielson, G., and Samuelson, O., *Svensk Kem. Tidskr.*, **62**, 221 (1950).

[4] Samuelson, *Svensk Kem. Tidskr.*, **52**, 115 (1940); **54**, 124 (1942).

[5] Jentsch, D., *Z. anal. Chem.*, **152**, 134 (1956).

[6] Teicher, H., and Gordon, L., *Anal. Chem.*, **23**, 930 (1951).

on an anion exchanger as a thiocyanate complex while the aluminum was washed out. MacNevin and Crummett[1] separated Pd(II) and Ir(III) by treating the chlorides with ammonia to produce $Pd(NH_3)_4^{++}$, which was retained on a cation exchange column while the iridium passed through as $IrCl_6^{3-}$.

Concentration of Extremely Dilute Electrolytes. An ion exchange column is very effective in collecting ionic substances from large volumes of very dilute solutions. By elution using a small volume of solution, a very considerable concentration effect can be achieved.

As examples may be cited the concentration of cations and anions in natural waters,[2-4] beryllium from bones,[5] transition metals from solutions containing relatively large amounts of ammonium salts,[6] and copper from milk[7] and mineral oils.[8]

PROBLEMS

25-1. The vapor pressures of benzene and toluene at 100°C are 1,335 and 557 mm, respectively. The normal boiling points are 80.2 and 110.8°C, respectively. Compare the values of the relative volatility calculated (a) from Eq. (25-2) and (b) from (25-5). *Ans.* (a) 2.40; (b) 2.34.

25-2. Calculate the number of theoretical plates required to obtain 99.9 mole per cent benzene at the top of the column and 99.9 mole per cent toluene in the still pot under conditions of total reflux. *Ans.* 15.

25-3. Calculate (a) the number of theoretical plates required to produce 98 mole per cent benzene at the top of column with 25 mole per cent benzene in the still pot, using a reflux ratio of 4 to 1. Calculate (b) the minimum reflux ratio for this separation. Estimate (c) the optimum number of plates from Eq. (25-15). *Ans.* (a) 8; (b) 2.23; (c) 8.

25-4. Using in each case a total volume of extractant equal to the volume of the aqueous phase, compare the fraction unextracted for $P = 10$ and for (a) one extraction, (b) five extractions, (c) infinite extractions. (d) How many extractions are required to obtain a yield of 99.9 per cent? *Ans.* (a) 0.091; (b) 0.0041; (c) 4.5×10^{-5}; (d) 7.

25-5. Taking $P = 10$, calculate the fraction of solute originally in tube 0 of a Craig multiple-extraction apparatus with equal volumes of phases and the fraction present in each tube after four extractions. *Ans.* 7×10^{-5}; 2.7×10^{-3}; 0.041; 0.27; 0.68.

25-6. In a particular partition chromatography column, the volumes of mobile phase, stationary phase, and inert phase are in the ratio $A_m : A_s : A_i = 0.20 : 0.05 : 0.75$; and the HETP is 0.005 cm. Two substances of partition coefficients 1.50 and 1.55 are to be separated. Calculate (a) the R_F values for the two substances; (b) the volume of

[1] MacNevin, W. M., and Crummett, W. B., *Anal. Chim. Acta*, **10**, 323 (1954).

[2] Nydahl, F., *Proc. Intern. Assoc. Theoret. Appl. Limnology*, **11**, 276 (1951).

[3] Calmon, C., *J. Am. Water Works Assoc.*, **46**, 470 (1954).

[4] McCoy, J. W., *Anal. Chim. Acta*, **6**, 259 (1952).

[5] Toribara, T. Y., and Sherman, R. K., *Anal. Chem.*, **25**, 1594 (1953).

[6] Riches, J. P. R., *Nature*, **158**, 96 (1946); *Chem. & Ind. London*, **1947**, 656.

[7] Cranston, H. A., and Thompson, J. B., *Ind. Eng. Chem., Anal. Ed.*, **18**, 323 (1946).

[8] Buchwald, H., and Wood, L. G., *Anal. Chem.*, **25**, 664 (1953).

eluant required to bring each of the band peaks in turn to a point 10 cm down a column of total area 1 cm^2; (c) the volume of eluant required to wash all but 0.13 per cent of the leading component from a 30-cm column; (d) the percentage of the lagging component that has been removed under the conditions of part c. Ans. (a) 0.7272, 0.7207; (b) 2.750, 2.775 ml; (c) 8.57 ml; (d) $t = 2.28$, 1.1 per cent.

25-7. For a particular gas chromatographic column, Keulemans[1] found the following empirical equation to express the HETP, cm, as a function of linear hydrogen gas velocity v, cm sec^{-1}: $h = 0.1 + 0.28/v + 0.05v$. (a) At what value of v was the column operating at maximum efficiency? (b) What relative increase in HETP would be caused by working at 0.5 or 1.5 times the optimum flow rate? Ans. (a) 2.37 cm sec^{-1}; (b) 17.5, 5.6 per cent.

25-8. A GLPC column such as one described by Porter, Deal, and Stross[2] having the following properties: $V_G^\circ = 13.1$ cm^3, $V_L = 2.58$ cm^3, $T = 378°K$, is operated under the following conditions: $F_c = 40.2$ cm^3 min^{-1}, $p_i = 1{,}340$ mm, $p_o = 760$ mm. If the retention time for n-hexane is 2.92 min, calculate the following quantities: V_R, V_R°, $(V_R^\circ)'$, P. If the partition coefficient of n-heptane using the same solvent is 57.0, what retention time is expected for this compound? Ans. 117.3 cm^3, 82.8 cm^3, 69.7 cm^3, 27.0, 5.64 min.

25-9. A GLPC column, like one described by Littlewood, Phillips, and Price,[3] using 2.82 g of silicone 702 as the stationary phase, is operated at 56.2°C and $p_i = 1{,}230$ mm, $p_o = 781$ cm, the atmospheric pressure being 760 mm. At a nitrogen flow rate of 11.0 cm^3 min^{-1} measured at 0°C and 760 mm, the retention time of methyl propionate vapor was observed to be 58.2 min; that of hydrogen was 2.7 min.

Calculate V_g for methyl propionate, assuming that hydrogen is not adsorbed by the liquid phase. Ans. 161 cm^3.

25-10. Mayer and Tompkins[4] found, in an ion exchange separation of Pr and Ce, using a column for which $r = 240$, that the elution peaks corresponded to $(N_F)_{max} = 113$ for Pr and 193 for Ce. (a) Assuming that the fraction of voids in the column was 0.30, estimate the partition coefficient between resin and solution for Pr and Ce. (b) Estimate D [cf. Eq. (25-79)] and E [cf. Eq. (25-80)] for Pr and Ce, and the distance that each band would have traveled down a 1-cm^2 column after the addition of 1 liter of eluant. (c) Estimate the fraction of Pr existing in solution in the 240th plate just as the Pr band emerges from the column. (d) Estimate the fractions of Pr and Ce remaining in the column after 153 free-column volumes of eluant have passed through. Ans. (a) 48.4, 82.7; (b) $D_{Pr} = 33.9$, $D_{Ce} = 57.9$, $E_{Pr} = 2.9 \times 10^{-2}$, $E_{Ce} = 1.7 \times 10^{-2}$, 29 cm, 17 cm; (c) 2.28×10^{-4}; (d) $t = 5.46$, $f_{Pr} \cong 0.001$ per cent, $f_{Ce} \cong 99.999$ per cent.

BIBLIOGRAPHY

Distillation

Carney, T. P.: "Laboratory Fractional Distillation," The Macmillan Company. New York, 1949.

Leslie, R. T., and Kuehner, E. C., *Anal. Chem.*, **30**, 629 (1958).

Rose, A., and Rose, E., in Weissberger, A. (ed.), "Technique of Organic Chemistry," vol. 4, pp. 1–174, Interscience Publishers, Inc., New York, 1951.

Zuiderweg, F. J., "Laboratory Manual of Batch Distillation," Interscience Publishers, Inc., New York, 1957.

[1] Keulemans, *op. cit.*, p. 143.
[2] Porter, Deal, and Stross, *op. cit.*
[3] Littlewood, Phillips, and Price, *op. cit.*
[4] Mayer and Tompkins, *op. cit.*

Extraction

Craig, L. C., and Craig, D. C., in Weissberger, "Technique of Organic Chemistry," vol. 3, pp. 171–311, Interscience, 1950.

Craig, L. C., *Anal. Chem.*, **21**, 85 (1949); **22**, 61 (1950); **23**, 41 (1951); **24**, 66 (1952); **26**, 110 (1954); **28**, 723 (1956).

Morrison, G. H., and Freiser, H., "Solvent Extraction in Analytical Chemistry," John Wiley & Sons, Inc., New York, 1957.

Morrison, G. H., and Freiser, H., *Anal. Chem.*, **30**, 632 (1958).

Gas-Liquid and Liquid-Liquid Partition Chromatography

Cassidy, H. G., in Weissberger, "Technique of Organic Chemistry," vol. 10, Interscience, 1957.

Lederer, E., and Lederer, M., "Chromatography," Elsevier Publishing Company, Amsterdam, 1955.

Keulemans, A. I. M., "Gas Chromatography," edited by Verver, C. G., Reinhold Publishing Corporation, New York, 1957.

Phillips, C., "Gas Chromatography," Academic Press, Inc., New York, 1956.

Desty, D. H., and Harbourn, C. L. A., "Vapour Phase Chromatography," Academic Press, Inc., New York, 1957.

Adsorption Chromatography

Cassidy, *op. cit.*

Strain, H. H., "Chromatographic Adsorption Analysis," Interscience Publishers, Inc., New York, 1947.

Brimley, R. C., and Barrett, F. C., "Practical Chromatography," Reinhold Publishing Corporation, New York, 1953.

Lederer, E. and Lederer, M., *op. cit.*

Paper Chromatography

Cassidy, *op. cit.*

Cramer, F., "Paper ʌChromatography," 2d ed., translated by L. Richards, The Macmillan Company, New York, 1954.

Block, R. J., Durrum, E. L., and Zweig, G., "A Manual of Paper Chromatography and Paper Electrophoresis," Academic Press, Inc., New York, 1955.

Strain, H. H., *Anal. Chem.*, **30**, 620 (1958).

Ion Exchange

Cassidy, *op. cit.*

Samuelson, O., "Ion Exchangers in Analytical Chemistry," John Wiley & Sons, Inc., New York, 1953.

Osborn, G. H., "Synthetic Ion Exchangers," Chapman & Hall, Ltd., London, 1955.

Osborn, G. H., *Analyst*, **78**, 220 (1953).

Kraus, K., in Yoe, J. H., and Koch, W. J., Jr. (eds.), "Trace Analysis," pp. 34–101, John Wiley & Sons, Inc., New York, 1957.

Kunin, R., McGarvey, F. X., and Zobian, D., *Anal. Chem.*, **30**, 681 (1958).

Inorganic Chromatography

Pollard, F. H., and McOmie, J. F. W., "Chromatographic Methods of Inorganic Analysis," Butterworth & Co. (Publishers) Ltd., London, 1953.

Smith, O. C., "Inorganic Chromatography," D. Van Nostrand Company, Inc., Princeton, N.J., 1953.

26. Statistics in Quantitative Analysis

The traditional role of statistics in quantitative analysis has long been the evaluation of scatter in experimental data for the purpose of estimating the "probable error." During the past ten or twenty years there has been an increasing awareness of contributions of the statistical approach to several other aspects of chemical analysis. The use of statistics in the sampling operation will be discussed in the next chapter. By proper design of experiments, guided by a statistical approach, the effects of experimental variables may be found more efficiently than by the traditional approach of holding all variables constant but one and systematically investigating each variable in turn. Trends in data may be sought to track down nonrandom sources of error. Quality-control charts are an important guide in evaluating day-by-day performance and in uncovering otherwise unsuspected variations or long-term trends.

The subject is much too large to treat in detail in a single chapter, but it is hoped that a brief discussion of the more important statistical operations will encourage the reader to seek more detailed information from the sources listed at the end of the chapter.

26-1. Errors in Quantitative Analysis[1]

Two broad classes of errors may be recognized. The first class, *determinate* or *systematic* errors, is composed of errors that can, at least in principle, be assigned to definite causes, even though the cause may not have been located. Such errors are characterized by being unidirectional. The magnitude may be constant from sample to sample, proportional to sample size, or variable in a more complex way. An example is the error

[1] For a critical discussion, see Sandell, E. B., in Kolthoff, I. M., and Elving, P. J. (eds.), "Treatise on Analytical Chemistry," part I, vol. 1, chap. 2, Interscience Publishers, Inc., New York, 1959.

caused by weighing a hygroscopic sample.   This error is always positive in sign; it increases with sample size but varies depending on the time required for weighing, with the humidity and temperature.   An example of a negative systematic error is that caused by solubility losses of a precipitate.

The second class, *indeterminate* or *random* errors, is brought about by the effects of uncontrolled variables.   Usually a relatively large number of experimental variables, each of which causes a small error, must be left uncontrolled.   For example, if a correction for solubility loss is made to eliminate the systematic error from this source, random errors due to fluctuations of temperature, volume of wash water, etc., remain.   Truly random errors are as likely to cause high as low results, and a small random error is much more probable than a large one.   By making the observation coarse enough, random errors would cease to exist.   Every observation would give the same result, but the result would be less precise than the average of a number of finer observations with random scatter.

The *precision* of a result is its reproducibility; the *accuracy* is its nearness to the truth.   A systematic error causes a loss of accuracy, and it may or may not impair the precision depending upon whether the error is constant or variable.   Random errors cause a lowering of reproducibility, but by making sufficient observations it is possible to overcome the scatter (within limits) so that the accuracy may not necessarily be affected.   Statistical treatment can properly be applied only to random errors.   One may raise the objection that it is not known in advance whether the errors are truly random, but here again the laws of probability can be applied to determine whether nonrandomness (trends, jumps, clustering, or the like) is a factor.   If it is, an effort should be made to locate and correct the systematic causes.

Even random errors may not follow the *normal law of error*, which is the fundamental starting point for analysis of data.   Once more, statistical tests may be applied to determine whether serious deviation from the normal law exists and to interpret the data accordingly.

26-2. The Normal Law of Error[1]

In statistics, a finite number of observations of a given kind is considered to represent a sample of an infinite *population* or *universe* of data. The properties of the universe of random errors can be described by means of the *normal law of error*, which follows the equation

$$\frac{dN}{N} = \frac{1}{\sigma \sqrt{2\pi}} \exp \left\{ - \frac{(x - \mu)^2}{2\sigma^2} \right\} dx \qquad (26\text{-}1)$$

[1] Compare Wilson, E. B., Jr., "An Introduction to Scientific Research," chap. 9, McGraw-Hill Book Company, Inc., New York, 1952.

where dN/N = fraction of the population with values in the interval x to $x + dx$; proportional, therefore, to the probability that a given value falls in this interval

μ = average value of the entire population

σ = *standard deviation* of the population

The distribution of errors for a particular population of data is given by the two *population parameters*[1] μ and σ. The *population mean* μ expresses the magnitude of the quantity being measured; the standard deviation σ expresses the scatter and is, therefore, an index of precision.

By introducing a variable y, given by

$$y = \frac{x - \mu}{\sigma} \tag{26-2}$$

it is possible to express the normal law in terms of a single variable, giving the equation

$$\frac{dN}{N} = \frac{1}{\sqrt{2\pi}} \exp\left(-y^2/2\right) dy = f(y)\, dy \tag{26-3}$$

which is plotted in Fig. 26-1. Values of the function $f(y)$ are listed in mathematical tables under the title *ordinates of the normal error curve*. The total area under the curve of Fig. 26-1, is

$$\frac{1}{\sqrt{2\pi}} \int_{-\infty}^{+\infty} \exp\left(-y^2/2\right) dy = 1 \tag{26-3a}$$

corresponding to a total probability of unity for the entire population. Thus the area under the curve between any two values of y gives the fraction of the total population having magnitudes of y between those two

TABLE 26-1. PROBABILITY OF ERROR IN SINGLE OBSERVATION FROM
NORMAL DISTRIBUTION

Absolute value of y	Probability of greater value	Probability of smaller value
0.674	0.50	0.50
1.00	0.3174	0.6826
1.282	0.20	0.80
1.645	0.10	0.90
1.960	0.05	0.95
2.00	0.0454	0.9546
2.576	0.01	0.99
3.00	0.0026	0.9974
3.291	0.001	0.999

[1] Properties of a population, such as μ and σ, are known as *parameters;* analogous properties of a finite sample are known as *statistics*.

values. In Table 26-1 are listed values of $\pm y$ beyond which lie various fractions of the total area under the curve of Fig. 26-1. From the definition of y it follows that $x - \mu = y\sigma$ and that the areas represent probabilities for the absolute deviation $|x - \mu|$ to exceed the value $y\sigma$. Since σ is the *standard deviation*, $y\sigma$ is the deviation of a single observation from the population mean measured in terms of the number of standard deviations.

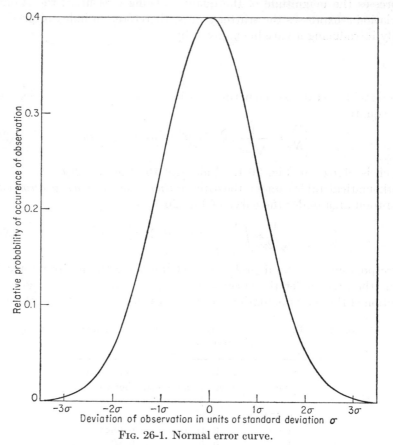

FIG. 26-1. Normal error curve.

The probability of an error greater than σ is 0.317; of an error greater than 2σ, 0.0454; and of an error greater than 3σ, 0.0026 for a normal distribution of errors. In each case, positive and negative deviations are equally probable.

The function $f(y)$ has the property of being a maximum for $y = 0$ and, therefore, for $x = \mu$. Thus, the average value is the most probable value of the population. This is the basis of one test for normal distribution.

26-3. The Normal Law of Error Applied to a Finite Sample

For a finite sample of n observations, the *sample mean* $\bar{x}$ is the arithmetic average of the n observations; $\bar{x}$ in the limit approaches the population mean μ as n approaches infinity.

Correspondingly, the *sample standard deviation* s approaches the population standard deviation σ in the limit. The sample standard deviation is given by the equation

$$s = \left\{ \sum_{i=1}^{i=n} \frac{(x_i - \bar{x})^2}{n-1} \right\}^{1/2} \tag{26-4}$$

As the number of observations is increased to a very large number N, the quantity $n - 1$ approaches N (relatively) more and more closely as N is increased. Thus

$$\sigma = \left\{ \sum_{i=1}^{i=N} \frac{(x_i - \mu)^2}{N} \right\}^{1/2} \tag{26-5}$$

The standard deviation of the sample is experimentally important as an estimate of the desired standard deviation of the population, which cannot actually be observed with a finite number of measurements. If a *random* sample is taken, the quantity s becomes a closer approximation to σ as the size of the sample is increased. Likewise, the sample average $\bar{x}$ becomes a closer estimate of the population mean μ as the size of a random sample is increased.

For many purposes it is more convenient to use the *variance*, which, for the sample, is s^2 or V

$$s^2 = V = \sum_{i=1}^{i=n} \frac{(x_i - \bar{x})^2}{n-1} \tag{26-6}$$

and which, for the population N, is σ^2

$$\sigma^2 = \sum_{i=1}^{i=N} \frac{(x_i - \mu)^2}{N} \tag{26-7}$$

In many practical papers the standard deviation of a finite number of observations is represented by σ, but strictly speaking the symbol σ should be reserved for the universe, or infinite population.

It will be observed from Eq. (26-7) that the variance σ^2 of the population is the arithmetic mean of the squares of the deviations of the individual values x_i from the population mean μ. On the other hand, from Eq. (26-6), the quantity $n - 1$ rather than N appears when a finite sample is considered. Obviously, for large values of n, it is immaterial whether $n - 1$ or n is used, but for small numbers of observations—which are especially important in analytical chemistry—the distinction is important, and we should recognize the reason for it.

If a finite number n of observations is made with a sample mean $\bar{x}$, there are n individual deviations $x_i - \bar{x}$. However, the sum of the n deviations is zero, and only $n - 1$ of the deviations are necessary to define the nth. This removes one *degree of freedom*, and there are left only $n - 1$ independently variable deviations. We can regard the sample variance as the average of the square of the independently variable deviations. For small numbers of observations, we want s to approximate as nearly as possible to σ, which would be observed with an infinite number. Now, for a small number n, the sample mean $\bar{x}$ will in general not coincide with the population mean μ, and we will set the difference $\bar{x} - \mu = \delta$.

$$(x_i - \mu) = (x_i - \bar{x}) + \delta$$

$$\sum_{i=1}^{i=n} (x_i - \mu)^2 = \sum_{i=1}^{i=n} (x_i - \bar{x})^2 + n\delta^2 + 2\delta \sum_{i=1}^{i=n} (x_i - \bar{x})$$

But the summation of the deviations, given by the last term, is zero; so

$$\sum_{i=1}^{i=n} (x_i - \mu)^2 = \sum_{i=1}^{i=n} (x_i - \bar{x})^2 + n\delta^2 \qquad (26\text{-}8)$$

It can be shown that the use of $n - 1$ as the divisor just compensates, when averaged over all values of n, for the fact that the sample mean and population mean are not identical.[1] Because of the relative improbability of drawing large deviations in a small sample, the sample variance would otherwise underestimate the population variance.

[1] It follows from the definition of σ [Eq. (26-5)] that, if the calculation expressed by Eq. (26-8) is repeated for a large number of samples, the value of $\Sigma(x_i - \mu)^2$, averaged over all values of n, approaches $n\sigma^2$. Similarly, the mean value of $n\delta^2$ approaches the quantity σ^2, since n times the variance of the mean $\bar{x}$ is given by $n(\sigma^2/n)$, as will be seen below, in Eq. (26-11).

Then, from Eq. (26-8) averaged over a large number of samples,

$$\sum (x_i - \bar{x})^2 \rightarrow n\sigma^2 - \sigma^2$$

or

$$s^2 = \sum \frac{(x_i - \bar{x})^2}{(n - 1)} \rightarrow \sigma^2$$

where the arrow has the meaning "is an estimate of." See Davies, O. L., "Statistical Methods in Research and Production," 3d ed., p. 50, Oliver & Boyd, Ltd., Edinburgh and London, 1957.

An alternative formulation of Eq. (26-6) is helpful in computing sample variance, especially when using a calculating machine. We write

$$s^2 = \frac{1}{n-1} \sum_{i=1}^{i=n} (x_i - \bar{x})^2$$

$$= \frac{1}{n-1} \left(\sum x_i^2 - 2\bar{x} \sum x_i + n\bar{x}^2 \right)$$

but, since $\Sigma x_i = n\bar{x}$,

$$s^2 = \frac{1}{n-1} \left\{ \sum x_i^2 - \frac{(\Sigma x_i)^2}{n} \right\} \tag{26-9}$$

A further aid, especially useful when a calculating machine is not available, is to subtract a constant quantity a from each observation. It can be readily shown that

$$s^2 = \frac{1}{n-1} \left\{ \sum (x_i - a)^2 - \frac{1}{n} \left[\sum (x_i - a) \right]^2 \right\} \tag{26-10}$$

The *residuals* $x_i - a$ can be kept small enough so that their squares can be looked up in short mathematical tables.

26-4. Sampling from a Population of Two Types of Units

A special case, which is of particular interest in sampling problems, is encountered when the population consists of only two types of units that are taken as such. The two types of units might be black and white marbles, satisfactory and unsatisfactory items from a production line, particles of ore mineral and gangue, etc. If p and q represent the fractions (by number) of the two kinds of units in the population, so that $p + q = 1$, and if n units are removed at random from an infinite population, then the most probable values for the numbers of the two kinds of units in the sample are clearly pn and qn. The actual numbers will fluctuate around these values with a standard deviation given by the Bernoulli equation[1]

$$\sigma = \sqrt{npq}$$

Example 26-1.   If the incidence of defective units coming from a production line is 2 per cent and if a random sample of 10,000 units is drawn, what is the expected number of defective units in the sample, and what is the standard deviation? The *expected number* is $0.02 \times 10,000 = 200$; the standard deviation is

$$s = \sqrt{10,000 \times 0.02 \times 0.98} = 14$$

[1] See Benedetti-Pichler, A. A., in Berl, W. M. (ed.), "Physical Methods in Chemical Analysis," vol. 3, p. 183, Academic Press, Inc., New York, 1956.

26-5. Measures of Central Value and Dispersion[1]

In general, the arithmetic mean is the most valuable statistic for measuring the central value of a sample of data, because for a normal distribution it is also the most probable value (mode) and the middle value (median). The mode and median are of relatively little use in analytical chemistry.

Several measures of dispersion are the *variance*, the *standard deviation*, the *coefficient of variation*, the *range*, and the *mean deviation*. Of these, the variance is the most important, because the variance s^2 of a finite sample is an unbiased estimate of σ^2, although the standard deviation s is not an unbiased estimate of σ.* Also, the variance is a quantity that occurs in many statistical operations, whereas the standard deviation is convenient only because it is expressed in the same units as the measured value. The *coefficient of variation* is merely the standard deviation expressed as a percentage of the arithmetic mean. It is useful mainly to show whether the relative or the absolute spread of values is constant as the values are changed. The *range* is the difference between the highest and lowest values of a sample of observations. It is of little use for large samples but becomes increasingly useful as the number of observations decreases, until, for a pair of observations, it, together with the mean, gives all the data. The *mean deviation*, or average deviation from the mean, is often cited in analytical papers but is a relatively useless statistic for small numbers of observations. For large bodies of normally distributed data, it approaches 0.8σ, but for reasonable numbers of observations it is a grossly biased estimate of precision because it gives equal weight to large and small deviations, which are not equally probable.[2] It tends to underestimate the dispersion and, therefore, to give a falsely optimistic estimate of precision.

26-6. Error of a Computed Result[3]

The estimation of the error of a computed result R from the errors of the component terms or factors A, B, and C depends upon whether the errors are determinate or random. The propagation of errors in computations is summarized in Table 26-2. The *absolute* determinate error ϵ or the variance $V = s^2$ for a random error is transmitted in addition or subtraction (note that the variance is additive both for a sum and for a dif-

---

[1] Dixon, W. J., and Massey, F. J., Jr., "Introduction to Statistical Analysis," 2d ed., p. 70, McGraw-Hill Book Company, Inc., New York, 1957.

* If the sampling distribution of a statistic has a mean equal to the corresponding universe parameter, the statistic is said to be an *unbiased* estimate of the parameter. The variance s^2 of a *random* sample is, *on the average*, equal to σ^2.

[2] Youden, W. J., "Statistical Methods for Chemists," p. 8, John Wiley & Sons, Inc., New York, 1951.

[3] Compare Benedetti-Pichler, *Ind. Eng. Chem., Anal. Ed.,* **8,** 373 (1936).

TABLE 26-2. ERROR OF A COMPUTED RESULT

Type of error\ \ \ Computation	Determinate	Random
Addition or subtraction $R = A + B - C$	$\epsilon_R = \epsilon_A + \epsilon_B - \epsilon_C$	$s_R^2 = s_A^2 + s_B^2 + s_C^2$
Multiplication or division $R = \dfrac{AB}{C}$	$\dfrac{\epsilon_R}{R} = \dfrac{\epsilon_A}{A} + \dfrac{\epsilon_B}{B} - \dfrac{\epsilon_C}{C}$	$\left(\dfrac{s_R}{R}\right)^2 = \left(\dfrac{s_A}{A}\right)^2 + \left(\dfrac{s_B}{B}\right)^2 + \left(\dfrac{s_C}{C}\right)^2$
General $R = f(A,B,C, \ldots)$	$\epsilon_R = \dfrac{\partial R}{\partial A}\epsilon_A + \dfrac{\partial R}{\partial B}\epsilon_B + \cdots$	$s_R^2 = \left(\dfrac{\partial R}{\partial A}\right)^2 s_A^2 + \left(\dfrac{\partial R}{\partial B}\right)^2 s_B^2 + \cdots$

ference). On the other hand, the *relative* determinate error ϵ_x/x or square of the relative standard deviation $(s_x/x)^2$ is additive in multiplication. The general case $R = f(A,B,C, \ldots)$ is valid only if A, B, C, $\ldots$, are independently variable; it is strictly true only for linear functions of A, B, C, $\ldots$, but is approximately valid for other cases if the relative errors are smaller than about 20 per cent of the mean values.[1]

26-7. Standard Deviation of the Mean

In Sec. 26-2 we have considered the standard deviation σ, which is related to the probable error of a single observation. If a series of random samples of size n is drawn from an infinite population; the average value of the various sets of n observations will show a smaller scatter as n is increased. As n increases, each sample average approaches the population average μ in the limit, and the scatter approaches zero. It can be shown[2] that the variance of the mean is inversely proportional to the number n, or

$$\sigma_m^2 = \frac{\sigma^2}{n} \tag{26-11}$$

In terms of the standard deviation,

$$\sigma_m = \frac{\sigma}{\sqrt{n}} \tag{26-12}$$

[1] Davies, *op. cit.*, p. 41.
[2] For a proof, see Wilson, *op. cit.*, p. 252.

The precision of a measurement can be increased by increasing the number of observations. However, because of the square-root-dependence expressed in Eq. (26-12), there is a practical limit to the improvement to be gained by replication. For example, to decrease the standard deviation by a factor of 10 requires 100 times as many observations.

Obviously, any systematic errors that are involved in a determination cannot be removed by replication. Consequently, the practical limit of useful replication has been reached when the standard deviation of the random errors is comparable to the determinate error.

26-8. The Confidence Interval

From Table 26-1, the *confidence interval* of a single observation may be expressed in terms of the variable y.

The population mean lies within the limits

$$\mu = x \pm 0.67\sigma \qquad \text{with 50 per cent confidence} \qquad (26\text{-}13a)$$
$$\mu = x \pm 1.96\sigma \qquad \text{with 95 per cent confidence} \qquad (26\text{-}13b)$$
$$\mu = x \pm 2.58\sigma \qquad \text{with 99 per cent confidence} \qquad (26\text{-}13c)$$

If the mean $\bar{x}$ of n measurements is taken, the population mean lies within the limits

$$\mu = \bar{x} \pm 0.67 \frac{\sigma}{\sqrt{n}} \qquad \text{with 50 per cent confidence} \qquad (26\text{-}14a)$$

$$\mu = \bar{x} \pm 1.96 \frac{\sigma}{\sqrt{n}} \qquad \text{with 95 per cent confidence} \qquad (26\text{-}14b)$$

$$\mu = \bar{x} \pm 2.58 \frac{\sigma}{\sqrt{n}} \qquad \text{with 99 per cent confidence} \qquad (26\text{-}14c)$$

In the older literature, the "probable error," corresponding to a confidence level of 50 per cent, was commonly cited. In modern practice, it is usual to employ a higher confidence level, such as 95 or 99 per cent, or to specify confidence limits of $\pm 2\sigma$ or $\pm 3\sigma$.

An obvious difficulty is that the population standard deviation is not usually known and can only be approximated for a finite number of measurements by the sample standard deviation s, calculated from Eq. (26-4). This difficulty is overcome by means of the quantity t (sometimes known as the "Student t"*), defined by

$$\pm t = (\bar{x} - \mu) \frac{\sqrt{n}}{s} \qquad (26\text{-}15)$$

which takes into account both the possible variation of the value of $\bar{x}$

* Named after the pseudonym of W. S. Gossett, who published a classic paper on the subject in *Biometrika*, **6**, 1 (1908).

from μ on the basis of the expected variance σ^2/n and the reliability of using s in place of σ.

Values of t can be found in tables for any desired number of observations n or degrees of freedom $n - 1$ and for various desired confidence levels. The confidence interval can be written

$$\mu = \bar{x} \pm \frac{ts}{\sqrt{n}} \qquad (26\text{-}16)$$

For purposes of illustration, a few values of t are listed in Table 26-3 for various confidence levels and corresponding to ν degrees of freedom, where $\nu = n - 1$. Note that the values for $\nu = \infty$ reduce to the values of Eqs. (26-14).

TABLE 26-3. VALUES OF t FOR ν DEGREES OF FREEDOM FOR VARIOUS
CONFIDENCE LEVELS

Confidence level, % / ν	50	90	95	99	99.5
1	1.000	6.314	12.706	63.657	127.32
2	0.816	2.920	4.303	9.925	14.089
3	0.765	2.353	3.182	5.841	7.453
4	0.741	2.132	2.776	4.604	5.598
5	0.727	2.015	2.571	4.032	4.773
6	0.718	1.943	2.447	3.707	4.317
7	0.711	1.895	2.365	3.500	4.029
8	0.706	1.860	2.306	3.355	3.832
9	0.703	1.833	2.262	3.250	3.690
10	0.700	1.812	2.228	3.169	3.581
15	0.691	1.753	2.131	2.947	3.252
20	0.687	1.725	2.086	2.845	3.153
25	0.684	1.708	2.060	2.787	3.078
∞	0.674	1.645	1.960	2.576	2.807

[With permission from Thompson, C. M., *Biometrika*, **32**, 168 (1941).]

A simpler procedure, particularly useful for small numbers of observations, is to base the confidence interval on the *range R*, the difference between the largest and smallest values in the sample. To a certain degree of confidence, the population mean lies within the limits

$$\mu = \bar{x} \pm c_n R$$

where $\bar{x}$ is the mean value of a random sample of n values drawn from a normal population, and c_n is a constant depending upon the number of

TABLE 26-4. VALUES OF c_n FOR SAMPLE OF n OBSERVATIONS FOR VARIOUS
CONFIDENCE LEVELS

No. of observations n	Confidence level, %			
	90	95	98	99
2	3.196	6.353	15.910	31.828
3	0.885	1.304	2.111	3.008
4	0.529	0.717	1.023	1.316
5	0.388	0.507	0.685	0.843
6	0.312	0.399	0.523	0.628

[With permission from Lord, E., *Biometrika*, **34**, 41 (1947).]

observations and the desired confidence level. Values of c_n are given in Table 26-4.

Other procedures for estimation of the standard deviation from the range are available, but all methods based on range should be used with caution, because of the uncertainty caused by a large fluctuation of an occasional observation. In any case, the use of the range is not usually recommended for samples of $n > 10$.

26-9. Combination of Observations

It often happens that a series of observations can be logically arranged into subgroups and that it is desired to calculate the variance of the entire series. For example, suppose that the precision of a standardization of a solution is being evaluated for a new primary standard. On each of several days, a set of values is observed, and it is desired not to include the possible deterioration of the standard solution from day to day into the estimate of precision.

Suppose that there are k subgroups, not necessarily containing the same number of observations, and N total observations. The variance is calculated by summing the squares of the deviations, $\Sigma(x_i - \overline{x_i})^2$, for each subgroup, then adding all the k sums and dividing by $N - k$, to give

$$s^2 = V = \frac{1}{N - k} \sum_k \sum_i (x_i - \overline{x_i})^2 \qquad (26\text{-}17)$$

The significance of dividing by $N - k$ is that, of the N deviations, only $N - k$ are independent, because one degree of freedom is lost in each subgroup.

For the case of two groups of observations consisting of n_A and n_B members, of standard deviations s_A and s_B, respectively, the variance is given by

$$V = \frac{(n_A - 1)s_A^2 + (n_B - 1)s_B^2}{n_A + n_B - 2} \tag{26-18}$$

26-10. Tests of Significance

Statistical methods are frequently used to give a yes or no answer to a particular question concerning the significance of data. The answer is qualified by a confidence level indicating the degree of certainty of the answer. This procedure is known as *hypothesis testing*.[1]

A common procedure is to set up a *null hypothesis*, which states that there is no significant difference between two sets of data or that a variable exerts no significant effect.[2] To enable a yes-or-no answer to be given, a confidence level, say 95 or 99 per cent, is chosen to express the probability that the answer is correct. Careful judgment must be exercised in selecting the confidence level. If it is chosen too severely (e.g., 99.9 per cent), a significant effect may be missed. Such an error is called an *error of the second kind*, or a type II error. On the other hand, if too much latitude is allowed (e.g., 80 per cent), an insignificant difference may be judged important. This is an *error of the first kind*, or a type I error.

The *t* test. An example of hypothesis testing is the *t* test (or Student's *t* test) based on the definition of *t* in Sec. 26-8 above. In this application the *t* test is used to test the hypothesis that two means do not differ significantly.

Equation (26-16) is applicable directly to the comparison of the mean $\bar{x}$ of n observations drawn at random from a normal population of mean μ. The quantity $t = (\bar{x} - \mu) \sqrt{n}/s$ is compared with the values found in a table of values of t (Table 26-3) at the desired confidence level and corresponding to ν degrees of freedom, where $\nu = n - 1$. If the value in question exceeds the tabular value, the null hypothesis is rejected, and a significant difference is indicated.

Example 26-2. The following values were obtained for the atomic weight of cadmium: 112.25, 112.36, 112.32, 112.21, 112.30, 112.36. Does the mean of these values (112.30) differ significantly from the accepted value 112.41?

The variance s^2 is $\Sigma(x_i - \bar{x})^2/(n - 1)$, or 0.00364, giving a standard deviation $s = 0.060$. The quantity t is $(112.30 - 112.41) \sqrt{6}/0.060 = -4.5$. From Table 26-3, for $\nu = 5$, t is 4.032 at the 99 per cent confidence level and 4.773 at the 99.5 per cent confidence level. A significant deviation is indicated; therefore, a systematic source of error is highly probable.

---

[1] Wilson, *op. cit.*, chap. 3.
[2] Fisher, R. A., "The Design of Experiments," 5th ed., Oliver & Boyd, Ltd., Edinburgh and London, 1949, states "Every experiment may be said to exist only in order to give the facts a chance of disproving the null hypothesis."

Such a test is limited in practical applicability because in it the population mean μ is regarded as known. If the deviation from a theoretical value is desired and *if there is a normal distribution of error around the theoretical value*, the theoretical value is the population mean μ. Again, if a relatively large sample of data, corresponding to $n > 30$, is available, its mean can be taken as a measure of μ, and the average of a smaller set can be compared with it adequately. However, it is often desirable to compare the means of two relatively small sets, of n_1 and n_2 observations, with means $\overline{x_1}$ and $\overline{x_2}$, respectively, when the *variances within the sets can be regarded as the same* within the limits of random sampling. To test for homogeneity of variance, the F test (see below, this section) is applied. The variance based on both samples [cf. Eq. (26-17)] is

$$V = s^2 = \frac{\Sigma(x_1 - \overline{x_1})^2 + \Sigma(x_2 - \overline{x_2})^2}{n_1 + n_2 - 2} \qquad (26\text{-}19)$$

The variance of $\overline{x_1}$ is s^2/n_1; that of $\overline{x_2}$ is s^2/n_2. The variance of the difference $\overline{x_1} - \overline{x_2}$ is the sum of the two, or

$$V_{\overline{x_1}-\overline{x_2}} = s^2\left(\frac{1}{n_1} + \frac{1}{n_2}\right) = s^2\left(\frac{n_1 + n_2}{n_1 n_2}\right) \qquad (26\text{-}20)$$

The quantity t is defined as the difference between the two means divided by its standard deviation [cf. Eq. (26-15)]

$$t = \frac{\overline{x_1} - \overline{x_2}}{s\left(\dfrac{1}{n_1} + \dfrac{1}{n_2}\right)^{1/2}} = \frac{\overline{x_1} - \overline{x_2}}{s}\left(\frac{n_1 n_2}{n_1 + n_2}\right)^{1/2} \qquad (26\text{-}21)$$

which may be compared with tables of t corresponding to $n_1 + n_2 - 2$ degrees of freedom.

To illustrate, suppose that two methods of analysis were applied to the same sample, with the results for percentage of component x that are shown in Table 26-5.

TABLE 26-5. APPLICATION OF ANALYTICAL METHODS A AND B TO SERIES OF IDENTICAL SAMPLES

Test	Method A	Method B	Difference
1	4.68	4.81	$d_1 = 0.13$
2	4.64	4.70	$d_2 = 0.06$
3	4.69	4.74	$d_3 = 0.05$
4	4.55	–	–
	$\overline{x_A} = 4.64$	$\overline{x_B} = 4.75$	$\overline{d} = 0.08$

Confining our attention to the first three columns, the variance based on both methods is 0.0037; the standard deviation of a single result is 0.0608; and t is given by

$$t = \frac{4.64 - 4.75}{0.0608} \left(\frac{4 \times 3}{7}\right)^{\frac{1}{2}} = -2.37$$

Disregarding the negative sign, the value of $t = 2.37$ for five degrees of freedom is to be compared with values of 2.015 for 90 per cent, 2.571 for 95 per cent, and 4.023 for 99 per cent confidence levels (cf. Table 26-3). Usually, a result giving a positive test at the 95 per cent level is regarded as significant, and one at the 99 per cent level is highly significant. In this instance, the t test suggests an affirmative result, but to be able to decide with more assurance whether methods A and B are significantly different, a greater number of tests must be run.

In the special case where $n_1 = n_2 = n$, Eq. (26-21) reduces to

$$t = \frac{\overline{x_1} - \overline{x_2}}{s} \sqrt{\frac{n}{2}} \qquad (26\text{-}22)$$

Also, in the special case where $n_1 = n$, $n_2 = \infty$, $\overline{x_2}$ becomes the population mean μ, and Eq. (26-21) reduces to (26-15).

Another type of application of the t test is to *individual* differences between sets of observations. In the above example, the same sample was analyzed by two methods. However, we may wish to determine whether there is a systematic difference between methods A and B irrespective of the sample. It is assumed that both methods have essentially the same standard deviation and also that this does not depend on the sample. In the fourth column of Table 26-5 are the differences between the two methods, for the three tests common to the two methods. The variance of the differences is

$$V_d = s_d^2 = \sum \frac{(d_i - \bar{d})^2}{n - 1} \qquad (26\text{-}23)$$

or, in the above example, $0.0038/2 = 0.0019$. The standard deviation of differences is $s_d = 0.0436$. The value of t is the mean difference divided by its standard deviation, or

$$t = \frac{\bar{d}}{s_d} \sqrt{n} \qquad (26\text{-}24)$$

Here the quantity $\sqrt{n}$ appears because the standard deviation of the *mean difference* is $s_d/\sqrt{n}$, if s_d is that of a single difference.

In the above example $t = (0.08/0.0436) \sqrt{3} = 3.2$. From the table, corresponding to $n - 1 = 2$ degrees of freedom, $t = 2.920$ at the 90 per cent confidence level and 4.303 at the 95 per cent level. Thus, a value of $t = 3.2$ would occur by chance alone less than once in ten trials, and the differences between methods A and B may, therefore, be judged to be real. Actually, it is risky to draw conclusions from so limited a group of data, which was presented here for the sake of simplicity, but, on the other hand, it is not necessary to have an enormous body of data to draw valid statistical conclusions.

The F test. In contrast to the t test, which is a comparison of means, the F *test* is a comparison of variances. The ratio between the two variances to be compared is the *variance ratio F* (for R. A. Fisher), defined by

$$F = \frac{s_1^2}{s_2^2} = \frac{V_1}{V_2} \tag{26-25}$$

Values of F are available in statistical tables at various desired significance levels. The values depend on the number of degrees of freedom ν_1 and ν_2 for the two variances V_1 and V_2. The tables are arranged with F values greater than unity; therefore, the two variances are compared in the order $V_1 > V_2$.

The values in Table 26-6 illustrate a small section of a table of F values, taken at the 95 per cent confidence level. The entries correspond to a probability of 0.95 that the variance ratio will not exceed the value in the table. Extensive tables are available for various confidence levels and degrees of freedom.

TABLE 26-6. VALUES OF F AT THE 95 PER CENT LEVEL

ν_2 \ ν_1	2	3	4	5	6	∞
2	19.00	19.16	19.25	19.30	19.33	19.50
3	9.55	9.28	9.12	9.01	8.94	8.53
4	6.94	6.59	6.39	6.26	6.16	5.63
5	5.79	5.41	5.19	5.05	4.95	4.36
6	5.14	4.76	4.53	4.39	4.28	3.67
∞	3.00	2.60	2.37	2.21	2.10	1.00

[With permission from Merrington, M., and Thompson, C. M., *Biometrika*, **33**, 73–88 (1943).]

To illustrate, suppose that two series of observations are made, one of six observations, of standard deviation $s_1 = 0.05$, another of four observations, of standard deviation $s_2 = 0.02$. We are to test whether s_1 is significantly greater than s_2. We have $\nu_1 = 5$, $\nu_2 = 3$, and, from the table, $F = 9.01$. The experimental variance ratio is

$$\frac{V_1}{V_2} = \frac{s_1^2}{s_2^2} = \frac{0.0025}{0.0004} = 6.25$$

On the basis of chance, the value of F would exceed 9.01 five per cent of the time. It is concluded that the null hypothesis is valid and that there is not a statistically significant divergence.[1]

[1] As applied above, the F test is *one-sided*, testing the null hypothesis that σ_1^2 and σ_2^2 (as estimated by s_1^2 and s_2^2) are equal; the alternative hypothesis being $\sigma_1^2 > \sigma_2^2$. The F test may also be applied as a *two-sided* test, in which the alternative to the null

The χ^2 (chi-square) test is a useful tool for testing the behavior of data if the theoretical behavior can be expressed quantitatively in terms of probabilities, or expected frequencies.

$$1, 2, \ldots, 9, 0$$

For example, if we were to examine the third digit of a five-place logarithm table, we would expect to find an equal probability, 0.1, of finding each of the ten digits. On the other hand, if we were to examine the last digit of students' buret readings estimated to 0.01 ml, we would find a considerable *number bias* in favor of certain digits, say, 0 and 5. Naturally, for a limited number of observations, a certain fluctuation is statistically expected, and it is this expectation that the chi-square test informs us about.

The quantity χ^2 is defined by

$$\chi^2 = \sum \frac{(f_i - F_i)^2}{F_i} \tag{26-26}$$

where f_i = observed frequency
$\quad\quad F_i$ = expected frequency
and where the summation is carried out over all classes of observations.

TABLE 26-7. CHI-SQUARE DISTRIBUTION
The column headings give the probability P that the tabular value will be exceeded;
ν = degrees of freedom.

P $\diagdown$ ν	0.995	0.99	0.95	0.90	0.50	0.10	0.05	0.01	0.005
1	0.00004	0.00016	0.0039	0.0158	0.455	2.71	3.84	6.63	7.88
2	0.0100	0.0201	0.1026	0.211	1.39	4.61	5.99	9.21	10.6
3	0.0717	0.115	0.352	0.584	2.37	6.25	7.81	11.3	12.8
4	0.207	0.297	0.711	1.064	3.36	7.78	9.49	13.3	14.9
5	0.412	0.554	1.15	1.61	4.35	9.24	11.1	15.1	16.7
6	0.676	0.872	1.64	2.20	5.35	10.6	12.6	16.8	18.5
8	1.34	1.65	2.73	3.49	7.34	13.4	15.5	20.1	22.0
10	2.16	2.56	3.94	4.87	9.34	16.0	18.3	23.2	25.2
15	4.60	5.23	7.26	8.55	14.3	22.3	25.0	30.6	32.8
20	7.43	8.26	10.85	12.44	19.3	28.4	31.4	37.6	40.0
30	13.79	14.95	18.49	20.60	29.3	40.3	43.8	50.9	53.7

[Abridged with permission from Thompson, C. M., *Biometrika*, **32**, 187–191 (1941).]

Example 26-3. An examination of the last digit of buret readings by sophomore quantitative-analysis students gave the following results:

hypothesis is $\sigma_1^2 \neq \sigma_2^2$. This doubles the probability that the null hypothesis is invalid and has the effect of changing the confidence level, in the above example, from 95 to 90 per cent.

Digit	f_i	$f_i - F_i$
0	375	216
1	132	27
2	129	30
3	118	41
4	123	36
5	252	93
6	117	42
7	118	41
8	143	16
9	83	76
	1,590	69,388 (sum of squares)

The expected frequency F_i is 159 in each class, assuming no number bias. The calculated value of x^2 is $69,388/159 = 437$ a value which, at nine degrees of freedom, lies far above the 99.9 percentile probability level and indicates pronounced number bias.

Another indication of number bias is obtained by comparing the observed standard deviation $s = \sqrt{69,388/9} = 88$ with that calculated from Bernoulli's equation $s = \sqrt{npq}$, which, for $n = 1,590$, $p = 0.1$, $q = 0.9$, gives $s = 12$ for ten *equal* classes of probability 0.1.

If the digits 0 and 5 are omitted on the grounds that these represent results in which students rounded off their readings to the nearest 0.5 ml, we may examine the remaining eight digits for number bias, as follows:

Digit	f_i	$f_i - F_i$
1	132	8
2	129	5
3	118	6
4	123	1
6	117	7
7	118	6
8	143	19
9	83	41
	963	2,253 (sum of squares)

The expected frequency is now $963/8 = 124$, leading to a x^2 of $2,253/124 = 18.1$, as compared with the tabular value of 14.1 for seven degrees of freedom, indicating a significant deviation at the 95 per cent confidence level. The standard deviation is $s = \sqrt{2,253/7} = 18$.

From Bernoulli's equation, for eight classes of equal probability and a total of 963 entries, we have $\sigma = \sqrt{963 \times 0.125 \times 0.875} = 10.2$. This corresponds to a frequency range of 124 ± 20 using 2σ confidence limits. It is interesting to note that only the digit 9 falls outside these limits. This one entry contributed 70 per cent of the observed x^2 value. Evidently the deficient frequency of the digit 9 appears largely in the abnormal frequency of the digit 0 and perhaps to a small extent in an abnormal frequency of the digit 8.

An interesting analysis of number bias in microbalance readings has been made by Gysel,[1] who concluded that number bias varies considerably from observer to observer and also depends on the manner of subdivision of instrument markings. Such bias can actually impose a limitation upon the accuracy of readings by an individual.

Distribution Normalcy Tests. The chi-square test can be used to find out whether an experimental distribution of error follows the normal curve. The method will be described here only in principle, because only in unusual cases would enough data be available. For a detailed example, see a paper by Nelson,[2] who studied the distribution of errors in 100 student observations. The steps are:

1. Prepare a frequency table showing the numbers of observations falling into a series of classes.

2. Calculate the sample mean $\bar{x}$ and the variance V.

3. Define a normal curve with the same mean, the same variance, and the same total number of observations.

4. Take differences between the observed and expected frequencies, and calculate χ^2 for each class.

5. Add the values of χ^2 to get a total value, and compare this value with tabular values to find the probability level corresponding to the value of χ^2. This probability level will express the likelihood that a random choice of values from a normal distribution would have given the observed distribution. For any reasonable number of observations, say, 100, it is necessary to be extremely cautious in concluding from the chi-square test that the population was nonrandom. Thus, a probability level below 1 or 0.1 per cent is commonly regarded as necessary. However, the existence of abnormalities in the frequency distribution is shown readily by abnormal contributions of certain classes to the total value of χ^2.

Another, and more simple, qualitative test for normalcy of distribution is the use of *probability paper* for plotting a distribution curve. If the cumulative probability of an observation is plotted as a function of the value of the observation, an s-shaped curve is observed, with the cumulative probability reaching 0.5 at the median value. By distorting the ordinates of the graph paper in the proper way, the cumulative probability can be made to be a straight line for a normal distribution. Such probability paper should be used with caution, because a fairly good straight line can be obtained from data that are far from normal. Also, deviations are difficult to judge, because points near the center of the graph carry far more weight than those near the ends.

[1] Gysel, H., *Mikrochim. Acta.*, **1953**, 266; **1956**, 577.

[2] Nelson, L. S., *J. Chem. Educ.*, **33**, 126 (1956).

26-11. Analysis of Variance

The technique of analysis of variance, developed largely by R. A. Fisher,[1] is a powerful tool in determining the separate effects of different sources of variation in experimental data.

In chemical analysis, for example, it is frequently an important question whether a particular method gives the same precision in the hands of several analysts, or whether analysts within a laboratory agree more closely among themselves than with another group in a separate laboratory, or whether the same relative precision is obtained by a given group of analysts regardless of variations in sample.

Variance analysis is most useful when applied to a set of experiments planned with statistical evaluation in mind. "Factorial" experiments, in which several factors are changed in all possible combinations in a single integrated experiment, allow the estimation of "interaction effects," or the simultaneous effects of two or more variables. Such interactions may be extremely important; yet they may escape detection completely by the classical method of experimentation in which the variables are changed one at a time, with all other conceivable sources of variation held constant.

When several factors are involved, the statistical design and analysis of variance become rather complicated. Therefore, we shall examine in detail only the simplest type of example, to illustrate the principles involved. More elaborate situations can readily be understood by an extension of the same principles.

The simplest application is to that of a *one-way classification with equal numbers*, such that a total of $N = nk$ observations are classified into k classes of n observations in each. As an illustration, there may be n standardizations of a single solution by k analysts. There is a single *assignable* source of variation (the different analysts) in addition to the random error inherent in the method, and it is desired to evaluate the magnitude of the variance from this source.

In Table 26-8, a set of observations is arranged in an order of k columns of n observations each. If $j = 1, 2, \ldots, n$ and $i = 1, 2, \ldots, k$, an observation x_{ij} is the jth observation of the ith class.

If the grand mean of the $N = nk$ observations is $\bar{x}$ and if $\bar{x}_i$ is the mean of the n observations of the ith class, we can write

$$(x_{ij} - \bar{x}) = (x_{ij} - \bar{x}_i) + (\bar{x}_i - \bar{x}) \tag{26-27}$$

Squaring both sides and summing over i and j, it can be shown by reason-

---

[1] Fisher, "Statistical Methods for Research Workers," Oliver & Boyd, Ltd., Edinburgh and London, 1954.

TABLE 26-8. OBSERVATIONS FOR ANALYSIS OF VARIANCE

Class no. Observation no.	$i = 1$	$i = 2$	$\cdots$	$\cdots\cdots$	$i = k$
$j = 1$	x_{11}	x_{21}	$\cdots$	x_{i1} $\cdots$	x_{k1}
$j = 2$	x_{12}	x_{22}	$\cdots$	x_{i2} $\cdots$	x_{k2}
.	.	.		.	.
.	.	.		.	.
.	.	.		.	.
.	x_{1j}	x_{2j}	$\cdots$	x_{ij} $\cdots$	x_{kj}
.	.	.		.	.
.	.	.		.	.
.	.	.		.	.
$j = n$	x_{1n}	x_{2n}	$\cdots$	x_{in} $\cdots$	x_{kn}
Mean of ith class	$\overline{x_1}$	$\overline{x_2}$	$\cdots$	$\overline{x_i}$ $\cdots$	$\overline{x_k}$

ing similar to that used in arriving at Eq. (26-8) that

$$\Sigma_{ij}(x_{ij} - \bar{x})^2 - \Sigma_{ij}(x_{ij} - \overline{x_i})^2 + n\Sigma_i(\overline{x_i} - \bar{x})^2 \qquad (26\text{-}28)$$

In Eq. (26-28), the quantity on the left-hand side is the *total sum of squares S*, obtained by summing the squares of each individual deviation from the grand mean. For simplicity of calculation, especially when using calculating machines, use can be made of the identity

$$S = \sum_{ij} (x_{ij} - \bar{x})^2 \equiv \sum_{ij} (x_{ij})^2 - \frac{\left(\sum_{ij} x_{ij}\right)^2}{N} \qquad (26\text{-}29a)$$

which is analogous to Eq. (26-9).

The first term on the right-hand side of Eq. (26-28) is $S_{j(i)}$, the sum of squares of j within i, or the sum of squares of the deviation *within* a class i. It is obtained by summing *within each class* the squares of the deviations from the average of that class and then summing over all the classes. Once more, use is made of the identity

$$S_{j(i)} = \sum_{ij} (x_{ij} - \overline{x_i})^2 \equiv \sum_{ij} (x_{ij})^2 - \frac{\sum_i \left(\sum_j x_{ij}\right)^2}{n} \qquad (26\text{-}29b)$$

The second term on the right-hand side of Eq. (26-28) is S_i, the sum of squares of deviations *between classes*, obtained by summing the squares of deviations of the class mean from the grand mean:

$$S_i = n \sum_i (\overline{x_i} - \bar{x})^2 \equiv \sum_i \frac{\left(\sum_i x_{ij}\right)^2}{n} - \frac{\left(\sum_{ij} x_{ij}\right)^2}{N} \qquad (26\text{-}29c)$$

If the classes do not all contain n members but do contain a variable number n_i, then $S_i = \sum_i n_i(\overline{x_i} - \bar{x})^2$, which is a weighted sum of squares. In each class, the multiplier n_i is used because it is desired to express the variance for a single observation, which is n_i times the variance of the mean of n_i observations. Obviously, the calculations are made more convenient by arranging all classes to contain an equal number of observations, as assumed above.

It is evident from Eq. (26-28) that

$$S = S_{j(i)} + S_i \qquad (26\text{-}30)$$

which simply states that the total sum of squares can be separated into a term $S_{j(i)}$ resulting from deviations *within* classes and a term S_i resulting from deviations *between* classes.

To calculate variances, the sum of squares is divided in each case by the number of degrees of freedom. Since there are k classes containing n observations in each, the total number of degrees of freedom is $nk - 1 = N - 1$. For S_i there are $k - 1$ degrees of freedom, because S_i is computed from the deviations of the k class means $\overline{x_i}$ from the over-all mean $\bar{x}$. For $S_{j(i)}$ there are $N - k = nk - k = n(k - 1)$ degrees of freedom, representing the difference between the total number of observations and the k class means used in the calculations. It will be noted that, just as the sum of squares is additive, so is the number of degrees of freedom; that is, the number $N - 1$ of total degrees of freedom is equal to the number $k - 1$ of degrees of freedom "between classes" plus the number $N - k$ of degrees of freedom "within classes."

It is convenient to summarize these observations in an *analysis-of-variance table;* Table 26-9 illustrates this type of table for the above case.

The over-all variance V contains contributions due to variances within classes as well as variances between classes.

TABLE 26-9. ANALYSIS-OF-VARIANCE TABLE FOR k CLASSES OF n OBSERVATIONS

Source of variation	Sum of squares	Degrees of freedom	Variance	Variance is estimate of
Between classes	S_i	$k - 1$	$V_i = \dfrac{S_i}{k - 1}$	$\sigma_i^2 = \sigma_0^2 + n\sigma_1^2$
Within classes	$S_{j(i)}$	$N - k$	$V_{j(i)} = \dfrac{S_{j(i)}}{N - k}$	σ_0^2
Total	S	$N - 1$	$V = \dfrac{S}{N - 1}$	–

The object of the analysis of variance is to determine whether the variance between classes is significantly greater than that within classes. The latter must be due to inherent error from nonassignable sources, because all members of the class were supposedly identical.

To express the effect of variance *between* classes on a single observation it is necessary to add to the variance *within* a class a variance due to the effect of the class. But, since the class effect is determined by considering the mean of n observations, the variance of a single observation is $n\sigma_1^2$, if σ_1^2 is the variance of the mean of classes. Thus V_i becomes an estimate of σ_i^2, which is given by

$$\sigma_i^2 = \sigma_0^2 + n\sigma_1^2 \qquad (26\text{-}31)$$

By means of the F test it can be determined whether σ_1^2 is significant. Under the null hypothesis $\sigma_1^2 = 0$ and $\sigma_i^2 = \sigma_0^2$. The ratio $F = \sigma_i^2/\sigma_0^2$ for $k - 1$ and for $N - k$ degrees of freedom is compared with tables of F at the desired confidence level to determine whether the ratio is significant. If the F test proves σ_1^2 to have a significant value, this can be estimated quantitatively by using Eq. (26-31).

Example 26-4. Suppose that five different laboratories A, B, C, D, E reported the following results (in ppm) for triplicate determinations of iron in water.

Determination	Laboratory A	B	C	D	E
1	10.3	9.5	12.1	7.6	13.6
2	9.8	8.6	13.0	8.3	14.5
3	11.4	8.9	12.4	8.2	15.1
Mean $\bar{x}_i$	10.5	9.0	12.5	8.0	14.4

It is desired to determine whether the variance between laboratories is significantly higher than that between replicate determinations by a single laboratory and whether there is a significant difference in precision among the various laboratories.

The following analysis-of-variance table is obtained by summing squares according to Eqs. (26-29) and arranging as shown in Table 26-9. It is noted that $n = 3$, $k = 5$.

Source of variation	Sum of squares	Degrees of freedom	Variance	Variance is estimate of
Between labs	$S_i = 80.39$	4	$V_i = 20.10$	$\sigma_i^2 = \sigma_0^2 + 3\sigma_1^2$
Within labs	$S_{j(i)} = 3.61$	10	$V_0 = 0.36$	σ_0^2
	$S = 84.00$	14	$V = 6.00$	–

The ratio $F = \sigma_i^2/\sigma_0^2 = 20.1/0.36 = 56$; this is compared with a value of 11.3 found in statistical tables of F values at four and ten degrees of freedom, at the 99.9 per cent confidence level. It is concluded that F is highly significant.

To estimate σ_1^2, we have, from Eq. (26-31),

$$20.10 = 0.36 + 3\sigma_1^2$$

and $\sigma_1^2 = 6.58$ = variance of the mean of three determinations between laboratories. To calculate confidence limits, we use Eq. (26-16). There are five values of $\bar{x}_i$; so there are four independent deviations from the grand mean and, therefore, four degrees of freedom for t. Equation (26-16) becomes $\mu = \bar{x} \pm ts/\sqrt{5} = 10.9 \pm 2.78(6.58/5)^{1/2}$, or $\mu = 10.9 \pm 3.2$ ppm, using the 95 per cent confidence level.

For determinations within a given laboratory, $\sigma_0^2 = 0.36$, or the standard deviation is $\sqrt{0.36} = 0.6$ ppm. Using Eq. (26-16), with two degrees of freedom, $t = 4.3$; and the 95 per cent confidence interval is $\mu_i = \bar{x}_i \pm 4.3 \times 0.6/\sqrt{3} = \bar{x}_i \pm 1.5$ ppm. This value may be compared with that estimated from Table 26-4, for three observations, $\mu_i = \bar{x}_i \pm 1.3R$. The range R varies between 0.7 for laboratory D and 1.6 for laboratory A.

26-12. Control Charts[1]

A control chart is a sequential plot of some quality characteristic. It might be a day-by-day plot of the average moisture content of grain samples, or the normality of a standard solution, or the percentage of a constituent in successive production lots, etc. The chart consists of a central line and two pairs of limit lines, the *inner* and *outer control limits*, or simply of a central line and one pair of control limits. By plotting a sequence of points in order, a continuous record of the quality characteristic is made available. Trends in data or sudden lack of precision can be made evident so that the causes may be sought. Control charts may be plotted for many statistics, but the most common are charts for averages and ranges of observations.

[1] For a comprehensive discussion, see Grant, E. L., "Statistical Quality Control," 2d ed., McGraw-Hill Book Company, Inc., New York, 1952.

The control chart is set up to answer the question of whether the data are in *statistical control*, i.e., whether the data may be regarded as random samples from a single population of data. Because of this feature of testing for randomness, the control chart may be useful in searching out systematic sources of error in laboratory research data as well as in evaluating plant-production or control-analysis data. An excellent discussion of the use of control charts in the analytical laboratory is given by Wernimont.[1] Several applications are discussed by Mitchell.[2]

To set up a control chart, individual observations might be plotted in sequential order and then compared with control limits established from sufficient past experience. For example, if the mean $\bar{x}$ and standard deviation s of a supposedly constant quantity have been established from, say, 20 past observations, these quantities may be taken as valid estimates of μ and σ for the population. Limits of $\pm 1.96\sigma$ corresponding to a confidence level of 95 per cent, might be set for control limits. The probability of a future observation falling outside these limits, based on chance, is only 1 in 20. A greater proportion of scatter might indicate a nonrandom distribution, i.e., a systematic error. Of course, if the control limits are set up with a limited sample, 20 in the above example, there is a certain probability that excessive scatter is caused by setting the initial control limits too rigidly because of inadequate estimates of μ and σ. To check this possibility, a new calculation based on a larger number of observations should be made. It is common practice in some industries to set inner control limits, or warning limits, at $\pm 1.96\sigma$ and outer control limits of $\pm 3.09\sigma$. The outer control limits correspond to a confidence level of 99.8 per cent, or a probability of 0.002 that a point will fall outside the limits. One-half of this probability corresponds to a high result and one-half to a low result. Special attention should be paid to one-sided deviation from the control limits, because systematic errors more often cause deviation in one direction than abnormally wide scatter. Two systematic errors of opposite sign would of course cause scatter, but it is unlikely that both would have entered at the same time. It is not necessary that the control chart be plotted in a time sequence. In any situation where relatively large numbers of units or small groups are to be compared, the control chart is a simple means of indicating whether any unit or group is out of line. Thus laboratories, production machines, test methods, or analysts may be put arbitrarily into a horizontal sequence.

Usually it is better to plot the means of small groups of observations on a control chart, rather than individual observations. The random scatter of averages of pairs of observations is $1/\sqrt{2} = 0.71$ as great as that of single observations, and the likelihood of two "wild" observations in the

[1] Wernimont, G., *Ind. Eng. Chem., Anal. Ed.*, **18**, 587 (1946).

[2] Mitchell, J. A., *Ind. Eng. Chem., Anal. Ed.*, **19**, 961 (1947).

same direction is vanishingly small. The groups of two to five observations should be chosen in such a way that only chance variations operate within the group, whereas assignable causes are sought for variations between groups. If duplicate analyses are performed each day, the pairs form logical groups.

Some measure of dispersion of the subgroup data should also be plotted as a parallel control chart. The most reliable measure of scatter is the standard deviation. For small groups, the range becomes increasingly significant as a measure of scatter, and it is usually a simple matter to plot the range as a vertical line and the mean as a point on this line for each group of observations.

To illustrate the procedure for setting control limits, consider the data in Table 26-10. For a normal distribution of error, the mean value of the range of subgroups becomes an increasingly valid basis for estimating the standard error of the population as the number of observed subgroups increases. Multiplying the mean value of the range by an appropriate factor taken from Table 26-10 permits establishment of upper and lower control limits. The mean value $\bar{R}$ of the range should be calculated from at least 20 subgroup ranges, although a temporary estimate may be taken from a smaller number and then adjusted as more data become available.

The control limits for ranges are unequal on the two sides of the average value, because R is always positive and has zero as a lower limit.

TABLE 26-10. FACTORS FOR DETERMINING FROM $\bar{R}$ THE 3σ CONTROL LIMITS FOR $\bar{x}$ AND R CHARTS

Number of observations in subgroup	Factor for $\bar{x}$ chart	Factors for R chart	
		Lower control limit	Upper control limit
n	A_2	D_3	D_4
2	1.88	0	3.27
3	1.02	0	2.57
4	0.73	0	2.28
5	0.58	0	2.11
6	0.48	0	2.00
8	0.37	0.14	1.86
10	0.31	0.22	1.78
12	0.27	0.28	1.72
15	0.22	0.35	1.65
20	0.18	0.41	1.59

Control limits for mean: $\bar{x} = \bar{\bar{x}} \pm A_2\bar{R}$

Control limits for range: $D_3\bar{R} < R < D_4\bar{R}$

[Selected values, with permission from Grant, E. L., "Statistical Quality Control," 2d ed., p. 513, McGraw-Hill Book Company, Inc., New York, 1952.]

An example of the use of a control chart is shown in Fig. 26-2, which illustrates a comparison of two weighing methods. The "single-swing" method and the method of multiple swings were compared. Four individual comparisons for two 1-gram and two 100-gram weights were made daily. Only four individual observations were outside the control limits, and only one standard deviation or daily variation appeared out of line. Although no assignable causes could be found for the occasional lack of control, it may be safely concluded that there is no appreciable superiority of the longer method of multiple swings over the more rapid single-swing method. Naturally, this conclusion is valid only for

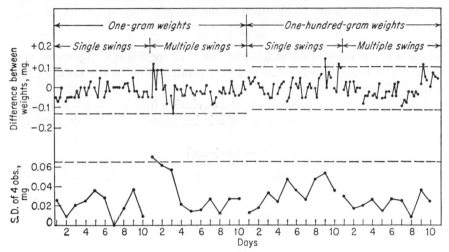

FIG. 26-2. Control chart for comparing weighing methods. [*With permission from Wernimont, G., Ind. Eng. Chem., Anal. Ed.,* **18,** 587 (1946).]

the particular balance tested, but a similar test could easily be made for any balance.

26-13. Regression Analysis[1]

In the analysis of data it is often desirable to determine whether two variable quantities are related and to express this relationship quantitatively. The present treatment will be limited to the case of a linear relationship, because this situation is by far the most important experimentally. Often a nonlinear relationship can be transformed into a linear one by plotting a simple function such as the logarithm, square root, or reciprocal of one or both of the variables.

If two variables x and y are related, two different situations may be recognized: (1) where both variables are subject to comparable experi-

[1] Compare Davies, O. L., "Statistical Methods in Research and Production," 3d ed., chap. 7, Oliver & Boyd, Ltd., Edinburgh and London, 1957.

mental error; (2) where one variable may be regarded as being determinable to so high a degree of precision that its uncertainty can be ignored. The latter situation is much more frequently encountered in analytical chemistry, because usually we are interested in determining whether there exists a statistically significant trend of results with some variable such as temperature, pH, sample size, etc., which exerts only a small effect and which can, therefore, be fixed as accurately as needed.

We shall consider here only the simplest case of a *single linear regression*, in which x is considered to be the accurately determinable independent variable and y the dependent variable subject to experimental uncertainty. The data are to be fitted to the straight line

$$y = a + bx$$

where a is the intercept and b is the slope, or *coefficient of regression of y on x*. The procedure is to fit the best straight line to the data by the *method of least squares*.

If x_i, y_i is any given observation, the deviation from the line is measured in the y direction, since the error of x is insignificant. The deviation is given by

$$y_i - (a + bx_i)$$

The values of a and b are chosen to make the sum of the squares of the deviations Q a minimum, where

$$Q = \sum_i \{y_i - (a + bx_i)\}^2 \tag{26-32}$$

This can be done in the usual way by the differential calculus, setting the derivatives of Q with respect to a and b equal to zero and solving for a and b.

The results are

$$a = \bar{y} - b\bar{x} \tag{26-33}$$

$$b = \frac{\Sigma(x_i - \bar{x})(y_i - \bar{y})}{\Sigma(x_i - \bar{x})^2} \tag{26-34}$$

where $\bar{y}$ is the mean of y's and $\bar{x}$ is the mean of x's.

It will be noted from Eq. (26-33) that the equation of the best straight line may be written

$$y - \bar{y} = b(x - \bar{x})$$

which indicates that *it is a line drawn through the point represented by the coordinates $\bar{x}, \bar{y}$ with a slope equal to b*.

The minimum sum of squares of deviations is given by substituting the values of a and b into the expression for Q. The result is

$$Q_{\min} = \Sigma(y_i - \bar{y})^2 - b^2\Sigma(x_i - \bar{x})^2 \tag{26-35}$$

This sum is useful for estimating the precision of the regression equation. The variance of the y's is the sum of the squares of the deviations divided by the number of degrees of freedom ($n - 2$, since two degrees of freedom corresponding to the two constants have been used up in finding the regression equation). Since the sum of squares of deviations was minimized, the best straight line corresponds to a *minimum variance* of vertical deviations—which justifies the method of least squares.

We may express the result as an analysis of variance, given in Table 26-11. The term "variance about regression" means that the deviations

TABLE 26-11. ANALYSIS OF VARIANCE OF REGRESSION

Source of variation	Sum of squares	Degrees of freedom	Variance
Due to regression	$b^2\Sigma(x_i - \bar{x})^2$	1	V_1
About regression	$\Sigma(y_i - \bar{y})^2 - b^2\Sigma(x_i - \bar{x})^2$	$n - 2$	V_2
Total	$\Sigma(y_i - \bar{y})^2$	$n - 1$	

of y are measured not from the mean (as in the usual definition of variance) but from the regression line. From the expression for Q_{min}, the total sum of squares of y is diminished by the amount $b^2\Sigma(x_i - \bar{x})^2$ when regression is taken into account.

In regression analysis, we can recognize two extreme cases. (1) If the sum of squares due to regression, $b^2\Sigma(x_i - \bar{x})^2$, were equal to the total sum of squares $\Sigma(y_i - \bar{y})^2$, the sum of squares about the regression would be zero, and all points would fall on the straight line. (2) The other extreme would be encountered if the sum of squares due to regression were zero, corresponding to $b = 0$, or a horizontal straight line passing through the mean value of y. In the first extreme, a perfect straight-line fit is observed; in the second, y is independent of x.

The F test can be applied to the variance ratio V_1/V_2. For a perfect straight line, V_1/V_2 is infinite; for no dependence of y on x, V_1/V_2 is zero.

A more useful test, which allows one to estimate the confidence interval of the slope, is the t test. It is important to realize that the quantities a and b in the regression line $y = a + bx$ are statistics that are estimates of the population parameters α and β. As the number of observations is increased without limit, the line

$$Y = \alpha + \beta X$$

is approached.

It can be shown[1] that, for a finite number of observations x_n, y_n, the

[1] Bennett, C. A., and Franklin, N. L., "Statistical Analysis in Chemistry and the Chemical Industry," p. 227, John Wiley & Sons, Inc., New York, 1954.

variance of b is given by

$$V_b = \frac{\sigma^2}{\Sigma(x_i - \bar{x})^2} \qquad (26\text{-}36)$$

where σ^2 is the population variance of y_i about a given x_i. Note that in simple linear regression it is implicitly assumed that the same variance σ^2 applies for all values of x.

Normally the population variance σ^2 is unknown, and it is therefore necessary to use the estimate s^2 from a finite number n of observations. This requires the introduction of the Student t, in a manner analogous to its use in testing a hypothesis concerning the mean of an unknown population.

The confidence interval for β is given by

$$\beta = b \pm \frac{ts}{\sqrt{\Sigma(x_i - \bar{x})^2}} \qquad (26\text{-}37)$$

where the value of t corresponds to $n - 2$ degrees of freedom and to the desired confidence level.

Before we consider the confidence level of the intercept α, it is well to recall that α simply represents the value of y corresponding to $x = 0$. This may not be a particularly important value of y; indeed it may not even correspond to physical reality, if x can never reach zero. Therefore, the confidence interval of α is best regarded as a special case of the confidence interval of Y.

Since the least-squares line is made to pass through the point $\bar{x}, \bar{y}$ and since the variance of x is negligible, the variance of $\bar{y}$ is given by V_2/n, where V_2 is the variance of a single measurement "about the regression" and $\bar{y}$ is the average of n measurements. The variance of y at any point x, y is the sum of two variances, namely, the variance of $\bar{y}$ and that of $b(x - \bar{x})$. The latter can be shown[1] to be equal to $V_2(x - \bar{x})^2/\Sigma(x_i - \bar{x})^2$. Thus,

$$s_y^2 = V_y = V_2 \left\{ \frac{1}{n} + \frac{(x - \bar{x})^2}{\Sigma(x_i - \bar{x})^2} \right\} \qquad (26\text{-}38)$$

The confidence interval for any desired value of y can be calculated from the t test,

$$Y = \alpha + \beta x = y \pm ts_y \qquad (26\text{-}39)$$

where t corresponds to $n - 2$ degrees of freedom and to the desired confidence level.

[1] *Ibid.*, p. 229.

Two special cases are of interest. The first is for $x = \bar{x}$; in this case $y = \bar{y}$, and Eq. (26-39) reduces to

$$\bar{Y} = \alpha + \beta\bar{x} = \bar{y} \pm t\sqrt{V_2/n} \qquad (26\text{-}40)$$

which gives the confidence interval of the mean in terms of the variance of the mean. The other special case is for $x = 0$; then $y = a$, and

$$\alpha = a \pm t\sqrt{V_2}\left\{\frac{1}{n} + \frac{\bar{x}^2}{\Sigma(x_i - \bar{x})^2}\right\}^{1/2} \qquad (26\text{-}41)$$

which gives the confidence interval of the intercept.

The interaction between the confidence limits for the slope and the intercept of a regression line is discussed by Mandel and Linnig.[1] If β and α represent the slope and intercept of the line of "best fit," then, for a given confidence level, say, 95 per cent, there exists, for each admissible slope b, a *range* of admissible intercept values a. It turns out that, if we imagine a coordinate plane of b versus a, these admissible values lie within an ellipse, with the point of best fit lying at the center. The ellipse is tilted with respect to the coordinate axes, because an increase in slope must be associated with a decrease in intercept. The use of such "joint-confidence ellipses" has been illustrated by Loscalzo and Benedetti-Pichler[2] in comparing two methods of titration of chloride. A detailed discussion of this method lies beyond the scope of the present treatment.

Example 26-5. To illustrate a control chart and regression analysis, consider the following set of replicate titration volumes arranged in the order in which the determinations were run: 41.41, 41.30, 41.59, 41.47, 41.53, 41.20, 41.33, 41.32, 41.51, 41.26, 41.58 ml. The mean is 41.41 ml; the standard deviation is 0.135 ml.

The upper control chart in Fig. 26-3 shows that the observations are in control and that they appear to show random fluctuations when plotted in sequence. It turns out, however, that the titrations were run at various pH values, which in sequence were 4.0, 3.0, 6.0, 4.5, 5.5, 2.0, 3.5, 3.2, 5.0, 2.5, and 5.7. When the observations are plotted as a function of pH, the lower control chart clearly shows a trend, which appears to be linear with pH. To show the significance of the trend, a regression analysis is carried out.

To simplify the numerical computations, the variables x and y were defined as follows:

$$x = 10 \text{ pH}$$
$$y = 100 \times (\text{titration volume} - 41 \text{ ml})$$

The mean values of x_i and y_i are

$$\bar{x}_i = \sum \frac{x_i}{n} = \frac{449}{11} = 40.82$$
$$\bar{y}_i = \sum \frac{y_i}{n} = \frac{450}{11} = 40.91$$

[1] Mandel, J., and Linnig, F. J., *Anal. Chem.*, **29**, 743 (1957).

[2] Loscalzo, A. G., and Benedetti-Pichler, A. A., *Anal. Chem.*, **30**, 2018 (1958).

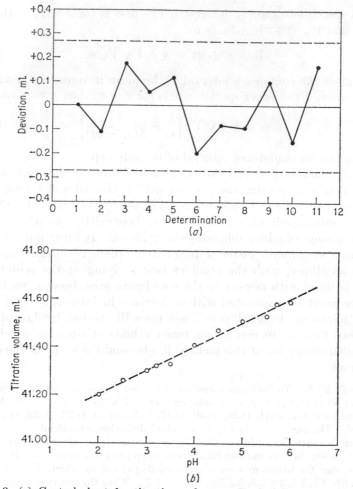

FIG. 26-3. (a) Control chart for titration volumes. Dashed lines are $\pm 2s$ limits. (b) Regression line for titration volumes. Dashed line is least-squares, best straight line.

To calculate the required sums of squares, the following short-cut formulas, analogous to Eqs. (26-9) and (26-10), were used:

$$\sum (x_i - \bar{x})(y_i - \bar{y}) = \sum x_i y_i - \frac{\Sigma x_i \Sigma y_i}{n}$$

$$= 20{,}195 - \frac{449 \times 450}{11} = 1{,}826.9$$

$$\sum (x_i - x)^2 = \sum x_i^2 - \frac{(\Sigma x_i)^2}{n}$$

$$= 20{,}173 - \frac{(449)^2}{11} = 1{,}845.6$$

$$\sum (y_i - \bar{y})^2 = \sum y_i^2 - \frac{(\Sigma y_i)^2}{n}$$

$$= 20,234 - \frac{(450)^2}{11} = 1,824.9$$

$$b = \frac{1,826.9}{1,845.6} = 0.9899$$

$$b^2 = 0.09798$$

$$a = \bar{y} - b\bar{x} = 40.91 - 0.9899 \times 40.82 = 0.50$$

The required least-squares line is

$$y = 0.50 + 0.9899x$$

or   Titration volume = $41.005 + 0.09899$ pH

The results are summarized in the analysis-of-variance table.

Source of variation	Sum of squares	Degrees of freedom	Variance
Due to regression	1,808.5	1	$V_1 = 1,808$
About regression	16.4	9	$V_2 = 1.8$
	1,824.9	10	–

To test for significance, the F value $V_1/V_2 = 1,000$ tells us that the regression is significant to a very high level of confidence, but it does not give us a measure of the confidence limits of the regression coefficient b.

Applying the t test, we have

$$s^2 = V_2 = 1.8$$

$t = 2.262$ at 95% confidence level, 9 degrees of freedom

and the confidence limits are given by

$$\beta = 0.9899 \pm 2.262 \sqrt{1.8/1,845.6} \qquad 95\% \text{ level}$$

$$= 0.990 \pm 0.072$$

The confidence limits of the intercept, calculated from Eq. (26-41), are

$$\alpha = 0.50 \pm 2.262 \sqrt{1.8} \left\{ \frac{1}{11} + \frac{(40.82)^2}{1,845.6} \right\}^{1/2}$$

or $\alpha = 0.50 \pm 3.0$

Note that, in the problem at hand, the intercept corresponds to pH = 0, which lies far beyond the experimental limits of pH and is, therefore, of little consequence.

A more significant set of limits here is the confidence interval of the mean,

$$\bar{Y} = 40.91 \pm 2.262 \sqrt{1.8/11}$$

or $\bar{Y} = 40.91 \pm 0.91$

Expressing the regression line by

$$y = \bar{y} + b(x - \bar{x})$$

and converting back to titration volume, we have

Titration volume = $(41.409 \pm 0.009) + (0.0990 \pm 0.0072)(\text{pH} - 4.08)$

with 95 per cent confidence that values will not by chance fall beyond the indicated limits.

It should be noted that the regression line should be interpreted with caution. In the first place, *its validity should not be inferred beyond the experimentally determined values of x.* For example, in the above instance of regression of titration volume with pH, the quantity a does not necessarily have physical reality at pH $= 0$, because no experiments were run at that value. Another example is a regression plot in which the theoretically expected relationship is $y = bx$, but the least-squares best straight line gives an intercept a at $x = 0$. The intercept may be wrongly interpreted as a "blank" value of y, when in fact it may merely have resulted from the fact that there is a finite uncertainty in the value of b for a limited set of data. Clearly, a value of y should actually be determined for $x = 0$.

Secondly, the quantity x does not necessarily *cause* the regression of y, for another factor z may vary in a regular way with x and may be the actual cause. For example, the rate of an air-oxidation reaction could vary with pH and be the actual cause of a regression of titration volume with pH. Again, the slope of a least-squares plot of absorbance against concentration is often interpreted directly as an extinction coefficient, whereas the slope may in fact be affected by a third variable, such as the slit width of a spectrophotometer.

Thirdly, the above regression analysis was carried out under the assumption that the absolute variance of y is independent of x. This may not be true. Actually a very important case in analytical chemistry is one in which the *relative* variance or coefficient of variation is independent of x. Thus, an instrument reading may be theoretically proportional to concentration with the same relative precision over a range of concentrations. This case can be handled in an analogous fashion.[1]

More complicated regression-analysis situations, such as linear regression with more than one independent variable and nonlinear regression, are encountered relatively infrequently in analytical chemistry and will not be considered here.

26-14. Statistical Design of Experiments.[2,3]

It has already been mentioned in connection with variance analysis that it is necessary to plan the experiments with statistical analysis in mind if maximum information is to be obtained from a given amount of experimental work.

Suppose that an experiment is to test the effect of n variables or *factors* at two values, which will be described as a low level and a high level. The factors are designated A, B, C, etc., and the levels A_0 and A_1, B_0

[1] Bennett and Franklin, *op. cit.*, p. 243.

[2] Youden, *op. cit.*, chaps. 8, 9, 10.

[3] Wilson, *op. cit.*, chap. 4.

and B_1, etc. To determine all the effects requires 2^n experiments, which can be set up according to a diagram, or *factorial design*.

Table 26-12 represents a factorial design for two factors at two levels. The entries in the tables represent the effects studied in each experiment,

TABLE 26-12. FACTORIAL DESIGN FOR TWO FACTORS AT TWO LEVELS

	A_0	A_1
B_0	(1)	a
B_1	b	ab

beginning with (1) as the low level of each factor. The entries a and b represent the separate effects of changing A alone and B alone; ab represents the *interaction* of A and B, or the combined effect of changing A and B.

An extension to three factors at two levels is shown in Table 26-13. The eight experiments represent three individual effects a, b, and c, three

TABLE 26-13. FACTORIAL DESIGN FOR THREE FACTORS AT TWO LEVELS

	A_0		A_1	
	B_0	B_1	B_0	B_1
C_0	(1)	b	a	ab
C_1	c	bc	ac	abc

interactions of two factors ab, ac, and bc, and one interaction of three factors abc.

An analysis-of-variance table for this design is shown in Table 26-14, together with a similar one for a design with four factors at two levels.

The numbers of degrees of freedom corresponding to increasing numbers of variable factors are 1, 2, 1 for a two-factor design, 1, 3, 3, 1 for

TABLE 26-14. ANALYSIS OF VARIANCE FOR FACTORIAL DESIGNS OF THREE FACTORS AND FOUR FACTORS AT TWO LEVELS

Source	Degrees of freedom	
	3 factors	4 factors
Effect of 1 factor	3	4
Effect of 2 factors	3	6
Effect of 3 factors	1	4
Effect of 4 factors	–	1
	7	15

a three-factor design and 1, 4, 6, 4, 1 for a four-factor design at two levels of each factor. These numbers correspond to the coefficients of a binomial expansion $(a + b)^n$.

As the number of factors increases, the number of experiments 2^n increases so rapidly that an excessive amount of experimental work may be involved to complete the entire factorial plan. Here the exercise of judgment on the part of the investigator may allow a considerable saving of effort with negligible loss of information. Let us say that five factors are judged to be of sufficient importance to merit testing at two levels. A complete factorial design requires $2^5 = 32$ experiments, with 1, 5, 10, 10, 5, 1 degrees of freedom associated respectively with 0, 1, 2, 3, 4, and 5 factors, varied simultaneously. These correspond to 5 *primary* effects due to a single variable, 10 *first-order* interactions, 10 *second-order* interactions, 5 *third-order* interactions and 1 *fourth-order* interaction. To the experimenter, the higher-order interactions become decreasingly important the greater the number of variables involved, and the corresponding experiments may be omitted. Usually, of the five variables, one or two may be considered *a priori* to have very little effect if any. This may be deduced from the primary effect. Accordingly, experiments corresponding to higher-order interactions may safely be omitted, because the likelihood of significance of a second- or higher-order interaction is even less than that of a primary interaction. In short, the higher-order interactions turn out to measure the basic error of the experimentation, and it is not necessary to make many estimates of this basic error. Such omission of selected interactions is known as *fractional replication*.

An excellent example of a complete factorial design of $2^4 = 16$ experiments, together with a discussion of the effect of half-replication, is given by Box.[1] It is important in fractional replication that the proper experiments be omitted, for one incorrect omission can lead to a situation in which there is no estimate for the effect of one factor and unnecessary estimates of higher-order interactions. If there is doubt about whether the primary effect of a specific variable is high enough to merit inclusion of its interactions, this variable can be tested early in the sequence of experiments, and the planned design can be altered accordingly. For an elementary discussion, see chap. 10 of Youden's book.[2]

A word of caution should be interjected in connection with the order in which statistically designed experiments should be run. With an ordered array of experimental variables such as that displayed in a factorial design, it is tempting to set up a systematic order of experimentation to ensure the completion of the design. Such a procedure may lead to incorrect conclusions if some unsuspected variable is exerting an effect. For example, suppose that an analyst has set up a factorial design to

[1] Box, G. E. P., *Analyst*, **77**, 879 (1952).

[2] Youden, *op. cit.*

test the effects of two variables, say, the temperature and acid concentration in a titration. Each titration is to be run in triplicate. Now, suppose that, for the sake of convenience, each set of replicates is run together and that a gradual change is occurring in the normality of the reagent. The replicates might show satisfactory agreement, being run in close succession, and a later set run, say, at a higher temperature might agree internally but differ significantly from the first set. It might then be falsely concluded that the effect was due to a temperature change. If the order of running the individual titrations had been randomized, divergence among supposed replicates would have revealed the presence of an unsuspected error.

Wernimont[1] has published an interesting example of a "nested design," which is an example of fractional replication. It was desired to evaluate an interlaboratory study of a method of acetyl determination. Results obtained by two analysts in each of eight laboratories were compared by having each analyst perform two tests on each of three days. The design is

		Laboratories				
		1	2	3	4	etc.
Analysts	1	2 1	2	etc.		
Days	1 2	3 1	2 3	etc.		
Tests	1 2 1 2	etc.				

The results indicated a greater variance among laboratories than between two analysts within a laboratory or between tests run by the same analyst on the same day or different days.

Another form of fractional replication that is often applicable is the *latin square*. Suppose that three factors are to be considered at four levels. We may be interested, for example, in a comparison of results obtained in four laboratories on four samples by four methods of analysis. A complete factorial design would require 4^3 or 64 observations. By distributing the four samples to each of the laboratories, we could set up the following design in which the samples are denoted by A, B, C, and D:

Method \ Lab	L_1	L_2	L_3	L_4
M_1	A	D	C	B
M_2	C	B	A	D
M_3	D	C	B	A
M_4	B	A	D	C

[1] Wernimont, G., *Anal. Chem.*, **23**, 1572 (1951).

The arrangement shown above is one of 576 possible ways of arranging the samples so that each column and each row contains all the samples. The actual pattern to be used should be selected at random. Since only 16 of the possible 64 experiments are included, this design corresponds to a *quarter-replication*.

The analysis-of-variance table indicates how the total sums of squares of deviations can be divided into four groups, the *residual* sources being an estimate of the error against which the assigned sources are tested by the F test. Thus the variances arising from differences in methods or laboratories may be tested for statistical significance.

TABLE 26-15. ANALYSIS OF VARIANCE FOR LATIN-SQUARE DESIGN

From square	Source of variation	Degrees of freedom
Rows	Between methods	3
Columns	Between laboratories	3
Letters	Between samples	3
	Residual	6
	Total	15

If we compare Table 26-15 with the last column of Table 26-14, we have an interesting comparison between two designs, both involving 16 experiments. The 2^4 factorial design permits a single estimate of the effect of each of four variables and of six interactions between two variables. The other five degrees of freedom may be regarded as error estimates. The latin-square design permits three estimates of the effects of each of three variables, and allows six error estimates.

26-15. Rejection of Observations

A question that often arises is the statistical justification for rejection of a divergent observation. The question is not a serious one if enough data are at hand to establish a reasonably valid estimate of the standard deviation. In the first place, the t test is available as a criterion, and in any event the effect of a single divergent result on the mean value is relatively small.

For small groups of three to eight replicates, however, the question is a more difficult one; it has been discussed, for example, by Blaedel, Meloche, and Ramsay.[1] The so-called "2.5*d*" (or "4*d*") rule states that an observation may be rejected if its deviation from the mean of the remaining observations exceeds 2.5 times (or 4 times) the average deviation of the remaining observations from their mean. This rule is based on the fact that, for an *infinite, normally distributed population*, the average deviation is 0.8 times the standard deviation, so that 2.5*d*

[1] Blaedel, W. J., Meloche, V. W., and Ramsay, J. A., *J. Chem. Educ.*, **28**, 643 (1951).

corresponds to about 3σ. For small numbers of replicates (three to eight) a bias is introduced in omitting the questionable value, and the average deviation is not a reliable estimate of standard deviation. The result is that both the $2.5d$ rule and the $4d$ rule lead to rejection of valid measurements (error of the first kind) much too frequently for the test to be useful.

This difficulty is avoided by the Q test,[1] which is relatively critical and which is statistically sound. Q is defined as the ratio of the divergence of the discordant value from its nearest neighbor to the range of the values. If the value of Q exceeds certain tabular values, which depend upon the number of observations, the questionable value may be rejected. The tabular values of Q correspond to a 90 per cent confidence limit that error of the first kind has been avoided. However, for small numbers of observations, say, three to five, the Q test allows rejection only of grossly divergent values. It therefore increases the probability of an error of the second kind, the retention of an erroneous result. Dean and Dixon have suggested the use of the median rather than the mean when the divergent result cannot be rejected with confidence. The median, of course, is a biased estimate, and on the average it is farther from the true value than the mean of all the observations.

The only valid justification for rejection of one reasonably divergent observation from a group of three or four appears to be the location of an assignable cause of determinate error. For groups of five or more, the omission of *both* the highest and the lowest value is preferred by some to the omission of any one observation.[2] From what has been said, it is dangerous practice to reject an intuitively doubtful observation, and it is best to repeat the determination until a statistically valid basis for retention or rejection is obtained. Otherwise the doubtful value should be retained.

PROBLEMS

26-1. The following values were observed for the normality of a particular solution of potassium permanganate using pure potassium iodide and arsenious oxide as primary standards:

Normality vs. KI	Normality vs. As_2O_3
0.44109	0.44118
0.44125	0.44122
0.44107	0.44127
0.44128	0.44117
0.44119	0.44124
0.44112	

[1] Dean, R. B., and Dixon, W. J., *Anal. Chem.*, **23**, 636 (1951).
[2] Wilson, *op. cit.*, p. 257.

Calculate the standard deviation of each set of standardizations. Is either method significantly more precise? Are the normality values obtained by the two methods significantly different? *Ans.*

$$s_1 = 0.000087 \qquad s_2 = 0.000042$$

$$\frac{s_1^2}{s_2^2} = 4.36 \qquad \text{significant at 95 per cent level}$$

Since $s_1^2 \neq s_2^2$, the t test [Eq. (26-21)] cannot be applied directly.[1] However, even for $s^2 = s_2^2 = 17.3 \times 10^{-10}$ (the smaller variance), the t calculated from Eq. (26-21) is only 1.96, which indicates that no significant difference exists between the means (0.44117 and 0.44122).

26-2. Suppose that the following numbers denote the relative frequency of occurrence of each of the digits in the last significant figure of an instrument reading:

Digit	Frequency	Digit	Frequency
0	324	5	308
1	267	6	313
2	292	7	284
3	264	8	311
4	319	9	268

Estimate the probability that this distribution could have occurred by chance. *Ans.* $\chi^2 = 16.2$, which, for nine degrees of freedom, would be exceeded about 5 per cent of the time.

Is the excess of even over odd digits significant? *Ans.* $\chi^2 = 9.57$, which is highly significant. For one degree of freedom, $\chi^2 = 7.88$ at the 0.5 per cent level.

26-3. Each of four analysts A, B, C, D carried out replicate sets of four determinations, with the following results:

Determination \ Analyst	A	B	C	D
1	20.13	20.14	20.19	20.19
2	20.16	20.12	20.11	20.15
3	20.09	20.04	20.12	20.16
4	20.14	20.06	20.15	20.10

Carry out an analysis of variance to determine whether the variance between analysts is significantly higher than that between determinations by a single analyst. *Ans.* Sum of squares "between analysts" = 0.0085, "within analysts" = 0.0175, $V_i = 0.00283$, $V_{j(i)} = 0.00146$. F is insignificant.

[1] See Bennett and Franklin, *op. cit.*, p. 177.

26-4. The following values were recorded for the potential E of an electrode, measured against the saturated calomel electrode, as a function of concentration C (moles liter^{-1}).

$-\log C$	E, mv	$-\log C$	E, mv
1.00	106	2.10	174
1.10	115	2.20	182
1.20	121	2.40	187
1.50	139	2.70	211
1.70	153	2.90	220
1.90	158	3.00	226

Fit the best straight line to these data, and express the result in terms of confidence intervals for the slope and intercept. Calculate the confidence interval for E at the average experimental value of $\log C$. *Ans.*

$$E = (49.6 \pm 5.1) - (58.95 \pm 2.43) \log C$$
$$\bar{E} = 166.0 \pm 1.6 \text{ mv} \qquad \text{at} - \log C = 1.975$$

26-5. The following represent control-analysis data on successive production batches: 11.7, 10.9, 11.3, 11.5, 11.1, 11.3, 10.8, 11.5, 11.2, 10.7, 11.2, 10.8, 11.3, 10.4, 10.9, 10.6, 10.7.

Prepare a control chart, using 95 per cent confidence limits based on the data at hand. Perform a regression analysis to determine whether the apparent downward trend is statistically significant. Derive the least-squares relationship between the ordinal number i of the sequence and the analytical result P. *Ans.* $P = (11.05 \pm 0.15) - (0.046 \pm 0.030)(i - 9)$, 95 per cent confidence level.

BIBLIOGRAPHY

Elementary Mathematical Statistics

Dixon, W. J., and Massey, F. J., Jr., "Introduction to Statistical Analysis," 2d ed., McGraw-Hill Book Company, Inc., New York, 1957.

Peters, C., and Van Voorhis, W. R., "Statistical Procedures and Their Mathematical Bases," McGraw-Hill Book Company, Inc., New York, 1940.

Wilks, S. S., "Elementary Statistical Analysis," Princeton University Press, Princeton, N.J., 1948.

Evaluation of Scientific Data (General)

Davies, O. L., "Statistical Methods in Research and Production," 3d ed., Oliver & Boyd, Ltd., Edinburgh and London, 1947.

Snedecor, G. W., "Statistical Methods Applied to Experiments in Agriculture and Biology," Iowa State College Press, Ames, Iowa, 1950.

Wilson, E. B., Jr., "An Introduction to Scientific Research," McGraw-Hill Book Company, Inc., New York, 1952.

Worthing, A. G., "Treatment of Experimental Data," John Wiley & Sons, Inc., New York, 1943.

Evaluation of Chemical Data

Bennett, C. A., and Franklin, N. L., "Statistical Analysis in Chemistry and the Chemical Industry," John Wiley & Sons, Inc., New York, 1954.

Gore, W. L., "Statistical Methods for Chemical Experimentation," Interscience Publishers, Inc., New York, 1952.

Youden, W. J., "Statistical Methods for Chemists," John Wiley & Sons, Inc., New York, 1951.

Design of Experiments

Fisher, R. A., "The Design of Experiments," 5th ed., Oliver & Boyd, Ltd., Edinburgh and London, 1949.

Federer, W. T., "Experimental Design," The Macmillan Company, New York, 1955.

Control Charts

Shewhart, W. A., "Economic Control of Quality of Manufactured Product," D. Van Nostrand, Company, Inc., Princeton, N.J., 1931.

Grant, E. L., "Statistical Quality Control," 2d ed., McGraw-Hill Book Company, Inc., New York, 1952.

27. Sampling

To the statistician, the process of sampling consists of drawing from a population a finite number of individuals to be examined. From sample statistics, such as mean and standard deviation, estimates are made of the population parameters. By appropriate tests of significance, confidence limits are placed on the estimates thus made. Sampling for chemical analysis is an example of statistical sampling in that conclusions are drawn about the composition of a much larger bulk of material from an analysis of a limited laboratory sample.

The process of sampling may involve an elaborate array of operations, such as crushing, grinding, subdivision, etc. Each operation makes a contribution to the variance of the analytical scheme. It is important to understand the basic principles underlying the sampling process in order that the accuracy of the sampling operation as well as that of the laboratory analysis can be made appropriate to the problem at hand. Otherwise too much or too little effort may be expended on the sampling operation, thereby either increasing the cost unnecessarily or failing to achieve the desired level of accuracy.

27-1. Statistical Criteria of Good Sampling

A sampling scheme is set up with several objectives in mind. These objectives can be stated in statistical terms as follows:

1. The sample mean should provide an unbiased[1] estimate of the population mean. This objective will be achieved only if all members of the population have an equal chance of being drawn into the sample.

2. The sample should provide an unbiased estimate of the population variance, in order that tests of significance may be applied.[2] This

---

[1] Cf. footnote*, Sec. 26-5, p. 544.
[2] Snedecor, G. W., "Statistical Methods," 4th ed., p. 455, Iowa State College Press, Ames, Iowa.

objective will be reached only if *every possible* sample of a given preselected size has an equal chance of being drawn.

These considerations may be illustrated by considering a population consisting of packages of a chemical coming along a conveyor belt. Each package has an equal chance of being drawn into the sample if the packages are chosen in a *random* fashion, as with the aid of a table of random numbers. Even if samples are chosen at regular intervals, a random choice of the first unit to be chosen fulfills the requirement of equal chance. Suppose, for example, that every tenth package is taken in regular sequence. If the first to be chosen was picked by the first appearance of a particular digit in a column of random numbers, each package was given a probability of 0.1 of appearing in the sample. However, this procedure could produce only ten *different* samples of a given size out of a great many possible samples; therefore, the second objective listed above would not be fulfilled. On the other hand, if the entire sample had been picked according to the column of random numbers, every possible one-in-ten sample would have had an equal probability of occurring.

3. A third objective may be stated in terms of efficiency. For a given expenditure of money or time, the sampling procedure should lead to estimates of the mean and variance that are as accurate as possible. Alternatively, the cost or effort of sampling should be minimized for a given accuracy. To accomplish this objective, it is often necessary to resort to a nonrandom sampling procedure, at least in part. If the population can be divided by a random procedure into a number of subdivisions or sections and if the variance between sections is large compared with the variance within sections, then it turns out that a more accurate result will on the average be obtained by using an organized sampling procedure than by using a completely randomized procedure to draw the same number of samples. Such a *stratified* procedure involves a risk of bias that cannot be estimated by the usual tests of significance; for these tests are based on probability theory, which in turn is based on the assumption of random selection. Randomness has been violated to some extent by the use of an orderly procedure. The risk can be minimized by making the procedure as truly representative as possible.

27-2. Sampling Units

It is useful to distinguish between type A material, like piles of coal or ore, that contains no unique subdivisions, and type B materials, occurring in discrete lots that can be specified as sampling units.[1] Type A materials present a special problem, for it is not possible to specify a routine procedure that will ensure a properly unbiased sample.

[1] Tanner, L., and Deming, W. E., *Am. Soc. Testing Materials Proc.*, **49**, 1181 (1949).

To illustrate the problem, consider a conical pile of coal produced by unloading freight cars by means of a conveyor belt. Such a pile has been subject to segregation because larger chunks have tended to roll down the sides of the cone, fine dust has tended to be blown by the wind, and small particulate matter has tended to settle under the source. Once the pile has been formed, it is well nigh impossible to specify a representative sampling procedure that does not involve subdividing the entire pile. On the other hand, if the coal had been sampled directly from the freight cars, it could have been regarded as type B material. Owing to segregation during transportation, it would then have been necessary to sample carefully *within* each freight car. (The question of the optimum number of freight cars to be selected at random, as compared with the number of samples to be taken within each car, will be considered in Sec. 27-6, under Stratified Sampling.) Better yet, the coal could have been sampled directly from the conveyor belt, where sections taken across the belt could be regarded as sampling units.

The problem of sampling from a moving stream, such as a conveyor belt or pipe line, is not quite so simple as it might at first appear. A segment across the moving stream is not a representative sample unless the entire cross section of the stream is moving at a uniform velocity. The proper sampling unit, therefore, is not necessarily that which is present at any one instant in a cross-sectional segment of stream but rather that which passes a given cross-sectional plane in a given interval of time. Often, if it is not practical to take the total effluent for a selected time interval as a sample, it is possible to design a moving orifice that can sample a cross-sectional plane.

27-3. Random and Regular Sampling

A *random* sampling procedure is one in which each portion of the whole is given an equal chance of appearing in the sample according to a procedure based completely upon chance and involving no periodicity or exercise of judgment.

In practice, a truly randomized selection procedure is seldom used in sampling a sequential series. Instead, it is common practice to take samples at regular intervals. The danger, of course, always exists that a cyclic variation of quality could fall into phase with the sampling operation, thereby leading to a biased sample. Such bias, however, would occur only if the time interval for the quality fluctuation happened to be comparable to the interval of the sampling sequence.[1] If the fluctuations are completely random, i.e., if the composition is "in control" in the sense of the quality-control chart, or if the period of fluctua-

[1] Davies, O. L., "Statistical Methods in Research and Production," 3d ed., p. 329, Oliver & Boyd, Ltd., Edinburgh and London, 1957.

tions is short compared with the sampling cycle, a systematic sampling procedure gives, in effect, a random sample. At the other extreme, if the fluctuation cycle is slow compared with the sampling period, the uniform sampling procedure is analogous to graphic integration to find the area under a curve. If the total area is divided into *uniform* strips, the heights of which are measured at their centers, the integration is more accurate than if strips of random widths were used. Likewise, a uniform sampling procedure, if frequent enough, would give the average composition more accurately than a random procedure. To avoid the possible coincidence of sampling and fluctuation cycles, it is advisable occasionally to change the sampling frequency.

27-4. Precision of Random Sampling of Uniform Units

It is of interest to compare several procedures for the analysis of a material composed of essentially uniform sampling units, e.g., headache tablets or bottles of peroxide, that can be sampled as such in a random fashion.

1. Each unit is analyzed separately, and the results are averaged. The analytical method has a standard deviation σ_1, estimated by s_1, for a single determination. To the variance s_1^2 must be added s_2^2, an estimate of the variance σ_2^2 due to differences among the units. If n such units are analyzed, the variance estimate of the mean is $(s_1^2 + s_2^2)/n$.

2. The n units are thoroughly mixed and divided into n parts before analysis. The process of mixing averages the composition, thus changing the variance σ_2^2 to σ_2^2/n per unit. Now, if only one unit is analyzed, the variance estimate is $s_1^2 + s_2^2/n$. If n analyses are carried out, the variance estimate of the mean is $s_1^2/n + s_2^2/n^2$, which of course is smaller than $(s_1^2 + s_2^2)/n$. Therefore, *a more precise result is obtained by mixing the units and performing n analyses on the mixture than by analyzing the n units separately and averaging the result.*

3. The pooled mixture is analyzed by a method in which the standard deviation is proportional to the magnitude being determined. This corresponds to a constant relative precision, a situation frequently encountered in chemical analysis. The standard deviation of determination for the whole sample is ns_1, or s_1 per unit. Alternatively, the variance of a determination for the whole sample is $n^2 s_1^2$; and, since the variance is proportional to the *square* of the sample size, the variance per unit is s_1^2. The total variance estimate is $s_1^2 + s_2^2/n$, which is the same as above, indicating that *the over-all precision is independent of sample size in a pooled sample when a method of constant relative precision is used.*

4. A single determination is carried out on the whole mixture by a method in which *the standard deviation is independent of the magnitude being determined.* The standard deviation s_1 for the whole sample

corresponds to a standard deviation of s_1/n per unit and to a variance of only s_1^2/n^2 per unit. The total variance estimate is $s_1^2/n^2 + s_2^2/n$, which is less than $(s_1^2 + s_2^2)/n$. This situation might occur, for example, in a trace analysis, in which the absolute rather than the relative error is essentially independent of sample size. *In this case, a single determination on the combined sample will give a more accurate result than the average of n separate unit analyses.*

Example 27-1. A random sample of ten pills is taken for analysis. Each pill contains 5 mg of active material, distributed normally with a standard deviation estimate of 0.1 mg. A single determination of active ingredient has a *relative* standard deviation estimate of 1 per cent of the amount present. Compare the standard deviations of the following analytical schemes:

  a. Analyze each pill separately, report mean of the ten determinations.

  b. Pool the sample, and run a single determination on one-tenth of the pooled sample.

  c. Same as scheme *b*, except report the mean of three determinations.

  d. Pool the sample, and run a single determination on the entire sample.

  Answer. We have $s_1 = 0.01x$, where $x =$ active ingredient, mg, and $s_2 = 0.1$ mg.

(a) $\qquad s^2 = \dfrac{s_1^2 + s_2^2}{n} = \dfrac{(0.05)^2 + (0.1)^2}{10} = 0.00125 \qquad s = 0.035$ mg

(b) $\qquad s^2 = s_1^2 + \dfrac{s_2^2}{n} = (0.05)^2 + \dfrac{(0.1)^2}{10} = 0.0035 \qquad s = 0.06$ mg

(c) $\qquad s^2 = \dfrac{s_1^2}{3} + \dfrac{s_2^2}{3n} = \dfrac{0.0035}{3} = 0.00117 \qquad\qquad s = 0.034$ mg

(d) $\qquad s^2 = \dfrac{s_1^2}{n^2} + \dfrac{s_2^2}{n} = \dfrac{(0.5)^2}{100} + \dfrac{(0.1)^2}{10} = 0.0035 \qquad s = 0.06$ mg

27-5. Estimation of Required Sample Size of Particulate Material

For solid particulate matter, it is qualitatively obvious that the necessary weight of sample taken at random from a bulk must be increased in relation to each of the following factors: (1) increase in variation of composition among the particles, (2) increase in the desired accuracy of analysis, and (3) increase in the particle size. For the general case of a complex mixture of several components, each containing the desired constituent at a different level and each existing in a wide range of particle sizes, a calculation of the minimum size of sample necessary to achieve a desired sampling accuracy would require so much preliminary data as to be entirely impracticable. However, the order of magnitude of sample size can readily be estimated by a procedure given by Baule and Benedetti-Pichler.[1,2]

The basis of the estimation is the Bernoulli equation (see Sec. 26-4)

[1] Baule, B., and Benedetti-Pichler, A. A., *Z. anal. Chem.* **74,** 442 (1928).

[2] Benedetti-Pichler, A. A., in Berl, W. M. (ed.), "Physical Methods in Chemical Analysis," vol. 3, p. 183, Academic Press, Inc., New York, 1956.

applied to the sampling of a binary population. If the population consists of N_1 units of A and N_2 units of B, the probability of drawing a unit of type A is given by $p = N_1/(N_1 + N_2)$ and the probability of drawing a unit of type B is $q = N_2/(N_1 + N_2)$. Now, if a series of samples of n units are drawn at random, the number of A units will fluctuate around the most probable value pn with a standard deviation given by

$$\sigma_n = \sqrt{npq} = \sqrt{np(1 - p)} \qquad (27\text{-}1)$$

Similarly, the number of B units will fluctuate around its most probable value qn with the same variance.

The *relative* standard deviation of the units of type A is given by

$$\frac{\sigma_n}{n_1} = \frac{\sigma_n}{pn} = \sqrt{\frac{1 - p}{pn}} \qquad (27\text{-}1a)$$

The corresponding relative standard deviation of the type B units is

$$\frac{\sigma_n}{n_2} = \frac{\sigma_n}{qn} = \sqrt{\frac{p}{(1 - p)n}} \qquad (27\text{-}1b)$$

where $n_1 = pn =$ number of A units drawn into the sample

$\qquad n_2 = qn =$ number of B units drawn into the sample

Let P represent the average percentage of the component x to be determined in the population, which is assumed to consist of uniform particles of two types A and B in the ratio $p/(1 - p)$. The A particles have density d_1 and contain P_1 per cent of the component; the B particles have density d_2 and contain P_2 per cent. The average density is d, and all particles have the same volume. It can be shown[1] that an error Δn_1 in the number of units of A contained in a sample of n units causes an error ΔP in the percentage of x, where ΔP is given by

$$\Delta P = \frac{\Delta n_1}{n} \frac{d_1 d_2}{d^2} (P_1 - P_2) \qquad (27\text{-}2)$$

If σ from Eq. (27-1) is substituted for Δn_1 in Eq. (27-2), the absolute standard deviation of P becomes

$$\sigma_P = \frac{d_1 d_2}{d^2} (P_1 - P_2) \sqrt{\frac{p(1 - p)}{n}} \qquad (27\text{-}3)$$

Solving for n, the number of particles required in the sample is given by

$$n = p(1 - p) \left(\frac{d_1 d_2}{d^2}\right)^2 \left(\frac{P_1 - P_2}{\sigma_P}\right)^2 \qquad (27\text{-}4)$$

[1] *Ibid.*

The number of particles must be increased in proportion to the reciprocal of the variance $1/\sigma_P^2$ that is desired and in proportion to $(P_1 - P_2)^2$, the square of the difference in percentage of desired constituent in particles A and B. The quantity $p(1 - p)$ reaches a maximum when $p = 0.5$; therefore, the number of sample particles reaches a maximum when equal numbers of A and B are present. The quantity d_1d_2/d^2 is unity when $d_1 = d_2$; but, since the average density d depends on the ratio $p/(1 - p)$, this factor increases most rapidly when both the densities and the proportions of A and B are disparate. Thus the factors $p(1 - p)$ and d_1d_2/d^2 tend somewhat to compensate for each other.

Example 27-2. A sample is composed of uniform particles of a mineral of density $d_1 = 5.2$ and gangue of density $d_2 = 2.7$. The percentage P_1 of metal in the mineral is 75; in the gangue the percentage $P_2 = 5$. If the sample contains $P = 60$ per cent metal, how many particles must be taken to ensure a standard deviation of less than 1 part per thousand in P, due to sampling error?

Answer. The fraction p of mineral particles is calculated from the following relationship, which is readily derived: $p/(1 - p) = d_2(P - P_2)/d_1(P_1 - P) = 1.903$, from which $p = 0.656$. The average density is given by $pd_1 + (1 - p)d_2 = 4.34$. $\sigma_P = 0.001 \times 60 = 0.06$, and n calculated from Eq. (27-4) is 1.7×10^5 particles. For spherical particles this corresponds to a sample weight of 1.23 g for particles of 0.01 cm diameter, or 1,230 g for particles of 0.1 cm diameter.

The above method of estimating sample size has been idealized in two ways. First, it has been assumed that only two components A and B exist in the sample. If more than two components are present, it is usually a simple matter to compute the necessary characteristics of an equivalent sample of just two components, chosen to give one fraction rich in the desired constituent and one fraction poor in it.[1,2]

The second simplification was in assuming that all particles were the same size. This leads to a more serious difficulty, because rarely is detailed information available about the particle-size distribution of a sample. It is apparent that, if the above calculation were carried out with the assumption that all particles were spheres of diameter equal to the mesh spacing of a screen that would pass all of the sample, the calculated sample size would be greater than that actually required. Benedetti-Pichler has shown by calculation[1,3] that the standard deviation will remain between 0.5 and 1.5 times that computed for uniform particles if any or all of the particles have volumes between 0.25 and 2.25 times as large as those assumed in the calculation. Within the same precision limits, up to 75 per cent of the particles can be smaller without size limit,

---

[1] *Ibid.*

[2] Benedetti-Pichler, "Essentials of Quantitative Analysis," The Ronald Press Company, New York, 1956.

[3] Benedetti-Pichler, in Berl, *op. cit.*

but only 18 per cent by weight can be twice the normal diameter, or 8 times the normal weight. Thus the most important consideration is to avoid abnormally large particles; or, to be on the safe side, one can base the calculation on the largest particles.

27-6. Stratified Sampling versus Completely Random Sampling

When the material to be sampled can be subdivided into logical sampling units, there are two fundamentally different approaches to random sampling. First, one can simply choose at random from the whole bulk of material a number of samples to be analyzed. Alternatively, the sampling can be stratified by first choosing from among the sampling units and then sampling within the units, again by a random procedure. It will be shown below that the stratified procedure will always yield results at least as precise as the simple random scheme and will give superior results whenever the variance between sampling units is appreciable compared with the variance within such units.

Statistically, this situation is described by stating that, if the whole population to be sampled is homogeneous, i.e., such that it can be described by a single set of parameters, a simple random sampling is as efficient as stratified sampling. On the other hand, if the population cannot be described by a single set of parameters but consists of a set of subpopulations that are appreciably different, then the stratified procedure consists in sampling the subpopulations to estimate their parameters and combining these estimates to obtain an estimate of the whole.

If the subpopulations or strata are unequal in size and in variance, it can be shown[1,2] that, to obtain an unbiased estimate of the population mean and to minimize the variance of the estimate, the number of samples taken from each stratum should be proportional to the size of the stratum and also to its standard deviation, or

$$\frac{n_r}{n} = \frac{w_r(\sigma_0)_r}{\Sigma w_r(\sigma_0)_r} \tag{27-5}$$

where n_r = number of samples from rth stratum
n = total number of samples desired
w_r = weight of stratum
$(\sigma_0)_r$ = standard deviation within rth stratum

It is intuitively clear that, in calculating the population mean, the stratum means must be weighted in proportion to the size of the strata,

---

[1] Neyman, J., *J. Roy. Statist. Soc.*, **97**, 558 (1934).

[2] Bennett, C. A., and Franklin, N. L., "Statistical Analysis in Chemistry and the Chemical Industry," pp. 61–63, 482–484, John Wiley & Sons, Inc., New York, 1954.

in order that the estimate of the population mean may be unbiased. Thus,

$$\bar{x} = \frac{\Sigma w_r \bar{x}_r}{\Sigma w_r} \qquad (27\text{-}6)$$

where $\bar{x}_r$ = mean of determined values in rth stratum
$\bar{x}$ = estimate of population mean
If the strata differ only in size but not in variance, σ_r is the same for all strata, and Eq. (27-5) becomes

$$\frac{n_r}{n} = \frac{w_r}{\Sigma w_r} \qquad (27\text{-}7)$$

which simply means that the numbers of samples within strata should be proportional to the sizes of the strata. This procedure is commonly called *representative sampling;* it gives an unbiased estimate of the population mean but leads to a larger variance of the estimate than the procedure represented by Eqs. (27-5) and (27-6) *unless the variance is uniform in all the strata.*

Example 27-3. A shipment of oil consists of equal numbers of 1-quart containers and 5-quart containers. A previous study has led to the expectation that the sulfur content of the 1-quart containers is 10 ppm with a standard deviation of 2 ppm and that of the 5-quart containers 15 ppm with a standard deviation of 3 ppm. If the analytical error is negligible, what is the optimum sampling scheme for a total of 24 samples to give an unbiased estimate of the sulfur content of the shipment, with a minimum of sampling error?

Answer. The two strata are the two sizes of containers, with $w_1 = 1$, $w_2 = 5$. The number of samples n_1 to be taken from the 1-quart containers is given by $n_1 = (n_1 + n_2)(2w_1)/(2w_1 + 3w_2)$, from which $n_1 = 3$, $n_2 = 21$. If the difference in the stratum variance had been neglected, the simple representative sampling scheme would have called for $n_1 = 24w_1/(w_1 + w_2) = 4$ and $n_2 = 20$. In either case the weighted average $\bar{x} = (1x_1 + 5x_2)/6$, where x_1 and x_2 are the average values from the two strata would give the sulfur content of the shipment.

A simpler case, but one frequently encountered in analytical chemistry, is that in which the strata are equal in size. In order to judge the effect of stratification, suppose that a variance-analysis study has been carried out. If there are k strata containing n observations in each, the analysis-of-variance table will be identical with Table 26-9, Sec. 26-11.

Let σ_0 and σ_i be the standard deviations of a single determination within strata and between strata, respectively. To calculate the variance of the mean of kn determinations, we recall that the mean is calculated by Eq. (27-6), which, for equal strata, is simply

$$\bar{x} = \frac{\Sigma \bar{x}_i}{k} \qquad (27\text{-}8)$$

The variance of $\bar{x}$ is $1/k^2$ times the variance of $\bar{x}_i$ (see Table 26-2, Sec. 26-6); so

$$V_{\bar{x}} = \frac{1}{k^2} V_{\bar{x}_i} = \frac{1}{k^2} \frac{\sigma_0^2}{n^2} = \frac{\sigma_0^2}{N^2} \qquad (27\text{-}9)$$

where $N = nk =$ total number of determinations.

It is important that the *variance of the mean is independent of the variance between strata* and depends only on the variance within strata and on the number of determinations.

Now suppose that the same number of samples had been drawn at random from the population as a whole. The variance of a single determination would be $\sigma_0^2 + \sigma_i^2$, and the variance of the mean of N determinations would be $(\sigma_0^2 + \sigma_i^2)/N$. This formula would be identical with Eq. (27-9) if the variance between sections were equal to zero.

Therefore, the stratified procedure must yield a result at least as good as the completely random procedure, and *will yield a superior result if the variance between strata is appreciable compared with the variance within strata.* The only qualification that must be made is that the *relative sizes* of the strata must be known. If there should be an appreciable error in sizes, the resulting bias in the estimate of the mean might more than compensate for the advantage in precision gained by stratification and, what is worse, introduce an unsuspected systematic error.

27-7. Minimization of Cost or Variance in Stratified Sampling

Suppose that the bulk of material to be analyzed is sampled by taking n_1 strata, each of which provides n_2 samples, and that n_3 determinations are to be carried out on each sample. The various strata are assumed to be equal in size and in variance within strata.

A practical question that arises is how to minimize the cost of determining an estimate of the population mean to within a desired variance. Alternatively, it may be desired to minimize the variance for a given allocation of funds, taking into account the relative costs of selecting the strata (c_1), sampling within the strata (c_2), and performing a determination (c_3).

The total cost of the procedure is

$$c = n_1 c_1 + n_1 n_2 c_2 + n_1 n_2 n_3 c_3 \qquad (27\text{-}10)$$

We suppose that an analysis of variance has been carried out and that the quantities s_1^2, s_2^2, and s_3^2 have been determined as estimates of the variance components σ_1^2, σ_2^2, and σ_3^2 for the two stages of sampling and the determination. These components contribute to the variance of the population mean that is being estimated. Thus,

$$\sigma^2 = \frac{\sigma_1^2}{n_1} + \frac{\sigma_2^2}{n_1 n_2} + \frac{\sigma_3^2}{n_1 n_2 n_3} \tag{27-11}$$

It can be shown[1] that, to minimize the cost c for a fixed value of σ^2, the values of n_1, n_2, and n_3 are given by

$$n_1 = \frac{\sqrt{\sigma_1^2/c_1}}{\sigma^2} \left(\sqrt{\sigma_1^2 c_1} + \sqrt{\sigma_2^2 c_2} + \sqrt{\sigma_3^2 c_3} \right) \tag{27-12}$$

$$n_2 = \sqrt{\sigma_2^2 c_1 / \sigma_1^2 c_2} \tag{27-13}$$

$$n_3 = \sqrt{\sigma_3^2 c_2 / \sigma_2^2 c_3} \tag{27-14}$$

The significant result is that *the optimum allocation of sampling after the first stage is independent of the desired over-all variance σ^2.* In other words, for different values of σ^2, the modification of the optimum sampling scheme consists of changing the number of strata n_1 sampled while maintaining constant the treatment of the various sections.

In a similar way, if the total cost c is fixed, it can be shown[2] that the optimum values of n_1, n_2, and n_3 are

$$n_1 = \frac{c \sqrt{\sigma_1^2/c_1}}{\sqrt{\sigma_1^2 c_1} + \sqrt{\sigma_2^2 c_2} + \sqrt{\sigma_3^2 c_3}} \tag{27-15}$$

$$n_2 = \sqrt{\sigma_2^2 c_1 / \sigma_1^2 c_2} \tag{27-16}$$

$$n_3 = \sqrt{\sigma_3^2 c_2 / \sigma_2^2 c_3} \tag{27-17}$$

showing that the *optimum allocation beyond the first stage is the same* for fixed total cost as for fixed total variance. The same principles are easily extended to any number of stages in a nested sampling design. Also, similar relationships are available for cases in which certain of the numbers n_1, n_2, n_3, etc., are fixed and either the total cost or the total variance is fixed.[3]

Example 27-4. If the standard deviation of sampling strata is 0.07, that of sampling within strata is 0.10, and that of a single determination is 0.21, and the relative costs are in the ratio $4:2:1$, calculate the optimum sampling scheme and minimum cost to give an over-all standard deviation of the mean of 0.08.

Answer. $n_1 = \sqrt{(0.07)^2/4} \, (\sqrt{(0.07)^2 \times 4} + \sqrt{(0.10)^2 \times 2}$
$\qquad + \sqrt{(0.21)^2 \times 1}) / (0.08)^2 = 2.7$
$\quad n_2 = \sqrt{(0.10)^2 \times 4 / (0.07)^2 \times 2} = 2.02$
$\quad n_3 = \sqrt{(0.21)^2 \times 2 / (0.1)^2 \times 1} = 2.97$

[1] *Ibid.*, p. 490.
[2] Marcuse, S., *Biometrics*, **5**, 189 (1949).
[3] *Ibid.*

Taking $n_1 = 3$, $n_2 = 2$, $n_3 = 3$, we calculate $\sigma_0 = 0.076$ and $c = 3 \times 4 + 6 \times 2 + 18 \times 1 = 42$ on the relative scale.

Example 27-5. Given the same standard deviations and relative costs as in the above example, calculate the minimum standard deviation that can be achieved for a cost of 30 times that of a single determination.

Answer. $n_1 = 30 \sqrt{(0.07)^2/4}/(\sqrt{(0.07)^2 \times 4} + \sqrt{(0.10)^2 \times 2} + \sqrt{(0.21)^2 \times 1}) = 2.14$

$n_2 = 2.02 \qquad n_3 = 2.97$

Taking $n_1 = 2$, $n_2 = 2$, $n_3 = 3$, we calculate $c = 28$ and

$$\sigma_0^2 = (0.07)^2/2 + (0.10)^2/4 + (0.21)^2/12 = 0.00862$$

so $\sigma_0 = 0.093$.

27-8. Sampling Procedures

From the statistical aspects of the sampling problem that have been considered above we may conclude that the bulk of material to be sampled should first be subdivided into real or imaginary sampling units, which might range from individual molecules in the case of homogeneous gases or liquid solutions to very large units such as carloads of coal. Next, it is helpful to know the relative variations to be expected between units and within units. By carrying out analysis-of-variance studies on stratified sampling schemes, it can be decided whether it is justified to continue stratification at several levels (nested sampling scheme) or to simplify the procedure. The decision will usually be based on considerations of cost and convenience as well as on the desired level of accuracy. As a rule, some stratification will turn out to be desirable, choosing strata that are known or suspected to have variations between them and taking samples proportional to the sizes of the strata.

For particulate material, the size of the sample should be commensurate with the maximum size of the particles, depending of course upon the variations in composition to be found among particles. If the same heterogeneity of composition exists at all stages of subdivision, then the calculations described in Sec. 27-5 would lead to the requirement that the same total number of particles be present in the sample at all stages of subdivision. This would, of course, mean that the sample weight could be decreased as the cube of the particle diameter. Actually, as the sample is ground to a finer mesh size a greater number of particles are usually required, because coarse granules are often made up of aggregates of finer particles, which differ in composition more than the agglomerates do. As a general rule, it is advisable to avoid carrying out more grinding than is necessary for efficient sampling and subsequent chemical treatment, in order to avoid the danger of changes of composition (e.g., dehydration or oxidation) during the grinding operation.[1]

The over-all sampling procedure may be divided into three steps: (1) collection of the gross sample, (2) reduction of the gross sample to a suitable size for the laboratory, and (3) preparation of the laboratory sample.[2] The details of the three steps differ considerably depending upon the physical character of the material to be sampled. Often the initial sample that must be taken to ensure sufficient precision of sampling is so large that considerable reduction in size is necessary. For particulate matter, the decreasing sample size must be accompanied by a corresponding decrease in particle size. For this purpose, a variety of crushing, grinding, mixing, and dividing machines have been devised, the details of which are beyond the scope of the present discussion. To prepare the laboratory sample requires packaging in a suitable form that ensures protection from changes in composition. For example, it is sometimes desirable to determine moisture immediately, before packaging the laboratory sample.

Some of the methods used for collecting samples will now be discussed in a general way, for several types of materials.

Material Present in Homogeneous Solution. For gases or liquids which contain no suspended matter and which can be regarded as homogeneous solutions, the sampling unit can be very small.

Example 27-6. What size of sample is required from a homogeneous solution of radioisotope present at a concentration of 10^{-8} M, if the standard deviation due to sampling is not to exceed 0.1 per cent (relative)?

Answer. This is an example of sampling from a population of two types, solute molecules A and solvent molecules B. In 1 liter of solution there are $N_1 = 10^{-8} \times 6 \times 10^{23} = 6 \times 10^{15}$ solute molecules and $N_2 - 55.5 \times 6 \times 10^{23} = 3.3 \times 10^{25}$ solvent molecules. Accordingly, $p = N_1/(N_1 + N_2) = 1.8 \times 10^{-10}$ and $q = 1$ (very nearly). From Eq. (27-1a), we have $\sigma_n/N = \sqrt{(1 - p)/pN} = 10^{-3}$, which yields $N = 10^6/p = 5.5 = 10^{15}$ molecules in the total sample. This corresponds to $5.5 \times 10^{15}/55.5 \times 6 \times 10^{23} = 1.6 \times 10^{-10}$ liters.

Henriques[3] has discussed equipment and methods for sampling gases in laboratory-scale apparatus and has stressed the necessity for stirring to achieve homogeneity when gas mixtures are being prepared. For intermittent sampling, evacuated bulbs can be used to gather spot samples. For continuous sampling of a flowing gas, provision must be made to ensure that the rate of collection of sample is a constant fraction of the flow rate.

[1] Hillebrand, W. F., Lundell, G. E. F., Bright, H. A., and Hoffman, J. I., "Applied Inorganic Analysis," 2d ed., pp. 819, 907, John Wiley & Sons, Inc., New York, 1953.

[2] Barnitt, J. P., in Furman, N. H. (ed.), "Scott's Standard Methods of Analysis," 5th ed., vol. 2, pp. 1301–1333, D. Van Nostrand Company, Inc., Princeton, N.J., 1939.

[3] Henriques, H. J., *Ind. Eng. Chem.*, **39**, 1564 (1947).

For liquids flowing in an open channel, Trebler and Harding[1] describe a device for taking samples at constant intervals, the size of the sample being proportional to the rate of flow over a weir. This is accomplished by means of a rotating scoop, with a bottom curvature designed to correspond to the mathematical formula for flow of a liquid over a weir, as a function of the height of liquid above the weir.

For homogeneous liquids flowing in pipes, the problem is to take a constant fraction of the total flow regardless of variations in the rate of flow. For a pipe that is always full, this can be done simply by means of a sampling tube extending one-half the distance from the wall to the center of the pipe, with the inner end of the sampling tube bent at an angle of 90° to face the direction of flow. For horizontal pipes that are only partly full, a specially shaped sampling orifice or multiple sampling orifices may be used to regulate the sample size in relation to flow rate. These devices afford only approximately representative samples.[2]

Liquids Containing Suspended Matter. Nonhomogeneity can be compensated for, at least for the most part, by taking a series of samples at various levels, meanwhile providing sufficient agitation to keep the solid matter suspended as uniformly as possible. A "sampling thief," a device that can be lowered to the desired depth and opened temporarily to gather a sample, is often used. In some instances it is possible to determine the ratio of weights of the two phases independently, for example, from the material balance. In such a case it is not necessary to draw a representative sample of the mixture, but only to carry out an analysis on each of the phases after they have been separated.

Solids in Particulate Form. As discussed above, material consisting of discrete lots is sampled by taking a random selection of such lots. When large variations exist within a lot, for example, when segregation has occurred during transportation, it is usually possible to resort to a representative sampling scheme within the lot or else to convert the lot into a flowing sample, which can then be sampled at random. If neither of these procedures is accessible, it may be possible to take samples from the composite pile while it is being formed, for instance, by taking samples at evenly spaced increments along lines drawn from several points around the base of the conical pile to the apex, after each lot is dumped at the apex.

Solids in Compact Form. Materials of this type are often in a form consisting of discrete lots such as ingots, slabs, sheets, or bales that can be subjected to random sampling procedures. The procedure of sampling within the lot depends, of course, upon the physical properties and geometry of the material.

[1] Trebler, H. A., and Harding, H. G., *Ind. Eng. Chem.*, **39**, 608 (1947).
[2] Barnitt, *op. cit.*

Sheets of metal can often be sampled conveniently and nondestructively by clamping a number of sheets together with edges flush and milling across the edges to obtain an edge sample.

Billets or ingots of nonferrous metals may be sampled by sawing completely across the specimen at several regularly spaced intervals along its length. The "sawdust" thus collected is combined to form the sample. Another way is to drill or punch holes at regularly spaced intervals along the diagonal of a block, preferably all the way through the specimen, or else halfway through, alternately from one side and then from the other. The punchings or drillings are sometimes melted together in a clean graphite crucible and granulated by pouring into distilled water or cast into thin slabs that can be sawed completely through in several places.

It is beyond the scope of this book to consider the details of the special sampling procedures that have been worked out for various types of materials. Reference should be made to the publications of testing organizations and government agencies, which have made studies of the sampling of many types of materials. For metals, nonmetallic construction materials, paper, paints, fuels, petroleum products, and soils, the "Books of Standards" and other publications of the American Society for Testing Materials[1,2] are recommended. The Journal of the Association of Official Agricultural Chemists regularly publishes tentative procedures for sampling and analysis of soils, fertilizers, foods, water, drugs, etc., and at 5-year intervals releases new editions of "Official Methods of Analysis."[3] Similar methods are published and revised periodically by the American Oil Chemists' Society[4] for vegetable fats, oils, soaps and related materials. Sampling procedures are given for many types of materials in "Scott's Standard Methods of Analysis,"[5] in which many references to the original literature are available.

PROBLEMS

27-1. A powdered sample consists of uniform particles of ore of density 4.5 and gangue of density 2.2, containing 60 and 15 per cent of metal M, respectively. If a sample of 0.20 g containing about 40 per cent M is taken for analysis and if the particles are assumed to have a uniform diameter of 0.01 mm, what is the expected standard deviation due to sampling? *Ans.* 0.002 per cent M.

[1] *Am. Soc. Testing Materials ASTM Standards.*

[2] "Methods for Chemical Analysis of Metals," 2d ed., American Society for Testing Materials, Philadelphia, 1950.

[3] Horwitz, W. (ed.), "Official Methods of Analysis of the Association of Official Agricultural Chemists," 8th ed., Association of Official Agricultural Chemists, Washington, D.C., 1955.

[4] Hopper, T. H. (ed.), "Official and Tentative Methods of the American Oil Chemists' Society," American Oil Chemists' Society, Chicago.

[5] Furman, "Scott's Standard Methods of Analysis," Van Nostrand, 1939.

27-2. A sample of ten randomly chosen bottles of hydrogen peroxide is to be analyzed for peroxide content. If the standard deviation of a single determination is 1 part per thousand and if the peroxide content of the bottles fluctuates about their mean with a standard deviation of 5 parts per thousand, how many analyses of the blended sample would give a result as accurate as the average of ten analyses run on the separate bottles? *Ans.* 2.

27-3. In a simple stratified sampling scheme the standard deviations between strata, within strata, and of a determination are in the ratio $2:5:1$. If the respective costs are in the ratio $3:2:1$, (a) what should be the relative numbers of strata, of samples within strata, and of determinations within samples to minimize the standard deviation, keeping the cost below 12 times that of running a determination. What is the standard deviation of the population-mean estimate? What would be the cost? (b) What should be the pattern if the result is to have a standard deviation of no more than twice that of a single determination? *Ans.* (a) $n_1 = 1$, $n_2 = 3$, $n_3 = 1$, $\sigma_0 = 3.56$, $c = 12$; (b) $n_1 = 4$, $n_2 = 3$, $n_3 = 1$, $\sigma_0 = 1.78$, $c = 48$.

27-4. How large a sample of an equimolar mixture of two gases, measured at 0°C and 10^{-6} mm pressure, must be taken if the error due to sampling is not to exceed 0.1 per cent (relative)? *Ans.* 2.8×10^{-5} ml.

Index